# PEARSON

ALWAYS LEARNING

W9-BTT-409

Halderman • Linder

# Advanced Fuel and Emissions

A Pearson Learning Solutions Publication
for Ivy Tech Community College

Taken from:
*Automotive Fuel and Emissions Control Systems*, Third Edition
by James D. Halderman and Jim Linder

*Advanced Engine Performance Diagnosis*, Fifth Edition
by James D. Halderman

Taken from:

*Automotive Fuel and Emissions Control Systems*, Third Edition
by James D. Halderman and Jim Linder
Copyright © 2012, 2009, 2006 by Pearson Education, Inc.
Published by Prentice Hall
Upper Saddle River, New Jersey 07458

*Advanced Engine Performance Diagnosis*, Fifth Edition
Copyright © 2012, 2009, 2006, 2002, 1998 by Pearson Education, Inc.
Published by Prentice Hall
Upper Saddle River, New Jersey 07458

This special edition published in cooperation with Pearson Learning Solutions.

All trademarks, service marks, registered trademarks, and registered service marks are the property of their respective owners and are used herein for identification purposes only.

Pearson Learning Solutions, 501 Boylston Street, Suite 900, Boston, MA 02116
A Pearson Education Company
www.pearsoned.com

Printed in the United States of America

1 2 3 4 5 6 7 8 9 10 V0ZN 17 16 15 14 13 12


000200010271649271

MM/FC

ISBN 10: 1-256-69193-3
ISBN 13: 978-1-256-69193-8

Dear Students,

The Ivy Tech Automotive Technology Program has partnered with Pearson Learning Solutions to create a custom textbook for the AUTC 109, 209, and 219 course sequence. This allows us to use only the content needed for your course from the books Automotive Fuel and Emissions Control Systems and Advanced Engine Performance Diagnosis.

Because content has been removed from Automotive Fuel and Emissions Control Systems and Chapters added from Advanced Engine Performance Diagnosis, you will notice gaps in the chapter numbers and the pagination of your text. Rest assured, these gaps mean you only buy what you need for the course in which you are enrolled. Plus, these gaps retain the integrity of the index that appears in the back of your book.

We are confindent that this approach will save you money while still providing you with the best resource for use in these courses.

Sincerely,

The Ivy Tech Automotive Technology Program and Pearson Learning Solutions

# PREFACE

**PROFESSIONAL TECHNICIAN SERIES** Part of Pearson Automotive's Professional Technician Series, the third edition of *Automotive Fuel and Emissions Control Systems* represents the future of automotive textbooks. The series is a full-color, media-integrated solution for today's students and instructors. The series includes textbooks that cover all 8 areas of ASE certification, plus additional titles covering common courses.

Current revisions are written by a team of very experienced writers and teachers. The series is also peer reviewed for technical accuracy.

## UPDATES TO THE THIRD EDITION

- All content is correlated to the latest NATEF tasks.
- A dramatic, new full-color design enhances the subject material.
- Three totally new chapters added to the third edition including:

  **Wide-band Oxygen Sensors** (chapter 18)

  **Gasoline Direct Injection Systems** (chapter 21)

  **Electronic Throttle Control Systems** (chapter 22)

- Expanded content on gasoline, alterative fuels and diesel fuel now in their own individual chapter (chapters 5, 6, and 7).
- Updated content on emission control devices (chapters 25, 26, 27, and 28)
- Over 40 new color photos and line drawings have been added to this edition.
- Content has been streamlined for easier reading and comprehension.

- This text is fully integrated with MyAutomotiveKit, an online supplement for homework, quizzing, testing, multimedia activities, and videos.
- Unlike other textbooks, this book is written so that the theory, construction, diagnosis, and service of a particular component or system is presented in one location. There is no need to search through the entire book for other references to the same topic.

**NATEF CORRELATED** NATEF certified programs need to demonstrate that they use course material that covers NATEF tasks. All Professional Technician textbooks have been correlated to the appropriate NATEF task lists. These correlations can be found in an appendix to each book.

**A COMPLETE INSTRUCTOR AND STUDENT SUPPLEMENTS PACKAGE** All Professional Technician textbooks are accompanied by a full set of instructor and student supplements. Please see page vi for a detailed list of supplements.

**A FOCUS ON DIAGNOSIS AND PROBLEM SOLVING** The Professional Technician Series has been developed to satisfy the need for a greater emphasis on problem diagnosis. Automotive instructors and service managers agree that students and beginning technicians need more training in diagnostic procedures and skill development. To meet this need and demonstrate how real-world problems are solved, "Real World Fix" features are included throughout and highlight how real-life problems are diagnosed and repaired.

The following pages highlight the unique core features that set the Professional Technician Series book apart from other automotive textbooks.

### chapter 1 — SHOP SAFETY

**OBJECTIVES:** After studying Chapter 1, the reader should be able to: • Identify situations where hearing protection should be worn. • Discuss how to safely handle tools and shop equipment. • Describe how to properly use a fire extinguisher. • Discuss shop safety procedures.

**KEY TERMS:** ANSI 1 • Bump cap 2 • Decibel (dB) 2 • Eye wash station 7 • Fire blankets 6 • Microbes 4 • "PASS" 5 • Personal protective equipment (PPE) 1 • Spontaneous combustion 3

#### PERSONAL PROTECTIVE EQUIPMENT

Safety is not just a buzzword on a poster in the work area. Safe work habits can reduce accidents and injuries, ease the workload, and keep employees pain free.

**SAFETY GLASSES** The most important **personal protective equipment (PPE)** a technician should wear all the time are safety glasses, which meet standard **ANSI** Z87.1. ● **SEE FIGURE 1–1.**

**STEEL-TOED SHOES** Steel-toed safety shoes are also a good investment. ● **SEE FIGURE 1–2.** If safety shoes are not available, then leather-topped shoes offer more protection than canvas or cloth covered shoes.

**GLOVES** Wear gloves to protect your hands from rough or sharp surfaces. Thin rubber gloves are recommended when working around automotive liquids such as engine oil, antifreeze, transmission fluid, or any other liquids that may be hazardous. Several types of gloves and their characteristics include:

- **Latex surgical gloves.** These gloves are relatively inexpensive, but tend to stretch, swell, and weaken when exposed to gas, oil, or solvents.
- **Vinyl gloves.** These gloves are also inexpensive and are not affected by gas, oil, or solvents. ● **SEE FIGURE 1-3.**
- **Polyurethane gloves.** These gloves are more expensive, yet very strong. Even though these gloves are also not affected by gas, oil, or solvents, they tend to be slippery.
- **Nitrile gloves.** These gloves are exactly like latex gloves, but are not affected by gas, oil, or solvents, yet they tend to be expensive.

**FIGURE 1–1** Safety glasses should be worn at all times when working on or around any vehicle or servicing any component.

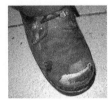

**FIGURE 1–2** Steel-toed shoes are a worthwhile investment to help prevent foot injury due to falling objects. Even these well-worn shoes can protect the feet of this service technician.

SHOP SAFETY **1**

**OBJECTIVES AND KEY TERMS** appear at the beginning of each chapter to help students and instructors focus on the most important material in each chapter. The chapter objectives are based on specific ASE and NATEF tasks.

### TECH TIP

**It Just Takes a Second**

Whenever removing any automotive component, it is wise to screw the bolts back into the holes a couple of threads by hand. This ensures that the right bolt will be used in its original location when the component or part is put back on the vehicle.

**TECH TIPS** feature real-world advice and "tricks of the trade" from ASE-certified master technicians.

### ✚ SAFETY TIP

**Shop Cloth Disposal**

Always dispose of oily shop cloths in an enclosed container to prevent a fire. ● **SEE FIGURE 1–69.** Whenever oily cloths are thrown together on the floor or workbench, a chemical reaction can occur, which can ignite the cloth even without an open flame. This process of ignition without an open flame is called **spontaneous combustion.**

**SAFETY TIPS** alert students to possible hazards on the job and how to avoid them.

### 🚗 REAL WORLD FIX

**Valve Springs Can Vary**

A technician was building a small block Chevrolet V-8 engine at home and was doing the final detailed checks, and found that many of the valve springs did not have the same tension. Using a borrowed valve spring tester, the technician visited a local parts store and measured all of the valve springs that the store had in stock. The technician selected and purchased the 16 valve springs that were within specification and within a very narrow range of tension. Although having all valve springs equal may or may not affect engine operation, the technician was pleased that all of the valve springs were equal.

**REAL WORLD FIXES** present students with actual automotive scenarios and shows how these common (and sometimes uncommon) problems were diagnosed and repaired.

### ❓ FREQUENTLY ASKED QUESTION

**How Many Types of Screw Heads Are Used in Automotive Applications?**

There are many, including Torx, hex (also called Allen), plus many others used in custom vans and motor homes. ● **SEE FIGURE 1–9.**

**FREQUENTLY ASKED QUESTIONS** are based on the author's own experience and provide answers to many of the most common questions asked by students and beginning service technicians.

**NOTE:** Most of these "locking nuts" are grouped together and are commonly referred to as *prevailing torque nuts*. This means that the nut will hold its tightness or torque and not loosen with movement or vibration.

**NOTES** provide students with additional technical information to give them a greater understanding of a specific task or procedure.

**CAUTION:** *Never* use hardware store (nongraded) bolts, studs, or nuts on any vehicle steering, suspension, or brake component. Always use the exact size and grade of hardware that is specified and used by the vehicle manufacturer.

**CAUTIONS** alert students about potential damage to the vehicle that can occur during a specific task or service procedure.

### ☠ WARNING

Do not use incandescent trouble lights around gasoline or other flammable liquids. The liquids can cause the bulb to break and the hot filament can ignite the flammable liquid which can cause personal injury or even death.

**WARNINGS** alert students to potential dangers to themselves during a specific task or service procedure.

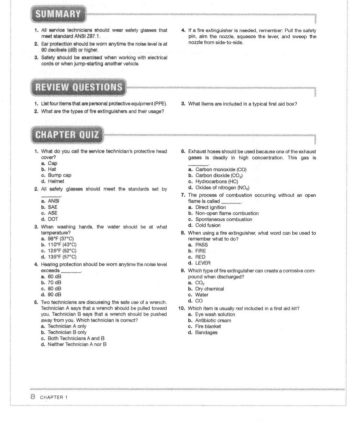

1. All service technicians should wear safety glasses that meet standard ANSI Z87.1.
2. Ear protection should be worn anytime the noise level is at 90 decibels (dB) or higher.
3. Safety should be exercised when working with electrical cords or when jump-starting another vehicle.
4. If a fire extinguisher is needed, remember: Pull the safety pin, aim the nozzle, squeeze the lever, and sweep the nozzle from side-to-side.

**REVIEW QUESTIONS**

1. List four items that are personal protective equipment (PPE).
2. What are the types of fire extinguishers and their usage?
3. What items are included in a typical first aid box?

**CHAPTER QUIZ**

1. What do you call the service technician's protective head cover?
   a. Cap
   b. Hat
   c. Bump cap
   d. Helmet
2. All safety glasses should meet the standards set by _____.
   a. ANSI
   b. SAE
   c. ASE
   d. DOT
3. When washing hands, the water should be at what temperature?
   a. 98°F (37°C)
   b. 110°F (43°C)
   c. 125°F (52°C)
   d. 135°F (57°C)
4. Hearing protection should be worn anytime the noise level exceeds _____.
   a. 60 dB
   b. 70 dB
   c. 80 dB
   d. 90 dB
5. Two technicians are discussing the safe use of a wrench. Technician A says that a wrench should be pulled toward you. Technician B says that a wrench should be pushed away from you. Which technician is correct?
   a. Technician A only
   b. Technician B only
   c. Both Technicians A and B
   d. Neither Technician A nor B
6. Exhaust hoses should be used because one of the exhaust gases is deadly in high concentration. This gas is _____.
   a. Carbon monoxide (CO)
   b. Carbon dioxide ($CO_2$)
   c. Hydrocarbons (HC)
   d. Oxides of nitrogen ($NO_x$)
7. The process of combustion occurring without an open flame is called _____.
   a. Direct ignition
   b. Non-open flame combustion
   c. Spontaneous combustion
   d. Cold fusion
8. When using a fire extinguisher, what word can be used to remember what to do?
   a. PASS
   b. FIRE
   c. RED
   d. LEVER
9. Which type of fire extinguisher can create a corrosive compound when discharged?
   a. $CO_2$
   b. Dry chemical
   c. Water
   d. CO
10. Which item is usually *not* included in a first aid kit?
    a. Eye wash solution
    b. Antibiotic cream
    c. Fire blanket
    d. Bandages

**THE SUMMARY, REVIEW QUESTIONS, AND CHAPTER QUIZ** at the end of each chapter help students review the material presented in the chapter and test themselves to see how much they've learned.

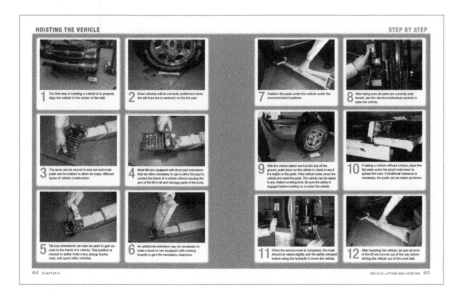

HOISTING THE VEHICLE                                         STEP BY STEP

**STEP BY STEP** photo sequences show in detail the steps involved in performing a specific task or service procedure.

# SUPPLEMENTS

**INSTRUCTOR SUPPLEMENTS**  The instructor supplement package has been completely revamped to reflect the needs of today's instructors. The all new **Online Instructor's Manual (ISBN: 0-13-254508-X)** is the cornerstone of the package.

To access supplementary materials online, instructors need to request an instructor access code. Go to www.pearsonhighered.com/irc to register for an instructor access code. Within 48 hours of registering, you will receive a confirming e-mail including an instructor access code. Once you have received your code, locate your text in the online catalog and click on the Instructor Resources button on the left side of the catalog product page. Select a supplement, and a login page will appear. Once you have logged in, you can access instructor material for all Prentice Hall textbooks. If you have any difficulties accessing the site or downloading a supplement, please contact Customer Service at http://247.prenhall.com.

Here you will find:

- PowerPoint presentations*
- Image Library containing every image in the book for use in class or customized PowerPoints*
- MyTest software and test bank*
- Chapter Quizzes

- Chapter Review Questions
- English and Spanish Glossary*
- NATEF Correlated task Sheets* also available as a printed supplement [ISBN: 0-13-254510-1]
- NATEF/ASE Correlation Charts

* All of these are available for download from www.pearsonhighered .com

## STUDENT SUPPLEMENTS

Today's student has more access to the Internet than ever, so all supplemental materials are downloadable at the following site for no additional charge:

## www.pearsoned.com/autostudent

On the site, students will find:

- PowerPoint presentations
- Chapter review questions and quizzes
- English and Spanish Glossary
- A full Spanish translation of the text

# ACKNOWLEDGMENTS

A large number of people and organizations have cooperated in providing the reference material and technical information used in this text. The author wishes to express sincere thanks to the following individuals for their special contributions:

Bill Fulton, Ohio Automotive Technology

Dan Marinucci, Communique'

Dave Scaler, Mechanic's Education Association

Dr. Norman Nall

John Thornton, Autotrain

Mark Warren

Randy Dillman

Rick Escalambre, Skyline College

Jim Morton, Automotive Training center (ATC)

Scot Manna

**TECHNICAL AND CONTENT REVIEWERS**  The following people reviewed the manuscript before production and checked it for technical accuracy and clarity of presentation. Their suggestions and recommendations were included in the final draft of the manuscript. Their input helped make this textbook clear and technically accurate while maintaining the easy-to-read style that has made other books from the same author so popular.

**Jim Anderson**
Greenville High School

**Victor Bridges**
Umpqua Community College

**Darrell Deeter**
Saddleback College

**Matt Dixon**
Southern Illinois University

**Dr. Roger Donovan**
Illinois Central College

**A. C. Durdin**
Moraine Park Technical College

**Herbert Ellinger**
Western Michigan University

**Al Engledahl**
College of Dupage

**Larry Hagelberger**
Upper Valley Joint Vocational School

**Oldrick Hajzler**
Red River College

**Betsy Hoffman**
Vermont Technical College

**Richard Krieger**
Michigan Institute of Technology

**Steven T. Lee**
Lincoln Technical Institute

**Carlton H. Mabe, Sr.**
Virginia Western Community College

**Roy Marks**
Owens Community College

**Tony Martin**
University of Alaska Southeast

**Kerry Meier**
San Juan College

**Fritz Peacock**
Indiana Vocational Technical College

**Dennis Peter**
NAIT (Canada)

**Kenneth Redick**
Hudson Valley Community College

**Jeff Rehkopf**
Florida State College

**Omar Trinidad**
Southern Illinois University

**Mitchell Walker**
St. Louis Community College at Forest Park

**Jennifer Wise**
Sinclair Community College

Special thanks to instructional designer **Alexis I. Skriloff James**

**PHOTO SEQUENCES**  The author wishes to thank Blaine Heeter, Mike Garblik, and Chuck Taylor of Sinclair Community College in Dayton, Ohio, and James (Mike) Watson who helped with many of the photos. A special thanks to Dick Krieger for his detailed and thorough review of the manuscript before publication.

Most of all, I wish to thank Michelle Halderman for her assistance in all phases of manuscript preparation.

—James D. Halderman
—Jim Linder

**JIM HALDERMAN** brings a world of experience, knowledge, and talent to his work. His automotive service experience includes working as a flat-rate technician, a business owner, and a professor of automotive technology at a leading U.S. community college for more than 20 years.

He has a Bachelor of Science Degree from Ohio Northern University and a Masters Degree in Education from Miami University in Oxford, Ohio. Jim also holds a U.S. Patent for an electronic transmission control device. He is an ASE certified Master Automotive Technician and Advanced Engine Performance (L1) ASE certified.

Jim is the author of many automotive textbooks all published by Prentice Hall.

Jim has presented numerous technical seminars to national audiences including the California Automotive Teachers (CAT) and the Illinois College Automotive Instructor Association (ICAIA). He is also a member and presenter at the North American Council of Automotive Teachers (NACAT). Jim was also named Regional Teacher of the Year by General Motors Corporation and an outstanding alumnus of Ohio Northern University.

Jim and his wife, Michelle, live in Dayton, Ohio. They have two children. You can reach Jim at

jim@jameshalderman.com

http://jameshalderman.com

**JIM LINDER** has spent most of his life in automotive service. His earliest start was as a gas station attendant. He has also worked in the automotive industry as a mechanic for seven years; as an automotive instructor at Lincoln Tech for eight years; and as a training manager, training developer, and district sales manager for Allen Test Products for eight years. Currently, he is an ATTP master instructor and board member on the Indiana IDEM Training Advisory Board. You can contact Jim at

jimlinder@juno.com

www.lindertech.com

# BRIEF CONTENTS

chapter 1     Service Information, Tools, and Safety   1

chapter 3     Gasoline Engine Operation and Specifications   46

chapter 4     Diesel Engine Operation and Diagnosis   60

chapter 5     Gasoline   81

chapter 6     Alternative Fuels   95

chapter 7     Diesel and Biodiesel Fuels   108

chapter 8     Intake and Exhaust Systems   113

chapter 9     Turbocharging and Supercharging   123

chapter 10    Engine Condition Diagnosis   135

chapter 11    On-Board Diagnosis   153

chapter 12    CAN and Network Communications   162

chapter 13    Temperature Sensors   179

chapter 14    Throttle Position Sensors   190

chapter 15    MAP/BARO Sensors   196

chapter 16    MASS AIRFLOW Sensors   205

chapter 17    Oxygen Sensors   212

chapter 18    Wide-Band Oxygen Sensors   229

chapter 19    Fuel Pumps, Lines, and Filters   238

chapter 20    Fuel-Injection Components and Operation   256

chapter 21    Gasoline Direct-Injection Systems   270

chapter 22    Electronic Throttle Control System   277

chapter 23    Fuel-Injection System Diagnosis and Service   286

chapter 24    Vehicle Emission Standards and Testing   306

chapter 25    Evaporative Emission Control Systems   317

chapter 26    Exhaust Gas Recirculation Systems   327

chapter 27    Positive Crankcase Ventilation and Secondary Air-Injection Systems   335

chapter 28    Catalytic Converters   343

chapter 29    Ignition System Operation and Diagnosis   354

chapter 30    Scan tools and Engine Performance Diagnosis   378

appendix      NATEF Task Correlation Chart   425

              English Glossary     428

              Spanish Glossary     437

              Index   449

Taken from: *Advanced Engine Performance Diagnosis*, Fifth Edition by James Halderman

chapter 4     Global OBD II and Mode $06   46

chapter 17    Fuel Trim Diagnosis   224

chapter 26    In-Vehicle Engine Service   362

chapter 27    Symptom-Based Diagnosis   372

# CONTENTS

## chapter 1
## SERVICE INFORMATION, TOOLS, AND SAFETY 1

- Objectives 1
- Key Terms 1
- Vehicle Identification 1
- Service Information 3
- Threaded Fasteners 4
- Hand Tools 7
- Basic Hand Tool List 16
- Tool Sets and Accessories 17
- Electrical Hand Tools 18
- Hand Tool Maintenance 18
- Trouble Lights 19
- Air and Electrically Operated Tools 19
- Personal Protective Equipment 21
- Safety Precautions 22
- Vehicle Protection 23
- Safety Lifting (Hoisting) a Vehicle 23
- Jacks and Safety Stands 25
- Drive-On Ramps 26
- Electrical Cord Safety 26
- Jump-Starting and Battery Safety 27
- Fire Extinguishers 27
- Fire Blankets 28
- First Aid and Eye Wash Stations 28
- Hybrid Electric Vehicle Safety Issues 29

SUMMARY 34
REVIEW QUESTIONS 34
CHAPTER QUIZ 34

## chapter 3
## GASOLINE ENGINE OPERATION AND SPECIFICATIONS 46

- Objectives 46
- Key Terms 46
- Purpose and Function 46
- Energy and Power 46
- Engine Construction Overview 46
- Engine Parts and Systems 47
- Four-Stroke Cycle Operation 49
- Engine Classification and Construction 49
- Engine Measurement 54
- Compression Ratio 55
- Torque and Horsepower 58

SUMMARY 59
REVIEW QUESTIONS 59
CHAPTER QUIZ 59

## chapter 4
## DIESEL ENGINE OPERATION AND DIAGNOSIS 60

- Objectives 60
- Key Terms 60
- Diesel Engines 60
- Three Phases of Combustion 62
- Fuel Tank and Lift Pump 63
- Injection Pump 63
- HEUI System 64
- Diesel Injector Nozzles 66
- Glow Plugs 67
- Engine-Driven Vacuum Pump 67
- Diesel Fuel Heaters 68
- Accelerator Pedal Position Sensor 68
- Diesel Engine Turbochargers 69
- Exhaust Gas Recirculation 70
- Diesel Particulate Matter 71
- Diesel Oxidation Catalyst 71
- Diesel Exhaust Particulate Filter 71
- Selective Catalytic Reduction 74
- Diesel Exhaust Smoke Diagnosis 74
- Diesel Performance Diagnosis 75
- Compression Testing 75
- Glow Plug Resistance Balance Test 77
- Injector Pop Testing 77
- Diesel Emission Testing 78

SUMMARY 79
REVIEW QUESTIONS 79
CHAPTER QUIZ 79

## chapter 5
## GASOLINE 81

- Objectives 81
- Key Terms 81
- Gasoline 81
- Refining 81
- Volatility 83
- Gasoline Combustion Process 84
- Normal and Abnormal Combustion 85
- Octane Rating 86
- High-Altitude Octane Requirements 87
- Gasoline Additives 87
- Gasoline Blending 89
- Reformulated Gasoline 89
- Testing Gasoline for Alcohol Content 90
- General Gasoline Recommendations 91

SUMMARY 94
REVIEW QUESTIONS 94
CHAPTER QUIZ 94

## chapter 6
## ALTERNATIVE FUELS 95

- Objectives 95
- Key Terms 95
- Ethanol 95
- Cellulose Ethanol 96
- E85 96
- Alternative-Fuel Vehicles 97
- Methanol 100
- Propane 101
- Compressed Natural Gas 102
- Liquefied Natural Gas 103
- P-Series Fuels 103
- Synthetic Fuels 104
- Safety Procedures When Working with Alternative Fuels 106

SUMMARY 106
REVIEW QUESTIONS 106
CHAPTER QUIZ 107

## chapter 7
## DIESEL AND BIODIESEL FUELS 108

- Objectives 108
- Key Terms 108
- Diesel Fuel 108
- Biodiesel 110
- E-Diesel Fuel 112

SUMMARY 112
REVIEW QUESTIONS 112
CHAPTER QUIZ 112

## chapter 8
## INTAKE AND EXHAUST SYSTEMS 113

- Objectives 113
- Key Terms 113
- Air Intake Filtration 113
- Throttle-Body Injection Intake Manifolds 115
- Port Fuel-Injection Intake Manifolds 116
- Exhaust Gas Recirculation Passages 118
- Exhaust Manifolds 118
- Mufflers 120

SUMMARY 121
REVIEW QUESTIONS 122
CHAPTER QUIZ 122

## chapter 9
## TURBOCHARGING AND SUPERCHARGING 123

- Objectives 123
- Key Terms 123
- Introduction 123
- Forced Induction Principles 123
- Superchargers 125
- Turbochargers 127

- Boost Control   129
- Turbocharger Failures   130
- Nitrous Oxide   132

SUMMARY   **133**
REVIEW QUESTIONS   **134**
CHAPTER QUIZ   **134**

## chapter 10
# ENGINE CONDITION DIAGNOSIS 135

- Objectives   135
- Key Terms   135
- Typical Engine-Related Complaints   135
- Engine Smoke Diagnosis   135
- The Driver Is Your Best Resource   136
- Visual Checks   136
- Engine Noise Diagnosis   138
- Oil Pressure Testing   139
- Oil Pressure Warning Lamp   140
- Compression Test   140
- Wet Compression Test   142
- Running (Dynamic) Compression Test   142
- Cylinder Leakage Test   143
- Cylinder Power Balance Test   144
- Power Balance Test Procedure   144
- Vacuum Tests   144
- Exhaust Restriction Test   146
- Testing Back Pressure with a Vacuum Gauge   147
- Testing Back Pressure with a Pressure Gauge   147
- Diagnosing Head Gasket Failure   147
- Dash Warning Lights   148

SUMMARY   **151**
REVIEW QUESTIONS   **151**
CHAPTER QUIZ   **151**

## chapter 11
# ON-BOARD DIAGNOSIS 153

- Objectives   153
- Key Terms   153

- On-Board Diagnostics Generation-II (OBD-II) Systems   153
- Diagnostic Executive and Task Manager   154
- Monitors   154
- OBD-II Monitor Information   155
- Enabling Criteria   156
- OBD-II DTC Numbering Designation   157
- OBD-II Freeze-Frame   158
- Enabling Conditions   158
- PCM Tests   159
- GLOBAL OBD-II   160
- Diagnosing Problems Using Mode Six   161

SUMMARY   **161**
REVIEW QUESTIONS   **161**
CHAPTER QUIZ   **161**

## chapter 12
# CAN AND NETWORK COMMUNICATIONS 162

- Objectives   162
- Key Terms   162
- Module Communications and Networks   162
- Network Fundamentals   162
- Module Communications Configuration   163
- Network Communications Classifications   165
- General Motors Communications Protocols   165
- Ford Network Communications Protocols   168
- Chrysler Communications Protocols   169
- Controller Area Network   170
- Honda/Toyota Communications   172
- European Bus Communications   172
- Network Communications Diagnosis   173
- OBD-II Data Link Connector   176

SUMMARY   **177**
REVIEW QUESTIONS   **177**
CHAPTER QUIZ   **178**

# chapter 13
# TEMPERATURE SENSORS 179

- Objectives 179
- Key Terms 179
- Engine Coolant Temperature Sensors 179
- Testing the Engine Coolant Temperature Sensor 180
- Intake Air Temperature Sensor 184
- Testing the Intake Air Temperature Sensor 186
- Transmission Fluid Temperature Sensor 186
- Cylinder Head Temperature Sensor 187
- Engine Fuel Temperature (EFT) Sensor 187
- Exhaust Gas Recirculation (EGR) Temperature Sensor 187
- Engine Oil Temperature Sensor 188
- Temperature Sensor Diagnostic Trouble Codes 188

SUMMARY 188
REVIEW QUESTIONS 188
CHAPTER QUIZ 189

# chapter 14
# THROTTLE POSITION SENSORS 190

- Objectives 190
- Key Terms 190
- Throttle Position Sensor Construction 190
- TP Sensor Computer Input Functions 191
- PCM Uses for the TP Sensor 191
- Testing the Throttle Position Sensor 192
- Testing a TP Sensor Using the Min/Max Function 193
- Testing the TP Sensor Using a Scan Tool 193
- TP Sensor Diagnostic Trouble Codes 194

SUMMARY 194
REVIEW QUESTIONS 194
CHAPTER QUIZ 194

# chapter 15
# MAP/BARO SENSORS 196

- Objectives 196
- Key Terms 196
- Air Pressure—High and Low 196
- Principles of Pressure Sensors 196
- Construction of MAP Sensors 196
- PCM Uses of the MAP Sensor 199

- Barometric Pressure Sensor 201
- Testing the MAP Sensor 202
- Fuel-Rail Pressure Sensor 203
- MAP/BARO Diagnostic Trouble Codes 203

SUMMARY 203
REVIEW QUESTIONS 203
CHAPTER QUIZ 204

# chapter 16
# MASS AIRFLOW SENSORS 205

- Objectives 205
- Key Terms 205
- Airflow Sensors 205
- Mass AirFlow Sensor Types 205
- Karman Vortex Sensors 207
- PCM Uses for Airflow Sensors 207
- Testing Mass Airflow Sensors 208
- MAF Sensor Contamination 209
- MAF-Related Diagnostic Trouble Codes 210

SUMMARY 210
REVIEW QUESTIONS 210
CHAPTER QUIZ 211

# chapter 17
# OXYGEN SENSORS 212

- Objectives 212
- Key Terms 212
- Oxygen Sensors 212
- Zirconia Oxygen Sensors 213
- Titania Oxygen Sensor 214
- Closed Loop and Open Loop 214
- PCM Uses of the Oxygen Sensor 214
- Oxygen Sensor Diagnosis 215
- Oxygen Sensor Waveform Analysis 218
- Hash 221
- Negative O2S Voltage 224
- Low O2S Readings 225
- High O2S Readings 225
- Post-Catalytic Converter Oxygen Sensor Testing 226
- Oxygen Sensor Visual Inspection 226
- O2S-Related Diagnostic Trouble Codes 227

SUMMARY 227
REVIEW QUESTIONS 227
CHAPTER QUIZ 228

## chapter 18
## WIDE-BAND OXYGEN SENSORS 229

- Objectives 229
- Key Terms 229
- Terminology 229
- Need For Wide-Band Sensors 229
- Conventional O2S Review 230
- Dual-Cell Planar Wide-Band Sensor Operation 232
- Dual-Cell Diagnosis 234
- Digital Multimeter Testing 234
- Single-Cell Wide-Band Oxygen Sensors 234
- Wide-Band Oxygen Sensor Pattern Failures 236

SUMMARY 236
REVIEW QUESTIONS 237
CHAPTER QUIZ 237

## chapter 19
## FUEL PUMPS, LINES, AND FILTERS 238

- Objectives 238
- Key Terms 238
- Fuel Delivery System 238
- Fuel Tanks 238
- Rollover Leakage Protection 240
- Fuel Lines 240
- Electronic Fuel Pumps 243
- Fuel Filters 248
- Fuel Pump Testing 248
- Fuel pump Current Draw Test 253
- Fuel pump Replacement 254

SUMMARY 254
REVIEW QUESTIONS 254
CHAPTER QUIZ 255

## chapter 20
## FUEL-INJECTION COMPONENTS AND OPERATION 256

- Objectives 256
- Key Terms 256
- Electronic Fuel-Injection Operation 256
- Speed-Density Fuel-Injection Systems 256
- Mass Airflow Fuel-Injection Systems 258

- Throttle-Body Injection 258
- Port Fuel Injection 258
- Fuel-Pressure Regulator 261
- Vacuum-Biased Fuel-Pressure Regulator 262
- Electronic Returnless Fuel System 262
- Mechanical Returnless Fuel System 263
- Demand Delivery System 263
- Fuel Injectors 264
- Central Port Injection 265
- Fuel-Injection Modes of Operation 266
- Idle Control 266
- Stepper Motor Operation 267

SUMMARY 268
REVIEW QUESTIONS 268
CHAPTER QUIZ 268

## chapter 21
## GASOLINE DIRECT-INJECTION SYSTEMS 270

- Objectives 270
- Key Terms 270
- Direct Fuel Injection 270
- Direct-Injection Fuel Delivery System 271
- GDI Fuel Injectors 272
- Modes of Operation 272
- Piston Top Designs 273
- Lexus Port-and Direct-Injection Systems 274
- Engine Start System 274
- GDI Service 275

SUMMARY 275
REVIEW QUESTIONS 276
CHAPTER QUIZ 276

## chapter 22
## ELECTRONIC THROTTLE CONTROL SYSTEM 277

- Objectives 277
- Key Terms 277
- Electronic Throttle Control (ETC) System 277
- Normal Operation of the ETC System 277
- Accelerator Pedal Position Sensor 278
- Throttle Body Assembly 278
- TP Sensor 280
- Diagnosis of ETC Systems 281

- ETC Throttle Follower Test 283
- Servicing Electronic Throttle Systems 283

SUMMARY 284
REVIEW QUESTIONS 284
CHAPTER QUIZ 284

## chapter 23
## FUEL-INJECTION SYSTEM DIAGNOSIS AND SERVICE 286

- Objectives 286
- Key Terms 286
- Port Fuel-Injection Pressure Regulator Diagnosis 286
- Diagnosing Electronic Fuel-Injection Problems Using Visual Inspection 287
- Scan Tool Vacuum Leak Diagnosis 288
- Port Fuel-Injection System Diagnosis 289
- Testing for an Injector Pulse 289
- Checking Fuel-Injector Resistance 291
- Measuring Resistance of Grouped Injectors 291
- Measuring Resistance of Individual Injectors 292
- Pressure-Drop Balance Test 293
- Injector Voltage-Drop Tests 293
- Scope-Testing Fuel Injectors 294
- Idle Air Speed Control Diagnosis 295
- Fuel-Injection Service 296
- Fuel-System Scan Tool Diagnostics 299

SUMMARY 305
REVIEW QUESTIONS 305
CHAPTER QUIZ 305

## chapter 24
## VEHICLE EMISSION STANDARDS AND TESTING 306

- Objectives 306
- Key Terms 306
- Emission Standards in the United States 306
- European Standards 308
- Exhaust Analysis Testing 308
- Exhaust Analysis and Combustion Efficiency 311
- HC Too High 312
- CO Too High 312
- Measuring Oxygen and Carbon Dioxide 313

- Photochemical Smog Formation 313
- Testing for Oxides of Nitrogen 314

SUMMARY 315
REVIEW QUESTIONS 315
CHAPTER QUIZ 316

## chapter 25
## EVAPORATIVE EMISSION CONTROL SYSTEMS 317

- Objectives 317
- Key Terms 317
- Evaporative Emission Control System 317
- Nonenhanced Evaporative Control Systems 318
- Enhanced Evaporative Control System 319
- Leak Detection Pump System 321
- Onboard Refueling Vapor Recovery 321
- Diagnosing The Evap System 322
- Evaporative System Monitor 323
- Typical Evap Monitor 324
- Evap System-Related Diagnostic Trouble Codes 325

SUMMARY 325
REVIEW QUESTIONS 326
CHAPTER QUIZ 326

## chapter 26
## EXHAUST GAS RECIRCULATION SYSTEMS 327

- Objectives 327
- Key Terms 327
- Exhaust Gas Recirculation Systems 327
- OBD-II EGR Monitoring Strategies 330
- Diagnosing a Defective EGR System 331
- EGR-Related OBD-II Diagnostic Trouble Codes 333

SUMMARY 333
REVIEW QUESTIONS 334
CHAPTER QUIZ 334

## chapter 27
## POSITIVE CRANKCASE VENTILATION AND SECONDARY AIR-INJECTION SYSTEMS 335

- Objectives 335
- Key Terms 335

- Crankcase Ventilation   335
- PCV-Related Diagnostic Trouble Codes   338
- Secondary Air-Injection System   339
- Secondary Air-Injection System Diagnosis   340
- Sai-Related Diagnostic Trouble Code   341

SUMMARY   341
REVIEW QUESTIONS   341
CHAPTER QUIZ   342


## chapter 28
## CATALYTIC CONVERTERS   343

- Objectives   343
- Key Terms   343
- Catalytic Converters   343
- OBD-II Catalytic Converter Performance   345
- Diagnosing Catalytic Converters   346
- Catalytic Converter Replacement Guidelines   348

SUMMARY   352
REVIEW QUESTIONS   352
CHAPTER QUIZ   352


## chapter 29
## IGNITION SYSTEM OPERATION AND DIAGNOSIS   354

- Objectives   354
- Key Terms   354
- Ignition System   354
- Ignition Switching and Triggering   356
- Distributor Ignition   360
- Waste-Spark Ignition Systems   361
- Coil-On-Plug Ignition   363
- Knock Sensors   365
- Ignition System Diagnosis   367
- Spark Plug Wire Inspection   369
- Spark Plugs   372
- Ignition Timing   375
- Ignition System Symptom Guide   376

SUMMARY   377
REVIEW QUESTIONS   377
CHAPTER QUIZ   377


## chapter 30
## SCAN TOOLS AND ENGINE PERFORMANCE DIAGNOSIS   378

- Objectives   378
- Key Terms   378
- The Eight-Step Diagnostic Procedure   378
- Scan Tools   384
- Retrieval of Diagnostic Information   384
- Troubleshooting Using Diagnostic Trouble Codes   385
- Flash Code Retrieval on OBD-I General Motors Vehicles   386
- Retrieving Ford Diagnostic Codes   387
- Flash Code Retrieval on Chrysler Vehicles   388
- OBD-II Diagnosis   388
- OBD-II Active Tests   391
- Service/Flash Programming   392
- Manufacturer's Diagnostic Routines   394
- Completing System Repairs   394
- Procedures for Resetting the PCM   395
- Road Test (Drive cycle)   395

SUMMARY   396
REVIEW QUESTIONS   396
CHAPTER QUIZ   396


## appendix
NATEF TASK CORRELATION CHART   425

ENGLISH GLOSSARY   428

SPANISH GLOSSARY   437

INDEX   449


TAKEN FROM: *ADVANCED ENGINE PERFORMANCE DIAGNOSIS*, FIFTH EDITION BY JAMES HALDERMAN


## chapter 4
## GLOBAL OBD II AND MODE $06   46

- Objectives   46
- Key Terms   46
- What Is Global OBD II?   46
- Global OBD II Modes   46
- Diagnosing Problems Using Mode $06   47

- Accessing Global OBD II   47
- Mode $06   48
- Oxygen Sensor Heater Mode $06 Test (General Motors)   50
- Engine Misfire Tests (FORD)   50
- Ford Oxygen Sensor Mode $06 Test   50
- General Motors Can Oxygen Sensor Mode $06 Test   50
- Ford EGR Tests   51
- General Motors Catalyst Efficiency Test   51
- General Motors Evap Test (CAN)   52
- Where to Get Mode $06 Information   52

SUMMARY   52

REVIEW QUESTIONS   52

CHAPTER QUIZ   52

# chapter 17
# FUEL TRIM DIAGNOSIS   224

- Objectives   224
- Key Terms   224
- Fuel Trim   224
- Base Pulse Width   225
- Measuring Pulse Width   226
- Fuel Trim   227
- The Need for Fuel Trim   227
- Short-Term Fuel Trim   227
- Long-Term Fuel Trim   228
- Using Fuel Trim as a Diagnostic Aid   228
- Fuel Trim Cells   228
- Fuel Trim Cell Diagnosis   229
- MAF Sensor Accuracy   229
- Volumetric Efficiency   230

SUMMARY   232

REVIEW QUESTIONS   232

CHAPTER QUIZ   232

# chapter 26
# IN-VEHICLE ENGINE SERVICE   362

- Objectives   362
- Key Terms   362
- Thermostat Replacement   362
- Water Pump Replacement   363
- Intake Manifold Gasket Inspection   363
- Intake Manifold Gasket Replacement   364
- Timing Belt Replacement   365
- Hybrid Engine Precautions   365

SUMMARY   371

REVIEW QUESTIONS   371

CHAPTER QUIZ   371

# chapter 27
# SYMPTOM-BASED DIAGNOSIS   372

- Objectives   372
- Key Terms   372
- Engine Hesitates, Sags, or Stumbles During Acceleration   372
- Rough Idle or Stalling   374
- Spark Knock (Ping or Detonation)   375
- Engine Cranks Okay, But Is Hard to Start   376
- Engine Does Not Crank or Cranks Slowly   377
- Poor Fuel Economy   377
- Dieseling or Run-On   378
- Backfire   378
- Lack of Power   379
- Surges   380
- Cuts Out or Misfires   380
- Rich Exhaust   380
- Lean Exhaust   381
- Symptoms of a Defective Component   381
- Excessive CO Exhaust Emissions   382
- Excessive HC Exhaust Emissions   382
- Excessive $NO_X$ Exhaust Emissions   383

SUMMARY   383

REVIEW QUESTIONS   384

CHAPTER QUIZ   384

## chapter 1

# SERVICE INFORMATION, TOOLS, AND SAFETY

**OBJECTIVES: After studying Chapter 1, the reader should be able to:** • Understand the ASE knowledge content for vehicle identification and the proper use of tools and shop equipment. • Retrieve vehicle service information. • Identify the strength ratings of threaded fasteners. • Describe how to safely hoist a vehicle. • Discuss how to safely use hand tools. • Identify the personal protective equipment (PPE) that all service technicians should wear. • Describe what tool is the best to use for each job. • Explain the difference between the brand name (trade name) and the proper name for tools. • Explain how to maintain hand tools. • Identify the precautions that should be followed when working on hybrid electric vehicles.

**KEY TERMS:** Bench grinder 21 • Bolts 4 • Breaker bar 9 • Bump cap 21 • Calibration codes 2 • Campaign 4 • Casting number 2 • Cheater bar 11 • Chisels 16 • Drive sizes 9 • Extensions 9 • Eye wash station 29 • Files 15 • Fire blanket 28 • Fire extinguisher classes 27 • GAWR 2 • Grade 5 • GVWR 2 • Hacksaws 16 • Hammers 12 • HEV 29 • LED 19 • Metric bolts 4 • Nuts 6 • PPE 21 • Pinch weld seam 24 • Pitch 4 • Pliers 13 • Punches 15 • Ratchet 9 • Recall 4 • Screwdrivers 11 • Snips 15 • Socket 9 • Socket adapter 11 • Spontaneous combustion 23 • SST 19 • Stud 4 • Tensile strength 6 • Trouble light 6 • TSB 3 • UNC 4 • UNF 4 • Universal joint 9 • VECI 2 • VIN 4 • Washers 7 • Wrenches 7

## VEHICLE IDENTIFICATION

**MAKE, MODEL, AND YEAR** All service work requires that the vehicle and its components be properly identified. The most common identification is the make, model, and year of the vehicle.

> **Make:** e.g., Chevrolet
> **Model:** e.g., Impala
> **Year:** e.g., 2008

**VEHICLE IDENTIFICATION NUMBER** The year of the vehicle is often difficult to determine exactly. A model may be introduced as the next year's model as soon as January of the previous year. Typically, a new model year starts in September or October of the year prior to the actual new year, but not always. This is why the **vehicle identification number,** usually abbreviated VIN, is so important. ● **SEE FIGURE 1–1.**

Since 1981, all vehicle manufacturers have used a VIN that is 17 characters long. Although every vehicle manufacturer assigns various letters or numbers within these 17 characters, there are some constants, including:

- The first number or letter designates the country of origin.
  ● **SEE CHART 1–1.**
- The fourth or fifth character is the car line/series.

- The sixth character is the body style.
- The seventh character is the restraint system.
- The eighth character is often the engine code. (Some engines cannot be determined by the VIN number.)
- The tenth character represents the year on all vehicles.
  ● **SEE CHART 1–2.**

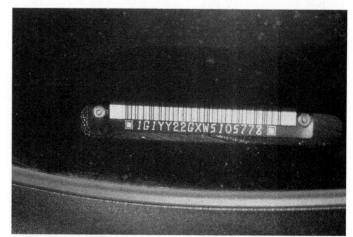

**FIGURE 1–1** Typical vehicle identification number (VIN) as viewed through the windshield.

| | | |
|---|---|---|
| 1 = United States | J = Japan | W = Germany |
| 2 = Canada | K = Korea | X = Russia |
| 3 = Mexico | L = China | Y = Sweden |
| 4 = United States | R = Taiwan | Z = Italy |
| 5 = United States | S = England | |
| 6 = Australia | T = Czechoslovakia | |
| 8 = Argentina | U = Romania | |
| 9 = Brazil | V = France | |

**CHART 1–1**

The first number or letter in the VIN identifies the country where the vehicle was made.

| | | |
|---|---|---|
| A = 1980/2010 | L = 1990/2020 | Y = 2000/2030 |
| B = 1981/2011 | M = 1991/2021 | 1 = 2001/2031 |
| C = 1982/2012 | N = 1992/2022 | 2 = 2002/2032 |
| D = 1983/2013 | P = 1993/2023 | 3 = 2003/2033 |
| E = 1984/2014 | R = 1994/2024 | 4 = 2004/2034 |
| F = 1985/2015 | S = 1995/2025 | 5 = 2005/2035 |
| G = 1986/2016 | T = 1996/2026 | 6 = 2006/2036 |
| H = 1987/2017 | V = 1997/2027 | 7 = 2007/2037 |
| J = 1988/2018 | W = 1998/2028 | 8 = 2008/2038 |
| K = 1989/2019 | X = 1999/2029 | 9 = 2009/2039 |

**CHART 1–2**

The pattern repeats every 30 years for the year of manufacture.

### VEHICLE SAFETY CERTIFICATION LABEL

A vehicle safety certification label is attached to the left side pillar post on the rearward-facing section of the left front door. This label indicates the month and year of manufacture as well as the **gross vehicle weight rating (GVWR),** the **gross axle weight rating (GAWR),** and the vehicle identification number (VIN).

### VECI LABEL

The **vehicle emissions control information (VECI)** label under the hood of the vehicle shows informative settings and emission hose routing information. ● **SEE FIGURE 1–2.**

The VECI label (sticker) can be located on the bottom side of the hood, the radiator fan shroud, the radiator core support, or on the strut towers. The VECI label usually includes the following information:

- Engine identification
- Emissions standard that the vehicle meets
- Vacuum hose routing diagram
- Base ignition timing (if adjustable)
- Spark plug type and gap

**FIGURE 1–2** The vehicle emissions control information (VECI) sticker is placed under the hood.

**FIGURE 1–3** A typical calibration code sticker on the case of a controller. The information on the sticker is often needed when ordering parts or a replacement controller.

- Valve lash
- Emission calibration code

### CALIBRATION CODES

**Calibration codes** are usually located on powertrain control modules (PCMs) or other controllers. Whenever diagnosing an engine operating fault, it is often necessary to use the calibration code to be sure that the vehicle is the subject of a technical service bulletin or other service procedure. ● **SEE FIGURE 1–3.**

### CASTING NUMBERS

When an engine part such as a block is cast, a number is put into the mold to identify the casting. ● **SEE FIGURE 1–4.** These **casting numbers** can be used to identify the part and check dimensions such as the cubic inch displacement and other information, such as the year of manufacture. Sometimes changes are made to the mold, yet

**FIGURE 1–4** Casting numbers on major components can be either cast or stamped.

the casting number is not changed. Most often the casting number is the best piece of identifying information that the service technician can use for identifying an engine.

## SERVICE INFORMATION

**SERVICE MANUALS** Service information is used by the service technician to determine specifications and service procedures and any needed special tools.

Factory and aftermarket service manuals contain specifications and service procedures. While factory service manuals cover just one year and one or more models of the same vehicle, most aftermarket service manufacturers cover multiple years and/or models in one manual.

Included in most service manuals are the following:

- Capacities and recommended specifications for all fluids
- Specifications including engine and routine maintenance items
- Testing procedures
- Service procedures including the use of special tools when needed

**ELECTRONIC SERVICE INFORMATION** Electronic service information is available mostly by subscription and provides access to an Internet site where service manual–type information is available. ● **SEE FIGURE 1–5.** Most vehicle manufacturers also offer electronic service information to their dealers and to most schools and colleges that offer corporate training programs.

**TECHNICAL SERVICE BULLETINS** **Technical service bulletins,** often abbreviated **TSB,** sometimes called *technical service information bulletins (TSIB),* are issued by the vehicle manufacturer to notify service technicians of a problem and include the necessary corrective action. Technical service

**FIGURE 1–5** Electronic service information is available from aftermarket sources such as All-Data and Mitchell-on-Demand, as well as on websites hosted by vehicle manufacturers.

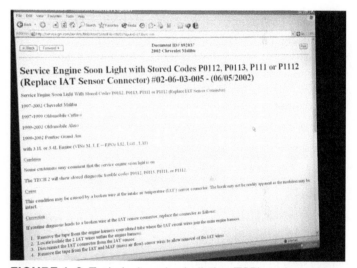

**FIGURE 1–6** Technical service bulletins (TSB) are issued by vehicle manufacturers when a fault occurs that affects many vehicles with the same problem. The TSB then provides the fix for the problem including any parts needed and detailed instructions.

bulletins are designed for dealership technicians but are republished by aftermarket companies and made available along with other service information to shops and vehicle repair facilities. ● **SEE FIGURE 1–6.**

**INTERNET** The Internet has opened the field for information exchange and access to technical advice. One of the most useful websites is the International Automotive Technician's Network at **www.iatn.net**. This is a free site, but service technicians must register to join. If a small monthly sponsor fee is paid, the shop or service technician can gain access to the archives, which include thousands of successful repairs in the searchable database.

? **FREQUENTLY ASKED QUESTION**

**What Should Be Included on a Work Order?**

A work order is a legal document that should include the following information:

1. Customer information
2. Identification of the vehicle including the VIN
3. Related service history information
4. The "three Cs":
   - Customer concern (complaint)
   - Cause of the concern
   - Correction or repairs that were required to return the vehicle to proper operation.

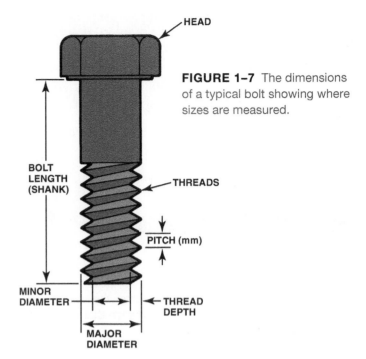

**FIGURE 1–7** The dimensions of a typical bolt showing where sizes are measured.

**RECALLS AND CAMPAIGNS** A **recall** or **campaign** is issued by a vehicle manufacturer and a notice is sent to all owners in the event of a safety-related fault or concern. While these faults may be repaired by shops, it is generally handled by a local dealer. Items that have created recalls in the past have included potential fuel system leakage problems, exhaust leakage, or electrical malfunctions that could cause a possible fire or the engine to stall. Unlike technical service bulletins whose cost is covered only when the vehicle is within the warranty period, a recall or campaign is always done at no cost to the vehicle owner.

## THREADED FASTENERS

**BOLTS AND THREADS** Most of the threaded fasteners used on vehicles are **bolts.** Bolts are called *cap* screws when they are threaded into a casting. Automotive service technicians usually refer to these fasteners as *bolts,* regardless of how they are used. In this chapter, they are called bolts. Sometimes, studs are used for threaded fasteners. A **stud** is a short rod with threads on both ends. Often, a stud will have coarse threads on one end and fine threads on the other end. The end of the stud with coarse threads is screwed into the casting. A nut is used on the opposite end to hold the parts together.

The fastener threads *must* match the threads in the casting or nut. The threads may be measured either in fractions of an inch (called fractional) or in metric units. The size is measured across the outside of the threads, called the *crest* of the thread. ● **SEE FIGURE 1–7.**

**FRACTIONAL BOLTS** Fractional threads are either coarse or fine. The coarse threads are called **unified national coarse (UNC),** and the fine threads are called **unified national fine (UNF).** Standard combinations of sizes and number of threads per inch (called **pitch**) are used. Pitch can be measured with a thread pitch gauge as shown in ● **FIGURE 1–8.** Bolts are identified by their diameter and length as measured from below the

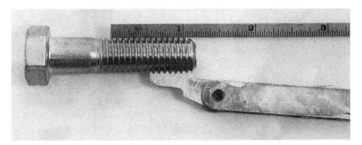

**FIGURE 1–8** Thread pitch gauge used to measure the pitch of the thread. This bolt has 13 threads to the inch.

? **FREQUENTLY ASKED QUESTION**

**How Many Types of Screw Heads Are Used in Automotive Applications?**

There are many, including Torx, hex (also called Allen), plus many others used in custom vans and motor homes. ● **SEE FIGURE 1–9.**

head and not by the size of the head or the size of the wrench used to remove or install the bolt.

Fractional thread sizes are specified by the diameter in fractions of an inch and the number of threads per inch. Typical UNC thread sizes would be 5/16-18 and 1/2-13. Similar UNF thread sizes would be 5/16-24 and 1/2-20. ● **SEE CHART 1–3.**

**METRIC BOLTS** The size of a **metric bolt** is specified by the letter *M* followed by the diameter in millimeters (mm) across the outside (crest) of the threads. Typical metric sizes would be M8 and M12. Fine metric threads are specified by the thread

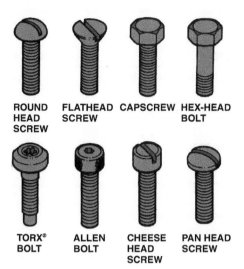

ROUND HEAD SCREW    FLATHEAD SCREW    CAPSCREW    HEX-HEAD BOLT

TORX® BOLT    ALLEN BOLT    CHEESE HEAD SCREW    PAN HEAD SCREW

**FIGURE 1–9** Bolts and screws have many different heads which determine what tool is needed.

## METRIC HEXAGON HEAD CAP SCREWS

### ALL MEASUREMENTS IN MILLIMETERS

M = NOMINAL THREAD DIAMETER
P = PITCH
D = HEAD SIZE ACROSS FLATS

| M | P | D | M | P | D | M | P | D |
|---|---|---|---|---|---|---|---|---|
| 1.6 | 0.35 | 3.2 | 10 | 1.00 | 17 | 20 | 1.50 | 30 |
| 1.7 | 0.35 | 3.5 | 10 | 1.25 | 17 | 20 | 2.50 | 30 |
| 2 | 0.40 | 4 | 10 | 1.50 | 17 | 22 | 1.50 | 32 |
| 2.3 | 0.40 | 4.5 | 12 | 1.25 | 19 | 22 | 2.50 | 32 |
| 2.5 | 0.45 | 5 | 12 | 1.50 | 19 | 24 | 2.00 | 36 |
| 3 | 0.50 | 5.5 | 12 | 1.75 | 19 | 24 | 3.00 | 36 |
| 3.5 | 0.60 | 6 | 14 | 1.50 | 22 | 27 | 3.00 | 41 |
| 4 | 0.70 | 7 | 14 | 2.00 | 22 | 30 | 3.50 | 46 |
| 5 | 0.80 | 8 | 16 | 1.50 | 24 | 33 | 3.50 | 50 |
| 6 | 1.00 | 10 | 16 | 2.00 | 24 | 36 | 4.00 | 55 |
| 7 | 1.00 | 11 | 18 | 1.50 | 27 | 39 | 4.00 | 60 |
| 8 | 1.00 | 13 | 18 | 2.50 | 27 | 42 | 4.50 | 65 |
| 8 | 1.25 | 13 | | | | 45 | 4.50 | 70 |

**FIGURE 1–10** The metric system specifies fasteners by diameter, length, and pitch.

diameter followed by X and the distance between the threads measured in millimeters (M8 X 1.5). ● **SEE FIGURE 1–10.**

**GRADES OF BOLTS**    Bolts are made from many different types of steel, and for this reason some are stronger than others. The strength or classification of a bolt is called the **grade.** The bolt heads are marked to indicate their grade strength.

The actual grade of bolts is two more than the number of lines on the bolt head. Metric bolts have a decimal number to indicate the grade. More lines or a higher grade number indicate a stronger bolt. In some cases, nuts and machine screws have similar grade markings. Higher grade bolts usually have threads that are rolled rather than cut, which also makes them stronger. ● **SEE FIGURE 1–11.**

| SIZE | THREADS PER INCH NC UNC | THREADS PER INCH NF UNF | OUTSIDE DIAMETER INCHES |
|---|---|---|---|
| 0 | .. | 80 | 0.0600 |
| 1 | 64 | .. | 0.0730 |
| 1 | .. | 72 | 0.0730 |
| 2 | 56 | .. | 0.0860 |
| 2 | .. | 64 | 0.0860 |
| 3 | 48 | .. | 0.0990 |
| 3 | .. | 56 | 0.0990 |
| 4 | 40 | .. | 0.1120 |
| 4 | .. | 48 | 0.1120 |
| 5 | 40 | .. | 0.1250 |
| 5 | .. | 44 | 0.1250 |
| 6 | 32 | .. | 0.1380 |
| 6 | .. | 40 | 0.1380 |
| 8 | 32 | .. | 0.1640 |
| 8 | .. | 36 | 0.1640 |
| 10 | 24 | .. | 0.1900 |
| 10 | .. | 32 | 0.1900 |
| 12 | 24 | .. | 0.2160 |
| 12 | .. | 28 | 0.2160 |
| 1/4 | 20 | .. | 0.2500 |
| 1/4 | .. | 28 | 0.2500 |
| 5/16 | 18 | .. | 0.3125 |
| 5/16 | .. | 24 | 0.3125 |
| 3/8 | 16 | .. | 0.3750 |
| 3/8 | .. | 24 | 0.3750 |
| 7/16 | 14 | .. | 0.4375 |
| 7/16 | .. | 20 | 0.4375 |
| 1/2 | 13 | .. | 0.5000 |
| 1/2 | .. | 20 | 0.5000 |
| 9/16 | 12 | .. | 0.5625 |
| 9/16 | .. | 18 | 0.5625 |
| 5/8 | 11 | .. | 0.6250 |
| 5/8 | .. | 18 | 0.6250 |
| 3/4 | 10 | .. | 0.7500 |
| 3/4 | .. | 16 | 0.7500 |
| 7/8 | 9 | .. | 0.8750 |
| 7/8 | .. | 14 | 0.8750 |
| 1 | 8 | .. | 1.0000 |
| 1 | .. | 12 | 1.0000 |
| 1 1/8 | 7 | .. | 1.1250 |
| 1 1/8 | .. | 12 | 1.1250 |
| 1 1/4 | 7 | .. | 1.2500 |
| 1 1/4 | .. | 12 | 1.2500 |
| 1 3/8 | 6 | .. | 1.3750 |
| 1 3/8 | .. | 12 | 1.3750 |
| 1 1/2 | 6 | .. | 1.5000 |
| 1 1/2 | .. | 12 | 1.5000 |
| 1 3/4 | 5 | .. | 1.7500 |
| 2 | 4 1/2 | .. | 2.0000 |
| 2 1/4 | 4 1/2 | .. | 2.2500 |
| 2 1/2 | 4 | .. | 2.5000 |
| 2 3/4 | 4 | .. | 2.7500 |
| 3 | 4 | .. | 3.0000 |
| 3 1/4 | 4 | .. | 3.2500 |
| 3 1/2 | 4 | .. | 3.5000 |
| 3 3/4 | 4 | .. | 3.7500 |
| 4 | 4 | .. | 4.0000 |

**CHART 1–3**

American standard is one method of sizing fasteners.

| SAE BOLT DESIGNATIONS | | | | |
|---|---|---|---|---|
| SAE GRADE NO. | SIZE RANGE | TENSILE STRENGTH, PSI | MATERIAL | HEAD MARKING |
| 1 | 1/4 through 1 1/2 | 60,000 | Low or medium carbon steel | |
| 2 | 1/4 through 3/4 | 74,000 | | |
| | 7/8 through 1 1/2 | 60,000 | | |
| 5 | 1/4 through 1 | 120,000 | Medium carbon steel, quenched and tempered | 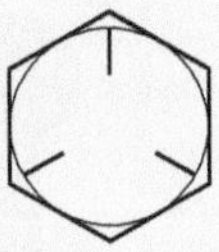 |
| | 1-1/8 through 1 1/2 | 105,000 | | |
| 5.2 | 1/4 through 1 | 120,000 | Low carbon martensite steel,* quenched and tempered | 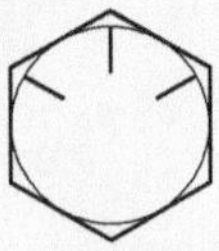 |
| 7 | 1/4 through 1 1/2 | 133,000 | Medium carbon alloy steel, quenched and tempered | 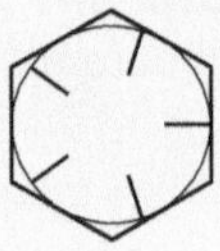 |
| 8 | 1/4 through 1 1/2 | 150,000 | Medium carbon alloy steel, quenched and tempered | 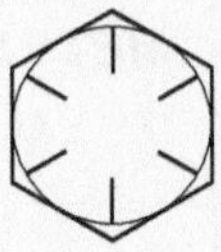 |
| 8.2 | 1/4 through 1 | 150,000 | Low carbon martensite steel,* quenched and tempered | 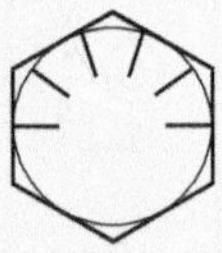 |

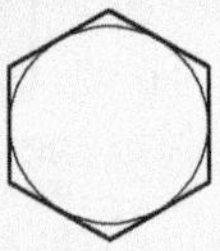

**CHART 1–4**

The tensile strength rating system as specified by the Society of Automotive Engineers (SAE).
*Martensite steel is steel that has been cooled rapidly, thereby increasing its hardness. It is named after a German metallurgist, Adolf Martens.

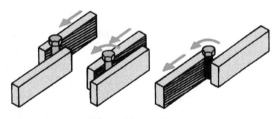

**ROLLING THREADS**

**FIGURE 1–11** Stronger threads are created by cold-rolling a heat-treated bolt blank instead of cutting the threads, using a die.

**CAUTION:** *Never* use hardware store (nongraded) bolts, studs, or nuts on any vehicle steering, suspension, or brake component. Always use the exact size and grade of hardware that is specified and used by the vehicle manufacturer.

**TENSILE STRENGTH OF FASTENERS** Graded fasteners have a higher tensile strength than nongraded fasteners. **Tensile strength** is the maximum stress used under tension (lengthwise force) without causing failure of the fastener. Tensile strength is specified in pounds per square inch (psi).

The strength and type of steel used in a bolt is supposed to be indicated by a raised mark on the head of the bolt. The type of mark depends on the standard to which the bolt was manufactured. Most often, bolts used in machinery are made to SAE Standard J429. ● **SEE CHART 1–4,** which shows the grade and specified tensile strength.

Metric bolt tensile strength property class is shown on the head of the bolt as a number, such as 4.6, 8.8, 9.8, and 10.9; the higher the number, the stronger the bolt. ● **SEE FIGURE 1–12.**

**NUTS** **Nuts** are the female part of a threaded fastener. Most nuts used on cap screws have the same hex size as the cap screw head. Some inexpensive nuts use a hex size larger than the cap screw head. Metric nuts are often marked with dimples to show their strength. More dimples indicate stronger nuts. Some nuts and cap screws use interference fit threads to keep them from accidentally loosening. This means that the shape of the nut is slightly distorted or that a section of the threads is deformed. Nuts can also be kept from loosening with a nylon washer fastened in the nut or with a nylon patch or strip on the threads. ● **SEE FIGURE 1–13.**

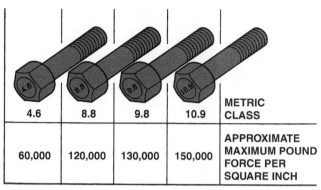

| | | | | METRIC CLASS |
|---|---|---|---|---|
| 4.6 | 8.8 | 9.8 | 10.9 | |
| 60,000 | 120,000 | 130,000 | 150,000 | APPROXIMATE MAXIMUM POUND FORCE PER SQUARE INCH |

**FIGURE 1–12** Metric bolt (cap screw) grade markings and approximate tensile strength.

**TECH TIP**

**A 1/2-Inch Wrench Does Not Fit a 1/2-Inch Bolt**

A common mistake made by persons new to the automotive field is to think that the size of a bolt or nut is the size of the head. The size of the bolt or nut (outside diameter of the threads) is usually smaller than the size of the wrench or socket that fits the head of the bolt or nut. Examples are given in the following table.

| Wrench Size | Thread Size |
|---|---|
| 7/16 in. | 1/4 in. |
| 1/2 in. | 5/16 in. |
| 9/16 in. | 3/8 in. |
| 5/8 in. | 7/16 in. |
| 3/4 in. | 1/2 in. |
| 10 mm | 6 mm |
| 12 mm or 13 mm* | 8 mm |
| 14 mm or 17 mm* | 10 mm |

*European (Système International d'Unités-SI) metric.

NOTE: Most of these "locking nuts" are grouped together and are commonly referred to as *prevailing torque nuts*. This means that the nut will hold its tightness or torque and not loosen with movement or vibration. Most prevailing torque nuts should be replaced whenever removed to ensure that the nut will not loosen during service. Always follow the manufacturer's recommendations. Anaerobic sealers, such as Loctite, are used on the threads where the nut or cap screw must be both locked and sealed.

**WASHERS** Washers are often used under cap screw heads and under nuts. ● **SEE FIGURE 1–14.** Plain flat washers are used to provide an even clamping load around the fastener. Lock washers are added to prevent accidental loosening. In some accessories, the washers are locked onto the nut to provide easy assembly.

| HEX NUT | JAM NUT | NYLON LOCK NUT | CASTLE NUT | ACORN NUT |

**FIGURE 1–13** Nuts come in a variety of styles, including locking (prevailing torque) types, such as the distorted thread and nylon insert type.

| FLAT WASHER | LOCK WASHER | STAR WASHER | STAR WASHER |

**FIGURE 1–14** Washers come in a variety of styles, including flat and serrated used to help prevent a fastener from loosening.

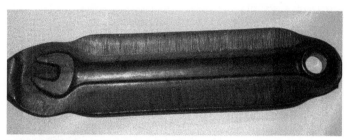

**FIGURE 1–15** A forged wrench after it has been forged but before the flashing, which is the extra material around the wrench, has been removed.

**TECH TIP**

**It Just Takes a Second**

Whenever removing any automotive component, it is wise to screw the bolts back into the holes a couple of threads by hand. This ensures that the right bolt will be used in its original location when the component or part is put back on the vehicle. Often, the same diameter of fastener is used on a component, but the length of the bolt may vary. Spending just a couple of seconds to put the bolts and nuts back where they belong when the part is removed can save a lot of time when the part is being reinstalled. Besides making certain that the right fastener is being installed in the right place, this method helps prevent bolts and nuts from getting lost or kicked away. How much time have you wasted looking for that lost bolt or nut?

## HAND TOOLS

**WRENCHES** Wrenches are the most used hand tool by service technicians. **Wrenches** are used to grasp and rotate threaded fasteners. Most wrenches are constructed of forged alloy steel, usually chrome-vanadium steel. ● **SEE FIGURE 1–15.**

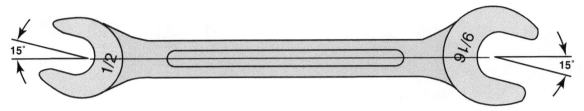

**FIGURE 1–16** A typical open-end wrench. The size is different on each end, and notice that the head is angled 15 degrees at the end.

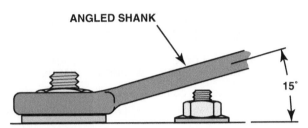

**FIGURE 1–17** The end of a box-end wrench is angled 15 degrees to allow clearance for nearby objects or other fasteners.

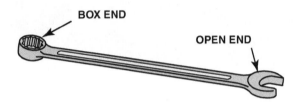

**FIGURE 1–18** A combination wrench has an open end at one end and a box end at the other end.

After the wrench is formed, the wrench is hardened, then tempered to reduce brittleness, and then chrome plated. There are several types of wrenches.

**OPEN-END WRENCH.** An open-end wrench is usually used to loosen or tighten bolts or nuts that do not require a lot of torque. Because of the open end, this type of wrench can be easily placed on a bolt or nut with an angle of 15 degrees, which allows the wrench to be flipped over and used again to continue to rotate the fastener. The major disadvantage of an open-end wrench is the lack of torque that can be applied due to the fact that the open jaws of the wrench contact only two flat surfaces of the fastener. An open-end wrench has two different sizes; one at each end. ● **SEE FIGURE 1–16.**

**BOX-END WRENCH.** A *box-end wrench,* also called a *closed-end wrench,* is placed over the top of the fastener and grips the points of the fastener. A box-end wrench is angled 15 degrees to allow it to clear nearby objects.

Therefore, a box-end wrench should be used to loosen or to tighten fasteners because it grasps around the entire head of the fastener. A box-end wrench has two different sizes; one at each end. ● **SEE FIGURE 1–17.**

Most service technicians purchase *combination wrenches,* which have the open end at one end and the same size box end on the other end. ● **SEE FIGURE 1–18.**

A combination wrench allows the technician to loosen or tighten a fastener using the box end of the wrench, turn it

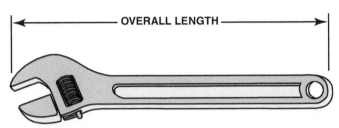

**FIGURE 1–19** An adjustable wrench. Adjustable wrenches are sized by the overall length of the wrench and not by how far the jaws open. Common sizes of adjustable wrenches include 8, 10, and 12 inch.

**FIGURE 1–20** The end of a typical line wrench, which shows that it is capable of grasping most of the head of the fitting.

around, and use the open end to increase the speed of rotating the fastener.

**ADJUSTABLE WRENCH.** An *adjustable wrench* is often used where the exact size wrench is not available or when a large nut, such as a wheel spindle nut, needs to be rotated but not tightened. An adjustable wrench should not be used to loosen or tighten fasteners because the torque applied to the wrench can cause the movable jaws to loosen their grip on the fastener, causing it to become rounded. ● **SEE FIGURE 1–19.**

**LINE WRENCHES.** Line wrenches are also called *flare-nut wrenches, fitting wrenches,* or *tube-nut wrenches* and are designed to grip almost all the way around a nut used to retain a fuel or refrigerant line and yet be able to be installed over the line. ● **SEE FIGURE 1–20.**

**SAFE USE OF WRENCHES** Wrenches should be inspected before use to be sure they are not cracked, bent, or damaged. All wrenches should be cleaned after use before being returned to the tool box. Always use the correct size of wrench for the fastener being loosened or tightened to help prevent the rounding of the flats of the fastener. When attempting to loosen a fastener, pull a wrench—do not push a wrench. If a wrench is pushed, your knuckles can be hurt when forced into another

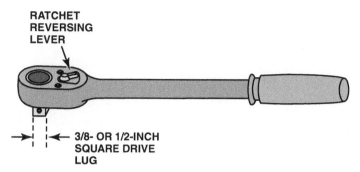

**FIGURE 1–21** A typical ratchet used to rotate a socket. A ratchet makes a ratcheting noise when it is being rotated in the opposite direction from loosening or tightening. A knob or lever on the ratchet allows the user to switch directions.

**FIGURE 1–22** A typical flex handle used to rotate a socket, also called a breaker bar because it usually has a longer handle than a ratchet and therefore can be used to apply more torque to a fastener than a ratchet.

TECH TIP

**Hide Those from the Boss**

An apprentice technician started working for a shop and put his top tool box on a workbench. Another technician observed that, along with a complete set of good-quality tools, the box contained several adjustable wrenches. The more experienced technician said, "Hide those from the boss." The boss does not want any service technician to use adjustable wrenches. If any adjustable wrench is used on a bolt or nut, the movable jaw often moves or loosens and starts to round the head of the fastener. If the head of the bolt or nut becomes rounded, it becomes that much more difficult to remove.

object if the fastener breaks loose or if the wrench slips. Always keep wrenches and all hand tools clean to help prevent rust and to allow for a better, firmer grip. Never expose any tool to excessive heat. High temperatures can reduce the strength ("draw the temper") of metal tools.

Never use a hammer on any wrench unless you are using a special "staking face" wrench designed to be used with a hammer. Replace any tools that are damaged or worn.

**RATCHETS, SOCKETS, AND EXTENSIONS** A **socket** fits over the fastener and grips the points and/or flats of the bolt or nut. The socket is rotated (driven) using either a long bar called a **breaker bar** (flex handle) or a ratchet. ● **SEE FIGURES 1–21 AND 1–22.**

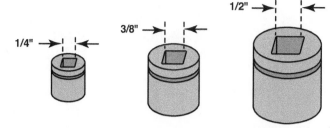

**FIGURE 1–23** The most commonly used socket drive sizes include 1/4-inch, 3/8-inch, and 1/2-inch drive.

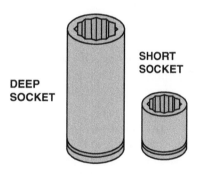

**FIGURE 1–24** A 6-point socket fits the head of a bolt or nut on all sides. A 12-point socket can round off the head of a bolt or nut if a lot of force is applied.

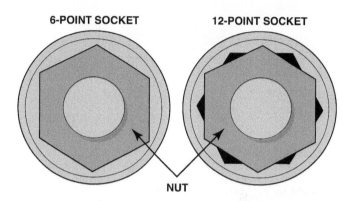

**FIGURE 1–25** Allows access to the nut that has a stud plus other locations needing great depth, such as spark plugs.

A **ratchet** is a tool that turns the socket in only one direction and allows the rotating of the ratchet handle back and forth in a narrow space. Socket **extensions** and **universal joints** are also used with sockets to allow access to fasteners in restricted locations.

**DRIVE SIZE.** Sockets are available in various **drive sizes,** including 1/4-inch, 3/8-inch, and 1/2-inch sizes for most automotive use. ● **SEE FIGURES 1–23 AND 1–24.**

Many heavy-duty truck and/or industrial applications use 3/4-inch and 1-inch sizes. The drive size is the distance of each side of the square drive. Sockets and ratchets of the same size are designed to work together.

**REGULAR AND DEEP WELL.** Sockets are available in regular length for use in most applications or in a deep well design that allows for access to a fastener that uses a long stud or other similar conditions. ● **SEE FIGURE 1–25.**

FIGURE 1–26 Using a clicker-type torque wrench to tighten connecting rod nuts on an engine.

 TECH TIP

**Right to Tighten**

It is sometimes confusing which way to rotate a wrench or screwdriver, especially when the head of the fastener is pointing away from you. To help visualize while looking at the fastener, say "righty tighty, lefty loosey."

**TORQUE WRENCHES** Torque wrenches are socket turning handles that are designed to apply a known amount of force to the fastener. The two basic types of torque wrenches are the following:

1. **Clicker type.** This type of torque wrench is first set to the specified torque, and then it "clicks" when the set torque value has been reached. When force is removed from the torque wrench handle, another click is heard. The setting on a clicker-type torque wrench should be set back to zero after use and checked for proper calibration regularly. ● **SEE FIGURE 1–26.**

2. **Beam-type.** This type of torque wrench is used to measure torque, but instead of presenting the value, the actual torque is displayed on the dial of the wrench as the fastener is being tightened. Beam-type torque wrenches are available in 1/4-inch, 3/8-inch, and 1/2-inch drives and both English and metric units. ● **SEE FIGURE 1–27.**

**SAFE USE OF SOCKETS AND RATCHETS** Always use the proper size socket that correctly fits the bolt or nut. All sockets and ratchets should be cleaned after use before being placed back into the toolbox. Sockets are available in short and deep well designs. Never expose any tool to excessive heat. High temperatures can reduce the strength ("draw the temper") of metal tools.

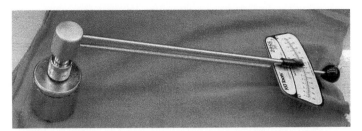

FIGURE 1–27 A beam-type torque wrench that displays the torque reading on the face of the dial. The beam display is read as the beam deflects, which is in proportion to the amount of torque applied to the fastener.

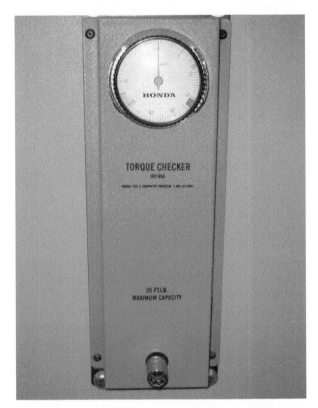

FIGURE 1–28 Torque wrench calibration checker.

 TECH TIP

**Check Torque Wrench Calibration Regularly**

Torque wrenches should be checked regularly. For example, Honda has a torque wrench calibration setup at each of their training centers. It is expected that a torque wrench be checked for accuracy before every use. Most experts recommend that torque wrenches be checked and adjusted as needed at least every year and more often if possible. ● **SEE FIGURE 1–28.**

Never use a hammer on a socket handle unless you are using a special "staking face" wrench designed to be used with a hammer. Replace any tools that are damaged or worn.

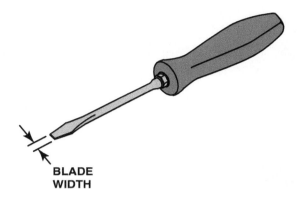

BLADE
WIDTH

FIGURE 1–29 A flat-tip (straight-blade) screwdriver. The width of the blade should match the width of the slot in the fastener being loosened or tightened.

FIGURE 1–30 Two stubby screwdrivers that are used to access screws that have limited space above. A straight blade is on top and a #2 Phillips screwdriver is on the bottom.

**TECH TIP**

**Use Socket Adapters with Caution**

A **socket adapter** allows the use of one size of socket and another drive size ratchet or breaker bar. Socket adapters are available and can be used for different drive size sockets on a ratchet. Combinations include the following:

- 1/4-in. drive—3/8-in. sockets
- 3/8-in. drive—1/4-in. sockets
- 3/8-in. drive—1/2-in. sockets
- 1/2-in. drive—3/8-in. sockets

Using a larger drive ratchet or breaker bar on a smaller size socket can cause the application of too much force to the socket, which could crack or shatter. Using a smaller size drive tool on a larger socket will usually not cause any harm but would greatly reduce the amount of torque that can be applied to the bolt or nut.

**TECH TIP**

**Avoid Using "Cheater Bars"**

Whenever a fastener is difficult to remove, some technicians will insert the handle of a ratchet or a breaker bar into a length of steel pipe sometimes called a **cheater bar.** The extra length of the pipe allows the technician to exert more torque than can be applied using the drive handle alone. However, the extra torque can easily overload the socket and ratchet, causing them to break or shatter, which could cause personal injury.

Also select the appropriate drive size. For example, for small work, such as on the dash, select a 1/4-inch drive. For most general service work, use a 3/8-inch drive, and for suspension and steering and other large fasteners, select a 1/2-inch drive. When loosening a fastener, always pull the ratchet toward you rather than push it outward.

## SCREWDRIVERS

**STRAIGHT-BLADE SCREWDRIVER.** Many smaller fasteners are removed and installed by using a **screwdriver.** Screwdrivers are available in many sizes and tip shapes. The most commonly used screwdriver is called a *straight blade* or *flat tip.*

Flat-tip screwdrivers are sized by the width of the blade, and this width should match the width of the slot in the screw. ● SEE FIGURE 1–29.

CAUTION: Do not use a screwdriver as a pry tool or as a chisel. Screwdrivers are hardened steel only at the tip and are not designed to be pounded on or used for prying because they could bend easily. Always use the proper tool for each application.

**PHILLIPS SCREWDRIVER.** Another type of commonly used screwdriver is called a Phillips screwdriver, named for Henry F. Phillips, who invented the crosshead screw in 1934. Because the shape of the crosshead screw and screwdriver, a Phillips screw can be driven with more torque than can be achieved with a slotted screw.

A Phillips head screwdriver is specified by the length of the handle and the size of the point at the tip. A #1 tip has a sharp point, a #2 tip is the most commonly used, and a #3 tip is blunt and is used only for larger sizes of Phillips head fasteners. For example, a #2 × 3-inch Phillips screwdriver would typically measure 6-inches from the tip of the blade to the end of the handle (3-inch long handle and 3-inch long blade) with a #2 tip.

Both straight-blade and Phillips screwdrivers are available with a short blade and handle for access to fasteners with limited room. ● SEE FIGURE 1–30.

**OFFSET SCREWDRIVERS.** Offset screwdrivers are used in places where a conventional screwdriver cannot fit. An offset screwdriver is bent at the ends and is used similarly to a wrench.

**FIGURE 1–31** An offset screwdriver is used to install or remove fasteners that do not have enough space above to use a conventional screwdriver.

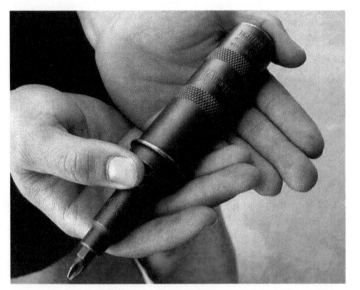

**FIGURE 1–32** An impact screwdriver used to remove slotted or Phillips head fasteners that cannot be broken loose using a standard screwdriver.

Most offset screwdrivers have a straight blade at one end and a Phillips end at the opposite end. ● **SEE FIGURE 1–31.**

**IMPACT SCREWDRIVER.** An *impact screwdriver* is used to break loose or tighten a screw. A hammer is used to strike the end after the screwdriver holder is placed in the head of the screw and rotated in the desired direction. The force from the hammer blow does two things: It applies a force downward holding the tip of the screwdriver in the slot and then applies a twisting force to loosen (or tighten) the screw. ● **SEE FIGURE 1–32.**

## SAFE USE OF SCREWDRIVERS
Always use the proper type and size screwdriver that matches the fastener. Try to avoid pressing down on a screwdriver because if it slips, the screwdriver tip could go into your hand, causing serious personal injury. All screwdrivers should be cleaned after use. Do not use a screwdriver as a pry bar; always use the correct tool for the job.

## HAMMERS AND MALLETS
**Hammers** and mallets are used to force objects together or apart. The shape of the back part of the hammer head (called the *peen*) usually determines

**FIGURE 1–33** A typical ball-peen hammer.

**FIGURE 1–34** A rubber mallet used to deliver a force to an object without harming the surface.

**FREQUENTLY ASKED QUESTION**

**What Is a Robertson Screwdriver?**

A Canadian named P. L. Robertson invented the Robertson screw and screwdriver in 1908, which uses a square-shaped tip with a slight taper. The Robertson screwdriver uses color-coded handles because different size screws required different tip sizes. The color and sizes include the following:

- Orange (#00)—Number 1 and 2 screws
- Yellow (#0)—Number 3 and 4 screws
- Green (#1)—Number 5, 6, and 7 screws
- Red (#2)—Number 8, 9, and 10 screws
- Black (#3)—Number 12 and larger screws

The Robertson screws are rarely found in the United States but are common in Canada.

the name. For example, a ball-peen hammer has a rounded end like a ball, and it is used to straighten oil pans and valve covers, using the hammer head, and for shaping metal, using the ball peen. ● **SEE FIGURE 1–33.**

**NOTE: A claw hammer has a claw used to remove nails and is not used for automotive service.**

A hammer is usually sized by the weight of the head of the hammer and the length of the handle. For example, a commonly used ball-peen hammer has an 8-ounce head with an 11-inch handle.

**MALLETS.** *Mallets* are a type of hammer with a large striking surface, which allows the technician to exert force over a larger area than a hammer, so as not to harm the part or component. Mallets are made from a variety of materials, including rubber, plastic, or wood. ● **SEE FIGURE 1–34.**

FIGURE 1–35 A dead-blow hammer that was left outside in freezing weather. The plastic covering was damaged, which destroyed this hammer. The lead shot is encased in the metal housing and then covered.

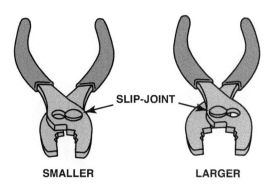

SMALLER          LARGER

FIGURE 1–36 Typical slip-joint pliers is a common house-hold pliers. The slip joint allows the jaws to be opened to two different settings.

**DEAD-BLOW HAMMER.** A shot-filled plastic hammer is called a *dead-blow hammer*. The small lead balls (shot) inside a plastic head prevent the hammer from bouncing off of the object when struck. ● **SEE FIGURE 1–35.**

## SAFE USE OF HAMMERS AND MALLETS
All mallets and hammers should be cleaned after use and not exposed to extreme temperatures. Never use a hammer or mallet that is damaged in any way and always use caution to avoid doing damage to the components and the surrounding area. Always follow the hammer manufacturer's recommended procedures and practices.

## PLIERS

**SLIP-JOINT PLIERS.** A **pliers** is capable of holding, twist-ing, bending, and cutting objects and is an extremely useful classification of tools. The common household type of pliers is called the *slip-joint pliers.* There are two different posi-tions where the junction of the handles meets to achieve a wide range of sizes of objects that can be gripped. ● **SEE FIGURE 1–36.**

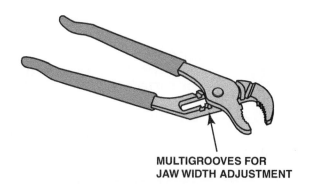

MULTIGROOVES FOR
JAW WIDTH ADJUSTMENT

FIGURE 1–37 Multigroove adjustable pliers is known by many names, including the trade name "Channel Locks®."

**MULTIGROOVE ADJUSTABLE PLIERS.** For gripping larger objects, a set of *multigroove adjustable pliers* is a commonly used tool of choice by many service technicians. Originally designed to remove the various size nuts holding rope seals used in water pumps, the name *water pump pliers* is also used. These types of pliers are commonly called by their trade name *Channel Locks®.* ● **SEE FIGURE 1–37.**

**LINESMAN'S PLIERS.** *Linesman's pliers* is a hand tool spe-cifically designed for cutting, bending, and twisting wire. While commonly used by construction workers and electricians, lines-man's pliers is a very useful tool for the service technician who deals with wiring. The center parts of the jaws are designed to grasp round objects such as pipe or tubing without slipping. ● **SEE FIGURE 1–38.**

**DIAGONAL PLIERS.** *Diagonal pliers* is designed to cut only. The cutting jaws are set at an angle to make it easier to cut wires. Diagonal pliers are also called *side cuts* or *dikes.* These pliers are constructed of hardened steel, and they are used mostly for cutting wire. ● **SEE FIGURE 1–39.**

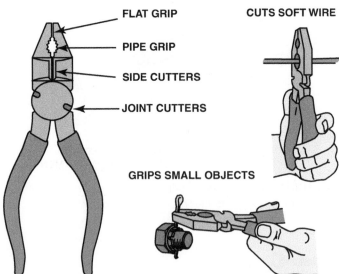

FLAT GRIP
PIPE GRIP
SIDE CUTTERS
JOINT CUTTERS

**FIGURE 1–38** Linesman's pliers are very useful because it can help perform many automotive service jobs.

CUTS SOFT WIRE

GRIPS SMALL OBJECTS

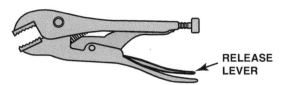

**FIGURE 1–40** Needle-nose pliers are used where there is limited access to a wire or pin that needs to be installed or removed.

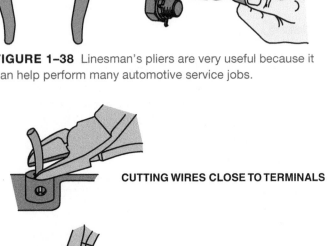

CUTTING WIRES CLOSE TO TERMINALS

PULLING OUT AND SPREADING COTTER PIN

**FIGURE 1–39** Diagonal-cut pliers is another common tool that has many names.

RELEASE LEVER

**FIGURE 1–41** Locking pliers are best known by their trade name Vise Grips®.

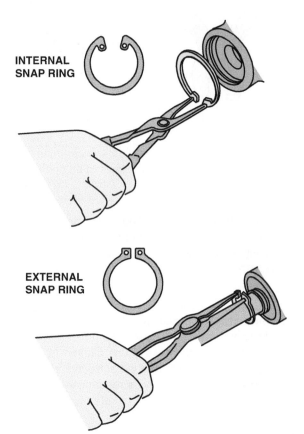

INTERNAL SNAP RING

EXTERNAL SNAP RING

**FIGURE 1–42** Snap-ring pliers are also called lock-ring pliers, and most are designed to remove internal and external snap rings (lock rings).

**NEEDLE-NOSE PLIERS.** *Needle-nose pliers* are designed to grip small objects or objects in tight locations. Needle-nose pliers have long, pointed jaws, which allow the tips to reach into narrow openings or groups of small objects. ● **SEE FIGURE 1–40.**

Most needle-nose pliers have a wire cutter located at the base of the jaws near the pivot. There are several variations of needle nose pliers, including right-angle jaws or slightly angled to allow access to certain cramped areas.

**LOCKING PLIERS.** *Locking pliers* are adjustable pliers that can be locked to hold objects from moving. Most locking pliers also have wire cutters built into the jaws near the pivot point. Locking pliers come in a variety of styles and sizes and are commonly referred to by the trade name *Vise Grips*®. The size is the length of the pliers, not how far the jaws open. ● **SEE FIGURE 1–41.**

**SNAP-RING PLIERS.** *Snap-ring pliers* is used to remove and install snap rings. Many snap-ring pliers are designed to be able to remove and install both inward and outward expanding snap

rings. Some snap-ring pliers can be equipped with serrated-tipped jaws for grasping the opening in the snap ring, while others are equipped with points that are inserted into the holes in the snap ring. ● **SEE FIGURE 1–42.**

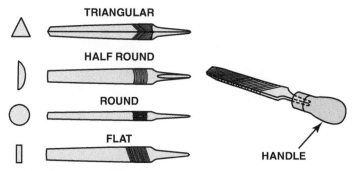

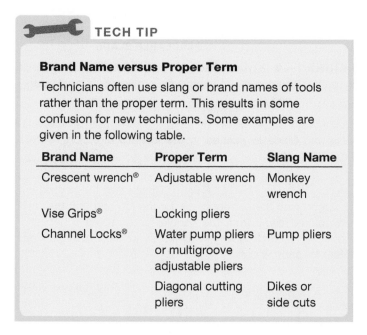

**FIGURE 1–43** Files come in many different shapes and sizes. Never use a file without a handle.

**SAFE USE OF PLIERS** Pliers should not be used to remove any bolt or other fastener. Pliers should be used only when specified for use by the vehicle manufacturer.

**FILES** Files are used to smooth metal and are constructed of hardened steel with diagonal rows of teeth. Files are available with a single row of teeth called a *single cut file,* as well as two rows of teeth cut at an opposite angle called a *double cut file.* Files are available in a variety of shapes and sizes from small flat files, half-round files, and triangular files. ● **SEE FIGURE 1–43.**

**SAFE USE OF FILES** Always use a file with a handle. Because files only cut when moved forward, a handle must be attached to prevent possible personal injury. After making a forward strike, lift the file and return the file to the starting position; avoid dragging the file backward.

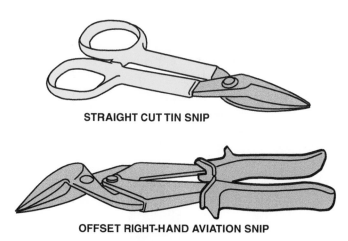

STRAIGHT CUT TIN SNIP

OFFSET RIGHT-HAND AVIATION SNIP

**FIGURE 1–44** Tin snips are used to cut thin sheets of metal or carpet.

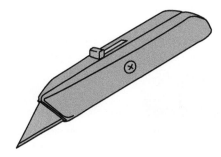

**FIGURE 1–45** A utility knife uses replaceable blades and is used to cut carpet and other materials.

**SNIPS** Service technicians are often asked to fabricate sheet metal brackets or heat shields and need to use one or more types of cutters available called **snips.** *Tin snips* are the simplest and are designed to make straight cuts in a variety of materials, such as sheet steel, aluminum, or even fabric. A variation of the tin snips is called *aviation tin snips.* There are three designs of aviation snips, including one designed to cut straight (called a *straight cut aviation snip*), one designed to cut left (called an *offset left aviation snip*), and one designed to cut right (called an *offset right aviation snip*). The handles are color coded for easy identification. These include yellow for straight, red for left, and green for right. ● **SEE FIGURE 1–44.**

**UTILITY KNIFE** A *utility knife* uses a replaceable blade and is used to cut a variety of materials such as carpet, plastic, wood, and paper products, such as cardboard. ● **SEE FIGURE 1–45.**

**SAFE USE OF CUTTERS** Whenever using cutters, always wear eye protection or a face shield to guard against the possibility of metal pieces being ejected during the cut. Always follow recommended procedures.

**PUNCHES** A **punch** is a small-diameter steel rod that has a smaller-diameter ground at one end. A punch is used to drive a pin out that is used to retain two components. Punches come in a variety of sizes, which are measured across the diameter of

PIN

**FIGURE 1–46** A punch used to drive pins from assembled components. This type of punch is also called a pin punch.

**FIGURE 1–47** Warning stamped on the side of a punch warning that goggles should be worn when using this tool. Always follow safety warnings.

the machined end. Sizes include 1/16-inch, 1/8-inch, 3/16-inch, and 1/4-inch. ● **SEE FIGURE 1–46.**

**CHISELS**    A **chisel** has a straight, sharp cutting end that is used for cutting off rivets or to separate two pieces of an assembly. The most common design of chisel used for automotive service work is called a *cold chisel.*

**SAFE USE OF PUNCHES AND CHISELS**    Always wear eye protection when using a punch or a chisel because the hardened steel is brittle and parts of the punch could fly off and cause serious personal injury. See the warning stamped on the side of this automotive punch in ● **FIGURE 1–47.**

The tops of punches and chisels can become rounded off from use, which is called "mushroomed." This material must be ground off to help avoid the possibility of the overhanging material being loosened and becoming airborne during use. ● **SEE FIGURE 1–48.**

**HACKSAWS**    A **hacksaw** is used to cut metals, such as steel, aluminum, brass, or copper. The cutting blade of a hacksaw is replaceable, and the sharpness and number of teeth can be varied to meet the needs of the job. Use 14 or 18 teeth per inch (TPI) for cutting plaster or soft metals, such as aluminum and copper. Use 24 or 32 teeth per inch for steel or pipe. Hacksaw blades should be installed with the teeth pointing away from the handle. This means that a hacksaw cuts only

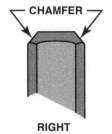

CHAMFER — MUSHROOM

RIGHT          WRONG

**FIGURE 1–48** Use a grinder or a file to remove the mushroom material on the end of a punch or chisel.

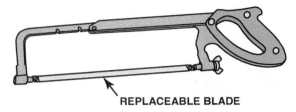

REPLACEABLE BLADE

**FIGURE 1–49** A typical hacksaw that is used to cut metal. If cutting sheet metal or thin objects, a blade with more teeth should be used.

while the blade is pushed in the forward direction. ● **SEE FIGURE 1–49.**

**SAFE USE OF HACKSAWS**    Check that the hacksaw is equipped with the correct blade for the job and that the teeth are pointed away from the handle. When using a hacksaw, move the hacksaw slowly away from you, then lift slightly and return for another cut.

## BASIC HAND TOOL LIST

The following is a typical list of hand tools every automotive technician should possess. Specialty tools are not included.

Safety glasses

Tool chest

1/4-in. drive socket set (1/4-inch to 9/16-inch standard and deep sockets; 6-mm to 15-mm standard and deep sockets)

1/4-in. drive ratchet

1/4-in. drive 2-in. extension

1/4-in. drive 6-in. extension

1/4-in. drive handle

3/8-in. drive socket set (3/8-in. to 7/8-in. standard and deep sockets; 10-mm to 19-mm standard and deep sockets)

3/8-in. drive Torx set (T40, T45, T50, and T55)

3/8-in. drive 13/16-in. plug socket

3/8-in. drive 5/8-in. plug socket

3/8-in. drive ratchet

3/8-in. drive 1 1/2-in. extension
3/8-in. drive 3-in. extension
3/8-in. drive 6-in. extension
3/8-in. drive 18-in. extension
3/8-in. drive universal
1/2-in. drive socket set (1/2-in. to 1-in. standard and
deep sockets)
1/2-in. drive ratchet
1/2-in. drive breaker bar
1/2-in. drive 5-in. extension
1/2-in. drive 10-in. extension
3/8-in. to 1/4-in. adapter
1/2-in. to 3/8-in. adapter
3/8-in. to 1/2-in. adapter
Crowfoot set (fractional in.)
Crowfoot set (metric)
3/8-in. through 1-in. combination wrench set
10-mm through 19-mm combination wrench set
1/16-in. through 1/4-in. hex wrench set
2-mm through 12-mm hex wrench set
3/8-in. hex socket
13-mm to 14-mm flare-nut wrench
15-mm to 17-mm flare-nut wrench
5/16-in. to 3/8-in. flare-nut wrench
7/16-in. to 1/2-in. flare-nut wrench
1/2-in. to 9/16-in. flare-nut wrench
Diagonal pliers
Needle pliers
Adjustable-jaw pliers
Locking pliers

Snap-ring pliers
Stripping or crimping pliers
Ball-peen hammer
Rubber hammer
Dead-blow hammer
Five-piece standard screwdriver set
Four-piece Phillips screwdriver set
#15 Torx screwdriver
#20 Torx screwdriver
Center punch
Pin punches (assorted sizes)
Chisel
Utility knife
Valve core tool
Filter wrench (large filters)
Filter wrench (smaller filters)
Test light
Feeler gauge
Scraper
Pinch bar
Magnet

## TOOL SETS AND ACCESSORIES

A beginning service technician may wish to start with a small set of tools before purchasing an expensive tool set. ● **SEE FIGURES 1–50 AND 1–51.**

**FIGURE 1–50** A typical beginning technician tool set that includes the basic tools to get started.

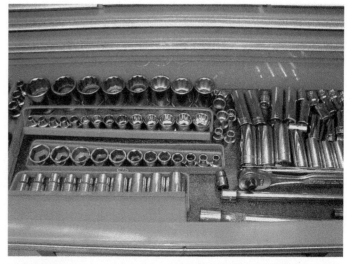

**FIGURE 1–51** A typical large tool box, showing just one of many drawers.

**FIGURE 1–52** A typical 12-volt test light.

 **TECH TIP**

**Need to Borrow a Tool More Than Twice? Buy It!**

Most service technicians agree that it is okay for a beginning technician to borrow a tool occasionally. However, if a tool has to be borrowed more than twice, then be sure to purchase it as soon as possible. Also, whenever a tool is borrowed, be sure that you clean the tool and let the technician you borrowed the tool from know that you are returning the tool. These actions will help in any future dealings with other technicians.

## ELECTRICAL HAND TOOLS

**TEST LIGHT**   A test light is used to test for electricity. A typical automotive test light consists of a clear plastic screwdriver-like handle that contains a lightbulb. A wire is attached to one terminal of the bulb, which the technician connects to a clean metal part of the vehicle. The other end of the bulb is attached to a point that can be used to test for electricity at a connector or wire. When there is power at the point and a good connection at the other end, the lightbulb lights. ● **SEE FIGURE 1–52.**

### SOLDERING GUNS

**ELECTRIC SOLDERING GUN.**   This type of soldering gun is usually powered by 110-volt AC and often has two power settings expressed in watts. A typical electric soldering gun will produce from 85 to 300 watts of heat at the tip, which is more than adequate for soldering.

**ELECTRIC SOLDERING PENCIL.**   This type of soldering iron is less expensive and creates less heat than an electric soldering gun. A typical electric soldering pencil (iron) creates 30 to 60 watts of heat and is suitable for soldering smaller wires and connections.

**BUTANE-POWERED SOLDERING IRON.**   A butane-powered soldering iron is portable and very useful for automotive service work because an electrical cord is not needed. Most butane-powered

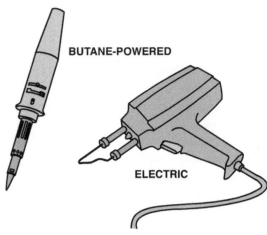

**FIGURE 1–53** An electric and butane-powered soldering guns used to make electrical repairs. Soldering guns are sold by the wattage rating. The higher the wattage, the greater the amount of heat created. Most solder guns used for automotive electrical work usually fall within the 60- to 160-watt range.

soldering irons produce about 60 watts of heat, which is enough for most automotive soldering. ● **SEE FIGURE 1–53.**

**ELECTRICAL WORK HAND TOOLS**   In addition to a soldering iron, most service technicians who do electrical-related work should have the following:

- Wire cutters
- Wire strippers
- Wire crimpers
- Heat gun for heat shrink tubing

**DIGITAL METER**   A digital meter is a necessary tool for any electrical diagnosis and troubleshooting. A digital multimeter, abbreviated DMM, is usually capable of measuring the following units of electricity:

- DC volts
- AC volts
- Ohms
- Amperes

## HAND TOOL MAINTENANCE

Most hand tools are constructed of rust-resistant metals, but they can still rust or corrode if not properly maintained. For best results and long tool life, the following steps should be taken:

- Clean each tool before placing it back into the toolbox.
- Keep tools separated. Moisture on metal tools will start to rust more readily if the tools are in contact with another metal tool.

**What Is an "SST"?**

Vehicle manufacturers often specify a **special service tool (SST)** to properly disassemble and assemble components, such as transmissions and other components. These tools are also called special tools and are available from the vehicle manufacturer or their tool supplier, such as Kent-Moore and Miller tools. Many service technicians do not have access to special service tools, so they use generic versions that are available from aftermarket sources.

- Line the drawers of the toolbox with a material that will prevent the tools from moving as the drawers are opened and closed. This helps to quickly locate the proper tool and size.

- Release the tension on all "clicker-type" torque wrenches.

- Keep the toolbox secure.

## TROUBLE LIGHTS

**INCANDESCENT** *Incandescent lights* use a filament that produces light when electric current flows through the bulb. This was the standard **trouble light,** also called a *work light* for many years until safety issues caused most shops to switch to safer fluorescent or LED lights. If incandescent lightbulbs are used, try to locate bulbs that are rated "rough service," which are designed to withstand shock and vibration more than conventional lightbulbs.

**FIGURE 1–54** A fluorescent trouble light operates cooler and is safer to use in the shop because it is protected against accidental breakage where gasoline or other flammable liquids would happen to come in contact with the light.

Do not use incandescent trouble lights around gasoline or other flammable liquids. The liquids can cause the bulb to break, and the hot filament can ignite the flammable liquid, which can cause personal injury or even death.

**FLUORESCENT** A trouble light is an essential piece of shop equipment and, for safety, should be fluorescent rather than incandescent. Incandescent lightbulbs can scatter or break if gasoline were to be splashed onto the bulb, creating a serious fire hazard. Fluorescent light tubes are not as likely to be broken and are usually protected by a clear plastic enclosure. Trouble lights are usually attached to a retractor, which can hold 20 to 50 feet of electrical cord. ● **SEE FIGURE 1–54.**

**LED TROUBLE LIGHT** **Light-emitting diode (LED)** trouble lights are excellent to use because they are shock resistant and long lasting and do not represent a fire hazard. Some trouble lights are battery powered and therefore can be used in places where an attached electrical cord could present problems.

## AIR AND ELECTRICALLY OPERATED TOOLS

**IMPACT WRENCH** An impact wrench, either air or electrically powered, is a tool that is used to remove and install fasteners. The air-operated 1/2-inch drive impact wrench is the most commonly used unit. ● **SEE FIGURE 1–55.**

**FIGURE 1–55** A typical 1/2-inch drive air impact wrench. The direction of rotation can be changed to loosen or tighten a fastener.

Electrically powered impact wrenches commonly include the following:

- Battery-powered units. ● **SEE FIGURE 1–56.**
- 110-volt AC-powered units. This type of impact is very useful, especially if compressed air is not readily available.

> ☠ **WARNING**
>
> Always use impact sockets with impact wrenches and always wear eye protection in case the socket or fastener shatters. Impact sockets are thicker walled and constructed with premium alloy steel. They are hardened with a black oxide finish to help prevent corrosion and distinguish them from regular sockets. ● **SEE FIGURE 1–57.**

**AIR RATCHET** An air ratchet is used to remove and install fasteners that would normally be removed or installed using a ratchet and a socket. ● **SEE FIGURE 1–58.**

**DIE GRINDER** A die grinder is a commonly used air-powered tool that can also be used to sand or remove gaskets and rust. ● **SEE FIGURE 1–59.**

**BENCH- OR PEDESTAL-MOUNTED GRINDER** These high-powered grinders can be equipped with a wire brush wheel and/or a stone wheel:

- **Wire brush wheel.** This type is used to clean threads of bolts as well as to remove gaskets from sheet metal engine parts.
- **Stone wheel.** This type is used to grind metal or to remove the mushroom from the top of punches or chisels. ● **SEE FIGURE 1–60.**

**FIGURE 1–56** A typical battery-powered 3/8-inch drive impact wrench.

**FIGURE 1–58** An air ratchet is a very useful tool that allows fast removal and installation of fasteners, especially in areas that are difficult to reach or do not have room enough to move a hand ratchet or wrench.

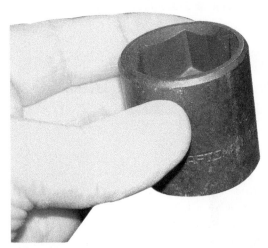

**FIGURE 1–57** A black impact socket. Always use an impact-type socket whenever using an impact wrench to avoid the possibility of shattering the socket, which could cause personal injury.

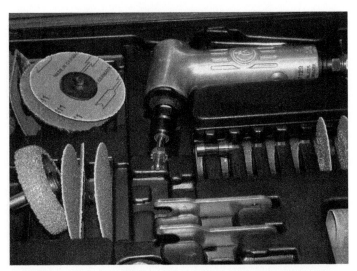

**FIGURE 1–59** This typical die grinder surface preparation kit includes the air-operated die grinder as well as a variety of sanding disks for smoothing surfaces or removing rust.

FIGURE 1–60 A typical pedestal grinder with a wire wheel on the left side and a stone wheel on the right side. Even though this machine is equipped with guards, safety glasses or a face shield should always be worn whenever using a grinder or wire wheel.

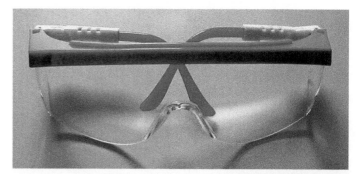

FIGURE 1–61 Safety glasses should be worn at all times when working on or around any vehicle or servicing any components.

> ☠ **WARNING**
>
> Always wear a face shield when using a wire wheel or a grinder.

Most **bench grinders** are equipped with a grinder wheel (stone) on one end and a wire brush wheel on the other end. A bench grinder is a very useful piece of shop equipment, and the wire wheel end can be used for the following:

- Cleaning threads of bolts
- Cleaning gaskets from sheet metal parts, such as steel valve covers

**CAUTION: Use a steel wire brush only on steel or iron components. If a steel wire brush is used on aluminum or copper-based metal parts, it can remove metal from the part.**

The grinding stone end of the bench grinder can be used for the following:

- Sharpening blades and drill bits
- Grinding off the heads of rivets or parts
- Sharpening sheet metal parts for custom fitting

## PERSONAL PROTECTIVE EQUIPMENT

Service technicians should wear **personal protective equipment (PPE)** to prevent personal injury. The personal protection devices include the following:

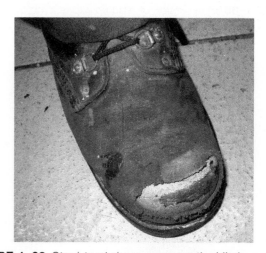

FIGURE 1–62 Steel-toed shoes are a worthwhile investment to help prevent foot injury due to falling objects. Even these well-worn shoes can protect the feet of this service technician.

**SAFETY GLASSES** Wear safety glasses at all times while servicing any vehicle and be sure that they meet standard ANSI Z87.1. ● **SEE FIGURE 1–61.**

**STEEL-TOED SAFETY SHOES** ● **SEE FIGURE 1–62.** If steel-toed safety shoes are not available, then leather-topped shoes offer more protection than canvas or cloth.

**BUMP CAP** Service technicians working under a vehicle should wear a **bump cap** to protect the head against under-vehicle objects and the pads of the lift. ● **SEE FIGURE 1–63.**

**HEARING PROTECTION** Hearing protection should be worn if the sound around you requires that you raise your voice (sound level higher than 90 dB). For example, a typical lawn-mower produces noise at a level of about 110 dB. This means that everyone who uses a lawnmower or other lawn or garden equipment should wear ear protection.

**GLOVES** Many technicians wear gloves not only to help keep their hands clean but also to help protect their skin from the effects of dirty engine oil and other possibly hazardous materials.

**FIGURE 1–63** One version of a bump cap is a molded plastic insert that is worn inside a regular cloth cap.

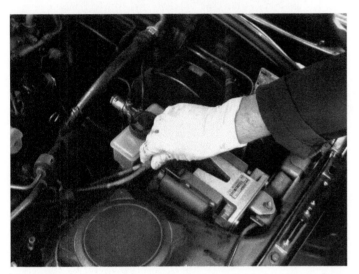

**FIGURE 1–64** Protective gloves are available in several sizes and materials.

Several types of gloves and their characteristics include the following:

- **Latex surgical gloves.** These gloves are relatively inexpensive but tend to stretch, swell, and weaken when exposed to gas, oil, or solvents.

- **Vinyl gloves.** These gloves are also inexpensive and are not affected by gas, oil, or solvents.

- **Polyurethane gloves.** These gloves are more expensive yet very strong. Even though these gloves are also not affected by gas, oil, or solvents, they do tend to be slippery.

- **Nitrile gloves.** These gloves are exactly like latex gloves but are not affected by gas, oil, or solvents, yet they tend to be expensive.

- **Mechanic's gloves.** These gloves are usually made of synthetic leather and spandex and provide thermo protection as well as protection from dirt and grime. ● **SEE FIGURE 1–64.**

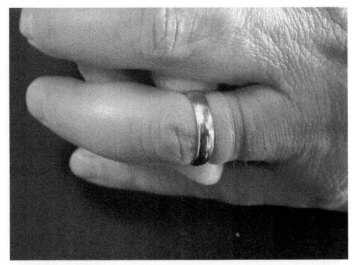

**FIGURE 1–65** Remove all jewelry before performing service work on any vehicle.

## SAFETY PRECAUTIONS

Besides wearing personal safety equipment, there are also many actions that should be performed to keep safe in the shop. These actions include the following:

- Remove jewelry that may get caught on something or act as a conductor to an exposed electrical circuit. ● **SEE FIGURE 1–65.**

- Take care of your hands. Keep your hands clean by washing with soap and hot water that is at least 110°F (43°C).

- Avoid loose or dangling clothing.

- When lifting any object, get a secure grip with solid footing. Keep the load close to your body to minimize the strain. Lift with your legs and arms, not your back.

- Do not twist your body when carrying a load. Instead, pivot your feet to help prevent strain on the spine.

- Ask for help when moving or lifting heavy objects.

- Push a heavy object rather than pull it. (This is opposite to the way you should work with tools—never push a wrench! If you do and a bolt or nut loosens, your entire weight is used to propel your hand[s] forward. This usually results in cuts, bruises, or other painful injury.)

- Always connect an exhaust hose to the tailpipe of any running vehicle to help prevent the buildup of carbon monoxide inside a closed garage space. ● **SEE FIGURE 1–66.**

- When standing, keep objects, parts, and tools with which you are working between chest height and waist height. If seated, work at tasks that are at elbow height.

- Always be sure the hood is securely held open.

**FIGURE 1-66** Always connect an exhaust hose to the tailpipe of a vehicle to be run inside a building.

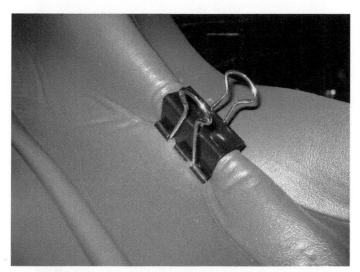

**FIGURE 1-67** A binder clip being used to keep a fender cover from falling off.

**FIGURE 1-68** Covering the interior as soon as the vehicle comes in for service helps improve customer satisfaction.

SAFETY TIP

**Shop Cloth Disposal**

Always dispose of oily shop cloths in an enclosed container to prevent a fire. ● **SEE FIGURE 1-69.** Whenever oily cloths are thrown together on the floor or workbench, a chemical reaction can occur, that can ignite the cloth even without an open flame. This process of ignition without an open flame is called **spontaneous combustion.**

## VEHICLE PROTECTION

**FENDER COVERS** Whenever working under the hood of any vehicle, be sure to use fender covers. They not only help protect the vehicle from possible damage but also provide a clean surface to place parts and tools. The major problem with using fender covers is that they tend to move and often fall off the vehicle. To help prevent the fender covers from falling off, secure them to a lip of the fender using a *binder clip* available at most office supply stores. ● **SEE FIGURE 1-67.**

**INTERIOR PROTECTION** Always protect the interior of the vehicle from accidental damage or dirt and grease by covering the seat, steering wheel, and floor with a protective covering. ● **SEE FIGURE 1-68.**

## SAFETY LIFTING (HOISTING) A VEHICLE

Many chassis and underbody service procedures require that the vehicle be hoisted or lifted off the ground. The simplest methods involve the use of drive-on ramps or a floor jack and safety (jack) stands, whereas in-ground or surface-mounted lifts provide greater access.

*Setting the pads is a critical part of this hoisting procedure.* All vehicle service information, including service, shop, and owner's manuals, include recommended locations to be used when hoisting (lifting) a vehicle. Newer vehicles have a triangle decal on the driver's door indicating the recommended lift points. The recommended standards for the lift points and lifting procedures are found in SAE Standard JRP-2184. ● **SEE FIGURE 1–70.**

These recommendations typically include the following points:

1. The vehicle should be centered on the lift or hoist so as not to overload one side or put too much force either forward or rearward. ● **SEE FIGURE 1–71.**

2. The pads of the lift should be spread as far apart as possible to provide a stable platform.

3. Each pad should be placed under a portion of the vehicle that is strong and capable of supporting the weight of the vehicle.

   a. Pinch welds at the bottom edge of the body are generally considered to be strong.

**FIGURE 1–69** All oily shop cloths should be stored in a metal container equipped with a lid to help prevent spontaneous combustion.

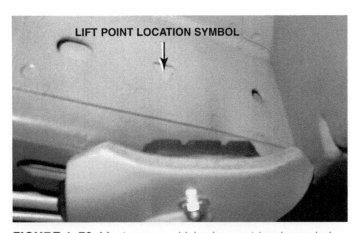

**FIGURE 1–70** Most newer vehicles have a triangle symbol indicating the recommended hoisting lift location.

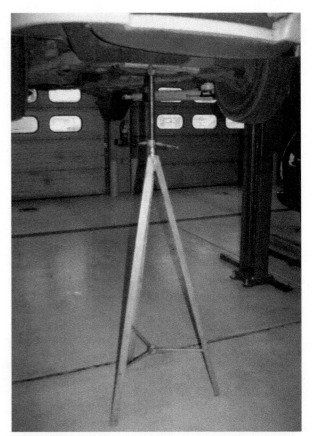

(a)

(b)

**FIGURE 1–71** (a) Tall safety stands can be used to provide additional support for the vehicle while on the hoist. (b) A block of wood should be used to avoid the possibility of doing damage to components supported by the stand.

**CAUTION: Even though pinch weld seams are the recommended location for hoisting many vehicles with unitized bodies (unit-body), care should be taken not to place the pad(s) too far forward or rearward. Incorrect placement of the vehicle on the lift could cause the vehicle to be imbalanced, and the vehicle could fall. This is exactly what happened to the vehicle in ● FIGURE 1–72.**

   b. Boxed areas of the body are the best places to position the pads on a vehicle without a frame. Be careful

**FIGURE 1–72** This training vehicle fell from the hoist because the pads were not set correctly. No one was hurt, but the vehicle was damaged.

to note whether the arms of the lift might come into contact with other parts of the vehicle before the pad touches the intended location. Commonly damaged areas include the following:

(1) Rocker panel moldings

(2) Exhaust system (including catalytic converter)

(3) Tires or body panels (● **SEE FIGURES 1–73 AND 1–74.**)

4. The vehicle should be raised about a foot (30 centimeters [cm]) off the floor, then stopped and shaken to check for stability. If the vehicle seems to be stable when checked at a short distance from the floor, continue raising the vehicle and continue to view the vehicle until it has reached the desired height. The hoist should be lowered onto the mechanical locks and then raised off of the locks before lowering.

**CAUTION: Do not look away from the vehicle while it is being raised (or lowered) on a hoist. Often one side or one end of the hoist can stop or fail, resulting in the vehicle being slanted enough to slip or fall, creating physical damage not only to the vehicle and/or hoist but also to the technician or others who may be nearby.**

**HINT: Most hoists can be safely placed at any desired height. For ease while working, the area in which you are working should be at chest level. When working on brakes or suspension components, it is not necessary to work on them down near the floor or over your head. Raise the hoist so that the components are at chest level.**

5. Before lowering the hoist, the safety latch(es) must be released and the direction of the controls reversed. The speed downward is often adjusted to be as slow as possible for additional safety.

(a)

(b)

**FIGURE 1–73** (a) An assortment of hoist pad adapters that are often needed to safely hoist many pickup trucks, vans, and sport utility vehicles (SUVs). (b) A view from underneath a Chevrolet pickup truck showing how the pad extensions are used to attach the hoist lifting pad to contact the frame.

## JACKS AND SAFETY STANDS

Floor jacks properly rated for the weight of the vehicle being raised are a common vehicle lifting tool. Floor jacks are portable and relatively inexpensive and must be used with safety (jack) stands. The floor jack is used to raise the vehicle off the ground, and safety stands should be placed under the frame on the body of the vehicle. The weight of the vehicle should never

(a)

(b)

**FIGURE 1–74** (a) The pad arm is just contacting the rocker panel of the vehicle. (b) The pad arm has dented the rocker panel on this vehicle because the pad was set too far inward underneath the vehicle.

be kept on the hydraulic floor jack because a failure of the jack could cause the vehicle to fall. ● **SEE FIGURE 1–75.** The jack is then slowly released to allow the vehicle weight to be supported on the safety stands. If the front or rear of the vehicle is being raised, the opposite end of the vehicle must be blocked.

CAUTION: Safety stands should be rated higher than the weight they support.

## DRIVE-ON RAMPS

Ramps are an inexpensive way to raise the front or rear of a vehicle. ● **SEE FIGURE 1–76.** Ramps are easy to store, but they can be dangerous because they can "kick out" when driving the vehicle onto the ramps.

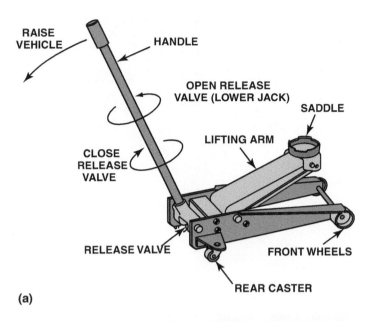

(a)

(b)

**FIGURE 1–75** (a) A typical 3-ton (6,000-pound) capacity hydraulic jack. (b) Whenever a vehicle is raised off the ground, a safety stand should be placed under the frame, axle, or body to support the weight of the vehicle.

CAUTION: Professional repair shops do not use ramps because they are dangerous to use. Use only with extreme care.

## ELECTRICAL CORD SAFETY

Use correctly grounded three-prong sockets and extension cords to operate power tools. Some tools use only two-prong plugs. Make sure these are double insulated and repair or replace any electrical cords that are cut or damaged to prevent the possibility of an electrical shock. When not in use, keep electrical cords off the floor to prevent tripping over them. Tape the cords down if they are placed in high-foot-traffic areas.

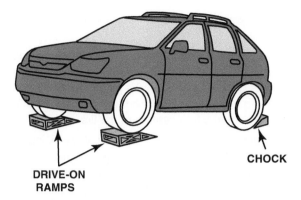

FIGURE 1–76 Drive-on-type ramps are dangerous to use. The wheels on the ground level must be chocked (blocked) to prevent accidental movement down the ramp.

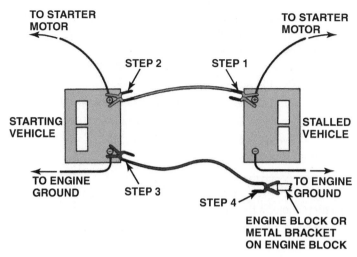

FIGURE 1–77 Jumper cable usage guide. Follow the same connections if using a portable jump box.

## JUMP-STARTING AND BATTERY SAFETY

To jump-start another vehicle with a dead battery, connect good-quality copper jumper cables as indicated in ● FIGURE 1–77 or a jump box. The last connection made should always be on the engine block or an engine bracket as far from the battery as possible. It is normal for a spark to be created when the jumper cables finally complete the jumping circuit, and this spark could cause an explosion of the gases around the battery. Many newer vehicles have special ground connections built away from the battery just for the purpose of jump-starting. Check the owner's manual or service information for the exact location.

Batteries contain acid and should be handled with care to avoid tipping them greater than a 45-degree angle. Always remove jewelry when working around a battery to avoid the possibility of electrical shock or burns, which can occur when the metal comes in contact with a 12-volt circuit and ground, such as the body of the vehicle.

FIGURE 1–78 The air pressure going to the nozzle should be reduced to 30 psi or less to help prevent personal injury.

### ✚ SAFETY TIP

**Air Hose Safety**

Improper use of an air nozzle can cause blindness or deafness. Compressed air must be reduced to less than 30 psi (206 kPa). ● SEE FIGURE 1–78. If an air nozzle is used to dry and clean parts, make sure the airstream is directed away from anyone else in the immediate area. Coil and store air hoses when they are not in use.

## FIRE EXTINGUISHERS

There are four **fire extinguisher classes.** Each class should be used on specific fires only:

- **Class A** is designed for use on general combustibles, such as cloth, paper, and wood.
- **Class B** is designed for use on flammable liquids and greases, including gasoline, oil, thinners, and solvents.
- **Class C** is used only on electrical fires.
- **Class D** is effective only on combustible metals, such as powdered aluminum, sodium, or magnesium.

The class rating is clearly marked on the side of every fire extinguisher. Many extinguishers are good for multiple types of fires. ● **SEE FIGURE 1–79.**

When using a fire extinguisher, remember the word "PASS":

P = Pull the safety pin.

A = Aim the nozzle of the extinguisher at the base of the fire.

S = Squeeze the lever to actuate the extinguisher.

S = Sweep the nozzle from side to side.

● **SEE FIGUR E 1–80.**

## TYPES OF FIRE EXTINGUISHERS
Types of fire extinguishers include the following:

- **Water.** A water fire extinguisher, usually in a pressurized container, is good to use on Class A fires by reducing

the temperature to the point where a fire cannot be sustained.

- **Carbon dioxide ($CO_2$).** A carbon dioxide fire extinguisher is good for almost any type of fire, especially Class B or Class C materials. A $CO_2$ fire extinguisher works by removing the oxygen from the fire, and the cold $CO_2$ also helps reduce the temperature of the fire.

- **Dry chemical (yellow).** A dry chemical fire extinguisher is good for Class A, B, or C fires by coating the flammable materials, which eliminates the oxygen from the fire. A dry chemical fire extinguisher tends to be very corrosive and will cause damage to electronic devices.

## FIRE BLANKETS

**Fire blankets** are required to be available in the shop areas. If a person is on fire, a fire blanket should be removed from its storage bag and thrown over and around the victim to smother the fire. ● **SEE FIGURE 1–81** showing a typical fire blanket.

## FIRST AID AND EYE WASH STATIONS

All shop areas must be equipped with a first aid kit and an eye wash station centrally located and kept stocked with emergency supplies. ● **SEE FIGURE 1–82.**

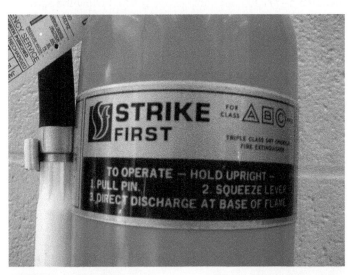

**FIGURE 1–79** A typical fire extinguisher designed to be used on Class A, B, or C fires.

**FIGURE 1–80** A $CO_2$ fire extinguisher being used on a fire set in an open drum during a demonstration at a fire training center.

**FIGURE 1–81** A treated wool blanket is kept in an easy-to-open wall-mounted holder and should be placed in a central location in the shop.

FIGURE 1–82 A first aid box should be centrally located in the shop and kept stocked with the recommended supplies.

FIGURE 1–83 A typical eye wash station. Often a thorough flushing of the eyes with water is the first and often the best treatment in the event of eye contamination.

**FIRST AID KIT**   A first aid kit should include the following:

- Bandages (variety)
- Gauze pads
- Roll gauze
- Iodine swab sticks
- Antibiotic ointment
- Hydrocortisone cream
- Burn gel packets
- Eye wash solution
- Scissors
- Tweezers
- Gloves
- First aid guide

Every shop should have a person trained in first aid. If there is an accident, call for help immediately.

**EYE WASH STATION**   An **eye wash station** should be centrally located and used whenever any liquid or chemical gets into the eyes. If such an emergency does occur, keep eyes in a constant stream of water and call for professional assistance. ● **SEE FIGURE 1–83.**

## HYBRID ELECTRIC VEHICLE SAFETY ISSUES

**Hybrid electric vehicles (HEVs)** use a high-voltage battery pack and an electric motor(s) to help propel the vehicle. ● **SEE FIGURE 1–84** for an example of a typical warning label on a hybrid electric vehicle. The gasoline or diesel engine also is equipped with a generator or a combination starter and an integrated starter generator (ISG) or integrated starter alternator (ISA).

**FIGURE 1–84** A warning label on a Honda hybrid warns that a person can be killed because of the high-voltage circuits under the cover.

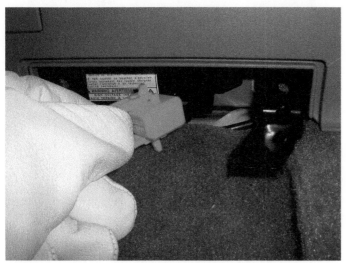

**FIGURE 1–85** The high-voltage disconnect switch is in the trunk area on a Toyota Prius. Insulated rubber lineman's gloves should be worn when removing this plug. (Courtesy of Tony Martin)

To safely work around a hybrid electric vehicle, the high-voltage (HV) battery and circuits should be shut off following these steps:

**STEP 1** Turn off the ignition key (if equipped) and remove the key from the ignition switch. (This will shut off all high-voltage circuits if the relay[s] is [are] working correctly.)

**STEP 2** Disconnect the high-voltage circuits.

**TOYOTA PRIUS** The cutoff switch is located in the trunk. To gain access, remove three clips holding the upper left portion of the trunk side cover. To disconnect the high-voltage system, pull the orange handled plug while wearing insulated rubber lineman's gloves. ● **SEE FIGURE 1–85.**

**FIGURE 1–86** The high-voltage shutoff switch on a Ford Escape hybrid. The switch is located under the carpet at the rear of the vehicle.

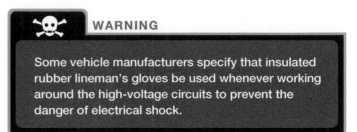

**WARNING**

Some vehicle manufacturers specify that insulated rubber lineman's gloves be used whenever working around the high-voltage circuits to prevent the danger of electrical shock.

**FORD ESCAPE/MERCURY MARINER** Ford and Mercury specify that the following steps should be included when working with the high-voltage (HV) systems of a hybrid vehicle:

■ Four orange cones are to be placed at the four corners of the vehicle to create a buffer zone.

■ High-voltage insulated gloves are to be worn with an outer leather glove to protect the inner rubber glove from possible damage.

■ The service technician should also wear a face shield, and a fiberglass hook should be in the area and used to move a technician in the event of electrocution.

The high-voltage shutoff switch is located in the rear of the vehicle under the right-side carpet. ● **SEE FIGURE 1–86.** Rotate the handle to the "service shipping" position, lift it out to disable the high-voltage circuit, and wait 5 minutes before removing high-voltage cables.

**HONDA CIVIC** To totally disable the high-voltage system on a Honda Civic, remove the main fuse (labeled number 1) from the driver's-side underhood fuse panel. This should be all that is necessary to shut off the high-voltage circuit. If this is not possible, then remove the rear seat cushion and seat back. Remove the metal switch cover labeled "up" and remove the red locking cover. Move the "battery module switch" down to disable the high-voltage system.

FIGURE 1–87 The shutoff switch on a GM parallel hybrid truck is green because this system uses 42 volts instead of higher, possibly fatal voltages used in other hybrid vehicles.

## CHEVROLET SILVERADO/GMC SIERRA PICKUP TRUCK

The high-voltage shutoff switch is located under the rear passenger seat. Remove the cover marked "energy storage box" and turn the green service disconnect switch to the horizontal position to turn off the high-voltage circuits. ● **SEE FIGURE 1–87.**

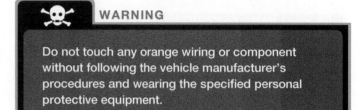

**WARNING**

Do not touch any orange wiring or component without following the vehicle manufacturer's procedures and wearing the specified personal protective equipment.

# HOISTING THE VEHICLE

**1** The first step in hoisting a vehicle is to properly align the vehicle in the center of the stall.

**2** Most vehicles will be correctly positioned when the left front tire is centered on the tire pad.

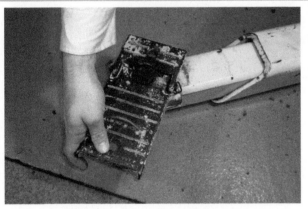

**3** The arms can be moved in and out and most pads can be rotated to allow for many different types of vehicle construction.

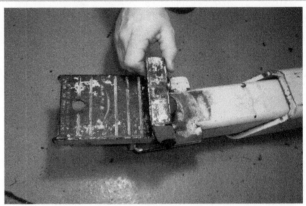

**4** Most lifts are equipped with short pad extensions that are often necessary to use to allow the pad to contact the frame of a vehicle without causing the arm of the lift to hit and damage parts of the body.

**5** Tall pad extensions can also be used to gain access to the frame of a vehicle. This position is needed to safely hoist many pickup trucks, vans, and sport utility vehicles.

**6** An additional extension may be necessary to hoist a truck or van equipped with running boards to give the necessary clearance.

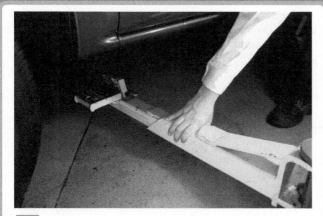

**7** Position the pads under the vehicle under the recommended locations.

**8** After being sure all pads are correctly positioned, use the electromechanical controls to raise the vehicle.

**9** With the vehicle raised 1 foot (30 cm) off the ground, push down on the vehicle to check to see if it is stable on the pads. If the vehicle rocks, lower the vehicle and reset the pads. The vehicle can be raised to any desired working level. Be sure the safety is engaged before working on or under the vehicle.

**10** If raising a vehicle without a frame, place the flat pads under the pinch weld seam to spread the load. If additional clearance is necessary, the pads can be raised as shown.

**11** When the service work is completed, the hoist should be raised slightly and the safety released before using the hydraulic lever to lower the vehicle.

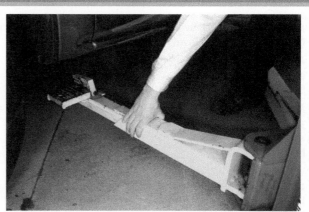

**12** After lowering the vehicle, be sure all arms of the lift are moved out of the way before driving the vehicle out of the work stall.

## SUMMARY

1. Bolts, studs, and nuts are commonly used as fasteners in the chassis. The sizes for fractional and metric threads are different and are not interchangeable. The grade is the rating of the strength of a fastener.

2. Whenever a vehicle is raised above the ground, it must be supported at a substantial section of the body or frame.

3. Wrenches are available in open end, box end, and combination open and box end.

4. An adjustable wrench should be used only where the proper size is not available.

5. Line wrenches are also called flare-nut wrenches, fitting wrenches, or tube-nut wrenches and are used to remove fuel or refrigerant lines.

6. Sockets are rotated by a ratchet or breaker bar, also called a flex handle.

7. Torque wrenches measure the amount of torque applied to a fastener.

8. Screwdriver types include straight blade (flat tip) and Phillips.

9. Hammers and mallets come in a variety of sizes and weights.

10. Pliers are a useful tool and are available in many different types, including slip-joint, multigroove, linesman's, diagonal, needle-nose, and locking pliers.

11. Other common hand tools include snap-ring pliers, files, cutters, punches, chisels, and hacksaws.

12. Hybrid electric vehicles should be depowered if any of the high-voltage components are going to be serviced.

## REVIEW QUESTIONS

1. List three precautions that must be taken whenever hoisting (lifting) a vehicle.

2. Describe how to determine the grade of a fastener, including how the markings differ between fractional and metric bolts.

3. List four items that are personal protective equipment (PPE).

4. List the types of fire extinguishers and their usage.

5. Why are wrenches offset 15 degrees?

6. What are the other names for a line wrench?

7. What are the standard automotive drive sizes for sockets?

8. Which type of screwdriver requires the use of a hammer or mallet?

9. What is inside a dead-blow hammer?

10. What type of cutter is available in left and right cutters?

## CHAPTER QUIZ

1. The correct location for the pads when hoisting or jacking the vehicle can often be found in the _____.
   a. Service manual
   b. Shop manual
   c. Owner's manual
   d. All of the above

2. For the best working position, the work should be _____.
   a. At neck or head level
   b. At knee or ankle level
   c. Overhead by about 1 foot
   d. At chest or elbow level

3. A high-strength bolt is identified by _____.
   a. A UNC symbol
   b. Lines on the head
   c. Strength letter codes
   d. The coarse threads

4. A fastener that uses threads on both ends is called a _____.
   a. Cap screw
   b. Stud
   c. Machine screw
   d. Crest fastener

5. When working with hand tools, always _____.
   a. Push the wrench—don't pull toward you
   b. Pull a wrench—don't push a wrench away from you

6. The proper term for Channel Locks® is _____.
   a. Vise Grips®
   b. Crescent wrench
   c. Locking pliers
   d. Multigroove adjustable pliers

7. The proper term for Vise Grips® is _____.
   a. Locking pliers
   b. Slip-joint pliers
   c. Side cuts
   d. Multigroove adjustable pliers

8. Two technicians are discussing torque wrenches. Technician A says that a torque wrench is capable of tightening a fastener with more torque than a conventional breaker bar or ratchet. Technician B says that a torque wrench should be calibrated regularly for the most accurate results. Which technician is correct?
   a. Technician A only
   b. Technician B only
   c. Both Technicians A and B
   d. Neither Technician A nor B

9. What type of screwdriver should be used if there is very limited space above the head of the fastener?
   a. Offset screwdriver
   b. Standard screwdriver
   c. Impact screwdriver
   d. Robertson screwdriver

10. What type of hammer is plastic coated, has a metal casing inside, and is filled with small lead balls?
   a. Dead-blow hammer
   b. Soft-blow hammer
   c. Sledgehammer
   d. Plastic hammer

# chapter 3

# GASOLINE ENGINE OPERATION AND SPECIFICATIONS

**OBJECTIVES:** **After studying Chapter 3, the reader should be able to:** • Prepare for Engine Repair (A1) ASE certification test content area "A" (General Engine Diagnosis). • Explain how a four-stroke cycle gasoline engine operates. • List the various characteristics by which vehicle engines are classified. • Discuss how a compression ratio is calculated. • Explain how engine size is determined. • Describe how displacement is affected by the bore and stroke of the engine.

**KEY TERMS:** Block 46 • Bore 54 • Bottom dead center (BDC) 49 • Boxer 49 • Cam-in-block design 51 • Camshaft 51 • Combustion 46 • Combustion chamber 46 • Compression ratio (CR) 55 • Connecting rod 49 • Crankshaft 49 • Cycle 49 • Cylinder 49 • Displacement 55 • Double overhead camshaft (DOHC) 51 • Exhaust valve 49 • External combustion engine 46 • Four-stroke cycle 49 • Intake valve 49 • Internal combustion engine 46 • Mechanical force 46 • Mechanical power 46 • Naturally aspirated 53 • Nonprincipal end 53 • Oil galleries 48 • Overhead valve (OHV) 51 • Pancake 49 • Piston stroke 49 • Principal end 53 • Pushrod engine 51 • Rotary engine 52 • Single overhead camshaft (SOHC) 51 • Stroke 54 • Supercharger 53 • Top dead center (TDC) 49 • Turbocharger 53 • Wankel engine 52

## PURPOSE AND FUNCTION

The purpose and function of an engine is to convert the heat energy of burning fuel into mechanical energy. In a typical vehicle, mechanical energy is then used to perform the following:

- Propel the vehicle
- Power the air-conditioning system and power steering
- Produce electrical power for use throughout the vehicle

## ENERGY AND POWER

Engines use energy to produce power. The chemical energy in fuel is converted to heat energy by the burning of the fuel at a controlled rate. This process is called **combustion.** If engine combustion occurs within the power chamber, the engine is called an **internal combustion engine.**

**NOTE: An external combustion engine burns fuel outside of the engine itself, such as a steam engine.**

Engines used in automobiles are internal combustion heat engines. They convert the chemical energy of the gasoline into heat within a power chamber that is called a **combustion chamber.** Heat energy released in the combustion chamber raises the temperature of the combustion gases within the chamber. The increase in gas temperature causes the pressure of the gases to increase. The pressure developed within the combustion chamber is applied to the head of a piston to produce a usable **mechanical force,** which is then converted into useful **mechanical power.**

## ENGINE CONSTRUCTION OVERVIEW

**BLOCK**   All automotive and truck engines are constructed using a solid frame, called a **block.** A block is constructed of cast iron or aluminum and provides the foundation for most of the engine components and systems. The block is cast and then machined to very close tolerances to allow other parts to be installed.

**ROTATING ASSEMBLY**   Pistons are installed in the block and move up and down during engine operation. Pistons are connected to connecting rods, which connect the pistons to the crankshaft. The crankshaft converts the up-and-down motion of the piston to rotary motion, which is then transmitted to the drive wheels and propels the vehicle. ● **SEE FIGURE 3–1.**

**CYLINDER HEADS**   All engines use a cylinder head to seal the top of the cylinders, which are in the engine block. The cylinder head on overhead valve (OHV) engines contain both intake

FIGURE 3–1 The rotating assembly for a V-8 engine that has eight pistons and connecting rods and one crankshaft.

FIGURE 3–2 A cylinder head with four valves per cylinder: two intake valves (larger) and two exhaust valves (smaller).

**?** FREQUENTLY ASKED QUESTION

**What Is a Flat-Head Engine?**

A flat-head engine is an older type of engine design that has the valves in the block. The valves are located next to the cylinders and the air-fuel mixture, and exhaust flows through the block to the intake and exhaust manifolds. Because the valves are in the block, the heads are flat and, therefore, are called flat-head engines. The most commonly known was the Ford flat-head V-8 produced from 1932 until 1953. Typical flat-head engines included:

- Inline 4-cylinder engines (many manufacturers)
- Inline 6-cylinder engines (many manufacturers)
- Inline 8-cylinder engines (many manufacturers)
- V-8s (Cadillac and Ford)
- V-12s (Cadillac and Lincoln)

FIGURE 3–3 The coolant temperature is controlled by the thermostat, which opens and allows coolant to flow to the radiator when the temperature reaches the rating temperature of the thermostat.

valves that allow air and fuel into the cylinder and exhaust valves, which allow the hot gases left over to escape from the engine. Cylinder heads are constructed of cast iron or aluminum and are then machined for the valves and other valve-related components. ● **SEE FIGURE 3–2.**

# ENGINE PARTS AND SYSTEMS

**INTAKE AND EXHAUST MANIFOLDS** Air and fuel enter the engine through an intake manifold and exit the engine through the exhaust manifold. Intake manifolds operate cooler than exhaust manifolds and are therefore constructed of nylon-reinforced plastic or aluminum. Exhaust manifolds must be able to withstand hot exhaust gases, so most are constructed from cast iron or steel tubing.

**COOLING SYSTEM** All engines must have a cooling system to control engine temperatures. While some older engines were air cooled, all current production passenger vehicle engines are cooled by circulating antifreeze coolant through passages in the block and cylinder head. The coolant picks up the heat from the engine and after the thermostat opens, the water pump circulates the coolant through the radiator where the excess heat is released to the outside air, cooling the coolant. The coolant is continuously circulated through the cooling system and the temperature is controlled by the thermostat. ● **SEE FIGURE 3–3.**

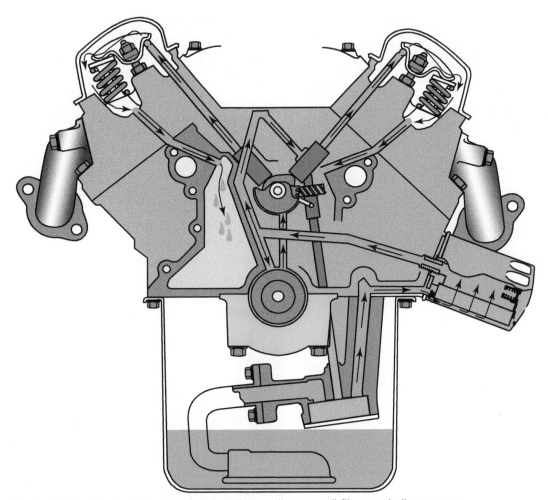

**FIGURE 3–4** A typical lubrication system, showing the oil pan, oil pump, oil filter, and oil passages.

**LUBRICATION SYSTEM**   All engines contain moving and sliding parts that must be kept lubricated to reduce wear and friction. The oil pan, bolted to the bottom of the engine block, holds 4 to 7 quarts (4 to 7 liters) of oil. An oil pump, which is driven by the engine, forces the oil through the oil filter and then into passages in the crankshaft and block. These passages are called **oil galleries.** The oil is also forced up to the valves and then falls down through openings in the cylinder head and block, then back into the oil pan. ● **SEE FIGURE 3–4:**

**FUEL SYSTEM AND IGNITION SYSTEM**   All engines require both a fuel system to supply fuel to the cylinders and an ignition system to ignite the air-fuel mixture in the cylinders. The fuel system includes the following components:

- Fuel tank, where fuel is stored and where most fuel pumps are located

- Fuel filter and lines, which transfer the fuel for the fuel tank to the engine

- Fuel injectors, which spray fuel into the intake manifold or directly into the cylinder, depending on the type of system used

The ignition system is designed to take 12 volts from the battery and convert it to 5,000 to 40,000 volts needed to jump the gap of a spark plug. Spark plugs are threaded into the cylinder head of each cylinder, and when the spark occurs, it ignites the air-fuel mixture in the cylinder, creating pressure and forcing the piston down in the cylinder. The following components are part of the ignition system:

- **Spark plugs.** Provide an air gap inside the cylinder where a spark occurs to start combustion

- **Sensor(s).** Includes crankshaft position (CKP) and camshaft position (CMP) sensors, used by the powertrain control module (PCM) to trigger the ignition coil(s) and the fuel injectors

- **Ignition coils.** Increase battery voltage to 5,000 to 40,000 volts

- **Ignition control module (ICM).** Controls when the spark plug fires

- **Associated wiring.** Electrically connects the battery, ICM, coil, and spark plugs

# FOUR-STROKE CYCLE OPERATION

**PRINCIPLES** The first **four-stroke cycle** engine was developed by a German engineer, Nickolaus Otto, in 1876. Most automotive engines use the four-stroke cycle of events. The process begins by the starter motor rotating the engine until combustion takes place. The four-stroke cycle is repeated for each cylinder of the engine. ● **SEE FIGURE 3–5.**

A piston that moves up and down, or reciprocates, in a **cylinder** can be seen in Figure 3–5. The piston is attached to a **crankshaft** with a **connecting rod.** This arrangement allows the piston to reciprocate (move up and down) in the cylinder as the crankshaft rotates. ● **SEE FIGURE 3–6.**

**OPERATION** Engine cycles are identified by the number of piston strokes required to complete the cycle. A **piston stroke** is a one-way piston movement either from top to bottom or bottom to top of the cylinder. During one stroke, the crankshaft rotates 180 degrees (1/2 revolution). A **cycle** is a complete series of events that continually repeats. Most automobile engines use a four-stroke cycle:

- **Intake stroke.** The **intake valve** is open and the piston inside the cylinder travels downward, drawing a mixture of air and fuel into the cylinder. The crankshaft rotates 180 degrees from **top dead center (TDC)** to **bottom dead center (BDC)** and the camshaft rotates 90 degrees.

- **Compression stroke.** As the engine continues to rotate, the intake valve closes and the piston moves upward in the cylinder, compressing the air-fuel mixture. The crankshaft rotates 180 degrees from bottom dead center (BDC) to top dead center (TDC) and the camshaft rotates 90 degrees.

- **Power stroke.** When the piston gets near the top of the cylinder, the spark at the spark plug ignites the air-fuel mixture, which forces the piston downward. The crankshaft rotates 180 degrees from top dead center (TDC) to bottom dead center (BDC) and the camshaft rotates 90 degrees.

- **Exhaust stroke.** The engine continues to rotate, and the piston again moves upward in the cylinder. The exhaust valve opens, and the piston forces the residual burned gases out of the **exhaust valve** and into the exhaust manifold and exhaust system. The crankshaft rotates 180 degrees from bottom dead center (BDC) to top dead center (TDC) and the camshaft rotates 90 degrees.

This sequence repeats as the engine rotates. To stop the engine, the electricity to the ignition system is shut off by the ignition switch, which stops the spark to the spark plugs.

The combustion pressure developed in the combustion chamber at the correct time will push the piston downward to rotate the crankshaft.

**THE 720-DEGREE CYCLE** Each cycle (four strokes) of events requires that the engine crankshaft make two complete revolutions, or 720 degrees (360 degrees × 2 = 720 degrees). Each stroke of the cycle requires that the crankshaft rotate 180 degrees. The greater the number of cylinders, the closer together the power strokes of the individual cylinders will occur. The number of degrees that the crankshaft rotates between power strokes can be expressed as an angle. To find the angle between cylinders of an engine, divide the number of cylinders into 720 degrees:

Angle with 3 cylinders: 720/3 = 240 degrees

Angle with 4 cylinders: 720/4 = 180 degrees

Angle with 5 cylinders: 720/5 = 144 degrees

Angle with 6 cylinders: 720/6 = 120 degrees

Angle with 8 cylinders: 720/8 = 90 degrees

Angle with 10 cylinders: 720/10 = 72 degrees

This means that in a 4-cylinder engine, a power stroke occurs at every 180 degrees of the crankshaft rotation (every 1/2 rotation). A V-8 is a much smoother operating engine because a power stroke occurs twice as often (every 90 degrees of crankshaft rotation).

# ENGINE CLASSIFICATION AND CONSTRUCTION

Engines are classified by several characteristics, including:

- **Number of strokes.** Most automotive engines use the four-stroke cycle.

- **Cylinder arrangement.** An engine with more cylinders is smoother operating because the power pulses produced by the power strokes are more closely spaced. An inline engine places all cylinders in a straight line. The 4-, 5-, and 6-cylinder engines are commonly manufactured inline engines. A V-type engine, such as a V-6 or V-8, has the number of cylinders split and built into a V shape. ● **SEE FIGURE 3–7.** Horizontally opposed 4- and 6-cylinder engines have two banks of cylinders that are horizontal, resulting in a low engine. This style of engine is used in Porsche and Subaru engines, and is often called the **boxer** or **pancake** engine design. ● **SEE FIGURE 3–8.**

- **Longitudinal and transverse mounting.** Engines may be mounted either parallel with the length of the vehicle (longitudinally) or crosswise (transversely). ● **SEE FIGURES 3–9 AND 3–10.** The same engine may be mounted in various vehicles in either direction.

**NOTE: Although it might be possible to mount an engine in different vehicles both longitudinally and transversely, the engine component parts may *not* be interchangeable. Differences can include different engine blocks and crankshafts, as well as different water pumps.**

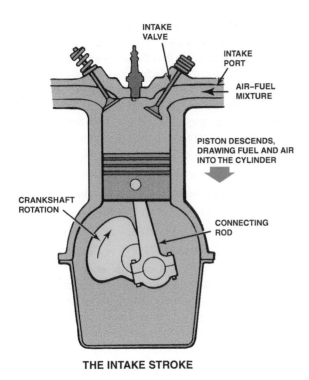

INTAKE VALVE

INTAKE PORT

AIR–FUEL MIXTURE

PISTON DESCENDS, DRAWING FUEL AND AIR INTO THE CYLINDER

CRANKSHAFT ROTATION

CONNECTING ROD

**THE INTAKE STROKE**

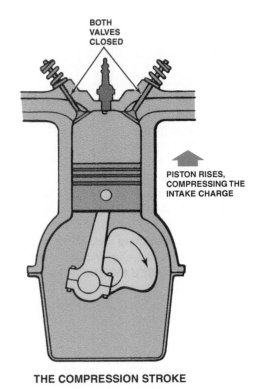

BOTH VALVES CLOSED

PISTON RISES, COMPRESSING THE INTAKE CHARGE

**THE COMPRESSION STROKE**

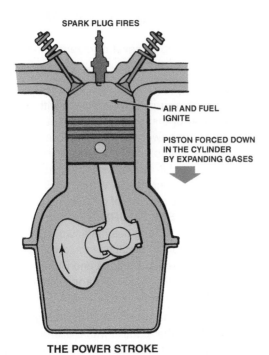

SPARK PLUG FIRES

AIR AND FUEL IGNITE

PISTON FORCED DOWN IN THE CYLINDER BY EXPANDING GASES

**THE POWER STROKE**

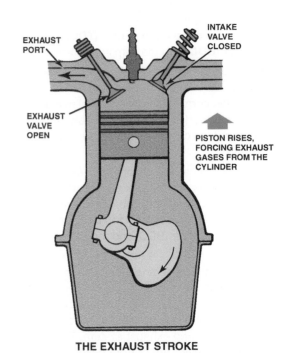

INTAKE VALVE CLOSED

EXHAUST PORT

EXHAUST VALVE OPEN

PISTON RISES, FORCING EXHAUST GASES FROM THE CYLINDER

**THE EXHAUST STROKE**

**FIGURE 3–5** The downward movement of the piston draws the air-fuel mixture into the cylinder through the intake valve on the intake stroke. On the compression stroke, the mixture is compressed by the upward movement of the piston with both valves closed. Ignition occurs at the beginning of the power stroke, and combustion drives the piston downward to produce power. On the exhaust stroke, the upward-moving piston forces the burned gases out the open exhaust valve.

**FIGURE 3–6** Cutaway of an engine showing the cylinder, piston, connecting rod, and crankshaft.

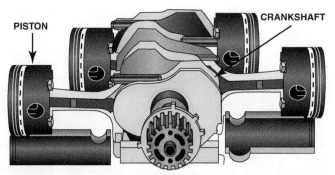

**FIGURE 3–8** A horizontally opposed engine design helps to lower the vehicle's center of gravity.

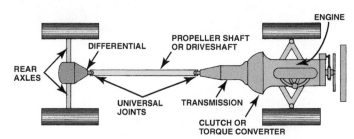

**FIGURE 3–9** A longitudinally mounted engine drives the rear wheels through a transmission, driveshaft, and differential assembly.

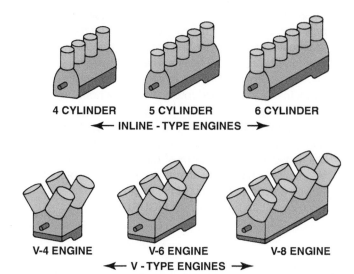

**4 CYLINDER**   **5 CYLINDER**   **6 CYLINDER**
← **INLINE - TYPE ENGINES** →

**V-4 ENGINE**   **V-6 ENGINE**   **V-8 ENGINE**
← **V - TYPE ENGINES** →

**FIGURE 3–7** Automotive engine cylinder arrangements.

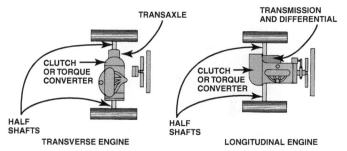

**FIGURE 3–10** Two types of front-engine, front-wheel drive mountings. A transaxle is used in most front wheel vehicles and the longitudinal engine is used by Audi and some other manufacturers.

- **Valve and camshaft number and location.** The number of valves per cylinder and the number and location of camshafts are major factors in engine operation. A typical older-model engine uses one intake valve and one exhaust valve per cylinder. Many newer engines use two intake and two exhaust valves per cylinder. The valves are opened by a **camshaft.** Some engines use one camshaft for the intake valves and a separate camshaft for the exhaust valves. When the camshaft is located in the block, the valves are operated by lifters, pushrods, and rocker arms.

  This type of engine can be called:

  - A **pushrod engine**
  - **Cam-in-block design**
  - **Overhead valve (OHV),** because an overhead valve engine has the valves located in the cylinder head
    - ● **SEE FIGURE 3–11.**

  When one overhead camshaft is used, the design is called a **single overhead camshaft (SOHC)** design. When two overhead camshafts are used, the design is called a **double overhead camshaft (DOHC)** design.
    - ● **SEE FIGURES 3–12 AND 3–13.**

**FIGURE 3–11** Cutaway of an overhead valve (OHV) V-8 engine showing the lifters, pushrods, roller rocker arms, and valves.

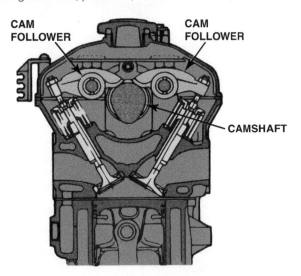

CAM FOLLOWER    CAM FOLLOWER

CAMSHAFT

**SINGLE OVERHEAD CAMSHAFT**

CAMSHAFT    LIFTER    CAMSHAFT

LIFTER

**DOUBLE OVERHEAD CAMSHAFT**

**FIGURE 3–12** SOHC engines usually require additional components, such as a rocker arm, to operate all of the valves. DOHC engines often operate the valves directly.

**FIGURE 3–13** A DOHC engine uses a camshaft for the intake valves and a separate camshaft for the exhaust valves in each cylinder head.

**?  FREQUENTLY ASKED QUESTION**

**What Is a Rotary Engine?**

A successful alternative engine design is the **rotary engine,** also called the **Wankel engine** after its inventor, Felix Heinrich Wankel (1902–1988), a German inventor. The Mazda RX-7 and RX-8 represent the only long-term use of the rotary engine. The rotating combustion chamber engine runs very smoothly, and it produces high power for its size and weight.

The basic rotating combustion chamber engine has a triangular-shaped rotor turning in a housing. The housing is in the shape of a geometric figure called a two-lobed epitrochoid. A seal on each corner, or apex, of the rotor is in constant contact with the housing, so the rotor must turn with an eccentric motion. This means that the center of the rotor moves around the center of the engine. The eccentric motion can be seen in ● **FIGURE 3–14.**

**NOTE: A V-type engine uses two banks or rows of cylinders. An SOHC design, therefore, uses two camshafts but only one camshaft per bank (row) of cylinders. A DOHC V-6, therefore, has four camshafts, two for each bank.**

■ **Type of fuel.** Most engines operate on gasoline, whereas some engines are designed to operate on ethanol (E85), methanol (M85), natural gas, propane, or diesel fuel.

■ **Cooling method.** Most engines are liquid cooled, but some older models were air cooled. Air-cooled engines, such as the original VW Beetle, could not meet exhaust emission standards.

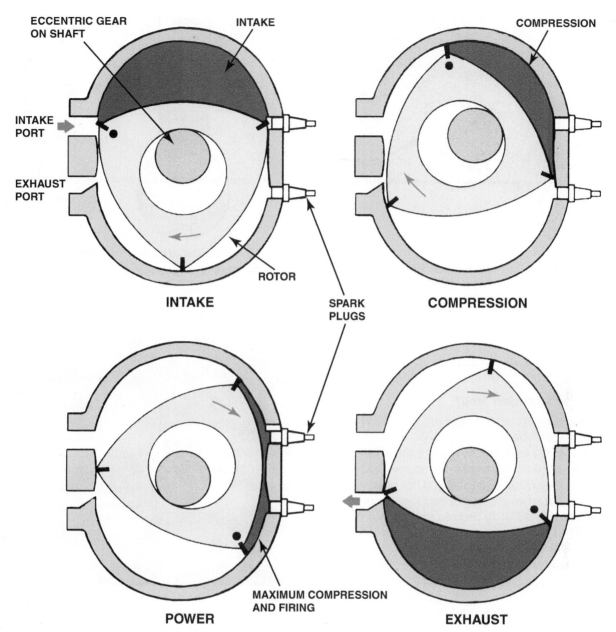

**FIGURE 3–14** A rotary engine operates on the four-stroke cycle but uses a rotor instead of a piston and crankshaft to achieve intake, compression, power, and exhaust stroke.

- **Type of induction pressure.** If atmospheric air pressure is used to force the air-fuel mixture into the cylinders, the engine is called **naturally aspirated.** Some engines use a **turbocharger** or **supercharger** to force the air-fuel mixture into the cylinder for even greater power.

**ENGINE ROTATION DIRECTION** The SAE standard for automotive engine rotation is counterclockwise (CCW) as viewed from the flywheel end (clockwise as viewed from the front of the engine). The flywheel end of the engine is the end to which the power is applied to drive the vehicle. This is called the **principal end** of the engine. The **nonprincipal end** of the engine is opposite the principal end and is generally referred to as the *front* of the engine, where the accessory belts are used. ● **SEE FIGURE 3–15.**

Therefore, in most rear-wheel-drive vehicles, the engine is mounted longitudinally with the principal end at the rear of the engine. Most transversely mounted engines also adhere to the same standard for direction of rotation. Many Honda engines, and some marine applications, may differ from this standard.

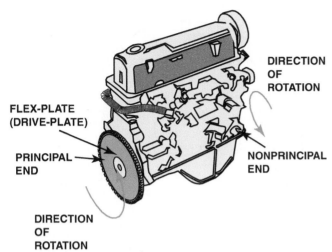

**FIGURE 3–15** Inline 4-cylinder engine showing principal and nonprincipal ends. Normal direction of rotation is clockwise (CW) as viewed from the front or accessory belt (nonprincipal) end.

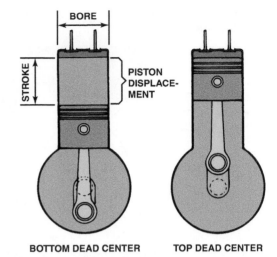

**FIGURE 3–16** The bore and stroke of pistons are used to calculate an engine's displacement.

**FIGURE 3–17** The distance between the centerline of the main bearing journal and the centerline of the connecting rod journal determines the stroke of the engine. This photo is a little unusual because it shows a V-6 with a splayed crankshaft used to even out the impulses on a 90-degree, V-6 engine design.

# ENGINE MEASUREMENT

**BORE** The diameter of a cylinder is called the **bore**. The larger the bore, the greater the area on which the gases have to work. Pressure is measured in units, such as pounds per square inch (PSI). The greater the area (in square inches), the higher the force exerted by the pistons to rotate the crankshaft. ● **SEE FIGURE 3–16.**

**STROKE** The **stroke** of an engine is the distance the piston travels from top dead center (TDC) to bottom dead center (BDC). This distance is determined by the throw of the crankshaft. The throw is the distance from the centerline of the crankshaft to the centerline of the crankshaft rod journal. The throw is one-half of the stroke. ● **SEE FIGURE 3–17.**

The longer this distance is, the greater the amount of air-fuel mixture that can be drawn into the cylinder. The more air-fuel mixture inside the cylinder, the more force will result when the mixture is ignited.

**NOTE: Changing the connecting rod length does *not* change the stroke of an engine. Changing the connecting rod only changes the position of the piston in the cylinder. Only the crankshaft determines the stroke of an engine.**

## DISPLACEMENT

**DISPLACEMENT** Engine size is described as displacement. **Displacement** is the cubic inch (cu. in.) or cubic centimeter (cc) volume displaced or how much air is moved by all of the pistons. A liter (L) is equal to 1,000 cubic centimeters; therefore, most engines today are identified by their displacement in liters:

$$1 \text{ L} = 1,000 \text{ cc}$$
$$1 \text{ L} = 61 \text{ cu. in.}$$
$$1 \text{ cu. in.} = 16.4 \text{ cc}$$

## CONVERSION

- To convert cubic inches to liters, divide cubic inches by 61.02:

$$\text{Liters} = \frac{\text{Cubic inches}}{61.02}$$

- To convert liters into cubic inches, multiply by 61.02:

$$\text{Cubic inches} = \text{Liters} \times 61.02$$

**CALCULATING CUBIC INCH DISPLACEMENT** The formula to calculate the displacement of an engine is basically the formula for determining the volume of a cylinder multiplied by the number of cylinders.

The formula is:

**Cubic inch displacement = π (pi) × R² × Stroke × Number of cylinders**

R = Radius of the cylinder or one-half of the bore.

The πR² part is the formula for the area of a circle. Applying the formula to a 6-cylinder engine:

- Bore = 4.000 in.
- Stroke = 3.000 in.
- π = 3.14
- R = 2 inches
- R² = 4 (2² or 2 × 2)

Cubic inches = 3.14 × 4 (R²) × 3 (stroke) × 6 (number of cylinders).

Cubic inches = 226 cubic inches

Because 1 cubic inch equals 16.4 cubic centimeters, this engine displacement equals 3,706 cubic centimeters or, rounded to 3,700 cubic centimeters, 3.7 liters. ● **SEE CHART 3–1** for an example of engine sizes for a variety of bore and stroke measurements.

**ENGINE SIZE CONVERSION** Many vehicle manufacturers will round the displacement so the calculated cubic inch displacement may not agree with the published displacement value. ● **SEE CHART 3–2.**

**TECH TIP**

### How Fast Can an Engine Rotate?

Most passenger vehicle engines are designed to rotate at low speed for the following reasons:

- Maximum efficiency is achieved at low engine speed. A diesel engine used in a large ship, for example, will rotate at about 100 RPM for maximum efficiency.
- Piston ring friction is the highest point of friction in the engine. The slower the engine speed, the less loss to friction from the piston rings.

However, horsepower is what is needed to get a vehicle down the road quickly. Horsepower is torque times engine speed divided by 5,252. Therefore, a high engine speed usually indicates a high horsepower. For example, a Formula 1 race car is limited to 2.4 liter V-8 but uses a 1.6 in. (40 mm) stroke. This extremely short stroke means that the engine can easily achieve the upper limit allowed by the rules of 18,000 RPM while producing over 700 horsepower.

The larger the engine, the more power the engine is capable of producing. Several sayings are often quoted about engine size:

"There is no substitute for cubic inches."
"There is no replacement for displacement."

Although a large engine generally uses more fuel, making an engine larger is often the easiest way to increase power.

## COMPRESSION RATIO

**DEFINITION** **Compression ratio (CR)** is the ratio of the difference in the cylinder volume when the piston is at the bottom of the stroke to the volume in the cylinder above the piston when the piston is at the top of the stroke. The compression ratio of an engine is an important consideration when rebuilding or repairing an engine. ● **SEE FIGURE 3–18.**

| If Compression Is Lower | If Compression Is Higher |
|---|---|
| Lower power | Higher power possible |
| Poorer fuel economy | Better fuel economy possible |
| Easier engine cranking | Harder to crank engine, especially when hot |
| More advanced ignition timing possible without spark knock (detonation) | Less ignition timing required to prevent spark knock (detonation) |

| V-8 ENGINE | | | | | |
|---|---|---|---|---|---|
| **Stroke** | **3.50** | **3.75** | **3.875** | **4.00** | **4.125** |
| **Bore** | Cu. In. | Cu. In. | Cu. In. | Cu. In. | Cu. In. |
| 3.00 | 199 | 212 | 219 | 226 | 233 |
| 3.125 | 214 | 229 | 237 | 244 | 252 |
| 3.250 | 232 | 249 | 257 | 265 | 274 |
| 3.375 | 251 | 269 | 277 | 286 | 295 |
| 3.500 | 269 | 288 | 298 | 308 | 317 |
| 3.625 | 288 | 309 | 319 | 330 | 339 |
| 3.750 | 309 | 332 | 343 | 354 | 365 |
| 3.875 | 331 | 354 | 366 | 378 | 390 |
| 4.00 | 352 | 377 | 389 | 402 | 414 |
| 4.125 | 373 | 399 | 413 | 426 | 439 |
| 6-CYLINDER ENGINE | | | | | |
| **Stroke** | **3.50** | **3.75** | **3.875** | **4.00** | **4.125** |
| **Bore** | Cu. In. | Cu. In. | Cu. In. | Cu. In. | Cu. In. |
| 3.00 | 148 | 159 | 164 | 169 | 175 |
| 3.125 | 161 | 172 | 178 | 184 | 190 |
| 3.250 | 174 | 186 | 193 | 199 | 205 |
| 3.375 | 188 | 201 | 208 | 215 | 222 |
| 3.500 | 202 | 216 | 223 | 228 | 238 |
| 3.625 | 216 | 232 | 239 | 247 | 255 |
| 3.750 | 232 | 249 | 257 | 265 | 273 |
| 3.875 | 248 | 266 | 275 | 283 | 292 |
| 4.00 | 264 | 283 | 292 | 301 | 311 |
| 4.125 | 280 | 299 | 309 | 319 | 329 |
| 4-CYLINDER ENGINE | | | | | |
| **Stroke** | **3.50** | **3.75** | **3.875** | **4.00** | **4.125** |
| **Bore** | Cu. In. | Cu. In. | Cu. In. | Cu. In. | Cu. In. |
| 3.00 | 99 | 106 | 110 | 113 | 117 |
| 3.125 | 107 | 115 | 119 | 123 | 126 |
| 3.250 | 116 | 124 | 129 | 133 | 137 |
| 3.375 | 125 | 134 | 139 | 143 | 148 |
| 3.500 | 135 | 144 | 149 | 152 | 159 |
| 3.625 | 144 | 158 | 160 | 165 | 170 |
| 3.750 | 155 | 166 | 171 | 177 | 182 |
| 3.875 | 165 | 177 | 183 | 189 | 195 |
| 4.00 | 176 | 188 | 195 | 201 | 207 |
| 4.125 | 186 | 200 | 206 | 213 | 220 |

**CHART 3-1**

To find the cubic inch displacement, find the bore that is closest to the actual value, then go across to the closest stroke value.

| LITERS TO CUBIC INCHES | | | | | |
|---|---|---|---|---|---|
| Liters | Cubic Inches | Liters | Cubic Inches | Liters | Cubic Inches |
| 1.0 | 61 | 3.2 | 196 | 5.4 | 330 |
| 1.3 | 79 | 3.3 | 200 / 201 | 5.7 | 350 |
| 1.4 | 85 | 3.4 | 204 | 5.8 | 351 |
| 1.5 | 91 | 3.5 | 215 | 6.0 | 366 / 368 |
| 1.6 | 97 / 98 | 3.7 | 225 | 6.1 | 370 |
| 1.7 | 105 | 3.8 | 229 / 231 / 232 | 6.2 | 381 |
| 1.8 | 107 / 110 / 112 | 3.9 | 239 / 240 | 6.4 | 389 / 390 / 391 |
| 1.9 | 116 | 4.0 | 241 / 244 | 6.5 | 396 |
| 2.0 | 121 / 122 | 4.1 | 250 / 252 | 6.6 | 400 |
| 2.1 | 128 | 4.2 | 255 / 258 | 6.9 | 420 |
| 2.2 | 132 / 133 / 134 / 135 | 4.3 | 260 / 262 / 265 | 7.0 | 425 / 427 / 428 / 429 |
| 2.3 | 138 / 140 | 4.4 | 267 | 7.2 | 440 |
| 2.4 | 149 | 4.5 | 273 | 7.3 | 445 |
| 2.5 | 150 / 153 | 4.6 | 280 / 281 | 7.4 | 454 |
| 2.6 | 156 / 159 | 4.8 | 292 | 7.5 | 460 |
| 2.8 | 171 / 173 | 4.9 | 300 / 301 | 7.8 | 475 / 477 |
| 2.9 | 177 | 5.0 | 302 / 304 / 305 / 307 | 8.0 | 488 |
| 3.0 | 181 / 182 / 183 | 5.2 | 318 | 8.8 | 534 |
| 3.1 | 191 | 5.3 | 327 | | |

**CHART 3-2**

Liters to cubic inches is often not exact and can result in representing several different engine sizes based on their advertised size in liters.

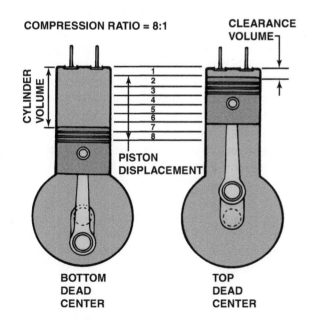

**FIGURE 3–18** Compression ratio is the ratio of the total cylinder volume (when the piston is at the bottom of its stroke) to the clearance volume (when the piston is at the top of its stroke).

**CALCULATING COMPRESSION RATIO** The compression ratio (CR) calculation uses the formula:

$$CR = \frac{\text{Volume in cylinder with piston at bottom of cylinder}}{\text{Volume in cylinder with piston at top center}}$$

● **SEE FIGURE 3–19.**

**For example:** What is the compression ratio of an engine with 50.3 cu. in. displacement in one cylinder and a combustion chamber volume of 6.7 cu. in.?

$$CR = \frac{50 + 6.7 \text{ cu. in}}{6.7 \text{ cu. in}} = \frac{57.0}{6.7} = 8.5$$

**CHANGING COMPRESSION RATIO** Any time an engine is modified, the compression ratio should be checked to make sure it is either the same as it was originally or has been changed to match the diesel compression ratio. Factors that can affect compression ratio include:

■ **Head gasket thickness.** A thicker than stock gasket will decrease the compression ratio and a thinner than stock gasket will increase the compression ratio.

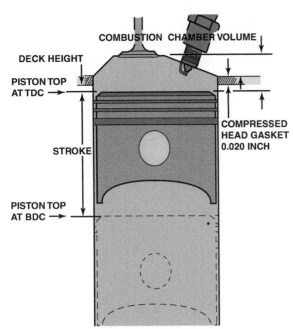

**FIGURE 3–19** Combustion chamber volume is the volume above the piston with the piston is at top dead center.

- **Increasing the cylinder size.** If the bore or stroke is increased, a greater amount of air will be compressed into the combustion chamber, which will increase the compression ratio.

# TORQUE AND HORSEPOWER

**DEFINITION OF TORQUE** *Torque* is the term used to describe a rotating force that may or may not result in motion. Torque is measured as the amount of force multiplied by the length of the lever through which it acts. If you use a 1 ft long wrench to apply 10 pounds (lb) of force to the end of the wrench to turn a bolt, then you are exerting 10 pound-feet (lb-ft) of torque. ● **SEE FIGURE 3–20.**

Torque is the twisting force measured at the end of the crankshaft and measured on a dynamometer. Engine torque is always expressed at a specific engine speed (RPM) or range of engine speeds where the torque is at the maximum. For example, an engine may be listed as producing 275 lb-ft @ 2,400 RPM.

The metric unit for torque is newton-meters, because the newton is the metric unit for force and the distance is expressed in meters.

  1 pound-foot = 1.3558 newton-meters
  1 newton-meter = 0.7376 pound-foot

**DEFINITION OF POWER** The term *power* means the rate of doing work. Power equals work divided by time. Work is achieved when a certain amount of mass (weight) is moved a

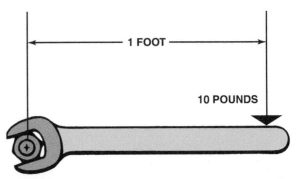

**FIGURE 3–20** Torque is a twisting force equal to the distance from the pivot point times the force applied expressed in units called pound-feet (lb-ft) or newton-meters (N-m).

**? FREQUENTLY ASKED QUESTION**

**Is Torque ft-lb or lb-ft?**
The definition of torque is a force (lb) applied to an object times the distance from that object (ft). Therefore, based on the definition of the term, torque should be:
lb-ft (a force times a distance)
Newton-meter (N-m) (a force times a distance)
  However, torque is commonly labeled, even on some torque wrenches, as ft-lb.

**🔧 TECH TIP**

**Quick-and-Easy Engine Efficiency Check**
A good, efficient engine is able to produce a lot of power from little displacement. A common rule of thumb is that an engine is efficient if it can produce 1 horsepower per cubic inch of displacement. Many engines today are capable of this feat, such as the following:

Ford: 4.6 liter V-8 (281 cu. in.): 305 hp
Chevrolet: 3.0 liter V-6 (207 cu. in.): 210 hp
Chrysler: 3.5 liter V-6 (214 cu. in.): 214 hp
Acura: 3.2 liter V-6 (195 cu. in.): 260 hp

  An engine is very powerful for its size if it can produce 100 hp per liter. This efficiency goal is harder to accomplish. Most factory stock engines that can achieve this feat are supercharged or turbocharged.

certain distance by a force. If the object is moved in 10 seconds or 10 minutes does not make a difference in the amount of work accomplished, but it does affect the amount of power needed. Power is expressed in units of foot-pounds per minute and power also includes the engine speed (RPM) where the maximum power is achieved. For example, an engine may be listed as producing 280 hp @ 4,400 RPM.

**HORSEPOWER AND ALTITUDE** Because the density of the air is lower at high altitude, the power that a normal engine can develop is greatly reduced at high altitude. According to SAE conversion factors, a nonsupercharged or nonturbocharged engine loses about 3% of its power for every 1,000 ft (300 m) of altitude.

Therefore, an engine that develops 200 brake horsepower at sea level will produce only about 116 brake horsepower at the top of Pike's Peak in Colorado at 14,110 ft (4,300 m) (3% × 14 – 42%). Supercharged and turbocharged engines are not as greatly affected by altitude as normally aspirated engines, which are those engines that breathe air at normal atmospheric pressure.

## SUMMARY

1. The four strokes of the four-stroke cycle are intake, compression, power, and exhaust.

2. Engines are classified by number and arrangement of cylinders and by number and location of valves and camshafts, as well as by type of mounting, fuel used, cooling method, and type of air induction.

3. Most engines rotate clockwise as viewed from the front (accessory) end of the engine. The SAE standard is counterclockwise as viewed from the principal (flywheel) end of the engine.

4. Engine size is called displacement and represents the volume displaced by all of the pistons.

## REVIEW QUESTIONS

1. What are the strokes of a four-stroke cycle?

2. If an engine at sea level produces 100 hp, how many horsepower would it develop at 6,000 ft of altitude?

## CHAPTER QUIZ

1. All overhead valve engines _____.
   a. Use an overhead camshaft
   b. Have the valves located in the cylinder head
   c. Operate by the two-stroke cycle
   d. Use the camshaft to close the valves

2. An SOHC V-8 engine has how many camshafts?
   a. One
   b. Two
   c. Three
   d. Four

3. The coolant flow through the radiator is controlled by the _____.
   a. Size of the passages in the block
   b. Thermostat
   c. Cooling fan(s)
   d. Water pump

4. Torque is expressed in units of _____.
   a. Pound-feet
   b. Foot-pounds
   c. Foot-pounds per minute
   d. Pound-feet per second

5. Horsepower is expressed in units of _____.
   a. Pound-feet
   b. Foot-pounds
   c. Foot-pounds per minute
   d. Pound-feet per second

6. A normally aspirated automobile engine loses about _____ power per 1,000 ft of altitude.
   a. 1%
   b. 3%
   c. 5%
   d. 6%

7. One cylinder of an automotive four-stroke cycle engine completes a cycle every _____.
   a. 90 degrees
   b. 180 degrees
   c. 360 degrees
   d. 720 degrees

8. How many rotations of the crankshaft are required to complete each stroke of a four-stroke cycle engine?
   a. One-fourth
   b. One-half
   c. One
   d. Two

9. A rotating force is called _____.
   a. Horsepower
   b. Torque
   c. Combustion pressure
   d. Eccentric movement

10. Technician A says that a crankshaft determines the stroke of an engine. Technician B says that the length of the connecting rod determines the stroke of an engine. Which technician is correct?
    a. Technician A only
    b. Technician B only
    c. Both Technicians A and B
    d. Neither Technician A nor B

# DIESEL ENGINE OPERATION AND DIAGNOSIS

**OBJECTIVES:** **After studying Chapter 4, the reader should be able to:** • Prepare for ASE Engine Performance (A8) certification test content area "C" (Fuel, Air Induction, and Exhaust Systems Diagnosis and Repair). • Explain how a diesel engine works. • Describe the difference between direct injection (DI) and indirect injection (IDI) diesel engines. • List the parts of the typical diesel engine fuel system. • Explain how glow plugs work. • List the advantages and disadvantages of a diesel engine.

**KEY TERMS:** Diesel exhaust fluid (DEF) 74 • Diesel exhaust particulate filter (DPF) 71 • Diesel oxidation catalyst (DOC) 71 • Differential pressure sensor (DPS) 72 • Direct injection (DI) 62 • Glow plug 67 • Heat of compression 60 • High-pressure common rail (HPCR) 64 • Hydraulic electronic unit injection (HEUI) 64 • Indirect injection (IDI) 62 • Injection pump 60 • Lift pump 63 • Opacity 78 • Particulate matter (PM) 71 • Pop tester 77 • Regeneration 72 • Selective catalytic reduction (SCR) 74 • Soot 71 • Urea 74 • Water-fuel separator 63

## DIESEL ENGINES

**FUNDAMENTALS** In 1892, a German engineer named Rudolf Diesel perfected the compression ignition engine that bears his name. The diesel engine uses heat created by compression to ignite the fuel, so it requires no spark ignition system.

The diesel engine requires compression ratios of 16:1 and higher. Incoming air is compressed until its temperature reaches about 1,000°F (540°C). This is called **heat of compression.** As the piston reaches the top of its compression stroke, fuel is injected into the cylinder, where it is ignited by the hot air.
● **SEE FIGURE 4–1.**

As the fuel burns, it expands and produces power. Because of the very high compression and torque output of a diesel engine, it is made heavier and stronger than the same size gasoline-powered engine.

A diesel engine uses a fuel system with a precision **injection pump** and individual fuel injectors. The pump delivers fuel to the injectors at a high pressure and at timed intervals. Each injector sprays fuel into the combustion chamber at the precise moment required for efficient combustion. ● **SEE FIGURE 4–2.**

**ADVANTAGES AND DISADVANTAGES** A diesel engine has several advantages compared to a similar size gasoline-powered engine, including:

1. More torque output
2. Greater fuel economy
3. Long service life

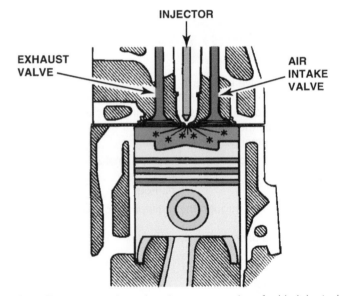

**FIGURE 4–1** Diesel combustion occurs when fuel is injected into the hot, highly compressed air in the cylinder.

A diesel engine has several disadvantages compared to a similar size gasoline-powered engine, including:

1. Engine noise, especially when cold and/or at idle speed
2. Exhaust smell
3. Cold weather startability
4. Vacuum pump that is needed to supply the vacuum needs of the heat, ventilation, and air-conditioning system

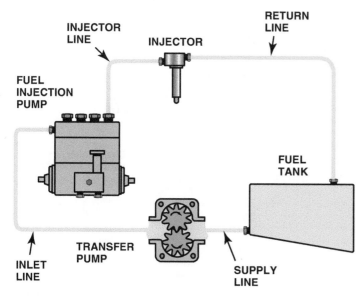

**FIGURE 4–2** A typical injector pump type of automotive diesel fuel-injection system.

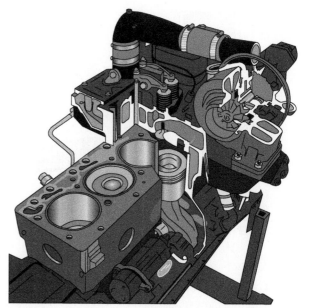

**FIGURE 4–3** A Cummins diesel engine as found in a Dodge pickup truck. A high-pressure pump (up to 30,000 PSI) is used to supply diesel fuel to this common rail, which has tubes running to each injector. Note the thick cylinder walls and heavy-duty construction.

| SYSTEM OR COMPONENT | DIESEL ENGINE | GASOLINE ENGINE |
|---|---|---|
| Block | Cast iron and heavy (● SEE FIGURE 4–3.) | Cast iron or aluminum and as light as possible |
| Cylinder head | Cast iron or aluminum | Cast iron or aluminum |
| Compression ratio | 17:1 to 25:1 | 8:1 to 12:1 |
| Peak engine speed | 2000 to 2500 RPM | 5000 to 8000 RPM |
| Pistons | Aluminum with combustion pockets and heavy-duty connecting rods (● SEE FIGURE 4–4.) | Aluminum, usually flat top or with valve relief but no combustion pockets |

**CHART 4–1**

Comparison between a typical gasoline and a diesel engine.

5. Heavier than a gasoline engine
6. Fuel availability
7. Extra cost compared to a gasoline engine

**CONSTRUCTION** Diesel engines must be constructed heavier than gasoline engines because of the tremendous pressures that are created in the cylinders during operation. ● **SEE CHART 4–1.** The torque output of a diesel engine is often double or more than the same size gasoline-powered engines.

**AIR-FUEL RATIOS** In a diesel engine, air is not controlled by a throttle as in a gasoline engine. Instead, the amount of fuel injected is varied to control power and speed. The air-fuel mixture

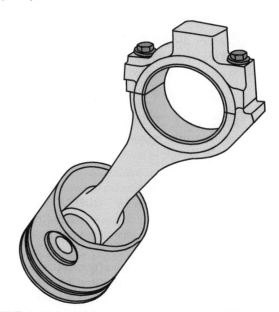

**FIGURE 4–4** A rod/piston assembly from a 5.9 liter Cummins diesel engine used in a Dodge pickup truck.

of a diesel can vary from as lean as 85:1 at idle to as rich as 20:1 at full load. This higher air-fuel ratio and the increased compression pressures make the diesel more fuel efficient than a gasoline engine, in part because diesel engines do not suffer from throttling losses. Throttling losses involve the power needed in a gasoline engine to draw air past a closed or partially closed throttle.

In a gasoline engine, the speed and power are controlled by the throttle valve, which controls the amount of air entering the engine. Adding more fuel to the cylinders of a gasoline engine without adding more air (oxygen) will not increase the speed or power of the engine. In a diesel engine, speed

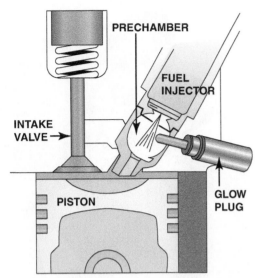

**FIGURE 4–5** An indirect injection diesel engine uses a prechamber and a glow plug.

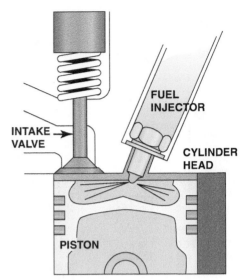

**FIGURE 4–6** A direct injection diesel engine injects the fuel directly into the combustion chamber. Many designs do not use a glow plug.

and power are not controlled by the amount of air entering the cylinders because the engine air intake is always wide open. Therefore, the engine always has enough oxygen to burn the fuel in the cylinder and will increase speed (and power) when additional fuel is supplied.

**NOTE: Many newer diesel engines are equipped with a throttle valve. This valve is used by the emission control system and is not designed to control the speed of the engine.**

**INDIRECT AND DIRECT INJECTION** In an **indirect injection** (abbreviated **IDI**) diesel engine, fuel is injected into a small prechamber, which is connected to the cylinder by a narrow opening. The initial combustion takes place in this prechamber. This has the effect of slowing the rate of combustion, which tends to reduce noise. ● **SEE FIGURE 4–5.**

All indirect diesel injection engines require the use of a glow plug which is an electrical heater that helps start the combustion process.

In a **direct injection** (abbreviated **DI**) diesel engine, fuel is injected directly into the cylinder. The piston incorporates a depression where initial combustion takes place. Direct injection diesel engines are generally more efficient than indirect injection engines, but have a tendency to produce greater amounts of noise. ● **SEE FIGURE 4–6.**

While some direct injection diesel engines use glow plugs to help cold starting and to reduce emissions, many direct injection diesel engines do not use glow plugs.

**DIESEL FUEL IGNITION** Ignition occurs in a diesel engine by injecting fuel into the air charge, which has been heated by compression to a temperature greater than the ignition point of the fuel or about 1,000°F (538°C). The chemical reaction of burning the fuel creates heat, which causes the gases to expand, forcing the piston to rotate the crankshaft. A four-stroke diesel engine requires two rotations of the crankshaft to complete one cycle.

- On the intake stroke, the piston passes TDC, the intake valve(s) opens, and filtered air enters the cylinder, while the exhaust valve(s) remains open for a few degrees to allow all of the exhaust gases to escape from the previous combustion event.
- On the compression stroke, after the piston passes BDC, the intake valve(s) closes and the piston travels up to TDC (completion of the first crankshaft rotation).
- On the power stroke, the piston nears TDC on the compression stroke and diesel fuel is injected into the cylinder by the injectors. The ignition of the fuel does not start immediately but the heat of compression starts the combustion phases in the cylinder. During this power stroke, the piston passes TDC and the expanding gases force the piston down, rotating the crankshaft.
- On the exhaust stroke, as the piston passes BDC, the exhaust valve(s) opens and the exhaust gases start to flow out of the cylinder. This continues as the piston travels up to TDC, pumping the spent gases out of the cylinder. At TDC, the second crankshaft rotation is complete.

# THREE PHASES OF COMBUSTION

There are three distinct phases or parts to the combustion in a diesel engine:

1. **Ignition delay.** Near the end of the compression stroke, fuel injection begins, but ignition does not begin immediately. This period is called *ignition delay*.

2. **Rapid combustion.** This phase of combustion occurs when the fuel first starts to burn, creating a sudden rise in

cylinder pressure. It is this sudden and rapid rise in combustion chamber pressure that causes the characteristic diesel engine knock.

3. **Controlled combustion.** After the rapid combustion occurs, the rest of the fuel in the combustion chamber begins to burn and injection continues. This process occurs in an area near the injector that contains fuel surrounded by air. This fuel burns as it mixes with the air.

## FUEL TANK AND LIFT PUMP

**PARTS INVOLVED** A fuel tank used on a vehicle equipped with a diesel engine differs from the one used with a gasoline engine in the following ways:

- The filler neck is larger for diesel fuel. The nozzle size is 15/16 in. (24 mm) instead of 13/16 in. (21 mm) for gasoline filler necks. Truck stop diesel nozzles for large over-the-road trucks are usually larger, 1.25 in. or 1.5 in. (32 mm or 38 mm) to allow for faster fueling of large-capacity fuel tanks.

- There are no evaporative emission control devices or a charcoal (carbon) canister. Diesel fuel is not as volatile as gasoline, and therefore diesel vehicles do not have evaporative emission control devices.

The diesel fuel is usually drawn from the fuel tank by a separate pump, called a **lift pump,** and delivers the fuel to the injection pump. Between the fuel tank and the lift pump is a **water-fuel separator.** Water is heavier than diesel fuel and sinks to the bottom of the separator. Part of normal routine maintenance on a vehicle equipped with a diesel engine is to drain the water from the water-fuel separator. A float is often used inside the separator, which is connected to a warning light on the dash that lights if the water reaches a level where it needs to be drained. The water separator is often part of the fuel filter assembly. Both the fuel filter and the water separator are common maintenance items.

**NOTE: Water can cause corrosive damage and wear to diesel engine parts because it is not a good lubricant. Water cannot be atomized by a diesel fuel injector nozzle and will often "blow out" the nozzle tip.**

Many diesel engines also use a *fuel temperature sensor.* The computer uses this information to adjust fuel delivery based on the density of the fuel. ● **SEE FIGURE 4–7.**

## INJECTION PUMP

**NEED FOR HIGH-PRESSURE FUEL PUMP** A diesel engine injection pump is used to increase the pressure of the diesel fuel from very low values from the lift pump to the extremely high pressures needed for injection.

**FIGURE 4–7** A fuel temperature sensor is being tested using an ice bath.

**FIGURE 4–8** A typical distributor-type diesel injection pump showing the pump, lines, and fuel filter.

- The lift pump is a *low-pressure, high-volume pump.*
- The high-pressure injection pump is a *high-pressure, low-volume pump.*

Injection pumps are usually driven by a gear off the camshaft at the front of the engine. As the injection pump shaft rotates, the diesel fuel is fed from a fill port to a high-pressure chamber. If a distributor-type injection pump is used, the fuel is forced out of the injection port to the correct injector nozzle through the high-pressure line. ● **SEE FIGURE 4–8.**

**NOTE: Because of the very tight tolerances in a diesel engine, the smallest amount of dirt can cause excessive damage to the engine and to the fuel-injection system.**

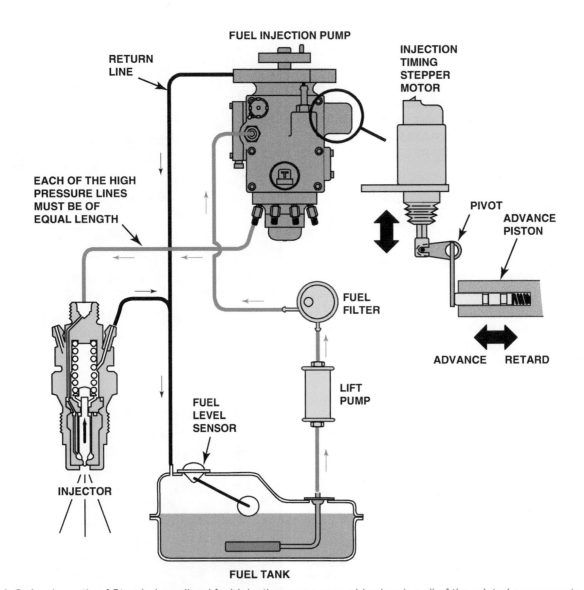

**FIGURE 4–9** A schematic of Standadyne diesel fuel-injection pump assembly showing all of the related components.

## DISTRIBUTOR INJECTION PUMP
A distributor diesel injection pump is a high-pressure pump assembly with lines leading to each individual injector. The high-pressure lines between the distributor, and the injectors must be the exact same length to ensure proper injection timing. The high-pressure fuel causes the injectors to open. Because of the internal friction of the lines, there is a slight delay before fuel pressure opens the injector nozzle. The injection pump itself creates the injection advance needed for engine speeds above idle often by using a stepper motor attached to the advance piston, and the fuel is then discharged into the lines. ● **SEE FIGURE 4–9.**

**NOTE: The lines expand some during an injection event. This is how timing checks are performed. The pulsing of the injector line is picked up by a probe used to detect the injection event similar to a timing light used to detect a spark on a gasoline engine.**

## HIGH-PRESSURE COMMON RAIL
Newer diesel engines use a fuel delivery system referred to as a **high-pressure common rail (HPCR)** design. Diesel fuel under high pressure, over

20,000 PSI (138,000 kPa), is applied to the injectors, which are opened by a solenoid controlled by the computer. Because the injectors are computer controlled, the combustion process can be precisely controlled to provide maximum engine efficiency with the lowest possible noise and exhaust emissions. ● **SEE FIGURE 4–10.**

## HEUI SYSTEM

### PRINCIPLES OF OPERATION
Ford 7.3, 6.0, and 6.4 liter (and Navistar) diesels use a system called a **hydraulic electronic unit injection** system, or **HEUI** system. The components used include:

- High-pressure engine oil pump and reservoir
- Pressure regulator for the engine oil
- Passages in the cylinder head for flow of fuel to the injectors

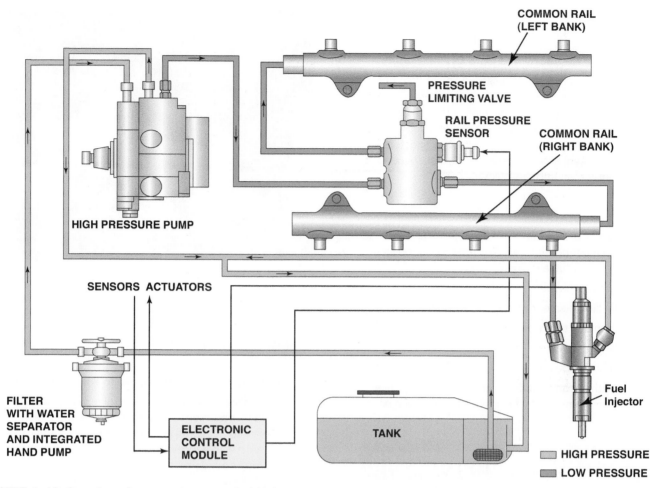

**FIGURE 4–10** Overview of a computer-controlled high-pressure common rail V-8 diesel engine.

**OPERATION** The engine oil is pressurized to provide an opening pressure strong enough to overcome the fuel pressure when the solenoid is commanded to open by the PCM. The system functions as follows:

- Fuel is drawn from the tank by the tandem fuel pump, which circulates fuel at low pressure through the fuel filter/water separator/fuel heater bowl, and then fuel is directed back to the fuel pump, where fuel is pumped at high pressure into the cylinder head fuel galleries.

- The injectors, which are hydraulically actuated by engine oil pressure from the high-pressure oil pump, are then fired by the powertrain control module (PCM). The control system for the fuel injectors is the PCM, and the injectors are fired based on sensor inputs received by the PCM.
  ● **SEE FIGURE 4–11.**

HEUI injectors rely on O-rings to keep fuel and oil from mixing or escaping, causing performance problems or engine damage. HEUI injectors use five O-rings. The three external O-rings should be replaced with updated O-rings if they fail.

**FIGURE 4–11** A HEUI injector from a Ford PowerStroke diesel engine. The O-ring grooves indicate the location of the O-rings that seal the fuel section of the injector from coolant and from the engine oil.

**Change Oil Regularly in a Ford Diesel Engine**

Ford 7.3, 6.0, and 6.4 liter diesel engines pump unfiltered oil from the sump to the high-pressure oil pump and then to the injectors. This means that not changing oil regularly can contribute to accumulation of dirt in the engine and will subject the fuel injectors to wear and potential damage as particles suspended in the oil get forced into the injectors.

The two internal O-rings are not replaceable and if these fail, the injector(s) must be replaced. The most common symptoms of injector O-ring trouble include:

- Oil getting in the fuel
- The fuel filter element turning black
- Long cranking times before starting
- Sluggish performance
- Reduction in power
- Increased oil consumption (This often accompanies O-ring problems or any fault that lets fuel in the oil.)

## DIESEL INJECTOR NOZZLES

**PARTS INVOLVED** Diesel injector nozzles are spring-loaded closed valves that spray fuel directly into the combustion chamber or precombustion chamber when the injector is opened. Injector nozzles are threaded or clamped into the cylinder head, one for each cylinder, and are replaceable as an assembly.

The tip of the injector nozzle has many holes to deliver an atomized spray of diesel fuel into the cylinder. Parts of a diesel injector nozzle include:

- **Heat shield.** This is the outer shell of the injector nozzle and may have external threads where it seals in the cylinder head.
- **Injector body.** This is the inner part of the nozzle and contains the injector needle valve and spring, and threads into the outer heat shield.
- **Diesel injector needle valve.** This precision machined valve and the tip of the needle seal against the injector body when it is closed. When the valve is open, diesel fuel is sprayed into the combustion chamber. This passage is controlled by a computer-controlled solenoid on diesel engines equipped with computer-controlled injection.
- **Injector pressure chamber.** The pressure chamber is a machined cavity in the injector body around the tip of the injector needle. Injection pump pressure forces fuel into this chamber, forcing the needle valve open.

**FIGURE 4–12** Typical computer-controlled diesel engine fuel injectors.

 TECH TIP

**Never Allow a Diesel Engine to Run Out of Fuel**

If a gasoline-powered vehicle runs out of gasoline, it is an inconvenience and a possible additional expense to get some gasoline. However, if a vehicle equipped with a diesel engine runs out of fuel, it can be a major concern.

Besides adding diesel fuel to the tank, the other problem is getting all of the air out of the pump, lines, and injectors so the engine will operate correctly.

The procedure usually involves cranking the engine long enough to get liquid diesel fuel back into the system, but at the same time keeping cranking time short enough to avoid overheating the starter. Consult service information for the exact service procedure if the diesel engine is run out of fuel.

**NOTE: Some diesel engines, such as the General Motors Duramax V-8, are equipped with a priming pump located under the hood on top of the fuel filter. Pushing down and releasing the priming pump with a vent valve open will purge any trapped air from the system. Always follow the vehicle manufacturer's instructions.**

**DIESEL INJECTOR NOZZLE OPERATION** The electric solenoid attached to the injector nozzle is computer controlled and opens to allow fuel to flow into the injector pressure chamber. ● **SEE FIGURE 4–12.**

The fuel flows down through a fuel passage in the injector body and into the pressure chamber. The high fuel pressure in the pressure chamber forces the needle valve upward, compressing the needle valve return spring and forcing the needle valve open.

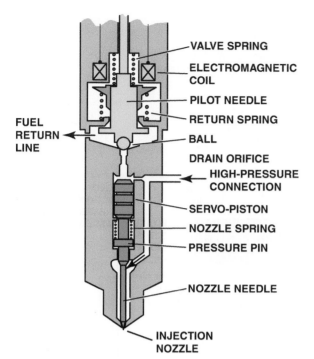

FIGURE 4–13 A Duramax injector showing all the internal parts.

FIGURE 4–14 A glow plug assortment showing the various types and sizes of glow plugs used. Always use the specified glow plugs.

When the needle valve opens, diesel fuel is discharged into the combustion chamber in a hollow cone spray pattern.

Any fuel that leaks past the needle valve returns to the fuel tank through a return passage and line. ● SEE FIGURE 4–13.

## GLOW PLUGS

**PURPOSE AND FUNCTION** Glow plugs are always used in diesel engines equipped with a precombustion chamber and may be used in direct injection diesel engines to aid starting. A **glow plug** is a heating element that uses 12 volts from the battery and aids in the starting of a cold engine by providing heat to help the fuel to ignite. ● SEE FIGURE 4–14.

As the temperature of the glow plug increases, the resistance of the heating element inside increases, thereby reducing the current in amperes needed by the glow plugs.

**OPERATION** Most glow plugs used in newer vehicles are controlled by the Powertrain Control Module, which monitors coolant temperature and intake air temperature. The glow plugs are turned on or pulsed on or off depending on the temperature of the engine. The PCM will also keep the glow plug turned on after the engine starts, to reduce white exhaust smoke (unburned fuel) and to improve idle quality after starting. ● SEE FIGURE 4–15.

The "wait to start" lamp (if equipped) will light when the engine and the outside temperatures are low to allow time for the glow plugs to get hot.

 **FREQUENTLY ASKED QUESTION**

**How Can You Tell if Gasoline Has Been Added to the Diesel Fuel by Mistake?**

If gasoline has been accidentally added to diesel fuel and is burned in a diesel engine, the result can be very damaging to the engine. The gasoline can ignite faster than diesel fuel, which would tend to increase the temperature of combustion. This high temperature can harm injectors and glow plugs, as well as pistons, head gaskets, and other major diesel engine components. If contaminated fuel is suspected, first smell the fuel at the filler neck. If the fuel smells like gasoline, then the tank should be drained and refilled with diesel fuel. If the smell test does not indicate a gasoline or any rancid smell, then test a sample for proper specific gravity.

NOTE: Diesel fuel designed for on-road use should be green. Red diesel fuel (high sulfur) should be found only in off-road or farm equipment.

**HEATED INLET AIR** Some diesel engines, such as the Dodge Cummins and the General Motors 6.6 liter Duramax V-8, use an electrical heater wire to warm the intake air to help in cold weather starting and running. ● SEE FIGURE 4–16.

## ENGINE-DRIVEN VACUUM PUMP

Because a diesel engine is unthrottled, it creates very little vacuum in the intake manifold. Several engine and vehicle components operate using vacuum, such as the exhaust gas

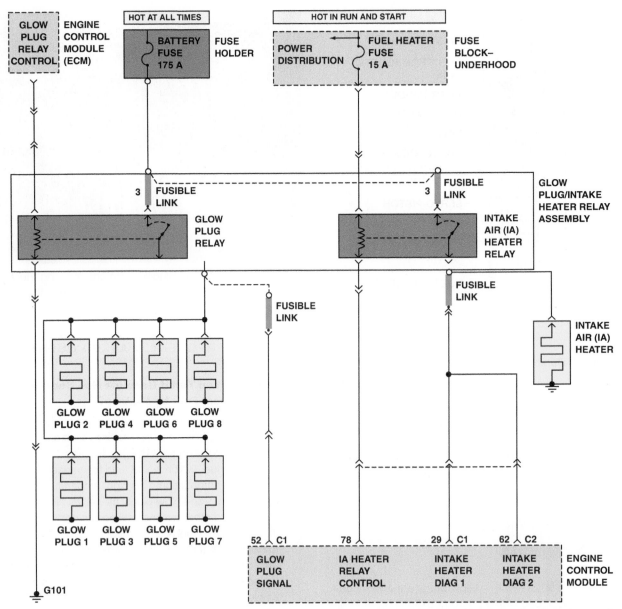

**FIGURE 4–15** A schematic of a typical glow plug circuit. Notice that the glow plug relay and intake air heater relay are both computer controlled.

recirculation (EGR) valve and the heating and ventilation blend and air doors. Most diesels used in cars and light trucks are equipped with an engine-driven vacuum pump to supply the vacuum for these components.

## DIESEL FUEL HEATERS

Diesel fuel heaters help prevent power loss and stalling in cold weather. The heater is placed in the fuel line between the tank and the primary filter. Some coolant heaters are thermostatically controlled, which allows fuel to bypass the heater once it has reached operating temperature.

## ACCELERATOR PEDAL POSITION SENSOR

Some light-truck diesel engines are equipped with an electronic throttle to control the amount of fuel injected into the engine. Because a diesel engine does not use a throttle in the air intake, the only way to control engine speed is by controlling the amount of fuel being injected into the cylinders. Instead of a mechanical link from the accelerator pedal to the diesel injection pump, a throttle-by-wire system uses an accelerator pedal position (APP) sensor. To ensure safety, it consists of three separate sensors that change in voltage as the accelerator pedal is depressed. ● **SEE FIGURE 4–17.**

**FIGURE 4–16** A wire-wound electric heater is used to warm the intake air on some diesel engines.

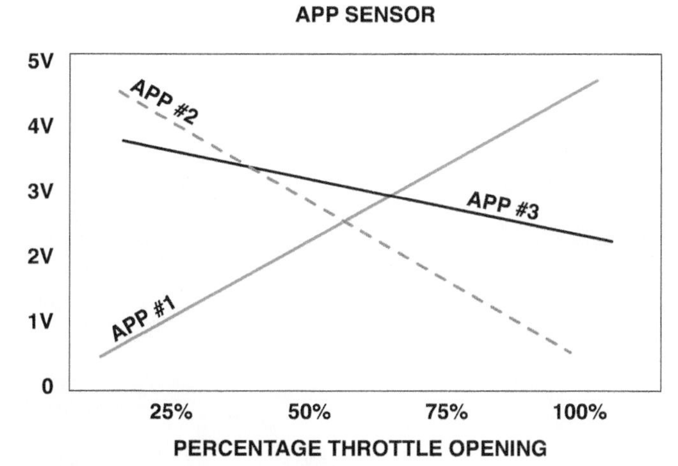

Turbocharger

**FIGURE 4–18** A Cummins diesel turbocharger is used to increase the power and torque of the engine.

## APP SENSOR

APP #2

APP #3

APP #1

5V

4V

3V

2V

1V

0

25%     50%     75%     100%

**PERCENTAGE THROTTLE OPENING**

**FIGURE 4–17** A typical accelerator pedal position (APP) sensor uses three different sensors in one package with each creating a different voltage as the accelerator is moved.

The computer checks for errors by comparing the voltage output of each of the three sensors inside the APP and compares them to what they should be if there are no faults. If an error is detected, the engine and vehicle speed are often reduced.

# DIESEL ENGINE TURBOCHARGERS

**TURBOCHARGED DIESELS** A turbocharger greatly increases engine power by pumping additional compressed air into the combustion chambers. This allows a greater quantity of fuel to be burned in the cylinders, resulting in greater power output. In a turbocharger, the turbine wheel spins as exhaust gas flows out of the engine and drives the turbine blades. The turbine spins the compressor wheel at the opposite end of the turbine shaft, pumping air into the intake system. ● **SEE FIGURE 4–18.**

**AIR CHARGE COOLER** The first component in a typical turbocharger system is an air filter through which ambient air passes before entering the compressor. The air is compressed, which raises its density (mass/unit volume). All currently produced light-duty diesels use an air charge cooler whose purpose is to cool the compressed air to further raise the air density. Cooler air entering the engine means more power can be produced by the engine. ● **SEE FIGURE 4–19.**

**VARIABLE TURBOCHARGER** A variable turbocharger is used on many diesel engines for boost control. Boost pressure is controlled independent of engine speed and a wastegate is not needed. The adjustable vanes mount to a unison ring that allows the vanes to move. As the position of the unison ring rotates, the vanes change angle. The vanes are opened to minimize flow at the turbine and exhaust back pressure at low engine speeds. To increase turbine speed, the vanes are closed. The velocity of the exhaust gases increases, as does the speed of the turbine. The unison ring is connected to a cam that is positioned by a rack-and-pinion gear. The turbocharger's vane position actuator solenoid connects to a hydraulic piston, which moves the rack to rotate the pinion gear and cam. ● **SEE FIGURE 4–20.**

The turbocharger vane position control solenoid valve is used to advance the unison ring's relationship to the turbine and thereby articulate the vanes. This solenoid actuates a spool valve that applies oil pressure to either side of a piston. Oil flow has three modes: apply, hold, and release.

- *Apply* moves the vanes toward a closed position.
- *Hold* maintains the vanes in a fixed position.
- *Release* moves the vanes toward the open position.

The turbocharger vane position actuation is controlled by the ECM, which can change turbine boost efficiency independent of

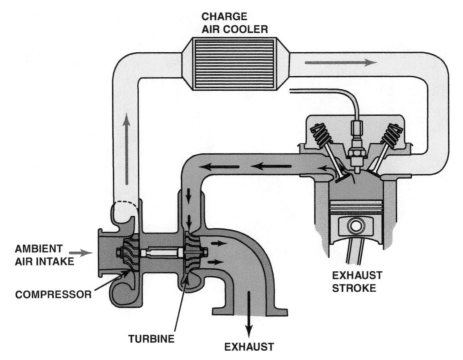

**FIGURE 4–19** An air charge cooler is used to cool the compressed air.

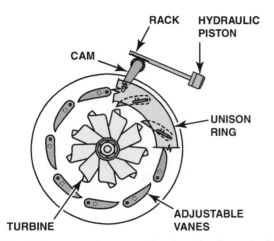

**FIGURE 4–20** A variable vane turbocharger allows the boost to be controlled without the need of a wastegate.

engine speed. The ECM provides a control signal to the valve solenoid along with a low-side reference. A pulse-width-modulated signal from the ECM moves the valve to the desired position.

# EXHAUST GAS RECIRCULATION

The EGR system recycles some exhaust gas back into the intake stream to cool combustion, which reduces oxides of nitrogen ($NO_x$) emissions. The EGR system includes:

- Plumbing that carries some exhaust gas from the turbocharger exhaust inlet to the intake ports

**FIGURE 4–21** A cutaway showing the exhaust cooler. The cooler the exhaust is, the more effective it is in controlling $NO_x$ emissions.

- EGR control valve
- Stainless steel cooling element used to cool the exhaust gases (● **SEE FIGURE 4–21.**)

The EGR valve is PCM controlled and often uses a DC stepper motor and worm gear to move the valve stem open. The gear is not attached to the valve and can only force it open. Return spring force closes the valve. The EGR valve and sensor assembly is a five-wire design. The PCM uses the position sensor to verify that valve action is as commanded.

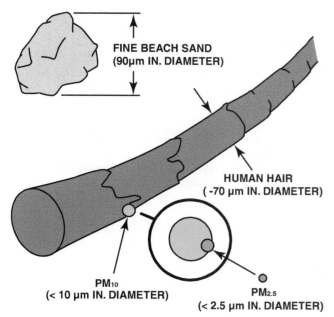

FINE BEACH SAND
(90μm IN. DIAMETER)

HUMAN HAIR
( -70 μm IN. DIAMETER)

PM₁₀
(< 10 μm IN. DIAMETER)

PM₂.₅
(< 2.5 μm IN. DIAMETER)

**FIGURE 4–22** Relative size of particulate matter to a human hair.

? FREQUENTLY ASKED QUESTION

**What Is the Big Deal for the Need to Control Very Small Soot Particles?**

For many years soot or particulate matter (PM) was thought to be less of a health concern than exhaust emissions from gasoline engines. It was felt that the soot could simply fall to the ground without causing any noticeable harm to people or the environment. However, it was discovered that the small soot particulates when breathed in are not expelled from the lungs like larger particles but instead get trapped in the deep areas of the lungs where they accumulate.

# DIESEL PARTICULATE MATTER

**PARTICULATE MATTER STANDARDS** **Particulate matter (PM),** also called **soot,** refers to tiny particles of solid or semisolid material suspended in the atmosphere. This includes particles between 0.1 micron and 50 microns in diameter. The heavier particles, larger than 50 microns, typically tend to settle out quickly due to gravity. Particulates are generally categorized as follows:

- **Total suspended particulate (TSP).** Refers to all particles between 0.1 and 50 microns. Up until 1987, the Environmental Protection Agency (EPA) standard for particulates was based on levels of TSP.

- **PM10.** Refers to particulate matter of 10 microns or less (approximately 1/6 the diameter of a human hair). EPA has a standard for particles based on levels of PM10.

- **PM2.5.** Refers to particulate matter of 2.5 microns or less (approximately 1/20 the diameter of a human hair), also called "fine" particles. In July 1997, the EPA approved a standard for PM2.5. ● **SEE FIGURE 4–22.**

**SOOT CATEGORIES** In general, soot particles produced by diesel combustion fall into the following categories.

- **Fine.** Less than 2.5 microns

- **Ultrafine.** Less than 0.1 micron, and make up 80% to 95% of soot

# DIESEL OXIDATION CATALYST

**PURPOSE AND FUNCTION** **Diesel oxidation catalysts (DOC)** are used in all light-duty diesel engines, since 2007. They consist of a flow-through honeycomb-style substrate structure that is wash coated with a layer of catalyst materials, similar to those used in a gasoline engine catalytic converter. These materials include the precious metals platinum and palladium, as well as other base metal catalysts.

Catalysts chemically react with exhaust gas to convert harmful nitrogen oxide into nitrogen dioxide, and to oxidize absorbed hydrocarbons. The chemical reaction acts as a combustor for the unburned fuel that is characteristic of diesel compression ignition. The main function of the DOC is to start a regeneration event by converting the fuel-rich exhaust gases to heat.

The DOC also reduces:

- Carbon monoxide (CO)

- Hydrocarbons (HC)

- Odor-causing compounds such as aldehydes and sulfur
  ● **SEE FIGURE 4–23.**

# DIESEL EXHAUST PARTICULATE FILTER

**PURPOSE AND FUNCTION** **Diesel exhaust particulate filters (DPFs)** are used in all light-duty diesel vehicles, since 2007, to meet the exhaust emissions standards. The heated exhaust gas from the DOC flows into the DPF, which captures diesel exhaust gas particulates (soot) to prevent them from being released into the atmosphere. This is done by forcing

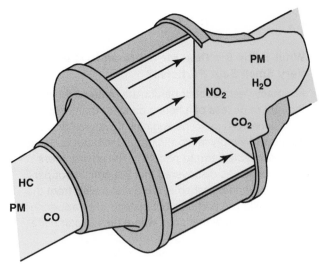

**FIGURE 4–23** Chemical reaction within the DOC.

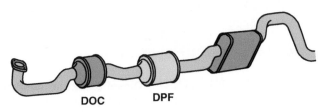

**FIGURE 4–24** Aftertreatment of diesel exhaust is handled by the DOC and DPF.

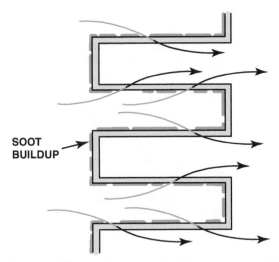

**FIGURE 4–25** The soot is trapped in the passages of the DPF. The exhaust has to flow through the sides of the trap and exit.

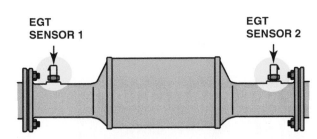

**FIGURE 4–26** EGT 1 and EGT 2 are used by the PCM to help control aftertreatment.

the exhaust through a porous cell which has a silicon carbide substrate with honeycomb-cell-type channels that trap the soot. The main difference between the DPF and a typical catalyst filter is that the entrance to every other cell channel in the DPF substrate is blocked at one end. So instead of flowing directly through the channels, the exhaust gas is forced through the porous walls of the blocked channels and exits through the adjacent open-ended channels. This type of filter is also referred to as a "wall-flow" filter. ● **SEE FIGURE 4–24.**

**OPERATION** Soot particulates in the gas remain trapped on the DPF channel walls where, over time, the trapped particulate matter will begin to clog the filter. The filter must therefore be purged periodically to remove accumulated soot particles. The process of purging soot from the DPF is described as **regeneration.** When the temperature of the exhaust gas is increased, the heat incinerates the soot particles trapped in the filter and is effectively renewed. ● **SEE FIGURE 4–25.**

**EXHAUST GAS TEMPERATURE SENSORS** The following two exhaust gas temperature sensors are used to help the PCM control the DPF.

- EGT sensor 1 is positioned between the DOC and the DPF where it can measure the temperature of the exhaust gas entering the DPF.

- EGT sensor 2 measures the temperature of the exhaust gas stream immediately after it exits the DPF.

The powertrain control module monitors the signals from the EGT sensors as part of its calibrations to control DPF regeneration. Proper exhaust gas temperatures at the inlet of the DPF are crucial for proper operation and for starting the regeneration process. Too high a temperature at the DPF will cause the DPF substrate to melt or crack. Regeneration will be terminated at temperatures above 1,470°F (800°C). With too low a temperature, self-regeneration will not fully complete the soot-burning process. ● **SEE FIGURE 4–26.**

**DPF DIFFERENTIAL PRESSURE SENSOR** The DPF **differential pressure sensor (DPS)** has two pressure sample lines.

- One line is attached before the DPF.
- The other is located after the DPF.

The exact location of the DPS varies by vehicle model type such as medium duty, pickup, or van. By measuring the exhaust supply (upstream) pressure from the DOC, and the post DPF (downstream) pressure, the PCM can determine differential pressure, also called "delta" pressure, across the DPF. Data from the DPF differential pressure sensor is used by the PCM to calibrate for controlling DPF exhaust system operation.

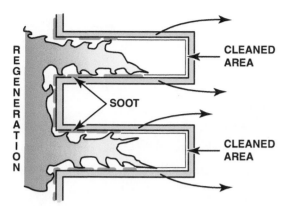

FIGURE 4–27 Regeneration burns the soot and renews the DPF.

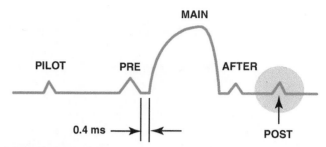

FIGURE 4–28 The post injection pulse occurs to create the heat needed for regeneration.

## DIESEL PARTICULATE FILTER REGENERATION

The primary reason for soot removal is to prevent the buildup of exhaust back pressure. Excessive back pressure increases fuel consumption, reduces power output, and can potentially cause engine damage. Several factors can trigger the diesel PCM to perform regeneration, including:

- Distance since last DPF regeneration
- Fuel used since last DPF regeneration
- Engine run time since last DPF regeneration
- Exhaust differential pressure across the DPF

## DPF REGENERATION PROCESS

A number of engine components are required to function together for the regeneration process to be performed, as follows:

1. PCM controls that impact DPF regeneration include late post injections, engine speed, and adjusting fuel pressure.

2. Adding late post injection pulses provides the engine with additional fuel to be oxidized in the DOC, which increases exhaust temperatures entering the DPF to 900°F (500°C) or higher. ● SEE FIGURE 4–27.

3. The intake air valve acts as a restrictor that reduces air entry to the engine, which increases engine operating temperature.

4. The intake air heater may also be activated to warm intake air during regeneration.

## TYPES OF DPF REGENERATION

DPF regeneration can be initiated in a number of ways, depending on the vehicle application and operating circumstances. The two main regeneration types are as follows:

- **Passive regeneration.** During normal vehicle operation when driving conditions produce sufficient load and exhaust temperatures, passive DPF regeneration may occur. This passive regeneration occurs without input from the PCM or the driver. A passive regeneration may typically occur while the vehicle is being driven at highway speed or towing a trailer.

 **FREQUENTLY ASKED QUESTION**

### Will the Postinjection Pulses Reduce Fuel Economy?

Maybe. Due to the added fuel-injection pulses and late fuel-injection timing, an increase in fuel consumption may be noticed on the driver information center (DIC) during the regeneration time period. A drop in overall fuel economy should not be noticeable. ● SEE FIGURE 4–28.

- **Active regeneration.** Active regeneration is commanded by the PCM when it determines that the DPF requires it to remove excess soot buildup and conditions for filter regeneration have been met. Active regeneration is usually not noticeable to the driver. The vehicle needs to be driven at speeds above 30 mph for approximately 20 to 30 minutes to complete a full regeneration. During regeneration, the exhaust gases reach temperatures above 1,000°F (550°C). Active regeneration is usually not noticeable to the driver.

 **WARNING**

Tailpipe outlet exhaust temperature will be greater than 572°F (300°C) during service regeneration. To help prevent personal injury or property damage from fire or burns, keep vehicle exhaust away from any object and people.

## ASH LOADING

Regeneration will not burn off ash. Only the particulate matter (PM) is burned off during regeneration. Ash is a noncombustible by-product from normal oil consumption. Ash accumulation in the DPF will eventually cause a restriction in the particulate filter. To service an ash-loaded DPF, the DPF will need to be removed from the vehicle and cleaned or replaced. Low ash content engine oil (API CJ-4) is required for vehicles with the DPF system. The CJ-4 rated oil is limited to 1% ash content.

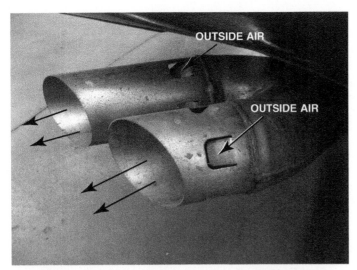

FIGURE 4–29 The exhaust is split into two outlets and has slits to help draw outside air in as the exhaust leaves the tailpipe. The end result is cooler exhaust gases exiting the tailpipe.

 **FREQUENTLY ASKED QUESTION**

**What Is an Exhaust Air Cooler?**

An exhaust air cooler is simply a section of tailpipe that has slits for air to enter. As hot exhaust rushes past the gap, outside air is drawn into the area which reduces the exhaust discharge temperature. The cooler significantly lowers exhaust temperature at the tailpipe from about 800°F (430°C) to approximately 500°F (270°C). ● **SEE FIGURE 4–29.**

## SELECTIVE CATALYTIC REDUCTION

**PURPOSE AND FUNCTION** Selective catalytic reduction (SCR) is a method used to reduce $NO_x$ emissions by injecting urea into the exhaust stream. Instead of using large amounts of exhaust gas recirculation (EGR), the SCR system uses urea. **Urea** is used as a nitrogen fertilizer. It is colorless, odorless, and nontoxic. Urea is called **diesel exhaust fluid (DEF)** in North America and AdBlue in Europe. ● **SEE FIGURE 4–30.**

The urea is injected into the catalyst where it sets off a chemical reaction that converts nitrogen oxides ($NO_x$) into nitrogen ($N_2$) and water ($H_2O$). Vehicle manufacturers size the onboard urea storage tank so that it needs to be refilled at about each scheduled oil change, or every 7,500 miles (12,000 km). A warning light alerts the driver when the urea level needs to be refilled. If the warning light is ignored and the diesel exhaust fluid is not refilled, current EPA regulations require that the operation of the engine be restricted and may not start unless the fluid is refilled. This regulation is designed to prevent the engine from

FIGURE 4–30 Diesel exhaust fluid cost $3 to $4 a gallon and is housed in a separate container that holds from 5 to 10 gallons, or enough to last until the next scheduled oil change in most diesel vehicles that use SCR.

being operated without the fluid, which, if not, would greatly increase exhaust emissions. ● **SEE FIGURE 4–31.**

**ADVANTAGES OF SCR** Using urea injection instead of large amounts of EGR results in the following advantages:

- Potential higher engine power output for the same size engine
- Reduced $NO_x$ emissions up to 90%
- Reduced HC and CO emissions up to 50%
- Reduced particulate matter (PM) by 50%

**DISADVANTAGES OF SCR** Using urea injection instead of large amounts of EGR results in the following disadvantages:

- Onboard storage tank required for the urea
- Difficult to find local sources of urea
- Increased costs to the vehicle owner due to having to refill the urea storage tank

## DIESEL EXHAUST SMOKE DIAGNOSIS

Although some exhaust smoke is considered normal operation for many diesel engines, especially older units, the cause of excessive exhaust smoke should be diagnosed and repaired.

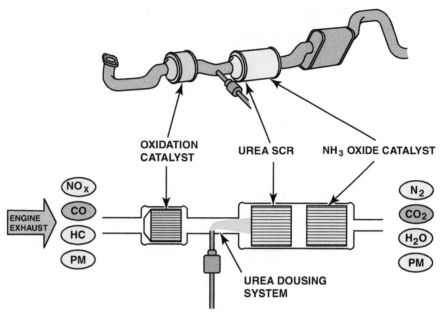

**FIGURE 4–31** Urea (diesel exhaust fluid) injection is used to reduce NO$_x$ exhaust emissions. It is injected after the diesel oxidation catalyst (DOC) and before the diesel particulate filter (DPF) on this 6.7 liter Ford diesel engine.

**BLACK SMOKE** Black exhaust smoke is caused by incomplete combustion because of a lack of air or a fault in the injection system that could cause an excessive amount of fuel in the cylinders. Items that should be checked include the following:

- Fuel specific gravity (API gravity)
- Injector balance test to locate faulty injectors using a scan tool
- Proper operation of the engine coolant temperature (ECT) sensor
- Proper operation of the fuel rail pressure (FRP) sensor
- Restrictions in the intake or turbocharger
- Engine oil usage

**WHITE SMOKE** White exhaust smoke occurs most often during cold engine starts because the smoke is usually condensed fuel droplets. White exhaust smoke is also an indication of cylinder misfire on a warm engine. The most common causes of white exhaust smoke include:

- Inoperative glow plugs
- Low engine compression
- Incorrect injector spray pattern
- Coolant leak into the combustion chamber

**GRAY OR BLUE SMOKE** Blue exhaust smoke is usually due to oil consumption caused by worn piston rings, scored cylinder walls, or defective valve stem seals. Gray or blue smoke can also be caused by a defective injector(s) or defective injector O-rings.

## DIESEL PERFORMANCE DIAGNOSIS

Diesel engines can be diagnosed using a scan tool in most cases, because most of the pressure sensors values can be displayed. Common faults include:

- Hard starting
- No start
- Extended cranking before starting
- Low power

Using a scan tool, check the sensor values in ● **CHART 4–2.** to help pin down the source of the problem. Also check the minimum pressures that are required to start the engine if a no-start condition is being diagnosed. ● **SEE FIGURE 4–32.**

## COMPRESSION TESTING

A compression test is fundamental for determining the mechanical condition of a diesel engine. Worn piston rings can cause low power and excessive exhaust smoke. To test the compression on a diesel engine, the following will have to be done:

- Remove the glow plug (if equipped) or the injector.
- Use a diesel compression gauge, as the compression is too high to use a gasoline engine compression gauge.

A diesel engine should produce at least 300 PSI (2,068 kPa) of compression pressure and all cylinders should be within 50 PSI (345 kPa) of each other. ● **SEE FIGURE 4–33.**

## DIESEL TROUBLESHOOTING CHART

### 5.9 Dodge Cummins 2003–2008

| | |
|---|---|
| Low-pressure pump | 8–12 PSI |
| Pump amperes | 4 A |
| Pump volume | 45 oz. in 30 sec. |
| High-pressure pump | 5,000–23,000 PSI |
| Idle PSI | 5,600–5,700 PSI |
| Electronic Fuel Control (EFC) maximum fuel pressure | Disconnect EFC to achieve maximum pressure |
| Injector volts | 90 V |
| Injector amperes | 20 A |
| Glow plug amperes | 60–80 A × 2 (120–160 A) |
| **Minimum PSI to start** | **5,000 PSI** |

### GM Duramax 2001–2008

| | |
|---|---|
| Low-pressure pump vacuum | 2–10 in. Hg |
| Pump amperes | NA |
| Pump volume | NA |
| High-pressure pump | 5 K-2.3 K-2.6 K PSI |
| Idle PSI | 5,000–6,000 PSI (30–40 MPa) |
| Fuel Rail Pressure Regulator (FRPR) maximum fuel pressure | Disconnect to achieve maximum pressure |
| Injector volts | 48 V or 93 V |
| Injector amperes | 20 A |
| Glow plug amperes | 160 A |
| **Minimum to start** | **1,500 PSI (10 MPa)** |

### Sprinter 2.7 2002–2006

| | |
|---|---|
| Low-pressure pump | 6–51 PSI |
| High-pressure pump | 800–23,000 PSI |
| Idle PSI | 4,900 PSI |
| Fuel Rail Pressure Control (FRPC) maximum fuel pressure | Apply power and ground to FRPC to achieve maximum pressure |
| Injector volts | 80 V |
| Injector amperes | 20 A |
| Glow plug amperes | 17 A each (85–95 A total) |
| **Minimum to start** | **3,200 PSI (1–1.2 V to start)** |

### 6.0 Powerstroke 2003–2008

| | |
|---|---|
| Low-pressure pump | 50–60 PSI |
| High-pressure pump | 500–4,000 PSI |
| Idle PSI | 500 PSI+ |
| Injection Pressure Regulator (IPR) maximum fuel pressure | Apply power and ground to IPR |
| Injector volts | 48 V |
| Injector amperes | 20 A |
| Glow plug amperes | 20–25 A each (160–200 A total) |
| **Minimum to start** | **500 PSI (0.85 V)** |

**CHART 4–2**

The values can be obtained by using a scan tool and basic test equipment. An inductive ammeter can be used to measure the glow plug current draw. Always follow the vehicle manufacturer's recommended procedures.

FIGURE 4–32 A pressure gauge checking the fuel pressure from the lift pump on a Cummins 6.7 liter diesel.

FIGURE 4–33 A compression gauge that is designed for the higher compression rate of a diesel engine should be used when checking the compression.

## GLOW PLUG RESISTANCE BALANCE TEST

Glow plugs increase in resistance as their temperature increases. All glow plugs should have about the same resistance when checked with an ohmmeter. A similar test of the resistance of the glow plugs can be used to detect a weak cylinder. This test is particularly helpful on a diesel engine that is not computer controlled. To test for even cylinder balance using glow plug resistance, perform the following on a warm engine:

1. Unplug, measure, and record the resistance of all glow plugs.

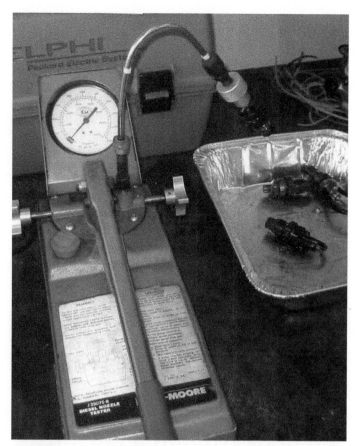

FIGURE 4–34 A typical pop tester used to check the spray pattern of a diesel engine injector.

2. With the wires still removed from the glow plugs, start the engine.

3. Allow the engine to run for several minutes to allow the combustion inside the cylinder to warm the glow plugs.

4. Turn off the engine and then measure and record the resistance of the glow plugs.

5. The resistance of all glow plugs should be higher than at the beginning of the test. A glow plug that is in a cylinder that is not firing correctly will not increase in resistance as much as the others.

6. Another test is to measure exhaust manifold temperature at each exhaust port using an infrared thermometer or a pyrometer. Misfiring cylinders will run cold.

## INJECTOR POP TESTING

A **pop tester** is a device used for checking a diesel injector nozzle for proper spray pattern. The handle is depressed and pop-off pressure is displayed on the gauge. ● **SEE FIGURE 4–34.**

The spray pattern should be a hollow cone, but will vary depending on design. The nozzle should also be tested for leakage (dripping of the nozzle) while under pressure. If the spray pattern is not correct, then cleaning, repairing, or replacing the injector nozzle may be necessary.

**Always Use Cardboard to Check for High-Pressure Leaks**

If diesel fuel is found on the engine, a high-pressure leak could be present. When checking for such a leak, wear protective clothing including safety glasses, a face shield, gloves, and a long-sleeved shirt. Then use a piece of cardboard to locate the high-pressure leak. When a Duramax diesel is running, the pressure in the common rail and injector tubes can reach over 20,000 PSI. At these pressures, the diesel fuel is atomized and cannot be seen but can penetrate the skin and cause personal injury. A leak will be shown as a dark area on the cardboard. When a leak is found, shut off the engine and find the exact location of the leak without the engine running.

CAUTION: Sometimes a leak can actually cut through the cardboard, so use extreme care.

# DIESEL EMISSION TESTING

**OPACITY TEST** The most common diesel exhaust emission test used in state or local testing programs is called the opacity test. **Opacity** means the percentage of light that is blocked by the exhaust smoke:

- A 0% opacity means that the exhaust has no visible smoke and does not block light from a beam projected through the exhaust smoke.
- A 100% opacity means that the exhaust is so dark that it completely blocks light from a beam projected through the exhaust smoke.
- A 50% opacity means that the exhaust blocks half of the light from a beam projected through the exhaust smoke.
  ● **SEE CHART 4–3.**

**SNAP ACCELERATION TEST** In a snap acceleration test, the vehicle is held stationary, with wheel chocks in place and brakes released as the engine is rapidly accelerated to high idle, with the transmission in neutral while smoke emissions are measured. This test is conducted a minimum of six times and the three most consistent measurements are averaged for a final score.

**ROLLING ACCELERATION TEST** Vehicles with a manual transmission are rapidly accelerated in low gear from an idle speed to a maximum governed RPM while the smoke emissions are measured.

| | |
|---|---|
| | 20% opacity |
| | 40% opacity |
| | 60% opacity |
| | 80% opacity |
| | 100% opacity |

**CHART 4–3**

An opacity test is sometimes used during a state emission test on diesel engines.

**FIGURE 4–35** The letters on the side of this injector on a Cummins 6.7 liter diesel indicate the calibration number for the injector.

 TECH TIP

**Do Not Switch Injectors**

In the past, it was common practice to switch diesel fuel injectors from one cylinder to another when diagnosing a dead cylinder problem. However, most high-pressure common rail systems used in new diesels utilize precisely calibrated injectors that should not be mixed up during service. Each injector has its own calibration number. ● **SEE FIGURE 4–35.**

**STALL ACCELERATION TEST** Vehicles with automatic transmissions are held in a stationary position with the parking brake and service brakes applied while the transmission is placed in "drive." The accelerator is depressed and held momentarily while smoke emissions are measured.

The standards for diesels vary according to the type of vehicle and other factors, but usually include a 40% opacity or less.

## SUMMARY

1. A diesel engine uses heat of compression to ignite the diesel fuel when it is injected into the compressed air in the combustion chamber.

2. There are two basic designs of combustion chambers used in diesel engines. Indirect injection (IDI) uses a pre-combustion chamber, whereas direct injection (DI) occurs directly into the combustion chamber.

3. The three phases of diesel combustion include:
   a. Ignition delay
   b. Rapid combustion
   c. Controlled combustion

4. The typical diesel engine fuel system consists of the fuel tank, lift pump, water-fuel separator, and fuel filter.

5. The engine-driven injection pump supplies high-pressure diesel fuel to the injectors.

6. The two most common types of fuel injection used in diesel engines are:
   a. Distributor-type injection pump
   b. Common rail design where all of the injectors are fed from the same fuel supply from a rail under high pressure

7. Injector nozzles are opened either by the high-pressure pulse from the distributor pump or electrically by the computer on a common rail design.

8. Glow plugs are used to help start a cold diesel engine and help prevent excessive white smoke during warm-up.

9. Emissions are controlled on newer diesel engines by using a diesel oxidation catalytic converter, a diesel exhaust particulate filter, exhaust gas recirculation, and a selective catalytic reduction system.

10. Diesel engines can be tested using a scan tool, as well as measuring the glow plug resistance or compression reading, to determine a weak or nonfunctioning cylinder.

## REVIEW QUESTIONS

1. What is the difference between direct injection and indirect injection?

2. What are the three phases of diesel ignition?

3. What are the two most commonly used types of diesel injection systems?

4. Why are glow plugs kept working after the engine starts?

5. What exhaust aftertreatment is needed to achieve exhaust emission standards for vehicles 2007 and newer?

6. What are the advantages and disadvantages of SCR?

## CHAPTER QUIZ

1. How is diesel fuel ignited in a warm diesel engine?
   a. Glow plugs
   b. Heat of compression
   c. Spark plugs
   d. Distributorless ignition system

2. Which type of diesel injection produces less noise?
   a. Indirect injection (IDI)
   b. Common rail
   c. Direct injection
   d. Distributor injection

3. Which diesel injection system requires the use of a glow plug?
   a. Indirect injection (IDI)
   b. High-pressure common rail
   c. Direct injection
   d. Distributor injection

4. The three phases of diesel ignition include _____.
   a. Glow plug ignition, fast burn, slow burn
   b. Slow burn, fast burn, slow burn
   c. Ignition delay, rapid combustion, controlled combustion
   d. Glow plug ignition, ignition delay, controlled combustion

5. What fuel system component is used in a vehicle equipped with a diesel engine that is seldom used on the same vehicle when it is equipped with a gasoline engine?
   a. Fuel filter
   b. Fuel supply line
   c. Fuel return line
   d. Water-fuel separator

6. The diesel injection pump is usually driven by a _____.
   a. Gear off the camshaft
   b. Belt off the crankshaft
   c. Shaft drive off the crankshaft
   d. Chain drive off the camshaft

7. Which diesel system supplies high-pressure diesel fuel to all of the injectors all of the time?
   a. Distributor
   b. Inline
   c. High-pressure common rail
   d. Rotary

8. Glow plugs should have high resistance when _____ and lower resistance when _____.
   a. Cold/warm
   b. Warm/cold
   c. Wet/dry
   d. Dry/wet

9. Technician A says that glow plugs are used to help start a diesel engine and are shut off as soon as the engine starts. Technician B says that the glow plugs are turned off as soon as a flame is detected in the combustion chamber. Which technician is correct?
   a. Technician A only
   b. Technician B only
   c. Both Technicians A and B
   d. Neither Technician A nor B

10. What part should be removed to test cylinder compression on a diesel engine?
    a. Injector
    b. Intake valve rocker arm and stud
    c. Glow plug
    d. Glow plug or injector

# chapter 5

# GASOLINE

**OBJECTIVES:** **After studying Chapter 5, the reader should be able to:** • Describe how the proper grade of gasoline affects engine performance. • List gasoline purchasing hints. • Discuss how volatility affects driveability. • Explain how oxygenated fuels can reduce CO exhaust emissions. • Discuss safety precautions when working with gasoline.

**KEY TERMS:** Air-fuel ratio 85 • Antiknock index (AKI) 86 • American Society for Testing and Materials (ASTM) 83 • British thermal unit (BTU) 84 • Catalytic cracking 82 • Cracking 82 • Detonation 85 • Distillation 81 • Distillation curve 83 • Driveability index (DI) 88 • E10 88 • Ethanol 88 • Fungible 82 • Gasoline 81 • Hydrocracking 82 • Octane rating 85 • Oxygenated fuels 88 • Petroleum 81 • Ping 85 • Reformulated gasoline (RFG) 89 • Reid vapor pressure (RVP) 83 • Spark knock 85 • Stoichiometric 85 • Tetraethyl lead (TEL) 86 • Vapor lock 83 • Volatility 83 • World Wide Fuel Charter (WWFC) 91

## GASOLINE

**DEFINITION** **Gasoline** is a term used to describe a complex mixture of various hydrocarbons refined from crude petroleum oil for use as a fuel in engines. Gasoline and air burns in the cylinder of the engine and produces heat and pressure, which is converted to rotary motion inside the engine and eventually powers the drive wheels of a vehicle. When combustion occurs, carbon dioxide and water are produced if the process is perfect and all of the air and all of the fuel are consumed in the process.

**CHEMICAL COMPOSITION** Gasoline is a combination of hydrocarbon molecules that have between five and 12 carbon atoms. The names of these various hydrocarbons are based on the number of carbon atoms and include:

- **Methane**—one carbon atom
- **Ethane**—two carbon atoms
- **Propane**—three carbon atoms
- **Butane**—four carbon atoms
- **Pentane**—five carbon atoms
- **Hexane**—six carbon atoms
- **Heptane**—seven carbon atoms (Used to test octane rating—has an octane rating of zero)
- **Octane**—eight carbon atoms (A type of octane is used as a basis for antiknock rating)

## REFINING

**TYPES OF CRUDE OIL** Refining is a complex combination of interdependent processing units that can separate crude oil into useful products such as gasoline and diesel fuel. As it comes out of the ground, **petroleum** (meaning "rock oil") crude can be as thin and light colored as apple cider or as thick and black as melted tar. A barrel of crude oil is 42 gallons, not 55 gallons as commonly used for industrial barrels. Typical terms used to describe the type of crude oil include:

- Thin crude oil has a high American Petroleum Institute (API) gravity, and therefore, is called *high-gravity* crude.
- Thick crude oil is called *low-gravity* crude. High-gravity-type crude contains more natural gasoline and its lower sulfur and nitrogen content makes it easier to refine.
- Low-sulfur crude oil is also known as "sweet" crude.
- High-sulfur crude oil is also known as "sour" crude.

**DISTILLATION** In the late 1800s, crude was separated into different products by boiling in a process called **distillation.** Distillation works because crude oil is composed of hydrocarbons with a broad range of boiling points.

In a distillation column, the vapor of the lowest-boiling hydrocarbons, propane and butane, rises to the top. The straight-run gasoline (also called naphtha), kerosene, and diesel fuel cuts are drawn off at successively lower positions in the column.

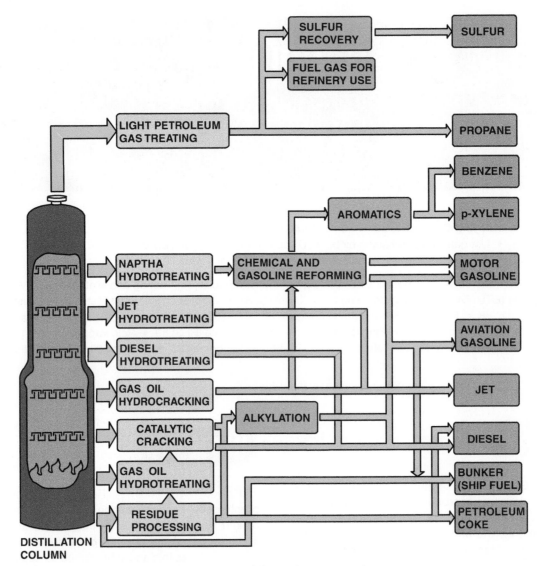

**FIGURE 5–1** The crude oil refining process showing most of the major steps and processes.

**CRACKING**  **Cracking** is the process where hydrocarbons with higher boiling points could be broken down (cracked) into lower-boiling hydrocarbons by treating them to very high temperatures. This process, called *thermal cracking*, was used to increase gasoline production starting in 1913.

Instead of high heat, today cracking is performed using a catalyst and is called **catalytic cracking.** A catalyst is a material that speeds up or otherwise facilitates a chemical reaction without undergoing a permanent chemical change itself. Catalytic cracking produces gasoline of higher quality than thermal cracking.

**Hydrocracking** is similar to catalytic cracking in that it uses a catalyst, but the catalyst is in a hydrogen atmosphere. Hydrocracking can break down hydrocarbons that are resistant to catalytic cracking alone, and it is used to produce diesel fuel rather than gasoline.

Other types of refining processes include:

- Reforming
- Alkylation
- Isomerization
- Hydrotreating
- Desulfurization

● **SEE FIGURE 5–1.**

**SHIPPING**  The gasoline is transported to regional storage facilities by railway tank car or by pipeline. In the pipeline method, all gasoline from many refiners is often sent through the same pipeline and can become mixed. All gasoline is said to be **fungible,** meaning that it is capable of being interchanged because each grade is created to specification so there is no reason to keep the different gasoline brands separated except for grade. Regular grade, mid-grade, and premium grades are separated in the pipeline and the additives are added at the regional storage facilities and then shipped by truck to individual gas stations.

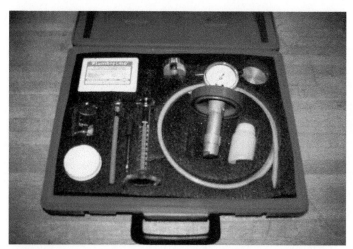

**FIGURE 5–2** A gasoline testing kit, including an insulated container where water at 100°F is used to heat a container holding a small sample of gasoline. The reading on the pressure gauge is the Reid vapor pressure (RVP).

## VOLATILITY

**DEFINITION OF VOLATILITY**   **Volatility** describes how easily the gasoline evaporates (forms a vapor). The definition of volatility assumes that the vapors will remain in the fuel tank or fuel line and will cause a certain pressure based on the temperature of the fuel.

**REID VAPOR PRESSURE (RVP)**   **Reid vapor pressure (RVP)** is the pressure of the vapor above the fuel when the fuel is at 100°F (38°C). Increased vapor pressure permits the engine to start in cold weather. Gasoline without air will not burn. Gasoline must be vaporized (mixed with air) to burn in an engine. ● **SEE FIGURE 5–2.**

**SEASONAL BLENDING**   Cold temperatures reduce the normal vaporization of gasoline; therefore, winter-blended gasoline is specially formulated to vaporize at lower temperatures for proper starting and driveability at low ambient temperatures. The **American Society for Testing and Materials (ASTM)** standards for winter-blend gasoline allow volatility of up to 15 pounds per square inch (PSI) RVP.

At warm ambient temperatures, gasoline vaporizes easily. However, the fuel system (fuel pump, carburetor, fuel-injector nozzles, etc.) is designed to operate with liquid gasoline. The volatility of summer-grade gasoline should be about 7.0 PSI RVP. According to ASTM standards, the maximum RVP should be 10.5 PSI for summer-blend gasoline.

**DISTILLATION CURVE**   Besides Reid vapor pressure, another method of classifying gasoline volatility is the **distillation curve**. A curve on a graph is created by plotting the temperature at which the various percentage of the fuel evaporates. A typical distillation curve is shown in ● **FIGURE 5–3.**

? FREQUENTLY ASKED QUESTION

**Why Do I Get Lower Gas Mileage in the Winter?**
Several factors cause the engine to use more fuel in the winter than in the summer, including:

- Gasoline that is blended for use in cold climates is designed for ease of starting and contains fewer heavy molecules, which contribute to fuel economy. The heat content of winter gasoline is lower than summer-blended gasoline.
- In cold temperatures, all lubricants are stiff, causing more resistance. These lubricants include the engine oil, as well as the transmission and differential gear lubricants.
- Heat from the engine is radiated into the outside air more rapidly when the temperature is cold, resulting in longer run time until the engine has reached normal operating temperature.
- Road conditions, such as ice and snow, can cause tire slippage or additional drag on the vehicle.

**DRIVEABILITY INDEX**   A distillation curve shows how much of a gasoline evaporates at what temperature range. To predict cold-weather driveability, an index was created called the **driveability index,** also called the *distillation index*, and abbreviated **DI.**

The DI was developed using the temperature for the evaporated percentage of 10% (labeled T10), 50% (labeled T50), and 90% (labeled T90). The formula for DI is:

**DI 5 1.5 3 T10 1 3 3 T50 1 T90**

The total DI is a temperature and usually ranges from 1,000°F to 1,200°F. The lower values of DI generally result in good cold-start and warm-up performance. A high DI number is less volatile than a low DI number.

**NOTE: Most premium-grade gasoline has a higher (worse) DI than regular-grade or midgrade gasoline, which could cause poor cold-weather driveability. Vehicles designed to operate on premium-grade gasoline are programmed to handle the higher DI, but engines designed to operate on regular-grade gasoline may not be able to provide acceptable cold-weather driveability.**

**VOLATILITY-RELATED PROBLEMS**   At higher temperatures, liquid gasoline can easily vaporize, which can cause **vapor lock.** Vapor lock is a *lean* condition caused by vaporized fuel in the fuel system. This vaporized fuel takes up space normally occupied by liquid fuel. Bubbles that form in the fuel cause vapor lock, preventing proper operation of the fuel-injection system.

Heat causes some fuel to evaporate, thereby causing bubbles. Sharp bends cause the fuel to be restricted at the bend. When the fuel flows past the bend, the fuel can expand to fill the space after the bend. This expansion drops the pressure, and

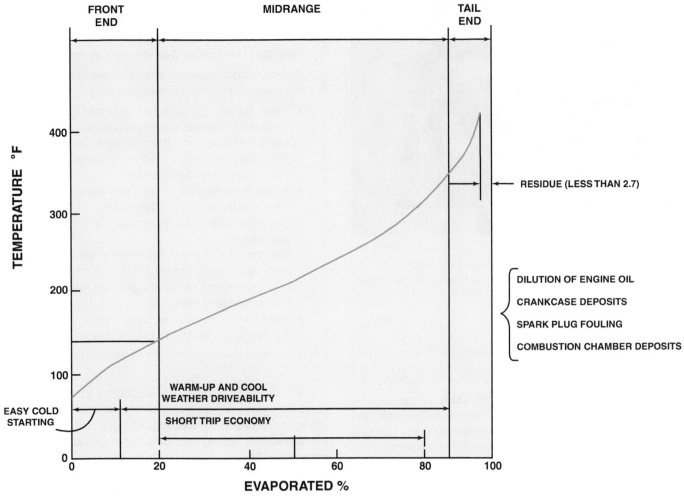

**FIGURE 5–3** A typical distillation curve. Heavier molecules evaporate at higher temperatures and contain more heat energy for power, whereas the lighter molecules evaporate easier for starting.

bubbles form in the fuel lines. When the fuel is full of bubbles, the engine is not being supplied with enough fuel and the engine runs lean. A lean engine will stumble during acceleration, will run rough, and may stall. Warm weather and alcohol-blended fuels both tend to increase vapor lock and engine performance problems.

If winter-blend gasoline (or high-RVP fuel) is used in an engine during warm weather, the following problems may occur:

1. Rough idle
2. Stalling
3. Hesitation on acceleration
4. Surging

# GASOLINE COMBUSTION PROCESS

**CHEMICAL REACTIONS** The combustion process involves the chemical combination of oxygen ($O_2$) from the air (about 21% of the atmosphere) with the hydrogen and carbon from the fuel. In a gasoline engine, a spark starts the combustion process, which takes about 3 ms (0.003 sec) to be completed inside the cylinder of an engine. The chemical reaction that takes place can be summarized as follows: hydrogen (H) plus carbon (C) plus oxygen ($O_2$) plus nitrogen (N) plus spark equals heat plus water ($H_2O$) plus carbon monoxide (CO) (if incomplete combustion) plus carbon dioxide ($CO_2$) plus hydrocarbons (HC) plus oxides of nitrogen ($NO_x$) plus many other chemicals. In an equation format it looks like this:

**H 1 C 1 $O_2$ 1 N 1 Spark 5 Heat 1 $CO_2$ 1 HC 1 $NO_x$**

**HEAT ENERGY** The heat produced by the combustion process is measured in **British thermal units (BTUs).** One BTU is the amount of heat required to raise one pound of water one Fahrenheit degree. The metric unit of heat is the *calorie* (cal). One calorie is the amount of heat required to raise the temperature of one gram (g) of water one Celsius degree:

Gasoline—About 130,000 BTUs per gallon

**AIR-FUEL RATIOS** Fuel burns best when the intake system turns it into a fine spray and mixes it with air before sending it into the cylinders. In fuel-injected engines, the fuel becomes a spray and mixes with the air in the intake manifold. There is a direct relationship between engine airflow and fuel requirements; this is called the **air-fuel ratio.**

The air-fuel ratio is the proportion by weight of air and gasoline that the injection system mixes as needed for engine combustion. The mixtures, with which an engine can operate without stalling, range from 8 to 1 to 18.5 to 1. ● **SEE FIGURE 5–4.**

These ratios are usually stated by weight, such as:

- 8 parts of air by weight combined with 1 part of gasoline by weight (8:1), which is the richest mixture that an engine can tolerate and still fire reliably.

- 18.5 parts of air mixed with 1 part of gasoline (18.5:1), which is the leanest practical ratio. Richer or leaner air-fuel ratios cause the engine to misfire badly or not run at all.

**STOICHIOMETRIC AIR-FUEL RATIO** The ideal mixture or ratio at which all of the fuel combines with all of the oxygen in the air and burns completely is called the **stoichiometric** ratio, a chemically perfect combination. In theory, this ratio for gasoline is an air-fuel mixture of 14.7 to 1. ● **SEE FIGURE 5–5.**

In reality, the exact ratio at which perfect mixture and combustion occurs depends on the molecular structure of gasoline, which can vary. The stoichiometric ratio is a compromise between maximum power and maximum economy.

## NORMAL AND ABNORMAL COMBUSTION

The **octane rating** of gasoline is the measure of its antiknock properties. *Engine knock* (also called **detonation, spark knock,** or **ping**) is a metallic noise an engine makes, usually during acceleration, resulting from abnormal or uncontrolled combustion inside the cylinder.

Normal combustion occurs smoothly and progresses across the combustion chamber from the point of ignition. ● **SEE FIGURE 5–6.**

Normal flame-front combustion travels between 45 and 90 mph (72 and 145 km/h). The speed of the flame front

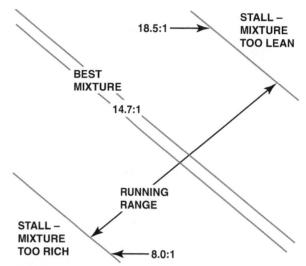

**FIGURE 5–4** An engine will not run if the air-fuel mixture is either too rich or too lean.

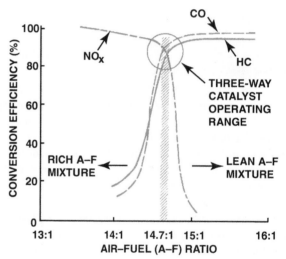

**FIGURE 5–5** With a three-way catalytic converter, emission control is most efficient with an air-fuel ratio between 14.65 to 1 and 14.75 to 1.

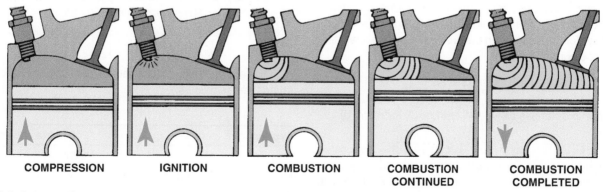

COMPRESSION   IGNITION   COMBUSTION   COMBUSTION CONTINUED   COMBUSTION COMPLETED

**FIGURE 5–6** Normal combustion is a smooth, controlled burning of the air-fuel mixture.

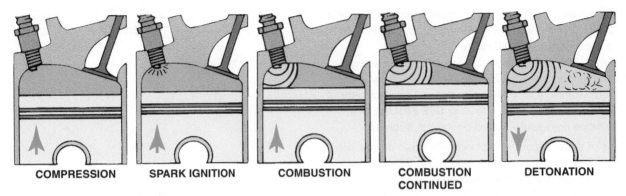

| COMPRESSION | SPARK IGNITION | COMBUSTION | COMBUSTION CONTINUED | DETONATION |

**FIGURE 5–7** Detonation is a secondary ignition of the air-fuel mixture. It is also called spark knock or pinging.

depends on the air-fuel ratio, combustion chamber design (determining amount of turbulence), and temperature.

During periods of spark knock (detonation), the combustion speed increases by up to 10 times to near the speed of sound. The increased combustion speed also causes increased temperatures and pressures, which can damage pistons, gaskets, and cylinder heads. ● **SEE FIGURE 5–7.**

One of the first additives used in gasoline was **tetraethyl lead (TEL).** TEL was added to gasoline in the early 1920s to reduce the tendency to knock. It was often called ethyl or high-test gasoline.

## OCTANE RATING

The antiknock standard or basis of comparison is the knock-resistant hydrocarbon isooctane, chemically called trimethylpentane ($C_8H_{18}$), also known as 2-2-4 trimethylpentane. If a gasoline tested had the exact same antiknock characteristics as isooctane, it was rated as 100-octane gasoline. If the gasoline tested had only 85% of the antiknock properties of isooctane, it was rated as 85 octane. Remember, octane rating is only a comparison test.

The two basic methods used to rate gasoline for antiknock properties (octane rating) are the *research method* and the *motor method.* Each uses a model of the special cooperative fuel research (CFR) single-cylinder engine. The research method and the motor method vary as to temperature of air, spark advance, and other parameters. The research method typically results in readings that are 6 to 10 points higher than those of the motor method. For example, a fuel with a research octane number (RON) of 93 might have a motor octane number (MON) of 85.

The octane rating posted on pumps in the United States is the average of the two methods and is referred to as (R + M) ÷ 2, meaning that, for the fuel used in the previous example, the rating posted on the pumps would be

$$\frac{RON + MON}{2} = \frac{93 + 85}{2} = 89$$

The pump octane is called the **antiknock index (AKI).**

**GASOLINE GRADES AND OCTANE NUMBER** The posted octane rating on gasoline pumps is the rating achieved by the average of the research and the motor methods. ● **SEE FIGURE 5–8.**

**FIGURE 5–8** A pump showing regular with a pump octane of 87, plus rated at 89, and premium rated at 93. These ratings can vary with brand as well as in different parts of the country.

 **FREQUENTLY ASKED QUESTION**

### What Grade of Gasoline Does the EPA Use When Testing Engines?

Due to the various grades and additives used in commercial fuel, the government (EPA) uses a liquid called indolene. Indolene has a research octane number of 96.5 and a motor method octane rating of 88, which results in an R + M ÷ 2 rating of 92.25.

Except in high-altitude areas, the grades and octane ratings are as follows:

| Grades | Octane rating |
| --- | --- |
| Regular | 87 |
| Midgrade (also called Plus) | 89 |
| Premium | 91 or higher |

**FIGURE 5–9** The posted octane rating in most high-altitude areas shows regular at 85 instead of the usual 87.

 **TECH TIP**

### Horsepower and Fuel Flow

To produce 1 hp, the engine must be supplied with 0.50 lb of fuel per hour (lb/hr). Fuel injectors are rated in pounds per hour. For example, a V-8 engine equipped with 25 lb/hr fuel injectors could produce 50 hp per cylinder (per injector) or 400 hp. Even if the cylinder head or block is modified to produce more horsepower, the limiting factor may be the injector flow rate.

The following are flow rates and resulting horsepower for a V-8 engine:

30 lb/hr: 60 hp per cylinder or 480 hp
35 lb/hr: 70 hp per cylinder or 560 hp
40 lb/hr: 80 hp per cylinder or 640 hp

Of course, injector flow rate is only one of many variables that affect power output. Installing larger injectors without other major engine modification could decrease engine output and drastically increase exhaust emissions.

# HIGH-ALTITUDE OCTANE REQUIREMENTS

As the altitude increases, atmospheric pressure drops. The air is less dense because a pound of air takes more volume. The octane rating of fuel does not need to be as high because the engine cannot take in as much air. This process will reduce the combustion (compression) pressures inside the engine. In mountainous areas, gasoline $(R + M) \div 2$ octane ratings are two or more numbers lower than normal (according to the SAE, about one octane number lower per 1,000 ft or 300 m in altitude).
● **SEE FIGURE 5–9.**

A secondary reason for the lowered octane requirement of engines running at higher altitudes is the normal enrichment of the air-fuel ratio and lower engine vacuum with the decreased air density. Some problems, therefore, may occur when driving out of high-altitude areas into lower-altitude areas where the octane rating must be higher. Most computerized engine control systems can compensate for changes in altitude and modify air-fuel ratio and ignition timing for best operation.

Because the combustion burn rate slows at high altitude, the ignition (spark) timing can be advanced to improve power. The amount of timing advance can be about 1 degree per 1,000 ft over 5,000 ft. Therefore, if driving at 8,000 ft of altitude, the ignition timing can be advanced 3 degrees.

High altitude also allows fuel to evaporate more easily. The volatility of fuel should be reduced at higher altitudes to prevent vapor from forming in sections of the fuel system, which can cause driveability and stalling problems. The extra heat generated in climbing to higher altitudes plus the lower atmospheric pressure at higher altitudes combine to cause vapor lock problems as the vehicle goes to higher altitudes.

# GASOLINE ADDITIVES

**DYE** Dye is usually added to gasoline at the distributor to help identify the grade and/or brand of fuel. In many countries, fuels are required to be colored using a fuel-soluble dye. In the United States and Canada, diesel fuel used for off-road use and not taxed is required to be dyed red for identification. Gasoline sold for off-road use in Canada is dyed purple.

**OCTANE IMPROVER ADDITIVES** When gasoline companies, under federal EPA regulations, removed tetraethyl lead from gasoline, other methods were developed to help maintain the antiknock properties of gasoline. Octane improvers (enhancers) can be grouped into three broad categories:

1. Aromatic hydrocarbons (hydrocarbons containing the benzene ring) such as xylene and toluene
2. Alcohols such as ethanol (ethyl alcohol), methanol (methyl alcohol), and tertiary butyl alcohol (TBA)
3. Metallic compounds such as methylcyclopentadienyl manganese tricarbonyl (MMT)

**NOTE: MMT has been proven to be harmful to catalytic converters and can cause spark plug fouling. However, MMT is currently one of the active ingredients commonly found in octane improvers available to the public and in some gasoline sold in Canada. If an octane boost additive has been used that contains MMT, the spark plug porcelain will be rust colored around the tip.**

Propane and butane, which are volatile by-products of the refinery process, are also often added to gasoline as octane improvers. The increase in volatility caused by the added propane and butane often leads to hot-weather driveability problems.

### Can Regular-Grade Gasoline Be Used If Premium Is the Recommended Grade?

Maybe. It is usually possible to use regular-grade or midgrade (plus) gasoline in most newer vehicles without danger of damage to the engine. Most vehicles built since the 1990s are equipped with at least one knock sensor. If a lower octane gasoline than specified is used, the engine ignition timing setting will usually cause the engine to spark knock, also called detonation or ping. This spark knock is detected by the knock sensor(s), which sends a signal to the computer. The computer then retards the ignition timing until the spark knock stops.

NOTE: Some scan tools will show the "estimated octane rating" of the fuel being used, which is based on knock sensor activity.

As a result of this spark timing retardation, the engine torque is reduced. While this reduction in power is seldom noticed, it will reduce fuel economy, often by 4 to 5 miles per gallon. If premium gasoline is then used, the PCM will gradually permit the engine to operate at the more advanced ignition timing setting. Therefore, it may take several tanks of premium gasoline to restore normal fuel economy. For best overall performance, use the grade of gasoline recommended by the vehicle manufacturer.

**FIGURE 5–10** This refueling pump indicates that the gasoline is blended with 10% ethanol (ethyl alcohol) and can be used in any gasoline vehicle. E85 contains 85% ethanol and can be used only in vehicles specifically designed to use it.

### What Is Meant by "Phase Separation?"

All alcohols absorb water, and the alcohol–water mixture can separate from the gasoline and sink to the bottom of the fuel tank. This process is called *phase separation*. To help avoid engine performance problems, try to keep at least a quarter tank of fuel at all times, especially during seasons when there is a wide temperature span between daytime highs and nighttime lows. These conditions can cause moisture to accumulate in the fuel tank as a result of condensation of the moisture in the air.

**OXYGENATED FUEL ADDITIVES** Oxygenated fuels contain oxygen in the molecule of the fuel itself. Examples of oxygenated fuels include methanol, ethanol, methyl tertiary butyl ether (MTBE), tertiary-amyl methyl ether (TAME), and ethyl tertiary butyl ether (ETBE).

Oxygenated fuels are commonly used in high-altitude areas to reduce carbon monoxide (CO) emissions. The extra oxygen in the fuel itself is used to convert harmful CO into carbon dioxide ($CO_2$). The extra oxygen in the fuel helps ensure that there is enough oxygen to convert all CO into $CO_2$ during the combustion process in the engine or catalytic converter.

**METHYL TERTIARY BUTYL ETHER (MTBE).** MTBE is manufactured by means of the chemical reaction of methanol and isobutylene. Unlike methanol, MTBE does not increase the volatility of the fuel and is not as sensitive to water as are other alcohols. The maximum allowable volume level, according to the EPA, is 15% but is currently being phased out because of health concerns, as well as MTBE contamination of drinking water if spilled from storage tanks.

**TERTIARY-AMYL METHYL ETHER.** Tertiary-amyl methyl ether (TAME) contains an oxygen atom bonded to two carbon atoms and is added to gasoline to provide oxygen to the fuel. It is slightly soluble in water, very soluble in ethers and alcohol, and soluble in most organic solvents including hydrocarbons.

**ETHYL TERTIARY BUTYL ETHER.** ETBE is derived from ethanol. The maximum allowable volume level is 17.2%. The use of ETBE is the cause of much of the odor from the exhaust of vehicles using reformulated gasoline.

**ETHANOL.** Ethanol, also called *ethyl alcohol* is drinkable alcohol and is usually made from grain. Adding 10% ethanol (ethyl alcohol or grain alcohol) increases the (R + M) ÷ 2 octane rating by three points. The alcohol added to the base gasoline, however, also raises the volatility of the fuel about 0.5 PSI. Most automobile manufacturers permit up to 10% ethanol if driveability problems are not experienced.

The oxygen content of a 10% blend of ethanol in gasoline, called **E10**, is 3.5% oxygen by weight. ● **SEE FIGURE 5–10.**

Keeping the fuel tank full reduces the amount of air and moisture in the tank. ● **SEE FIGURE 5–11.**

**FIGURE 5–11** A container with gasoline containing alcohol. Notice the separation line where the alcohol–water mixture separated from the gasoline and sank to the bottom.

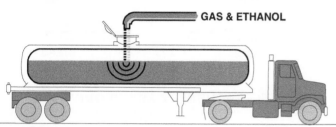

**FIGURE 5–12** In-line blending is the most accurate method for blending ethanol with gasoline because computers are used to calculate the correct ratio.

## GASOLINE BLENDING

Gasoline additives, such as ethanol and dyes, are usually added to the fuel at the distributor. Adding ethanol to gasoline is a way to add oxygen to the fuel itself. Gasoline containing an addition that has oxygen is called *oxygenated fuel*. There are three basic methods used to blend ethanol with gasoline to create E10 (10% ethanol, 90% gasoline):

1. **In-line blending.** Gasoline and ethanol are mixed in a storage tank or in the tank of a transport truck while it is being filled. Because the quantities of each can be accurately measured, this method is most likely to produce a well-mixed blend of ethanol and gasoline. ● **SEE FIGURE 5–12.**

2. **Sequential blending.** This method is usually performed at the wholesale terminal and involves adding a measured amount of ethanol to a tank truck followed by a measured amount of gasoline. ● **SEE FIGURE 5–13.**

3. **Splash blending.** Splash blending can be done at the retail outlet or distributor and involves separate purchases of ethanol and gasoline. In a typical case, a distributor can purchase gasoline, and then drive to another supplier and purchase ethanol. The ethanol is then added (splashed) into the tank of gasoline. This method is the least-accurate method of blending and can result in ethanol concentration for E10 that should be 10% to range from 5% to over 20% in some cases. ● **SEE FIGURE 5–14.**

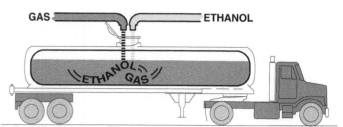

**FIGURE 5–13** Sequential blending uses a computer to calculate the correct ratio as well as the prescribed order in which the products are loaded.

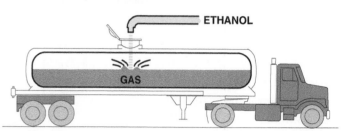

**FIGURE 5–14** Splash blending occurs when the ethanol is added to a tanker with gasoline and is mixed as the truck travels to the retail outlet.

> **? FREQUENTLY ASKED QUESTION**
>
> **Is Water Heavier Than Gasoline?**
>
> Yes. Water weighs about 8.3 pounds per gallon, whereas gasoline weighs about 6 pounds per gallon. The density as measured by specific gravity includes:
>
> Water = 1.000 (the baseline for specific gravity)
>
> Gasoline = 0.730 to 0.760
>
> This means that any water that gets into the fuel tank will sink to the bottom.

## REFORMULATED GASOLINE

Reformulated gasoline (RFG) is manufactured to help reduce emissions. The gasoline refiners reformulate gasoline by using additives that contain at least 2% oxygen by weight and reducing the additive benzene to a maximum of 1% by volume. Two other major changes done at the refineries are as follows:

1. **Reduce light compounds.** Refineries eliminate butane, pentane, and propane, which have a low boiling point and evaporate easily. These unburned hydrocarbons are released into the atmosphere during refueling and through the fuel tank vent system, contributing to smog formation. Therefore, reducing the light compounds from gasoline helps reduce evaporative emissions.

2. **Reduce heavy compounds.** Refineries eliminate heavy compounds with high boiling points such as aromatics and olefins. The purpose of this reduction is to reduce the amount of unburned hydrocarbons that enter the catalytic

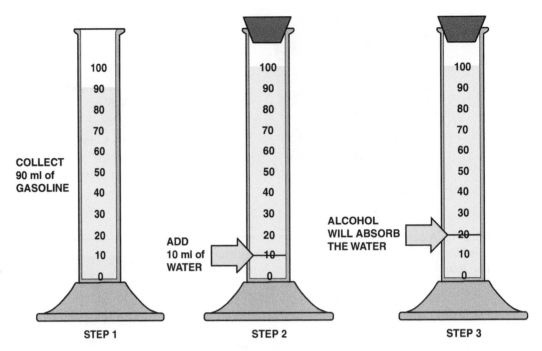

FIGURE 5–15 Checking gasoline for alcohol involves using a graduated cylinder and adding water to check if the alcohol absorbs the water.

Labels in figure:
COLLECT 90 ml of GASOLINE — STEP 1
ADD 10 ml of WATER — STEP 2
ALCOHOL WILL ABSORB THE WATER — STEP 3

converter, which makes the converter more efficient, thereby reducing emissions.

Because many of the heavy compounds are eliminated, a drop in fuel economy of about 1 mpg has been reported in areas where reformulated gasoline is being used. Formaldehyde is formed when RFG is burned, and the vehicle exhaust has a unique smell when reformulated gasoline is used.

## TESTING GASOLINE FOR ALCOHOL CONTENT

Take the following steps when testing gasoline for alcohol content:

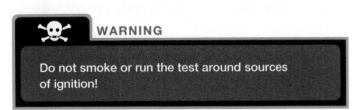

WARNING

Do not smoke or run the test around sources of ignition!

1. Pour suspect gasoline into a graduated cylinder.
2. Carefully fill the graduated cylinder to the 90-mL mark.
3. Add 10 mL of water to the graduated cylinder by counting the number of drops from an eyedropper.
4. Put the stopper in the cylinder and shake vigorously for 1 minute. Relieve built-up pressure by occasionally removing the stopper. Alcohol dissolves in water and will drop to the bottom of the cylinder.
5. Place the cylinder on a flat surface and let it stand for 2 minutes.

? FREQUENTLY ASKED QUESTION

**How Does Alcohol Content in the Gasoline Affect Engine Operation?**

In most cases, the use of gasoline containing 10% or less of ethanol (ethyl alcohol) has little or no effect on engine operation. However, because the addition of 10% ethanol raises the volatility of the fuel slightly, occasional rough idle or stalling may be noticed, especially during warm weather. The rough idle and stalling may also be noticeable after the engine is started, driven, then stopped for a short time. Engine heat can vaporize the alcohol-enhanced fuel causing bubbles to form in the fuel system. These bubbles in the fuel prevent the proper operation of the fuel injection system and result in a hesitation during acceleration, rough idle, or in severe cases repeated stalling until all the bubbles have been forced through the fuel system, replaced by cooler fuel from the fuel tank.

6. Take a reading near the bottom of the cylinder at the boundary between the two liquids.
7. For percent of alcohol in gasoline, subtract 10 from the reading.

For example,

**The reading is 20 mL: 20 − 10 = 10% alcohol**

If the increase in volume is 0.2% or less, it may be assumed that the test gasoline contains no alcohol. ● **SEE FIGURE 5–15.** Alcohol content can also be checked using an electronic tester. See the step-by-step sequence at the end of the chapter.

**FIGURE 5–16** The gas cap on a Ford vehicle notes that BP fuel is recommended.

 **TECH TIP**

**The Sniff Test**

Problems can occur with stale gasoline from which the lighter parts of the gasoline have evaporated. Stale gasoline usually results in a no-start situation. If stale gasoline is suspected, sniff it. If it smells rancid, replace it with fresh gasoline.

**NOTE: If storing a vehicle, boat, or lawnmower over the winter, put some gasoline stabilizer into the gasoline to reduce the evaporation and separation that can occur during storage. Gasoline stabilizer is frequently available at lawnmower repair shops or marinas.**

 **FREQUENTLY ASKED QUESTION**

**What Is "Top-Tier" Gasoline?**

Top-tier gasoline is gasoline that has specific standards for quality, including enough detergent to keep all intake valves clean. Four automobile manufacturers, including BMW, General Motors, Honda, and Toyota, developed the standards. Top-tier gasoline exceeds the quality standards developed by the **World Wide Fuel Charter (WWFC)** that was established in 2002 by vehicle and engine manufacturers. The gasoline companies that agreed to make fuel that matches or exceeds the standards as a top-tier fuel include ChevronTexaco and ConocoPhillips. Ford has specified that BP fuel, sold in many parts of the country, is the recommended fuel to use in Ford vehicles. ● **SEE FIGURE 5–16.**

## GENERAL GASOLINE RECOMMENDATIONS

The fuel used by an engine is a major expense in the operation cost of the vehicle. The proper operation of the engine depends on clean fuel of the proper octane rating and vapor pressure for the atmospheric conditions.

To help ensure proper engine operation and keep fuel costs to a minimum, follow these guidelines:

1. Purchase fuel from a busy station to help ensure that it is fresh and less likely to be contaminated with water or moisture.

2. Keep the fuel tank above one-quarter full, especially during seasons in which the temperature rises and falls by more than 20°F between daytime highs and nighttime lows. This helps to reduce condensed moisture in the fuel tank and could prevent gas line freeze-up in cold weather.

   **NOTE: Gas line freeze-up occurs when the water in the gasoline freezes and forms an ice blockage in the fuel line.**

3. Do not purchase fuel with a higher octane rating than is necessary. Most newer engines are equipped with a detonation (knock) sensor that signals the vehicle computer to retard the ignition timing when spark knock occurs. Therefore, an operating difference may not be noticeable to the driver when using a low-octane fuel, except for a decrease in power and fuel economy. In other words, the engine with a knock sensor will tend to operate knock free on regular fuel, even if premium, higher-octane fuel is specified. Using premium fuel may result in more power and greater fuel economy. The increase in fuel economy, however, would have to be substantial to justify the increased cost of high-octane premium fuel. Some drivers find a good compromise by using midgrade (plus) fuel to benefit from the engine power and fuel economy gains without the cost of using premium fuel all the time.

4. Avoid using gasoline with alcohol in warm weather, even though many alcohol blends do not affect engine driveability. If warm-engine stumble, stalling, or rough idle occurs, change brands of gasoline.

5. Do not purchase fuel from a retail outlet when a tanker truck is filling the underground tanks. During the refilling procedure, dirt, rust, and water may be stirred up in the underground tanks. This undesirable material may be pumped into your vehicle's fuel tank.

### Why Should I Keep the Fuel Gauge Above One-Quarter Tank?

The fuel pickup inside the fuel tank can help keep water from being drawn into the fuel system unless water is all that is left at the bottom of the tank. Over time, moisture in the air inside the fuel tank can condense, causing liquid water to drop to the bottom of the fuel tank (water is heavier than gasoline—about 8 lb per gallon for water and about 6 lb per gallon for gasoline). If alcohol-blended gasoline is used, the alcohol can absorb the water and the alcohol–water combination can be burned inside the engine. However, when water combines with alcohol, a separation layer occurs between the gasoline at the top of the tank and the alcohol–water combination at the bottom. When the fuel level is low, the fuel pump will draw from this concentrated level of alcohol and water. Because alcohol and water do not burn as well as pure gasoline, severe driveability problems can occur such as stalling, rough idle, hard starting, and missing.

 TECH TIP

### Do Not Overfill the Fuel Tank

Gasoline fuel tanks have an expansion volume area at the top. The volume of this expansion area is equal to 10% to 15% of the volume of the tank. This area is normally not filled with gasoline, but rather is designed to provide a place for the gasoline to expand into, if the vehicle is parked in the hot sun and the gasoline expands. This prevents raw gasoline from escaping from the fuel system. A small restriction is usually present to control the amount of air and vapors that can escape the tank and flow to the charcoal canister.

This volume area could be filled with gasoline if the fuel is slowly pumped into the tank. Since it can hold an extra 10% (2 gallons in a 20-gallon tank), some people deliberately try to fill the tank completely. When this expansion volume is filled, liquid fuel (rather than vapors) can be drawn into the charcoal canister. When the purge valve opens, liquid fuel can be drawn into the engine, causing an excessively rich air-fuel mixture. Not only can this liquid fuel harm vapor recovery parts, but overfilling the gas tank could also cause the vehicle to fail an exhaust emission test, particularly during an enhanced test when the tank could be purged while on the rollers.

**FIGURE 5–17** Many gasoline service stations have signs posted warning customers to place plastic fuel containers on the ground while filling. If placed in a trunk or pickup truck bed equipped with a plastic liner, static electricity could build up during fueling and discharge from the container to the metal nozzle, creating a spark and possible explosion. Some service stations have warning signs not to use cell phones while fueling to help avoid the possibility of an accidental spark creating a fire hazard.

6. Do not overfill the gas tank. After the nozzle clicks off, add just enough fuel to round up to the next dime. Adding additional gasoline will cause the excess to be drawn into the charcoal canister. This can lead to engine flooding and excessive exhaust emissions.

7. Be careful when filling gasoline containers. Always fill a gas can on the ground to help prevent the possibility of static electricity buildup during the refueling process. ● **SEE FIGURE 5–17.**

**1** A fuel composition tester (SPX Kent-Moore J-44175) is the recommended tool, by General Motors, to use to test the alcohol content of gasoline.

**2** This battery-powered tester uses light-emitting diodes (LEDs), meter lead terminals, and two small openings for the fuel sample.

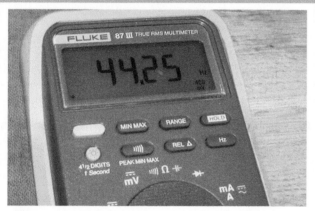

**3** The first step is to verify the proper operation of the tester by measuring the air frequency by selecting AC hertz on the meter. The air frequency should be between 35 and 48 Hz.

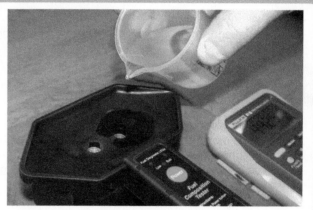

**4** After verifying that the tester is capable of correctly reading the air frequency, gasoline is poured into the testing cell of the tool.

**5** Record the AC frequency as shown on the meter and subtract 50 from the reading. (e.g., 60.50 − 50.00 = 10.5). This number (10.5) is the percentage of alcohol in the gasoline sample.

**6** Adding additional amounts of ethyl alcohol (ethanol) increases the frequency reading.

1. Gasoline is a complex blend of hydrocarbons. Gasoline is blended for seasonal usage to achieve the correct volatility for easy starting and maximum fuel economy under all driving conditions.

2. Winter-blend fuel used in a vehicle during warm weather can cause a rough idle and stalling because of its higher Reid vapor pressure (RVP).

3. Abnormal combustion (also called detonation or spark knock) increases both the temperature and the pressure inside the combustion chamber.

4. Most regular-grade gasoline today, using the (R + M) ÷ 2 rating method, is 87 octane; midgrade (plus) is 89; and premium grade is 91 or higher.

5. Oxygenated fuels contain oxygen to lower CO exhaust emissions.

6. Gasoline should always be purchased from a busy station, and the tank should not be overfilled.

## REVIEW QUESTIONS

1. What is the difference between summer-blend and winter-blend gasoline?

2. What is Reid vapor pressure?

3. What is vapor lock?

4. What does the (R + M) ÷ 2 gasoline pump octane rating indicate?

5. What are the octane improvers that may be used during the refining process?

6. What is stoichiometric?

## CHAPTER QUIZ

1. Winter-blend gasoline _____.
   a. Vaporizes more easily than summer-blend gasoline
   b. Has a higher RVP
   c. Can cause engine driveability problems if used during warm weather
   d. All of the above

2. Vapor lock can occur _____.
   a. As a result of excessive heat near fuel lines
   b. If a fuel line is restricted
   c. During both a and b
   d. During neither a nor b

3. Technician A says that spark knock, ping, and detonation are different names for abnormal combustion. Technician B says that any abnormal combustion raises the temperature and pressure inside the combustion chamber and can cause severe engine damage. Which technician is correct?
   a. Technician A only
   b. Technician B only
   c. Both Technicians A and B
   d. Neither Technician A nor B

4. Technician A says that the research octane number is higher than the motor octane number. Technician B says that the octane rating posted on fuel pumps is an average of the two ratings. Which technician is correct?
   a. Technician A only
   b. Technician B only
   c. Both Technicians A and B
   d. Neither Technician A nor B

5. Technician A says that in going to high altitudes, engines produce lower power. Technician B says that most engine control systems can compensate the air-fuel mixture for changes in altitude. Which technician is correct?
   a. Technician A only
   b. Technician B only
   c. Both Technicians A and B
   d. Neither Technician A nor B

6. Which method of blending ethanol with gasoline is the most accurate?
   a. In-line
   b. Sequential
   c. Splash
   d. All of the above are equally accurate methods

7. What can be used to measure the alcohol content in gasoline?
   a. Graduated cylinder      c. Scan tool
   b. Electronic tester       d. Either a or b

8. To avoid problems with the variation of gasoline, all government testing uses _____ as a fuel during testing procedures.
   a. MTBE (methyl tertiary butyl ether)
   b. Indolene
   c. Xylene
   d. TBA (tertiary butyl alcohol)

9. Avoid topping off the fuel tank because _____.
   a. It can saturate the charcoal canister
   b. The extra fuel simply spills onto the ground
   c. The extra fuel increases vehicle weight and reduces performance
   d. The extra fuel goes into the expansion area of the tank and is not used by the engine

10. Using ethanol-enhanced or reformulated gasoline can result in reduced fuel economy.
    a. True                    b. False

**OBJECTIVES:** **After studying Chapter 6, the reader should be able to:** • Describe how alternative fuels affect engine performance. • List alternatives to gasoline. • Discuss how alternative fuels affect driveability. • Explain how alternative fuels can reduce CO exhaust emissions. • Discuss safety precautions when working with alternative fuels.

**KEY TERMS:** AFV 97 • Anhydrous ethanol 96 • Biomass 101 • Cellulose ethanol 96 • Cellulosic biomass 96 • Coal to liquid (CTL) 105 • Compressed natural gas (CNG) 102 • E85 96 • Ethanol 95 • Ethyl alcohol 95 • FFV 97 • Fischer-Tropsch 104 • Flex fuels 97 • FTD 105 • Fuel compensation sensor 97 • Gas to liquid (GTL) 105 • Grain alcohol 95 • Liquid petroleum gas (LPG) 101 • LP-gas 101 • M85 101 • Methanol 100 • Methanol to gasoline (MTG) 105 • NGV 102 • Propane 101 • Switchgrass 96 • Syncrude 105 • Syn-gas 101 • Synthetic fuel 104 • Underground coal gasification (UCG) 105 • V-FFV 98 • Variable fuel sensor 97

## ETHANOL

**ETHANOL TERMINOLOGY** **Ethanol** is also called **ethyl alcohol** or **grain alcohol,** because it is usually made from grain and is the type of alcohol found in alcoholic drinks such as beer, wine, and distilled spirits like whiskey. Ethanol is composed of two carbon atoms and six hydrogen atoms with one added oxygen atom. ● **SEE FIGURE 6–1.**

**ETHANOL PRODUCTION** Conventional ethanol is derived from grains, such as corn, wheat, or soybeans. Corn, for example, is converted to ethanol in either a dry or wet milling process. In dry milling operations, liquefied cornstarch is produced by heating cornmeal with water and enzymes. A second enzyme converts the liquefied starch to sugars, which are fermented by yeast into ethanol and carbon dioxide. Wet milling operations separate the fiber, germ (oil), and protein from the starch before it is fermented into ethanol.

The majority of the ethanol in the United States is made from:

- Corn
- Grain
- Sorghum
- Wheat
- Barley
- Potatoes

In Brazil, the world's largest ethanol producer, it is made from sugarcane. Ethanol can be made by the dry mill process

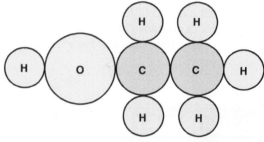

**FIGURE 6–1** The ethanol molecule showing two carbon atoms, six hydrogen atoms, and one oxygen atom.

**?** **FREQUENTLY ASKED QUESTION**

**Does Ethanol Production Harm the Environment?**

The production of ethanol is referred to as being carbon neutral because the amount of $CO_2$ released during production is equal to the amount of $CO_2$ that would be released if the corn or other products were left to decay.

in which the starch portion of the corn is fermented into sugar and then distilled into alcohol.

The major steps in the dry mill process include:

1. **Milling.** The feedstock passes through a hammer mill that turns it into a fine powder called *meal.*

2. **Liquefaction.** The meal is mixed with water and then passed through cookers where the starch is liquefied.

Heat is applied at this stage to enable liquefaction. Cookers use a high-temperature stage of about 250°F to 300°F (120°C to 150°C) to reduce bacteria levels and then a lower temperature of about 200°F (95°C) for a holding period.

3. **Saccharification.** The mash from the cookers is cooled and a secondary enzyme is added to convert the liquefied starch to fermentable sugars (dextrose).

4. **Fermentation.** Yeast is added to the mash to ferment the sugars to ethanol and carbon dioxide.

5. **Distillation.** The fermented mash, now called beer, contains about 10% alcohol plus all the nonfermentable solids from the corn and yeast cells. The mash is pumped to the continuous-flow, distillation system where the alcohol is removed from the solids and the water. The alcohol leaves the top of the final column at about 96% strength, and the residue mash, called *silage*, is transferred from the base of the column to the co-product processing area.

6. **Dehydration.** The alcohol from the top of the column passes through a dehydration system where the remaining water will be removed. The alcohol product at this stage is called **anhydrous ethanol** (pure, no more than 0.5% water).

7. **Denaturing.** Ethanol that will be used for fuel must be denatured, or made unfit for human consumption, with a small amount of gasoline (2% to 5%), methanol, or denatonium benzoate. This is done at the ethanol plant.

## CELLULOSE ETHANOL

**TERMINOLOGY** **Cellulose ethanol** can be produced from a wide variety of cellulose biomass feedstock, including:

- Agricultural plant wastes (corn stalks, cereal straws)
- Plant wastes from industrial processes (sawdust, paper pulp)
- Energy crops grown specifically for fuel production.

These nongrain products are often referred to as **cellulosic biomass.** Cellulosic biomass is composed of cellulose and lignin, with smaller amounts of proteins, lipids (fats, waxes, and oils), and ash. About two-thirds of cellulosic materials are present as cellulose, with lignin making up the bulk of the remaining dry mass.

**REFINING CELLULOSE BIOMASS** As with grains, processing cellulose biomass involves extracting fermentable sugars from the feedstock. But the sugars in cellulose are locked in complex carbohydrates called polysaccharides (long chains of simple sugars). Separating these complex structures into fermentable sugars is needed to achieve the efficient and economic production of cellulose ethanol.

Two processing options are employed to produce fermentable sugars from cellulose biomass:

- Acid hydrolysis is used to break down the complex carbohydrates into simple sugars.
- Enzymes are employed to convert the cellulose biomass to fermentable sugars. The final step involves microbial fermentation, yielding ethanol and carbon dioxide.

**NOTE: Cellulose ethanol production substitutes biomass for fossil fuels. The greenhouse gases produced by the combustion of biomass are offset by the $CO_2$ absorbed by the biomass as it grows in the field.**

## E85

**WHAT IS E85?** Vehicle manufacturers have available vehicles that are capable of operating on gasoline plus ethanol or a combination of gasoline and ethanol called **E85.** E85 is composed of 85% ethanol and 15% gasoline.

Pure ethanol has an octane rating of about 113. E85, which contains 35% oxygen by weight, has an octane rating of about 100 to 105. This compares to a regular unleaded gasoline, which has a rating of 87. ● **SEE FIGURE 6–2.**

**NOTE: The octane rating of E85 depends on the exact percent of ethanol used, which can vary from 81% to 85%. It also depends on the octane rating of the gasoline used to make E85.**

**FIGURE 6–2** Some retail stations offer a variety of fuel choices, such as this station in Ohio where E10 and E85 are available.

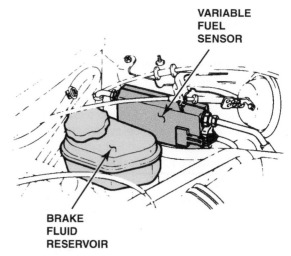

**FIGURE 6–3** The location of the variable fuel sensor can vary, depending on the make and model of vehicle, but it is always in the fuel line between the fuel tank and the fuel injectors.

## HEAT ENERGY OF E85
E85 has less heat energy than gasoline.

**Gasoline = 114,000 BTUs per gallon**

**E85 = 87,000 BTUs per gallon**

This means that the fuel economy is reduced by 20% to 30% if E85 is used instead of gasoline.

**Example:** A Chevrolet Tahoe 5.3-liter V-8 with an automatic transmission has an EPA rating of 15 mpg in the city and 20 mpg on the highway when using gasoline. If this same vehicle was fueled with E85, the EPA fuel economy rating drops to 11 mpg in the city and 15 mpg on the highway.

# ALTERNATIVE-FUEL VEHICLES

The 15% gasoline in this blend helps the engine start, especially in cold weather. Vehicles equipped with this capability are commonly referred to as **alternative-fuel vehicles (AFVs),** **flex fuels,** and **flexible fuel vehicles,** or **FFVs.** Using E85 in a flex-fuel vehicle can result in a power increase of about 5%. For example, an engine rated at 200 hp using gasoline or E10 could produce 210 hp if using E85.

**NOTE: E85 may test as containing less than 85% ethanol if tested in cold climates because it is often blended according to outside temperature. A lower percentage of ethanol with a slightly higher percentage of gasoline helps engines start in cold climates.**

These vehicles are equipped with an electronic sensor in the fuel supply line that detects the presence and percentage of ethanol. The PCM then adjusts the fuel injector on-time and ignition timing to match the needs of the fuel being used.

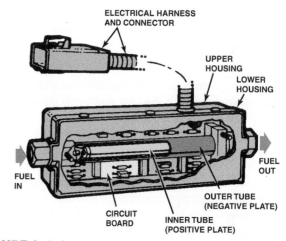

**FIGURE 6–4** A cutaway view of a typical variable fuel sensor.

E85 contains less heat energy, and therefore will use more fuel, but the benefits include a lower cost of the fuel and the environmental benefit associated with using an oxygenated fuel.

General Motors, Ford, Chrysler, Mazda, and Honda are a few of the manufacturers offering E85 compatible vehicles. E85 vehicles use fuel system parts designed to withstand the additional alcohol content, modified driveability programs that adjust fuel delivery and timing to compensate for the various percentages of ethanol fuel, and a **fuel compensation sensor** that measures both the percentage of ethanol blend and the temperature of the fuel. This sensor is also called a **variable fuel sensor.** ● SEE FIGURES 6–3 AND 6–4.

## E85 FUEL SYSTEM REQUIREMENTS
Most E85 vehicles are very similar to non-E85 vehicles. Fuel system components may be redesigned to withstand the effects of higher concentrations of ethanol. In addition, since the stoichiometric point for ethanol is 9:1 instead of 14.7:1 as for gasoline, the air-fuel mixture has to be adjusted for the percentage of ethanol present in the fuel tank. In order to determine this percentage

## TECH TIP

### Purchase a Flex-Fuel Vehicle

If purchasing a new or used vehicle, try to find a flex-fuel vehicle. Even though you may not want to use E85, a flex-fuel vehicle has a more robust fuel system than a conventional fuel system designed for gasoline or E10. The enhanced fuel system components and materials usually include:

- Stainless steel fuel rail
- Graphite commutator bars instead of copper in the fuel pump motor (ethanol can oxidize into acetic acid, which can corrode copper)
- Diamond-like carbon (DLC) corrosion-resistant fuel injectors
- Alcohol-resistant O-rings and hoses

The cost of a flex-fuel vehicle compared with the same vehicle designed to operate on gasoline is a no-cost or a low-cost option.

**FIGURE 6–5** A pump for E85 (85% ethanol and 15% gasoline). E85 is available in more locations every year.

**FIGURE 6–6** A flex-fuel vehicle often has a yellow gas cap, which is labeled E85/gasoline.

of ethanol in the fuel tank, a compensation sensor is used. The fuel compensation sensor is the only additional piece of hardware required on some E85 vehicles. The fuel compensation sensor provides both the ethanol percentage and the fuel temperature to the PCM. The PCM uses this information to adjust both the ignition timing and the quantity of fuel delivered to the engine. The fuel compensation sensor uses a microprocessor to measure both the ethanol percentage and the fuel temperature. This information is sent to the PCM on the signal circuit. The compensation sensor produces a square wave frequency and pulse width signal. The normal frequency range of the fuel compensation sensor is 50 hertz, which represents 0% ethanol and 150 hertz, which represents 100% ethanol. The pulse width of the signal varies from 1 millisecond to 5 milliseconds. One millisecond would represent a fuel temperature of −40°F (−40°C), and 5 milliseconds would represent a fuel temperature of 257°F (125°C). Since the PCM knows both the fuel temperature and the ethanol percentage of the fuel, it can adjust fuel quantity and ignition timing for optimum performance and emissions.

The benefits of E85 vehicles are less pollution, less $CO_2$ production, and less dependence on oil. ● **SEE FIGURE 6–5.**

Ethanol-fueled vehicles generally produce the same pollutants as gasoline vehicles; however, they produce less CO and $CO_2$ emissions. While $CO_2$ is not considered a pollutant, it is thought to lead to global warming and is called a greenhouse gas.

**FLEX-FUEL VEHICLE IDENTIFICATION** Flexible fuel vehicles (FFVs) can be identified by:

- Emblems on the side, front, and/or rear of the vehicle
- Yellow fuel cap showing E85/gasoline (● **SEE FIGURE 6–6**)

## ? FREQUENTLY ASKED QUESTION

### How Does a Sensorless Flex-Fuel System Work?

Many General Motors flex-fuel vehicles do not use a fuel compensation sensor and instead use the oxygen sensor to detect the presence of the lean mixture and the extra oxygen in the fuel.

The powertrain control module (PCM) then adjusts the injector pulse-width and the ignition timing to optimize engine operation to the use of E85. This type of vehicle is called a **virtual flexible fuel vehicle**, abbreviated **V-FFV**. The virtual flexible fuel vehicle can operate on pure gasoline or blends up to 85% ethanol.

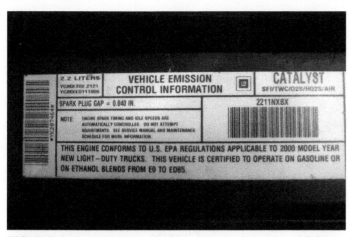

**FIGURE 6-7** A vehicle emission control information (VECI) sticker on a flexible fuel vehicle indicating that it can use ethanol from 0 to 85%.

- Vehicle emission control information (VECI) label under the hood (● **SEE FIGURE 6-7**)
- Vehicle identification number (VIN)

Vehicles that are flexible fuel include:

### Chrysler

**2004+**
- 4.7L Dodge Ram Pickup 1500 Series
- 2.7L Dodge Stratus Sedan
- 2.7L Chrysler Sebring Sedan
- 3.3L Caravan and Grand Caravan SE

**2003–2004**
- 2.7L Dodge Stratus Sedan
- 2.7L Chrysler Sebring Sedan

**2003**
- 3.3L Dodge Cargo Minivan

**2000–2003**
- 3.3L Chrysler Voyager Minivan
- 3.3L Dodge Caravan Minivan 3.3L Chrysler Town and Country Minivan

**1998–1999**
- 3.3L Dodge Caravan Minivan
- 3.3L Plymouth Voyager Minivan
- 3.3L Chrysler Town & Country Minivan

### Ford Motor Company
*Ford offers the flex fuel capability as an option on select vehicles—see the owner's manual.

**2004+**
- 4.0L Explorer Sport Trac
- 4.0L Explorer (4-door)
- 3.0L Taurus Sedan and Wagon

**2002–2004**
- 4.0L Explorer (4-door)
- 3.0L Taurus Sedan and Wagon

**2002–2003**
- 3.0L Supercab Ranger Pickup 2WD

**2001**
- 3.0L Supercab Ranger Pickup 2WD
- 3.0L Taurus LX, SE, and SES Sedan

**1999–2000**
- 3.0L Ranger Pickup 4WD and 2WD

### General Motors
*Select vehicles only—see your owner's manual.

**2005+**
- 5.3L Vortec-Engine Avalanche
- 5.3L Vortec-Engine Police Package Tahoe

**2003–2005**
- 5.3L V8 Chevy Silverado* and GMC Sierra* Half-Ton Pickups 2WD and 4WD
- 5.3L Vortec-Engine Suburban, Tahoe, Yukon, and Yukon XL

**2002**
- 5.3L V8 Chevy Silverado* and GMC Sierra* Half-Ton Pickups 2WD and 4WD
- 5.3L Vortec-Engine Suburban, Tahoe, Yukon, and Yukon XL
- 2.2L Chevy S10 Pickup 2WD
- 2.2L Sonoma GMC Pickup 2WD

**2000–2001**
- 2.2L Chevy S10 Pickup 2WD
- 2.2L GMC Sonoma Pickup 2WD

### Isuzu

**2000–2001**
- 2.2L Hombre Pickup 2WD

Mazda

**1999–2003**
- 3.0L Selected B3000 Pickups

### Mercedes-Benz

**2005+**
- 2.6L C240 Luxury Sedan and Wagon

**2003**
- 3.2L C320 Sport Sedan and Wagon

### Mercury

**2002–2004**
- 4.0L Selected Mountaineers

**2000–2004**
- 3.0L Selected Sables

### Nissan

**2005+**
- 5.6L DOHC V8 Engine

*Select vehicles only—see the owner's manual or VECI sticker under the hood.

### Avoid Resetting Fuel Compensation

Starting in 2006, General Motors vehicles designed to operate on E85 do not use a fuel compensation sensor, but instead use the oxygen sensor and refueling information to calculate the percentage of ethanol in the fuel. The PCM uses the fuel level sensor to sense that fuel has been added and starts to determine the resulting ethanol content by using the oxygen sensor. However, if a service technician were to reset fuel compensation by clearing long-term fuel trim, the PCM starts the calculation based on base fuel, which is gasoline with less than or equal to 10% ethanol (E10). If the fuel tank has E85, then the fuel compensation cannot be determined unless the tank is drained and refilled with base fuel. Therefore, avoid resetting the fuel compensation setting unless it is known that the fuel tank contains gasoline or E10 only.

## HOW TO READ A VEHICLE IDENTIFICATION NUMBER

The vehicle identification number (VIN) is required by federal regulation to contain specific information about the vehicle. The following chart shows the character in the eighth position of the VIN number from Ford Motor Company, General Motors, and Chrysler that designates their vehicles as flexible fuel vehicles.

#### Ford Motor Company

| Vehicle | 8th Character |
|---|---|
| Ford Crown Victoria | V |
| Ford F-150 | V |
| Ford Explorer | K |
| Ford Ranger | V |
| Ford Taurus | 2 |
| Lincoln Town Car | V |
| Mercury Mountaineer | K |
| Mercury Sable | 2 |
| Mercury Grand Marquis | V |

#### General Motors

| Vehicle | 8th Character |
|---|---|
| Chevrolet Avalanche | Z |
| Chevrolet Impala | K |
| Chevrolet Monte Carlo | K |
| Chevrolet S-10 Pickup | 5 |
| Chevrolet Sierra | Z |
| Chevrolet Suburban | Z |
| Chevrolet Tahoe | Z |
| GMC Yukon and Yukon XL | Z |
| GMC Silverado | Z |
| GMC Sonoma | 5 |

### How Long Can Oxygenated Fuel Be Stored Before All of the Oxygen Escapes?

The oxygen in oxygenated fuels, such as E10 and E85, is not in a gaseous state like the $CO_2$ in soft drinks. The oxygen is part of the molecule of ethanol or other oxygenates and does not bubble out of the fuel. Oxygenated fuels, just like any fuel, have a shelf life of about 90 days.

#### Chrysler

| Vehicle | 8th Character |
|---|---|
| Chrysler Sebring | T |
| Chrysler Town & Country | E, G or 3 |
| Dodge Caravan | E, G or 3 |
| Dodge Cargo Minivan | E, G or 3 |
| Dodge Durango | P |
| Dodge Ram | P |
| Dodge Stratus | T |
| Plymouth Voyageur | E, G or 3 |

#### Mazda

| Vehicle | 8th Character |
|---|---|
| B3000 Pickup | V |

#### Nissan

| Vehicle | 4th Character |
|---|---|
| Titan | B |

#### Mercedes Benz

Check owner's manual or the VECI sticker under the hood.

NOTE: For additional information on E85 and for the location of E85 stations in your area, go to www.e85fuel.com.

## METHANOL

**METHANOL TERMINOLOGY** Methanol, also known as *methyl alcohol, wood alcohol,* or *methyl hydrate,* is a chemical compound formula that includes one carbon atom and four hydrogen atoms and one oxygen. ● SEE FIGURE 6–8.

Methanol is a light, volatile, colorless, tasteless, flammable, poisonous liquid with a very faint odor. It is used as an antifreeze, a solvent, and a fuel. Methanol burns in air, forming $CO_2$ (carbon dioxide) and $H_2O$ (water). A methanol flame is almost colorless. Because of its poisonous properties, methanol is also

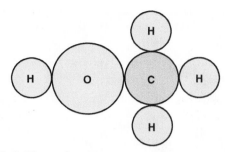

**FIGURE 6–8** The molecular structure of methanol showing the one carbon atom, four hydrogen atoms, and one oxygen atom.

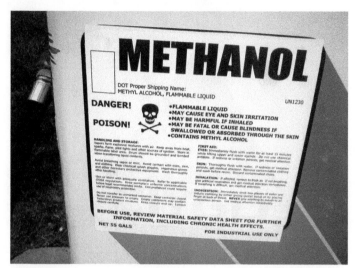

**FIGURE 6–9** Sign on methanol pump shows that methyl alcohol is a poison and can cause skin irritation and other personal injury. Methanol is used in industry as well as being a fuel.

used to denature ethanol. Methanol is often called wood alcohol because it was once produced chiefly as a by-product of the destructive distillation of wood. ● **SEE FIGURE 6–9.**

**PRODUCTION OF METHANOL** The biggest source of methanol in the United States is coal. Using a simple reaction between coal and steam, a gas mixture called **syn-gas** (*synthesis gas*) is formed. The components of this mixture are carbon monoxide and hydrogen, which, through an additional chemical reaction, are converted to methanol.

Natural gas can also be used to create methanol and is re-formed or converted to synthesis gas, which is later made into methanol.

Biomass can be converted to synthesis gas by a process called partial oxidation, and later converted to methanol. **Biomass** is organic material, such as:

- Urban wood wastes
- Primary mill residues
- Forest residues
- Agricultural residues
- Dedicated energy crops (e.g., sugarcane and sugar beets) that can be made into fuel

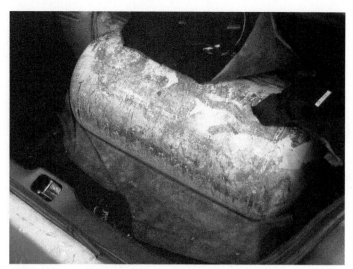

**FIGURE 6–10** Propane fuel storage tank in the trunk of a Ford taxi.

Electricity can be used to convert water into hydrogen, which is then reacted with carbon dioxide to produce methanol.

Methanol is toxic and can cause blindness and death. It can enter the body by ingestion, inhalation, or absorption through the skin. Dangerous doses will build up if a person is regularly exposed to fumes or handles liquid without skin protection. If methanol has been ingested, a doctor should be contacted immediately. The usual fatal dose is 4 fl oz (100 to 125 mL).

**M85** Some flexible fuel vehicles are designed to operate on 85% methanol and 15% gasoline called **M85.** Methanol is very corrosive and requires that the fuel system components be constructed of stainless steel and other alcohol-resistant rubber and plastic components. The heat content of M85 is about 60% of that of gasoline.

## PROPANE

**Propane** is the most widely used of all of the alternative fuels. Propane is normally a gas but is easily compressed into a liquid and stored in inexpensive containers. When sold as a fuel, it is also known as **liquefied petroleum gas (LPG)** or **LP-gas** because the propane is often mixed with about 10% of other gases such as butane, propylene, butylenes, and mercaptan to give the colorless and odorless propane a smell. Propane is nontoxic, but if inhaled can cause asphyxiation through lack of oxygen. Propane is heavier than air and lays near the floor if released into the atmosphere. Propane is commonly used in forklifts and other equipment used inside warehouses and factories because the exhaust from the engine using propane is not harmful. Propane is a by-product of petroleum refining of natural gas. In order to liquefy the fuel, it is stored in strong tanks at about 300 PSI (2,000 kPa). The heating value of propane is less than that of gasoline; therefore, more is required, which reduces the fuel economy. ● **SEE FIGURE 6–10.**

FIGURE 6–11 The blue sticker on the rear of this vehicle indicates that it is designed to use compressed natural gas.

FIGURE 6–12 A CNG storage tank from a Honda Civic GX shown with the fixture used to support it while it is being removed or installed in the vehicle. Honda specifies that three technicians be used to remove or install the tank through the rear door of the vehicle due to the size and weight of the tank.

## COMPRESSED NATURAL GAS

**CNG VEHICLE DESIGN** Another alternative fuel that is often used in fleet vehicles is **compressed natural gas,** or **CNG,** and vehicles using this fuel are often referred to as **natural gas vehicles (NGVs).** Look for the blue CNG label on vehicles designed to operate on compressed natural gas. ● **SEE FIGURE 6–11.**

Natural gas has to be compressed to about 3,000 PSI (20,000 kPa) or more, so that the weight and the cost of the storage container is a major factor when it comes to preparing a vehicle to run on CNG. The tanks needed for CNG are typically constructed of 0.5-inch-thick (3 mm) aluminum reinforced

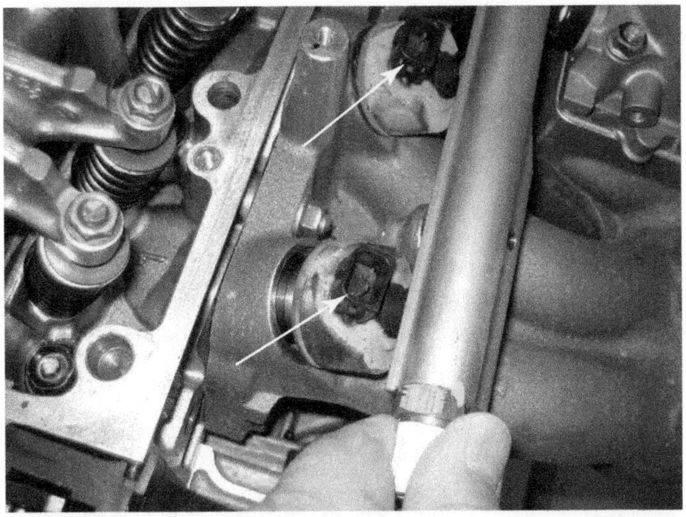

FIGURE 6–13 The fuel injectors used on this Honda Civic GX CNG engine are designed to flow gaseous fuel instead of liquid fuel and cannot be interchanged with any other type of injector.

with fiberglass. ● **SEE FIGURE 6–12.** The octane rating of CNG is about 130 and the cost per gallon is about half of the cost of gasoline. However, the heat value of CNG is also less, and therefore more is required to produce the same power and the miles per gallon is less.

**CNG COMPOSITION**    Compressed natural gas is made up of a blend of:

- Methane
- Propane
- Ethane
- N-butane
- Carbon dioxide
- Nitrogen

Once it is processed, it is at least 93% methane. Natural gas is nontoxic, odorless, and colorless in its natural state. It is odorized during processing, using ethyl mercaptan ("skunk"), to allow for easy leak detection. Natural gas is lighter than air and will rise when released into the air. Since CNG is already a vapor, it does not need heat to vaporize before it will burn, which improves cold start-up and results in lower emissions during cold operation. However, because it is already in a gaseous state, it does displace some of the air charge in the intake manifold. This leads to about a 10% reduction in engine power as compared to an engine operating on gasoline. Natural gas also burns slower than gasoline; therefore, the ignition timing must be advanced more when the vehicle operates on natural gas. The stoichiometric ratio, the point at which all the air and fuel is used or burned is 16.5:1 compared to 14.7:1 for gasoline. This means that more air is required to burn one pound of natural gas than is required to burn one pound of gasoline. ● **SEE FIGURE 6–13.**

**What Is the Amount of CNG Equal to in Gasoline?**

To achieve the amount of energy of one gallon of gasoline, 122 cubic feet of compressed natural gas (CNG) is needed. While the octane rating of CNG is much higher than gasoline (130 octane), using CNG instead of gasoline in the same engine would result in a reduction 10% to 20% of power due to the lower heat energy that is released when CNG is burned in the engine.

The CNG engine is designed to include:

- Increased compression ratio
- Strong pistons and connecting rods
- Heat-resistant valves
- Fuel injectors designed for gaseous fuel instead of liquid fuel

**CNG FUEL SYSTEMS** When completely filled, the CNG tank has 3,600 PSI of pressure in the tank. When the ignition is turned on, the alternate fuel electronic control unit activates the high-pressure lock-off, which allows high-pressure gas to pass to the high-pressure regulator. The high-pressure regulator reduces the high-pressure CNG to approximately 170 PSI and sends it to the low-pressure lock-off. The low-pressure lock-off is also controlled by the alternate fuel electronic control unit and is activated at the same time that the high-pressure lock-off is activated. From the low-pressure lock-off, the CNG is directed to the low-pressure regulator. This is a two-stage regulator that first reduces the pressure to approximately 4 to 6 PSI in the first stage and then to 4.5 to 7 inches of water in the second stage. Twenty-eight inches of water is equal to 1 PSI, therefore, the final pressure of the natural gas entering the engine is very low. From here, the low-pressure gas is delivered to the gas mass sensor/mixture control valve. This valve controls the air-fuel mixture. The CNG gas distributor adapter then delivers the gas to the intake stream.

CNG vehicles are designed for fleet use that usually have their own refueling capabilities. One of the drawbacks to using CNG is the time that it takes to refuel a vehicle. The ideal method of refueling is the slow fill method. The slow filling method compresses the natural gas as the tank is being fueled. This method ensures that the tank will receive a full charge of CNG; however, this method can take three to five hours to accomplish. If more than one vehicle needs filling, the facility will need multiple CNG compressors to refuel the vehicles.

There are three commonly used CNG refilling station pressures:

P24—2,400 PSI
P30—3,000 PSI
P36—3,600 PSI

**FIGURE 6–14** This CNG pump is capable of supplying compressed natural gas at either 3,000 PSI or 3,600 PSI. The price per gallon is higher for the higher pressure.

Try to find and use a station with the highest refilling pressure. Filling at lower pressures will result in less compressed natural gas being installed in the storage tank, thereby reducing the driving range. ● **SEE FIGURE 6–14.**

The fast fill method uses CNG that is already compressed. However, as the CNG tank is filled rapidly, the internal temperature of the tank will rise, which causes a rise in tank pressure. Once the temperature drops in the CNG tank, the pressure in the tank also drops, resulting in an incomplete charge in the CNG tank. This refueling method may take only about five minutes; however, it will result in an incomplete charge to the CNG tank, reducing the driving range.

## LIQUEFIED NATURAL GAS

Natural gas can be turned into a liquid if cooled to below −260°F (−127°C). The natural gas condenses into a liquid at normal atmospheric pressure and the volume is reduced by about 600 times. This means that the natural gas can be more efficiently transported over long distances where no pipelines are present when liquefied.

Because the temperature of liquefied natural gas (LNG) must be kept low, it is only practical for use in short haul trucks where they can be refueled from a central location.

## P-SERIES FUELS

P-series alternative fuel is patented by Princeton University and is a non-petroleum- or natural gas-based fuel suitable for use in flexible fuel vehicles or any vehicle designed to operate on E85 (85% ethanol, 15% gasoline). P-series fuel is recognized by the United States Department of Energy as being an alternative fuel,

**FREQUENTLY ASKED QUESTION**

## What Is a Tri-Fuel Vehicle?

In Brazil, most vehicles are designed to operate on ethanol or gasoline or any combination of the two. In this South American country, ethanol is made from sugarcane, is commonly available, and is lower in price than gasoline. Compressed natural gas (CNG) is also being made available so many vehicle manufacturers in Brazil, such as General Motors and Ford, are equipping vehicles to be capable of using gasoline, ethanol, or CNG. These vehicles are called tri-fuel vehicles.

but is not yet available to the public. P-series fuels are blends of the following:

- Ethanol (ethyl alcohol)
- Methyltetrahydrofuron, abbreviated MTHF
- Natural gas liquids, such as pentanes
- Butane

The ethanol and MTHF are produced from renewable feedstocks, such as corn, waste paper, biomass, agricultural waste, and wood waste (scraps and sawdust). The components used in P-type fuel can be varied to produce regular grade, premium grade, or fuel suitable for cold climates.
● **SEE CHART 6–1** for the percentages of the ingredients based on fuel grade.
● **SEE CHART 6–2** for a comparison of the most frequently used alternative fuels.

## SYNTHETIC FUELS

**Synthetic fuels** can be made from a variety of products, using several different processes. Synthetic fuel must, however, make these alternatives practical only when conventional petroleum products are either very expensive or not available.

**FISCHER-TROPSCH** Synthetic fuels were first developed using the **Fischer-Tropsch** method and have been in use since the 1920s to convert coal, natural gas, and other fossil fuel

| COMPOSITION OF P-SERIES FUELS (BY VOLUME) | | | |
|---|---|---|---|
| COMPONENT | REGULAR GRADE | PREMIUM GRADE | COLD WEATHER |
| Pentanes plus | 32.5% | 27.5% | 16.0% |
| MTHF | 32.5% | 17.5% | 26.0% |
| Ethanol | 35.0% | 55.0% | 47.0% |
| Butane | 0.0% | 0.0% | 11.0% |

**CHART 6–1**

P-series fuel varies in composition, depending on the octane rating and temperature.

| ALTERNATIVE FUEL COMPARISON CHART | | | | | |
|---|---|---|---|---|---|
| CHARACTERISTIC | PROPANE | CNG | METHANOL | ETHANOL | REGULAR UNLEADED GAS |
| Octane | 104 | 130 | 100 | 100 | 87–93 |
| BTU per gallon | 91,000 | N.A. | 70,000 | 83,000 | 114,000–125,000 |
| Gallon equivalent | 1.15 | 122 cubic feet— 1 gallon of gasoline | 1.8 | 1.5 | 1 |
| On-board fuel storage | Liquid | Gas | Liquid | Liquid | Liquid |
| Miles/gallon as compared to gas | 85% | N.A. | 55% | 70% | 100% |
| Relative tank size required to yield driving range equivalent to gas | Tank is 1.25 times larger | Tank is 3.5 times larger | Tank is 1.8 times larger | Tank is 1.5 times larger | |
| Pressure | 200 PSI | 3,000-3,600 PSI | N.A. | N.A. | N.A. |
| Cold weather capability | Good | Good | Poor | Poor | Good |
| Vehicle power | 5-10% power loss | 10-20% power loss | 4% power increase | 5% power increase | Standard |
| Toxicity | Nontoxic | Nontoxic | Highly toxic | Toxic | Toxic |
| Corrosiveness | Noncorrosive | Noncorrosive | Corrosive | Corrosive | Minimally corrosive |
| Source | Natural gas/ petroleum refining | Natural gas/ crude oil | Natural gas/coal | Sugar and starch crops/biomass | Crude oil |

**CHART 6–2**

The characteristics of alternative fuels compared to regular unleaded gasoline shows that all have advantages and disadvantages.

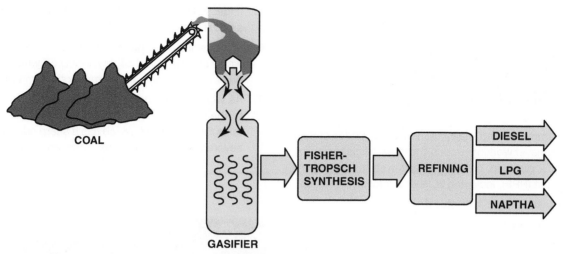

COAL

GASIFIER

FISHER-TROPSCH SYNTHESIS → REFINING → DIESEL / LPG / NAPTHA

**FIGURE 6–15** A Fischer-Tropsch processing plant is able to produce a variety of fuels from coal.

products into a fuel that is high in quality and clean-burning. The process for producing Fischer-Tropsch fuels was patented by two German scientists, Franz Fischer and Hans Tropsch, during World War I. The Fischer-Tropsch method uses carbon monoxide and hydrogen (the same synthesis gas used to produce hydrogen fuel) to convert coal and other hydrocarbons to liquid fuels in a process similar to hydrogenation, another method for hydrocarbon conversion. The process using natural gas, also called **gas-to-liquid (GTL)** technology, uses a catalyst, usually iron or cobalt, and incorporates steam re-forming to give off the by-products of carbon dioxide, hydrogen, and carbon monoxide. ● **SEE FIGURE 6–15.**

Whereas traditional fuels emit environmentally harmful particulates and chemicals, namely sulfur compounds, Fischer-Tropsch fuels combust with no soot or odors and emit only low levels of toxins. Fischer-Tropsch fuels can also be blended with traditional transportation fuels with little equipment modification, as they use the same engine and equipment technology as traditional fuels.

The fuels contain a very low sulfur and aromatic content and they produce virtually no particulate emissions. Researchers also expect reductions in hydrocarbon and carbon monoxide emissions. Fischer-Tropsch fuels do not differ in fuel performance from gasoline and diesel. At present, Fischer-Tropsch fuels are very expensive to produce on a large scale, although research is under way to lower processing costs. Diesel fuel created using the Fischer-Tropsch diesel **(FTD)** process is often called *GTL diesel*. GTL diesel can also be combined with petroleum diesel to produce a GTL blend. This fuel product is currently being sold in Europe and plans are in place to introduce it in North America.

## COAL TO LIQUID (CTL)

Coal is very abundant in the United States and coal can be converted to a liquid fuel through a process called **coal to liquid (CTL).** The huge cost is the main obstacle to these plants. The need to invest $1.4 billion per plant before it can make product is the reason no one has built a CTL plant yet in the United States. Investors need to be convinced that the cost of oil is going to remain high in order to get them to commit this kind of money.

A large plant might be able to produce 120,000 barrels of liquid fuel a day and would consume about 50,000 tons of coal per day. However, such a plant would create about 6,000 tons of $CO_2$ per day. These $CO_2$ emissions, which could contribute to global warming, and the cost involved make CTL a technology that is not likely to expand.

Two procedures can be used to convert coal-to-liquid fuel:

1. **Direct.** In the direct method, coal is broken down to create liquid products. First the coal is reacted with hydrogen ($H_2$) at high temperatures and pressure with a catalyst. This process creates a synthetic crude, called **syncrude,** which is then refined to produce gasoline or diesel fuel.

2. **Indirect.** In the indirect method, coal is first turned into a gas and the molecules are reassembled to create the desired product. This process involves turning coal into a gas called syn-gas. The syngas is then converted into liquid, using the Fischer-Tropsch (FT) process.

Russia has been using CTL by injecting air into the underground coal seams. Ignition is provided and the resulting gases are trapped and converted to liquid gasoline and diesel fuel through the Fischer-Tropsch process. This underground method is called **underground coal gasification (UCG).**

## METHANOL TO GASOLINE

Exxon Mobil has developed a process for converting methanol (methyl alcohol) into gasoline in a process called **methanol-to-gasoline (MTG).** The MTG process was discovered by accident when a gasoline additive made from methanol was being created. The process instead created olefins (alkenes), paraffins (alkenes), and aromatic compounds, which in combination are known as gasoline. The process uses a catalyst and is currently being produced in New Zealand.

## FUTURE OF SYNTHETIC FUELS

Producing gasoline and diesel fuels by other methods besides refining from crude oil has usually been more expensive. With the increasing cost of crude oil, alternative methods are now becoming economically feasible. Whether or not the diesel fuel or gasoline is created from coal, natural gas, or methanol, or created by refining crude oil, the transportation and service pumps are already in place. Compared to using compressed natural gas or other similar alternative fuels, synthetic fuels represent the lowest cost.

## SAFETY PROCEDURES WHEN WORKING WITH ALTERNATIVE FUELS

All fuels are flammable and many are explosive under certain conditions. Whenever working around compressed gases of any kind (CNG, LNG, propane, or LPG), always wear personal protective equipment (PPE), including at least the following items:

1. Safety glasses and/or face shield.

2. Protective gloves.

3. Long-sleeved shirt and pants to help protect bare skin from the freezing effects of gases under pressure in the event that the pressure is lost.

4. If any fuel gets on the skin, the area should be washed immediately.

5. If fuel spills on clothing, change into clean clothing as soon as possible.

6. If fuel spills on a painted surface, flush the surface with water and air dry. If simply wiped off with a dry cloth, the paint surface could be permanently damaged.

7. As with any fuel-burning vehicle, always vent the exhaust to the outside. If methanol fuel is used, the exhaust contains *formaldehyde*, which has a sharp odor and can cause severe burning of the eyes, nose, and throat.

 **WARNING**

Do not smoke or have an open flame in the area when working around or refueling any vehicle.

## SUMMARY

1. Flexible fuel vehicles (FFVs) are designed to operate on gasoline or gasoline-ethanol blends up to 85% ethanol (E85).

2. Ethanol can be made from grain, such as corn, or from cellulosic biomass, such as switchgrass.

3. E85 has fewer BTUs of energy per gallon compared with gasoline and will therefore provide lower fuel economy.

4. Older flexible fuel vehicles used a fuel compensation sensor but newer models use the oxygen sensor to calculate the percentage of ethanol in the fuel being burned.

5. Methanol is also called methyl alcohol or wood alcohol and, while it can be made from wood, it is mostly made from natural gas.

6. Propane is the most widely used alternative fuel. Propane is also called liquefied petroleum gas (LPG).

7. Compressed natural gas (CNG) is available for refilling in several pressures, including 2,400 PSI, 3,000 PSI, and 3,600 PSI.

8. P-series fuel is recognized by the United States Department of Energy as being an alternative fuel. P-series fuel is a non-petroleum-based fuel suitable for use in a flexible fuel vehicle. However, P-series fuel is not commercially available.

9. Synthetic fuels are usually made using the Fischer-Tropsch method to convert coal or natural gas into gasoline and diesel fuel.

10. Safety procedures when working around alternative fuel include wearing the necessary personal protective equipment (PPE), including safety glasses and protective gloves.

## REVIEW QUESTIONS

1. Ethanol is also known by what other terms?

2. The majority of ethanol in the United States is made from what farm products?

3. How is a flexible fuel vehicle identified?

4. Methanol is also known by what other terms?

5. What other gases are often mixed with propane?

6. Why is it desirable to fill a compressed natural gas (CNG) vehicle with the highest pressure available?

7. P-series fuel is made of what products?

8. The Fischer-Tropsch method can be used to change what into gasoline?

1. Ethanol can be produced from what products?
   a. Switchgrass
   c. Sugarcane
   b. Corn
   d. Any of the above

2. E85 means that the fuel is made from _____.
   a. 85% gasoline, 15% ethanol
   b. 85% ethanol, 15% gasoline
   c. Ethanol that has 15% water
   d. Pure ethyl alcohol

3. A flex-fuel vehicle can be identified by _____.
   a. Emblems on the side, front, and/or rear of the vehicle
   b. VECI
   c. VIN
   d. Any of the above

4. Methanol is also called _____.
   a. Methyl alcohol
   c. Methyl hydrate
   b. Wood alcohol
   d. All of the above

5. Which alcohol is dangerous (toxic)?
   a. Methanol
   b. Ethanol
   c. Both ethanol and methanol
   d. Neither ethanol nor methanol

6. Which is the most widely used alternative fuel?
   a. E85
   c. CNG
   b. Propane
   d. M85

7. Liquefied petroleum gas (LPG) is also called _____.
   a. E85
   c. Propane
   b. M85
   d. P-series fuel

8. How much compressed natural gas (CNG) does it require to achieve the energy of one gallon of gasoline?
   a. 130 cubic feet
   c. 105 cubic feet
   b. 122 cubic feet
   d. 91 cubic feet

9. When refueling a CNG vehicle, why is it recommended that the tank be filled to a high pressure?
   a. The range of the vehicle is increased
   b. The cost of the fuel is lower
   c. Less of the fuel is lost to evaporation
   d. Both a and c

10. Producing liquid fuel from coal or natural gas usually uses which process?
    a. Syncrude
    c. Fischer-Tropsch
    b. P-series
    d. Methanol to gasoline (MTG)

# chapter 7

# DIESEL AND BIODIESEL FUELS

**OBJECTIVES:** After studying Chapter 7, the reader should be able to: • Explain diesel fuel specifications. • List the advantages and disadvantages of biodiesel. • Discuss API gravity. • Explain E-diesel specifications.

**KEY TERMS:** API gravity 109 • ASTM 108 • B20 110 • Biodiesel 110 • Cetane number 108 • Cloud point 108 • Diesohol 112 • E-diesel 112 • Petrodiesel 111 • PPO 111 • SVO 111 • UCO 111 • ULSD 110 • WVO 111

## DIESEL FUEL

**FEATURES OF DIESEL FUEL**   Diesel fuel must meet an entirely different set of standards than gasoline. Diesel fuel contains 12% more heat energy than the same amount of gasoline. The fuel in a diesel engine is not ignited with a spark, but is ignited by the heat generated by high compression. The pressure of compression (400 to 700 PSI or 2,800 to 4,800 kPa) generates temperatures of 1,200°F to 1,600°F (700°C to 900°C), which speeds the preflame reaction to start the ignition of fuel injected into the cylinder.

**DIESEL FUEL REQUIREMENTS**   All diesel fuel must have the following characteristics:

- **Cleanliness.** It is imperative that the fuel used in a diesel engine be clean and free from water. Unlike the case with gasoline engines, the fuel is the lubricant and coolant for the diesel injector pump and injectors. Good-quality diesel fuel contains additives such as oxidation inhibitors, detergents, dispersants, rust preventatives, and metal deactivators.

- **Low-temperature fluidity.** Diesel fuel must be able to flow freely at all expected ambient temperatures. One specification for diesel fuel is its "pour point," which is the temperature below which the fuel would stop flowing.

- **Cloud point** is another concern with diesel fuel at lower temperatures. **Cloud point** is the low-temperature point when the waxes present in most diesel fuels tend to form crystals that can clog the fuel filter. Most diesel fuel suppliers distribute fuel with the proper pour point and cloud point for the climate conditions of the area.

**CETANE NUMBER**   The cetane number for diesel fuel is the opposite of the octane number for gasoline. The **cetane number** is a measure of the ease with which the fuel can be ignited.

The cetane rating of the fuel determines, to a great extent, its ability to start the engine at low temperatures and to provide smooth warm-up and even combustion. The cetane rating of diesel fuel should be between 45 and 50. The higher the cetane rating, the more easily the fuel is ignited.

**SULFUR CONTENT**   The sulfur content of diesel fuel is very important to the life of the engine. Sulfur in the fuel creates sulfuric acid during the combustion process, which can damage engine components and cause piston ring wear. Federal regulations are getting extremely tight on sulfur content to less than 15 parts per million (ppm). High-sulfur fuel contributes to acid rain.

**DIESEL FUEL COLOR**   Diesel fuel intended for use on the streets and highways is clear or green in color. Diesel fuel to be used on farms and off-road use is dyed red. ● **SEE FIGURE 7–1.**

**GRADES OF DIESEL FUEL**   **American Society for Testing Materials (ASTM)** also classifies diesel fuel by volatility (boiling range) into the following grades:

**GRADE #1**   This grade of diesel fuel has the lowest boiling point and the lowest cloud and pour points, as well as a lower BTU content—less heat per pound of fuel. As a result, grade #1 is suitable for use during low-temperature (winter) operation. Grade #1 produces less heat per pound of fuel compared to grade #2 and may be specified for use in diesel engines involved in frequent changes in load and speed, such as those found in city buses and delivery trucks.

**GRADE #2**   This grade has a higher boiling point, cloud point, and pour point as compared with grade #1. It is usually specified where constant speed and high loads are encountered, such as in long-haul trucking and automotive diesel applications. Most diesel is Grade #2.

(a)

(b)

**FIGURE 7–1** (a) Regular diesel fuel on the left has a clear or greenish tint, whereas fuel for off-road use is tinted red for identification. (b) A fuel pump in a farming area that clearly states the red diesel fuel is for off-road use only.

## DIESEL FUEL SPECIFIC GRAVITY TESTING

The density of diesel fuel should be tested whenever there is a driveability concern. The density or specific gravity of diesel fuel is measured in units of **API gravity.** API gravity is an arbitrary scale expressing the gravity or density of liquid petroleum products devised jointly by the American Petroleum Institute and the National Bureau of Standards. The measuring scale is calibrated in terms of degrees API. Oil with the least specific gravity has the highest API gravity. The formula for determining API gravity is as follows:

**Degrees API gravity = (141.5 ÷ specific gravity at 60°F) − 131.5**

The normal API gravity for #1 diesel fuel is 39 to 44 (typically 40). The normal API gravity for #2 diesel fuel is 30 to 39 (typically 35). A hydrometer calibrated in API gravity units should be used to test diesel fuel. ● **SEE FIGURE 7–2.**

**FIGURE 7–2** Testing the API viscosity of a diesel fuel sample using a hydrometer.

**How Can You Tell If Gasoline Has Been Added to the Diesel Fuel by Mistake?**

If gasoline has been accidentally added to diesel fuel and is burned in a diesel engine, the result can be very damaging to the engine. The gasoline can ignite faster than diesel fuel, which would tend to increase the temperature of combustion. This high temperature can harm injectors and glow plugs, as well as pistons, head gaskets, and other major diesel engine components. If contaminated fuel is suspected, first smell the fuel at the filler neck. If the fuel smells like gasoline, then the tank should be drained and refilled with diesel fuel. If the smell test does not indicate a gasoline smell (or any rancid smell), then test a sample for proper API gravity.

**NOTE: Diesel fuel designed for on-road use should be green in color. Red diesel fuel (high sulfur) should be found only in off-road or farm equipment.**

● **SEE CHART 7–1** for a comparison among specific gravity, weight density, pounds per gallon, and API gravity of diesel fuel.

## DIESEL FUEL HEATERS

Diesel fuel heaters, either coolant or electric, help prevent power loss and stalling in cold weather. The heater is placed in the fuel line between the tank and the primary filter. Some coolant heaters are thermostatically controlled, which allows fuel to bypass the heater once it has reached operating temperature. ● **SEE FIGURE 7–3.**

## API GRAVITY COMPARISON CHART
### Values for API Scale Oil

| API GRAVITY SCALE | SPECIFIC GRAVITY | WEIGHT DENSITY, LB/FT | POUNDS PER GALLON |
|---|---|---|---|
| 0 | | | |
| 2 | | | |
| 4 | | | |
| 6 | | | |
| 8 | | | |
| 10 | 1.0000 | 62.36 | 8.337 |
| 12 | 0.9861 | 61.50 | 8.221 |
| 14 | 0.9725 | 60.65 | 8.108 |
| 16 | 0.9593 | 59.83 | 7.998 |
| 18 | 0.9465 | 59.03 | 7.891 |
| 20 | 0.9340 | 58.25 | 7.787 |
| 22 | 0.9218 | 57.87 | 7.736 |
| 24 | 0.9100 | 56.75 | 7.587 |
| 26 | 0.8984 | 56.03 | 7.490 |
| 28 | 0.8871 | 55.32 | 7.396 |
| 30 | 0.8762 | 54.64 | 7.305 |
| 32 | 0.8654 | 53.97 | 7.215 |
| 34 | 0.8550 | 53.32 | 7.128 |
| 36 | 0.8448 | 52.69 | 7.043 |
| 38 | 0.8348 | 51.06 | 6.960 |
| 40 | 0.8251 | 50.96 | 6.879 |
| 42 | 0.8155 | 50.86 | 6.799 |
| 44 | 0.8030 | 50.28 | 6.722 |
| 46 | 0.7972 | 49.72 | 6.646 |
| 48 | 0.7883 | 49.16 | 6.572 |
| 50 | 0.7796 | 48.62 | 6.499 |
| 52 | 0.7711 | 48.09 | 6.429 |
| 54 | 0.7628 | 47.57 | 6.359 |
| 56 | 0.7547 | 47.07 | 6.292 |
| 58 | 0.7467 | 46.57 | 6.225 |
| 60 | 0.7389 | 46.08 | 6.160 |
| 62 | 0.7313 | 45.61 | 6.097 |
| 64 | 0.7238 | 45.14 | 6.034 |
| 66 | 0.7165 | 44.68 | 5.973 |
| 68 | 0.7093 | 44.23 | 5.913 |
| 70 | 0.7022 | 43.79 | 5.854 |
| 72 | 0.6953 | 43.36 | 5.797 |
| 74 | 0.6886 | 42.94 | 5.741 |
| 76 | 0.6819 | 42.53 | 5.685 |
| 78 | 0.6754 | 41.12 | 5.631 |
| 80 | 0.6690 | 41.72 | 5.577 |
| 82 | 0.6628 | 41.33 | 5.526 |
| 84 | 0.6566 | 40.95 | 5.474 |
| 86 | 0.6506 | 40.57 | 5.424 |
| 88 | 0.6446 | 40.20 | 5.374 |
| 90 | 0.6388 | 39.84 | 5.326 |
| 92 | 0.6331 | 39.48 | 5.278 |
| 94 | 0.6275 | 39.13 | 5.231 |
| 96 | 0.6220 | 38.79 | 5.186 |
| 98 | 0.6116 | 38.45 | 5.141 |
| 100 | 0.6112 | 38.12 | 5.096 |

**CHART 7–1**

The API gravity scale is based on the specific gravity of the fuel.

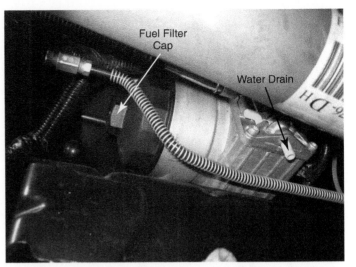

**FIGURE 7–3** A fuel heater is part of the fuel filter and water separator located on the frame rail of a Ford pickup truck equipped with a PowerStroke 6.0 liter V-8 diesel engine.

### ULTRA-LOW-SULFUR DIESEL FUEL

Diesel fuel is used in diesel engines and is usually readily available throughout the United States, Canada, and Europe, where many more cars are equipped with diesel engines. Diesel engines manufactured to 2007 or newer standards must use ultra-low-sulfur diesel fuel containing less than 15 ppm of sulfur compared to the older, low-sulfur specification of 500 ppm. The purpose of the lower sulfur amount in diesel fuel is to reduce emissions of sulfur oxides ($SO_x$) and particulate matter (PM) from heavy-duty highway engines and vehicles that use diesel fuel. The emission controls used on 2007 and newer diesel engines require the use of **ultra-low-sulfur diesel (ULSD)** for reliable operation.

Ultra-low-sulfur diesel (ULSD) will eventually replace the current highway diesel fuel, low-sulfur diesel, which can have as much as 500 ppm of sulfur. ULSD is required for use in all model year 2007 and newer vehicles equipped with advanced emission control systems. ULSD looks lighter in color and has less smell than other diesel fuel.

## BIODIESEL

### DEFINITION OF BIODIESEL

**Biodiesel** is a domestically produced, renewable fuel that can be manufactured from vegetable oils, animal fats, or recycled restaurant greases. Biodiesel is safe, biodegradable, and reduces serious air pollutants such as particulate matter (PM), carbon monoxide, and hydrocarbons. Biodiesel is defined as mono-alkyl esters of long-chain fatty acids derived from vegetable oils or animal fats which conform to ASTM D6751 specifications for use in diesel engines. Biodiesel refers to the pure fuel before blending with diesel fuel.
● **SEE FIGURE 7–4.**

**FIGURE 7–4** A pump decal indicating that the biodiesel fuel is ultra-low-sulfur diesel (ULSD) and must be used in 2007 and newer diesel vehicles.

**BIODIESEL BLENDS** Biodiesel blends are denoted as "BXX" with "XX" representing the percentage of biodiesel contained in the blend (i.e., **B20** is 20% biodiesel, 80% petroleum diesel). Blends of 20% biodiesel with 80% petroleum diesel (B20) can generally be used in unmodified diesel engines; however, users should consult their OEM and engine warranty statement. Biodiesel can also be used in its pure form (B100), but it may require certain engine modifications to avoid maintenance and performance problems and may not be suitable for wintertime use. Most diesel engine or vehicle manufacturers of diesel vehicles allow the use of B5 (5% biodiesel). For example, Cummins, used in Dodge trucks, allows the use of B20 only if the optional extra fuel filter has been installed. Users should consult their engine warranty statement for more information on fuel blends of greater than 20% biodiesel.

In general, B20 costs 30 to 40 cents more per gallon than conventional diesel. Although biodiesel costs more than regular diesel fuel, often called **petrodiesel,** fleet managers can make the switch to alternative fuels without purchasing new vehicles, acquiring new spare parts inventories, rebuilding refueling stations, or hiring new service technicians.

**FEATURES OF BIODIESEL** Biodiesel has the following characteristics:

1. Purchasing biodiesel in bulk quantities decreases the cost of fuel.
2. Biodiesel maintains similar horsepower, torque, and fuel economy.
3. Biodiesel has a higher cetane number than conventional diesel, which increases the engine's performance.
4. It is nontoxic, which makes it safe to handle, transport, and store. Maintenance requirements for B20 vehicles and petrodiesel vehicles are the same.
5. Biodiesel acts as a lubricant and this can add to the life of the fuel system components.

### I Thought Biodiesel Was Vegetable Oil?

Biodiesel is vegetable oil with the glycerin component removed by means of reacting the vegetable oil with a catalyst. The resulting hydrocarbon esters are 16 to 18 carbon atoms in length, almost identical to the petroleum diesel fuel atoms. This allows the use of biodiesel fuel in a diesel engine with no modifications needed. Biodiesel-powered vehicles do not *need* a second fuel tank, whereas vegetable-oil-powered vehicles do. There are three main types of fuel used in diesel engines. These are:

- Petroleum diesel, a fossil hydrocarbon with a carbon chain length of about 16 carbon atoms.
- Biodiesel, a hydrocarbon with a carbon chain length of 16 to 18 carbon atoms.
- Vegetable oil is a triglyceride with a glycerin component joining three hydrocarbon chains of 16 to 18 carbon atoms each, called **straight vegetable oil (SVO)**. Other terms used when describing vegetable oil include:
  - **Pure plant oil (PPO)**—a term most often used in Europe to describe SVO
  - **Waste vegetable oil (WVO)**—this oil could include animal or fish oils from cooking
  - **Used cooking oil (UCO)**—a term used when the oil may or may not be pure vegetable oil

Vegetable oil is not liquid enough at common ambient temperatures for use in a diesel engine fuel delivery system designed for the lower-viscosity petroleum diesel fuel. Vegetable oil needs to be heated to obtain a similar viscosity to biodiesel and petroleum diesel. This means that a heat source needs to be provided before the fuel can be used in a diesel engine. This is achieved by starting on petroleum diesel or biodiesel fuel until the engine heat can be used to sufficiently warm a tank containing the vegetable oil. It also requires purging the fuel system of vegetable oil with petroleum diesel or biodiesel fuel prior to stopping the engine to avoid the vegetable oil's thickening and solidifying in the fuel system away from the heated tank. The use of vegetable oil in its natural state does, however, eliminate the need to remove the glycerin component. Many vehicle and diesel engine fuel system suppliers permit the use of biodiesel fuel that is certified as meeting testing standards. None permit the use of vegetable oil in its natural state.

**NOTE: For additional information on biodiesel and the locations where it can be purchased, visit www .biodiesel.org.**

## E-DIESEL FUEL

**DEFINITION OF E-DIESEL**    **E-diesel,** also called **diesohol** outside of the United States, is standard No. 2 diesel fuel that contains up to 15% ethanol. While E-diesel can have up to 15% ethanol by volume, typical blend levels are from 8% to 10%.

**CETANE RATING OF E-DIESEL**    The higher the cetane number, the shorter the delay between injection and ignition. Normal diesel fuel has a cetane number of about 50. Adding 15% ethanol lowers the cetane number. To increase the cetane number back to that of conventional diesel fuel, a cetane-enhancing additive is added to E-diesel. The additive used to increase the cetane rating of E-diesel is ethylhexylnitrate or ditertbutyl peroxide.

E-diesel has better cold-flow properties than conventional diesel. The heat content of E-diesel is about 6% less than conventional diesel, but the particulate matter (PM) emissions are reduced by as much as 40%, 20% less carbon monoxide, and a 5% reduction in oxides of nitrogen (NOX).

Currently, E-diesel is considered to be experimental and can be used legally in off-road applications or in mass-transit buses with EPA approval. For additional information, visit www.e-diesel.org.

## SUMMARY

1. Diesel fuel produces 12% more heat energy than the same amount of gasoline.

2. Diesel fuel requirements include cleanliness, low-temperature fluidity, and proper cetane rating.

3. Emission control devices used on 2007 and newer engines require the use of ultra-low-sulfur diesel (ULSD) that has less than 15 ppm of sulfur.

4. The density of diesel fuel is measured in a unit called API gravity.

5. The cetane rating of diesel fuel is a measure of the ease with which the fuel can be ignited.

6. Biodiesel is the blend of vegetable-based liquid with regular diesel fuel. Most diesel engine manufacturers allow the use of a 5% blend, called B20 without any changes to the fuel system or engine.

7. E-diesel is a blend of ethanol with diesel fuel up to 15% ethanol by volume.

## REVIEW QUESTIONS

1. What is meant by the cloud point?

2. What is ultra-low-sulfur diesel?

3. Biodiesel blends are identified by what designation?

## CHAPTER QUIZ

1. What color is diesel fuel dyed if it is for off-road use only?
   - **a.** Red
   - **b.** Green
   - **c.** Blue
   - **d.** Yellow

2. What clogs fuel filters when the temperature is low on a vehicle that uses diesel fuel?
   - **a.** Alcohol
   - **b.** Sulfur
   - **c.** Wax
   - **d.** Cetane

3. The specific gravity of diesel fuel is measured in what units?
   - **a.** Hydrometer units
   - **b.** API gravity
   - **c.** Grade number
   - **d.** Cetane number

4. What rating of diesel fuel indicates how well a diesel engine will start?
   - **a.** Specific gravity rating
   - **b.** Sulfur content
   - **c.** Cloud point
   - **d.** Cetane rating

5. Ultra-low-sulfur diesel fuel has how much sulfur content?
   - **a.** 15 ppm
   - **b.** 50 ppm
   - **c.** 500 ppm
   - **d.** 1,500 ppm

6. E-diesel is diesel fuel with what additive?
   - **a.** Methanol
   - **b.** Sulfur
   - **c.** Ethanol
   - **d.** Vegetable oil

7. Biodiesel is regular diesel fuel with vegetable oil added.
   - **a.** True
   - **b.** False

8. B20 biodiesel has how much regular diesel fuel?
   - **a.** 20%
   - **b.** 40%
   - **c.** 80%
   - **d.** 100%

9. Most diesel fuel is what grade?
   - **a.** Grade #1
   - **b.** Grade #2
   - **c.** Grade #3
   - **d.** Grade #4

10. Most manufacturers of vehicles equipped with diesel engines allow what type of biodiesel?
    - **a.** B100
    - **b.** B80
    - **c.** B20
    - **d.** B5

# chapter 8

# INTAKE AND EXHAUST SYSTEMS

**OBJECTIVES:** **After studying Chapter 8, the reader should be able to:** • Prepare for ASE Engine Performance (A8) certification test content area "C" (Air Induction and Exhaust Systems Diagnosis and Repair). • Discuss the purpose and function of intake air system components. • Explain the differences between throttle-body fuel-injection manifolds and port fuel-injection manifolds. • List the materials used in exhaust manifolds and exhaust systems. • Describe the purpose and function of the exhaust system components.

**KEY TERMS:** EGR 118 • Hangers 120 • Helmholtz resonator 115 • Micron 113 • Plenum 117

## AIR INTAKE FILTRATION

**NEED FOR AIR FILTERING** Gasoline must be mixed with air to form a combustible mixture. Air movement into an engine occurs due to low pressure (vacuum) being created in the engine. ● **SEE FIGURE 8–1.**

Air contains dirt and other materials that cannot be allowed to reach the engine. Just as fuel filters are used to clean impurities from gasoline, an air cleaner and filter are used to remove contaminants from the air. The three main jobs of the air cleaner and filter include:

1. Clean the air before it is mixed with fuel
2. Silence air intake noise
3. Act as a flame arrester in case of a backfire

The automotive engine uses about 9,000 gallons (34,000 liters) of air for every gallon of gasoline burned at an air-fuel ratio of 14.7:1 by weight. Without proper filtering of the air before it enters the engine, dust and dirt in the air can seriously damage engine parts and shorten engine life.

Abrasive particles can cause wear any place inside the engine where two surfaces move against each other, such as piston rings against the cylinder wall. The dirt particles then pass by the piston rings and into the crankcase. From the crankcase, the particles circulate throughout the engine in the oil. Large amounts of abrasive particles in the oil can damage other moving engine parts.

The filter that cleans the intake air is in a two-piece air cleaner housing made of either:

■ Stamped steel

■ Composite (usually nylon reinforced plastic) materials

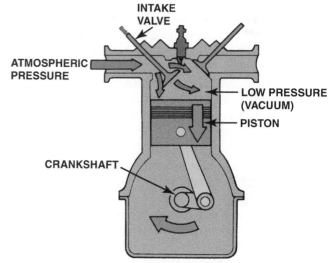

**FIGURE 8–1** Downward movement of the piston lowers the air pressure inside the combustion chamber. The pressure differential between the atmosphere and the inside of the engine forces air into the engine.

**AIR FILTER ELEMENTS** The paper air filter element is the most common type of filter. It is made of a chemically treated paper stock that contains tiny passages in the fibers. These passages form an indirect path for the airflow to follow. The airflow passes through several fiber surfaces, each of which traps microscopic particles of dust, dirt, and carbon. Most air filters are capable of trapping dirt and other particles larger than 10 to 25 microns in size. One **micron** is equal to 0.000039 in.

**NOTE: A person can only see objects that are 40 microns or larger in size. A human hair is about 50 microns in diameter.**

● **SEE FIGURE 8–2.**

FIGURE 8–2 Dust and dirt in the air are trapped in the air filter so they do not enter the engine. A restricted air filter reduces the amount of air that can enter the engine thereby reducing engine power and performance.

FIGURE 8–3 Most air filter housings are located on the side of the engine compartment and use flexible rubber hose to direct the airflow into the throttle body of the engine.

**FILTER REPLACEMENT** Manufacturers recommend cleaning or replacing the air filter element at periodic intervals, usually listed in terms of distance driven or months of service. The distance and time intervals are based on so-called normal driving. More frequent air filter replacement is necessary when the vehicle is driven under dusty, dirty, or other severe conditions.

It is best to replace a filter element before it becomes too dirty to be effective. A dirty air filter that passes contaminants can cause engine wear.

**REMOTELY MOUNTED AIR FILTERS AND DUCTS** Air cleaner and duct design depend on a number of factors such as the size, shape, and location of other engine compartment components, as well as the vehicle body structure.

Port fuel-injection systems generally use a horizontally mounted throttle body.

Some systems also have a mass airflow (MAF) sensor between the throttle body and the air cleaner. Because placing the air cleaner housing next to the throttle body would cause engine and vehicle design problems, it is more efficient to use this remote air cleaner placement. ● **SEE FIGURE 8–3.**

Turbocharged engines present a similar problem. The air cleaner connects to the air inlet elbow at the turbocharger. However, the tremendous heat generated by the turbocharger makes it impractical to place the air cleaner housing too close to the turbocharger. Remote air cleaners are connected to the turbocharger air inlet elbow or fuel-injection throttle body by composite ducting that is usually retained by clamps. The ducting used may be rigid or flexible, but all connections must be airtight.

**AIR FILTER RESTRICTION INDICATOR** Some vehicles, especially pickup trucks that are often driven in dusty conditions, are equipped with an air filter restriction indicator. The purpose of this device is to give a visual warning when the air filter is restricted and needs to be replaced. The device operates

FIGURE 8–4 A typical air filter restriction indicator used on a General Motors truck engine. The indicator turns red when it detects enough restriction to require a filter replacement.

by detecting the slight drop in pressure that occurs when an air filter is restricted. The calibration before the red warning bar or "replace air filter" message appears varies, but is usually:

- 15 to 20 in. of water (in. $H_2O$) for gasoline engines
- 20 to 30 in. of water (in. $H_2O$) for diesel engines

The unit of inches of water is used to measure the difference in air pressure before and after the air filter. The unit is very small, because 28 in. of water is equal to a pound per square inch (PSI).

Some air filter restriction indicators, especially on diesel engines, include an electrical switch used to light a dash-mounted warning lamp when the air filter needs to be replaced. ● **SEE FIGURE 8–4.**

(a)

(b)

**FIGURE 8–5** (a) Note the discovery as the air filter housing was opened during service on a Pontiac. The nuts were obviously deposited by squirrels (or some other animal). (b) Not only was the housing filled with nuts, but also this air filter was extremely dirty, indicating that this vehicle had not been serviced for a long time.

🔧 **TECH TIP**

**Always Check the Air Filter**

Always inspect the air filter and the air intake system carefully during routine service. Debris or objects deposited by animals can cause a restriction to the airflow and can reduce engine performance. ● **SEE FIGURE 8–5.**

## THROTTLE-BODY INJECTION INTAKE MANIFOLDS

**TERMINOLOGY** The *intake manifold* is also called an *inlet manifold.* Smooth engine operation can occur only when each combustion chamber produces the same pressure as every

**FIGURE 8–6** A resonance tube, called a Helmholtz resonator, is used on the intake duct between the air filter and the throttle body to reduce air intake noise during engine acceleration.

**❓ FREQUENTLY ASKED QUESTION**

**What Does This Tube Do?**

What is the purpose of the odd-shape tube attached to the inlet duct between the air filter and the throttle body, as seen in ● **FIGURE 8–6?**

The tube shape is designed to dampen out certain resonant frequencies that can occur at specific engine speeds. The length and shape of this tube are designed to absorb shock waves that are created in the air intake system and to provide a reservoir for the air that will then be released into the airstream during cycles of lower pressure. This resonance tube is often called a **Helmholtz resonator,** named for the discoverer of the relationship between shape and value of frequency, Herman L. F. von Helmholtz (1821–1894) of the University of Hönizsberg in East Prussia. The overall effect of these resonance tubes is to reduce the noise of the air entering the engine.

other chamber in the engine. For this to be achieved, each cylinder must receive an intake charge exactly like the charge going into the other cylinders in quality and quantity. The charges must have the same physical properties and the same air-fuel mixture.

A throttle-body fuel injector forces finely divided droplets of liquid fuel into the incoming air to form a combustible air-fuel mixture. ● **SEE FIGURE 8–7** for an example of a typical throttle-body injection (TBI) unit.

**INTAKE AIR SPEEDS** These droplets start to evaporate as soon as they leave the throttle-body injector nozzles. *The droplets stay in the charge as long as the charge flows at high velocities.* At maximum engine speed, these velocities may reach 300 ft per second. Separation of the droplets from the charge as it passes through the manifold occurs when the velocity drops

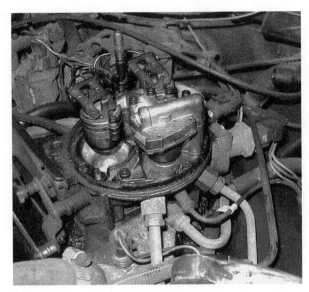

**FIGURE 8–7** A throttle-body injection (TBI) unit used on a GM V-6 engine.

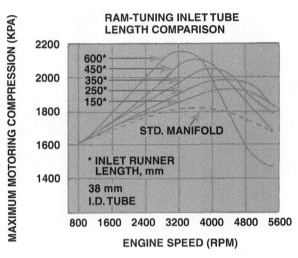

**FIGURE 8–9** The graph shows the effect of sonic tuning of the intake manifold runners. The longer runners increase the torque peak and move it to a lower RPM. The 600 mm intake runner is about 24 in. long.

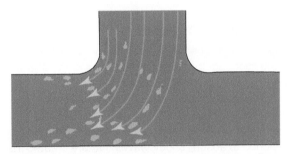

**FIGURE 8–8** Heavy fuel droplets separate as they flow around an abrupt bend in an intake manifold.

below 50 ft per second. Intake charge velocities at idle speeds are often below this value. When separation occurs—at low engine speeds—extra fuel must be supplied to the charge in order to have a combustible mixture reach the combustion chamber.

Manifold sizes and shapes represent a compromise.

- They must have a cross section large enough to allow charge flow for maximum power.

- The cross section must be small enough that the flow velocities of the charge will be high enough to keep the fuel droplets in suspension. This is required so that equal mixtures reach each cylinder. Manifold cross-sectional size is one reason why engines designed especially for racing will not run at low engine speeds.

- Racing manifolds must be large enough to reach maximum horsepower. This size, however, allows the charge to move slowly, and the fuel will separate from the charge at low engine speeds. Fuel separation leads to poor accelerator response. ● **SEE FIGURE 8–8.**

Standard passenger vehicle engines are primarily designed for economy during light-load, partial-throttle operation. Their manifolds, therefore, have a much smaller cross-sectional area than do those of racing engines. This small size will help keep flow velocities of the charge high throughout the normal operating speed range of the engine.

## PORT FUEL-INJECTION INTAKE MANIFOLDS

**TERMINOLOGY** The size and shape of port fuel-injected engine intake manifolds can be optimized because the only thing in the manifold is air. The fuel injector is located in the intake manifold about 3 to 4 in. (70 to 100 mm) from the intake valve. Therefore, the runner length and shape are designed for tuning only. There is no need to keep an air-fuel mixture thoroughly mixed (homogenized) throughout its trip from the TBI unit to the intake valve. Intake manifold runners are tuned to improve engine performance.

- Long runners build low-RPM torque.
- Shorter runners provide maximum high-RPM power.
  ● **SEE FIGURES 8–9 AND 8–10.**

**VARIABLE INTAKES** Some engines with four valve heads utilize a dual or variable intake runner design. At lower engine speeds, long intake runners provide low-speed torque. At higher engine speeds, shorter intake runners are opened by means of a computer-controlled valve to increase high-speed power.

Many intake manifolds are designed to provide both short runners best for higher engine speed power and longer runners best for lower engine speed torque. The valve(s) that control the flow of air through the passages of the intake manifold are computer controlled. ● **SEE FIGURE 8–11.**

**PLASTIC INTAKE MANIFOLDS** Most intake manifolds are made from thermoplastic molded from fiberglass-reinforced nylon by either casting or by injection molding. Some manifolds are molded in two parts and bonded together. Plastic intake manifolds are lighter than aluminum manifolds and can better insulate engine heat from the fuel injectors.

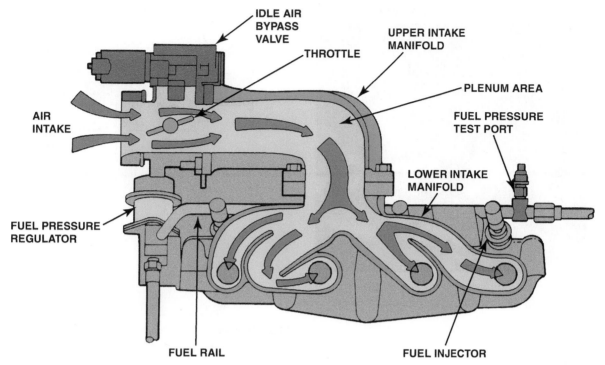

FIGURE 8–10 Airflow through the large diameter upper intake manifold is distributed to smaller diameter individual runners in the lower manifold in this two-piece manifold design.

FIGURE 8–11 The air flowing into the engine can be directed through long or short runners for best performance and fuel economy.

FIGURE 8–12 Many plastic intake manifolds are constructed using many parts glued together to form complex passages for airflow into the engine.

Plastic intake manifolds have smoother interior surfaces than do other types of manifolds, resulting in greater airflow. ● SEE FIGURE 8–12.

## UPPER AND LOWER INTAKE MANIFOLDS Many intake manifolds are constructed in two parts.

- A lower section attaches to the cylinder heads and includes passages from the intake ports.
- An upper manifold, usually called the **plenum,** connects to the lower unit and includes the long passages needed to help provide the ram effect that helps the engine

deliver maximum torque at low engine speeds. The throttle body attaches to the upper intake.

The use of a two-part intake manifold allows for easier manufacturing as well as assembly, but can create additional locations for leaks.

If the lower intake manifold gasket leaks, not only could a vacuum leak occur affecting the operation of the engine, but a coolant leak or an oil leak can also occur if the manifold has coolant flowing through it. A leak at the gasket(s) of the upper intake manifold usually results in a vacuum (air) leak only.

FIGURE 8–13 A typical long exhaust gas line used to cool the exhaust gases before being recirculated back into the intake manifold.

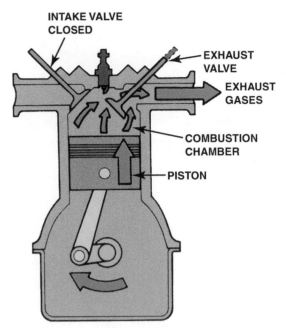

FIGURE 8–14 The exhaust gases are pushed out of the cylinder by the piston on the exhaust stroke.

## EXHAUST GAS RECIRCULATION PASSAGES

**PURPOSE AND FUNCTION** To reduce the emission of oxides of nitrogen (NOx), engines have been equipped with **exhaust gas recirculation (EGR)** valves. From 1973 until recently, they were used on almost all vehicles. Most EGR valves are mounted on the intake manifold. Because of the efficiency of computer-controlled fuel injection, some newer engines do not require an EGR system to meet emission standards. These engines' variable valve timing to close the exhaust valve sooner than normal, trapping some exhaust in the cylinder, is an alternative to using an EGR valve.

On engines with EGR systems, the EGR valve opens at speeds above idle on a warm engine. When open, the valve allows a small portion of the exhaust gas (5% to 10%) to enter the intake manifold.

The EGR system has some means of interconnecting of the exhaust and intake manifolds. The EGR valve controls the gas flow through the passages.

- On V-type engines, the intake manifold crossover is used as a source of exhaust gas for the EGR system. A cast passage connects the exhaust crossover to the EGR valve.
- On inline-type engines, an external tube is generally used to carry exhaust gas to the EGR valve.

**EXHAUST GAS COOLERS** The exhaust gases are more effective in reducing oxide of nitrogen (NOx) emissions if the exhaust is cooled before being drawn into the cylinders. This tube is often designed to be long so that the exhaust gas is cooled before it enters the EGR valve. ● **SEE FIGURE 8–13.**

## EXHAUST MANIFOLDS

**PURPOSE AND FUNCTION** The exhaust manifold is designed to collect high-temperature spent gases from the individual head exhaust ports and direct them into a single outlet connected to the exhaust system. ● **SEE FIGURE 8–14.**

The hot gases are sent to an exhaust pipe, then to a catalytic converter, to the muffler, to a resonator, and on to the tailpipe, where they are vented to the atmosphere. The exhaust system is designed to meet the following needs.

- Provide the least possible amount of restriction or back-pressure
- Keep the exhaust noise at a minimum

Exhaust gas temperature will vary according to the power produced by the engine. The manifold must be designed to operate at both engine idle and continuous full power. Under full-power conditions, the exhaust manifold can become red-hot, causing a great deal of expansion.

The temperature of an exhaust manifold can exceed 1,500°F (815°C).

**CONSTRUCTION** Most exhaust manifolds are made from the following:

- Cast iron
- Steel tubing

During vehicle operation, manifold temperatures usually reach the high-temperature extremes. The manifold is bolted to the head in a way that will allow expansion and contraction. In some cases, hollow-headed bolts are used to maintain

FIGURE 8–15 This exhaust manifold (red area) is equipped with a heat shield to help retain heat and reduce exhaust emissions.

FIGURE 8–16 Many exhaust manifolds are constructed of steel tubing and are free flowing to improve engine performance.

a gas-tight seal while still allowing normal expansion and contraction.

Many exhaust manifolds have heat shields to help keep exhaust heat off the spark plug wires and to help keep the heat from escaping to improve exhaust emissions. ● **SEE FIGURE 8–15.**

Exhaust systems are especially designed for the engine-chassis combination. The exhaust system length, pipe size, and silencer are designed, where possible, to make use of the tuning effect within the exhaust system. Tuning occurs when the exhaust pulses from the cylinders are emptied into the manifold between the pulses of other cylinders. ● **SEE FIGURE 8–16.**

**EXHAUST MANIFOLD GASKETS** Exhaust heat will expand the manifold more than it will expand the head. The heat causes the exhaust manifold to slide on the sealing surface of the head. The heat also causes thermal stress. When the

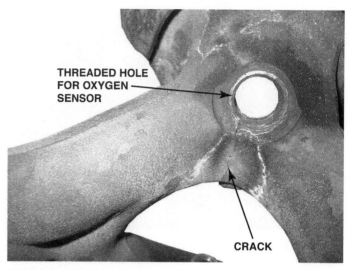

THREADED HOLE FOR OXYGEN SENSOR

CRACK

FIGURE 8–17 A crack in an exhaust manifold is often not visible because a heat shield usually covers the area. A crack in the exhaust manifold upstream of the oxygen sensor can fool the sensor and affect engine operation.

**?** **FREQUENTLY ASKED QUESTION**

**How Can a Cracked Exhaust Manifold Affect Engine Performance?**

Cracks in an exhaust manifold will not only allow exhaust gases to escape and cause noise, but also allow air to enter the exhaust manifold. ● **SEE FIGURE 8–17.**

Exhaust flows from the cylinders as individual puffs or pressure pulses. Behind each of these pressure pulses, a low pressure (below atmospheric pressure) is created. Outside air at atmospheric pressure is then drawn into the exhaust manifold through the crack. This outside air contains 21% oxygen and is measured by the oxygen sensor (O2S). The air passing the O2S signals the engine computer that the engine is operating too lean (excess oxygen) and the computer, not knowing that the lean indicator is false, adds additional fuel to the engine. The result is that the engine will be operating richer (more fuel than normal) and spark plugs could become fouled by fuel, causing poor engine operation.

manifold is removed from the engine for service, the stress is relieved, which may cause the manifold to warp slightly. Exhaust manifold gaskets are included in gasket sets to seal slightly warped exhaust manifolds. These gaskets *should* be used, even if the engine did not originally use exhaust manifold gaskets. When an exhaust manifold gasket has facing on one side only, put the facing side against the head and put the manifold against the perforated metal core. The manifold can slide on the metal of the gasket just as it slid on the sealing surface of the head.

FIGURE 8–18 Typical exhaust manifold gaskets. Note how they are laminated to allow the exhaust manifold to expand and contract due to heating and cooling.

Gaskets are used on new engines with tubing- or header-type exhaust manifolds. They may have several layers of steel for high-temperature sealing. The layers are spot welded together. Some are embossed where special sealing is needed. ● SEE FIGURE 8–18.

Many new engines do not use gaskets with cast exhaust manifolds. The flat surface of the new cast-iron exhaust manifold fits tightly against the flat surface of the new head.

 TECH TIP

**Using the Correct Tool Saves Time**

When cast-iron exhaust manifolds are removed, the stresses built up in the manifolds often cause the manifolds to twist or bend. This distortion even occurs when the exhaust manifolds have been allowed to cool before removal. Attempting to reinstall distorted exhaust manifolds is often a time-consuming and frustrating exercise.

However, special spreading jacks can be used to force the manifold back into position so that the fasteners can be lined up with the cylinder head. ● SEE FIGURE 8–19.

## MUFFLERS

**PURPOSE AND FUNCTION** When the exhaust valve opens, it rapidly releases high-pressure gas. This sends a strong air pressure wave through the atmosphere inside the exhaust system, which produces a sound we call an explosion. It is the same sound produced when the high-pressure gases from burned gunpowder are released from a gun. In an engine, the pulses are released one after another. The explosions come so fast that they blend together in a steady roar.

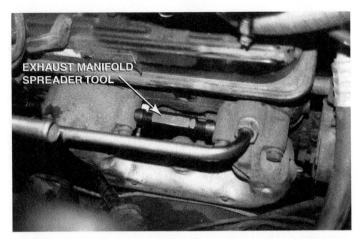

FIGURE 8–19 An exhaust manifold spreader tool is absolutely necessary when reinstalling exhaust manifolds. When they are removed from the engine, the manifolds tend to warp slightly even though the engine is allowed to cool before being removed. The spreader tool allows the technician to line up the bolt holes without harming the manifold.

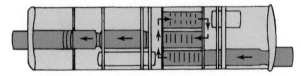

FIGURE 8–20 Exhaust gases expand and cool as they travel through passages in the muffler.

Sound is air vibration. When the vibrations are large, the sound is loud. The muffler catches the large bursts of high-pressure exhaust gas from the cylinder, smoothing out the pressure pulses and allowing them to be released at an even and constant rate. It does this through the use of perforated tubes within the muffler chamber. The smooth-flowing gases are released to the tailpipe. In this way, the muffler silences engine exhaust noise. ● SEE FIGURE 8–20.

**CONSTRUCTION** Most mufflers have a larger inlet diameter than outlet diameter. As the exhaust enters the muffler, it expands and cools. The cooler exhaust is denser and occupies less volume. The diameter of the outlet of the muffler and the diameter of the tailpipe can be reduced with no decrease in efficiency.

Sometimes resonators are used in the exhaust system and the catalytic converter also acts as a muffler. They provide additional expansion space at critical points in the exhaust system to smooth out the exhaust gas flow.

The tailpipe carries the exhaust gases from the muffler to the air, away from the vehicle. In most cases, the tailpipe exit is at the rear of the vehicle, below the rear bumper. In some cases, the exhaust is released at the side of the vehicle, just ahead of or just behind the rear wheel.

The muffler and tailpipe are supported with brackets, called **hangers,** which help to isolate the exhaust noise from

**FIGURE 8–21** A hole in the muffler allows condensed water to escape.

**FIGURE 8–22** A high-performance aftermarket air filter often can increase airflow into the engine for more power.

 **FREQUENTLY ASKED QUESTION**

**Why Is There a Hole in My Muffler?**

Many mufflers are equipped with a small hole in the lower rear part to drain accumulated water. About 1 gallon of water is produced in the form of steam for each gallon of gasoline burned. The water is formed when gasoline is burned in the cylinder. Water consists of two molecules of hydrogen and one of oxygen ($H_2O$). The hydrogen (H) comes from the fuel and the oxygen (O) comes from the air. During combustion, the hydrogen from the fuel combines with some of the oxygen in the air to form water vapor. The water vapor condenses on the cooler surfaces of the exhaust system, especially in the muffler, until the vehicle has been driven long enough to fully warm the exhaust above the boiling point of water (212°F [100°C]). ● **SEE FIGURE 8–21.**

 **HIGH-PERFORMANCE TIP**

**More Airflow = More Power**

One of the most popular high-performance modifications is to replace the factory exhaust system with a low-restriction design and to replace the original air filter and air filter housing with a low-restriction unit, as shown in ● **FIGURE 8–22.**

The installation of an aftermarket air filter not only increases power, but also increases air induction noise, which many drivers prefer. The aftermarket filter housing, however, may not be able to effectively prevent water from being drawn into the engine if the vehicle is traveling through deep water.

Almost every modification that increases performance has a negative effect on some other part of the vehicle, or else the manufacturer would include the change at the factory.

the rest of the vehicle. The types of exhaust system hangers include:

- Rubberized fabric with metal ends that hold the muffler and tailpipe in position so that they do not touch any metal part, to isolate the exhaust noise from the rest of the vehicle

- Rubber material that looks like large rubber bands, which slip over the hooks on the exhaust system and the hooks attached to the body of the vehicle

## SUMMARY

1. All air entering an engine must be filtered.

2. Engines that use throttle-body injection units are equipped with intake manifolds that keep the airflow speed through the manifold at 50 to 300 ft per second.

3. Most intake manifolds have an EGR valve that regulates the amount of recirculated exhaust that enters the engine to reduce NOx emissions.

4. Exhaust manifolds can be made from cast iron or steel tubing.

5. The exhaust system also contains a catalytic converter, exhaust pipes, and muffler. The entire exhaust system is supported by rubber hangers that isolate the noise and vibration of the exhaust from the rest of the vehicle.

1. Why is it necessary to have intake charge velocities of about 50 ft per second?

2. Why can port fuel-injected engines use larger (and longer) intake manifolds and still operate at low engine speed?

3. What is a tuned runner in an intake manifold?

4. How does a muffler quiet exhaust noise?

## CHAPTER QUIZ

1. Intake charge velocity has to be _____ to prevent fuel droplet separation.
   a. 25 ft per second
   b. 50 ft per second
   c. 100 ft per second
   d. 300 ft per second

2. The air filter restriction indicator uses what to detect when it signals to replace the filter?
   a. Number of hours of engine operation
   b. Number of miles or vehicle travel
   c. The amount of light that can past through the filter
   d. The amount of restriction measured in inches of water

3. Why are the EGR gases cooled before entering the engine on some engines?
   a. Cool exhaust gas is more effective at controlling NOx emissions
   b. To help prevent the exhaust from slowing down
   c. To prevent damage to the intake valve
   d. To prevent heating the air-fuel mixture in the cylinder

4. The air-fuel mixture flows through the intake manifold on what type of system?
   a. Port fuel-injection systems
   b. Throttle-body fuel-injection systems
   c. Both a port-injected and throttle-body injected engine
   d. Any fuel-injected engine

5. Air filters can remove particles and dirt as small as _____.
   a. 5 to 10 microns
   b. 10 to 25 microns
   c. 30 to 40 microns
   d. 40 to 50 microns

6. Why do many port fuel-injected engines use long intake manifold runners?
   a. To reduce exhaust emissions
   b. To heat the incoming air
   c. To increase high-RPM power
   d. To increase low-RPM torque

7. Exhaust passages are included in some intake manifolds. Technician A says that the exhaust passages are used for exhaust gas recirculation (EGR) systems. Technician B says that the upper intake is often called the plenum. Which technician is correct?
   a. Technician A only
   b. Technician B only
   c. Both Technicians A and B
   d. Neither Technician A nor B

8. The upper portion of a two-part intake manifold is often called the _____.
   a. Housing
   b. Lower part
   c. Plenum
   d. Vacuum chamber

9. Technician A says that a cracked exhaust manifold can affect engine operation. Technician B says that a leaking lower intake manifold gasket could cause a vacuum leak. Which technician is correct?
   a. Technician A only
   b. Technician B only
   c. Both Technicians A and B
   d. Neither Technician A nor B

10. Technician A says that some intake manifolds are plastic. Technician B says that some intake manifolds are constructed in two parts or sections: upper and lower. Which technician is correct?
    a. Technician A only
    b. Technician B only
    c. Both Technicians A and B
    d. Neither Technician A nor B

# chapter 9

# TURBOCHARGING AND SUPERCHARGING

**OBJECTIVES:** After studying Chapter 9, the reader should be able to: • Prepare for ASE Engine Performance (A8) certification test content area "C" (Fuel, Air Induction, and Exhaust Systems Diagnosis and Repair). • Explain the difference between a turbocharger and a supercharger. • Describe how the boost levels are controlled. • Discuss maintenance procedures for turbochargers and superchargers.

**KEY TERMS:** Boost 123 • BOV 130 • Bypass valve 126 • CBV 130 • Dry system 132 • Dump valve 130 • Forced induction systems 124 • Intercooler 129 • Naturally (normally) aspirated 123 • Nitrous oxide ($N_2O$) 132 • Positive displacement 126 • Power adder 132 • Roots supercharger 126 • Supercharger 125 • Turbocharger 127 • Turbo lag 128 • Vent valve 130 • Volumetric efficiency 123 • Wastegate 129 • Wet system 132

## INTRODUCTION

**AIRFLOW REQUIREMENTS** Naturally aspirated engines with throttle plates use atmospheric pressure to push an air-fuel mixture into the combustion chamber vacuum created by the downstroke of a piston. The mixture is then compressed before ignition to increase the force of the burning, expanding gases. The greater the compression of the air-fuel mixture, the higher the engine power output resulting from combustion.

A four-stroke engine can take in only so much air, and how much fuel it needs for proper combustion depends on how much air it takes in. Engineers calculate engine airflow requirements using three factors:

1. Engine displacement
2. Engine revolutions per minute (RPM)
3. Volumetric efficiency

**VOLUMETRIC EFFICIENCY** **Volumetric efficiency** is a measure of how well an engine breathes. It is a comparison of the actual volume of air-fuel mixture drawn into an engine to the theoretical maximum volume that could be drawn in. Volumetric efficiency is expressed as a percentage. If the engine takes in the airflow volume slowly, a cylinder might fill to capacity. It takes a definite amount of time for the airflow to pass through all the curves of the intake manifold and valve port. Therefore, volumetric efficiency decreases as engine speed increases because of the shorter amount of time for the cylinders to be filled with air during the intake stroke. At high speed, it may drop to as low as 50%.

The average stock gasoline engine never reaches 100% volumetric efficiency. A new engine is about 85% efficient.

A race engine usually has 95% or better volumetric efficiency. These figures apply only to naturally aspirated engines. However, with either turbochargers or superchargers, engines can easily achieve more than 100% volumetric efficiency. Many vehicles are equipped with a supercharger or a turbocharger from the factory to increase power. ● **SEE FIGURES 9–1 AND 9–2.**

## FORCED INDUCTION PRINCIPLES

**PURPOSE AND FUNCTION** The amount of force an air-fuel charge produces when it is ignited is largely a function of the charge density. Charge density is a term used to define the amount of the air-fuel charge introduced into the cylinders. Density is the mass of a substance in a given amount of space. ● **SEE FIGURE 9–3.**

The greater the density of an air-fuel charge forced into a cylinder, the greater the force it produces when ignited, and the greater the engine power.

An engine that uses atmospheric pressure for its intake charge is called a **naturally (normally) aspirated** engine. A better way to increase air density is to use some type of air pump, such as a turbocharger or supercharger.

When air is pumped into the cylinder, the combustion chamber receives an increase of air pressure, known as **boost,** and can be measured in the following ways:

- Pounds per square inch (PSI)
- Atmospheres (ATM) (1 atmosphere is 14.7 PSI)
- Bars (1 bar is 14.7 PSI)

FIGURE 9–1 A supercharger on a Ford V-8.

FIGURE 9–2 A turbocharger on a Toyota engine.

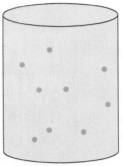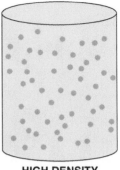

LOW DENSITY         HIGH DENSITY

FIGURE 9–3 The more air and fuel that can be packed in a cylinder, the greater the density of the air-fuel charge.

Pumping air into the intake system under pressure forces it through the bends and restrictions of the air intake system at a greater speed than it would travel under normal atmospheric pressure. This added pressure allows more air to enter the intake port before the intake valve closes. By increasing the airflow into the intake, more fuel can be mixed with the air while still maintaining the same air-fuel ratio. The denser the air-fuel charge entering the engine during its intake stroke, the greater the potential energy released during combustion. In addition to the increased power resulting from combustion, there are several other advantages of supercharging an engine including the following:

- It increases the air-fuel charge density to provide high-compression pressure when power is required but allows the engine to run on lower pressures when additional power is not required.

- The pumped air pushes the remaining exhaust from the combustion chamber during intake and exhaust valve overlap. (Overlap is when both the intake and the exhaust valves are partially open when the piston is near the top at the end of the exhaust stroke and the beginning of the intake stroke.)

- The forced airflow and removal of hot exhaust gases lowers the temperature of the cylinder head, pistons, and valves and helps extend the life of the engine.

A supercharger or turbocharger pressurizes air to greater than atmospheric pressure. The pressurization above atmospheric pressure, or boost, can be measured in the same way as atmospheric pressure. Atmospheric pressure drops as altitude increases, but boost pressure remains the same. If a supercharger develops 12 PSI (83 kPa) boost at sea level, it will develop the same amount at a 5,000-foot altitude because boost pressure is measured inside the intake manifold. ● SEE FIGURE 9–4.

**BOOST AND COMPRESSION RATIOS** Boost increases the amount of air entering the cylinder during the intake stroke. This extra air causes the effective compression ratio to be greater than the mechanical compression ratio designed into

While boost pressure increases air density, friction heats air in motion and causes an increase in temperature. This increase in temperature works in the opposite direction, decreasing air density. Because of these and other variables, an increase in pressure does not always result in greater air density.

**FORCED INDUCTION PRINCIPLES** **Forced induction systems** use an air pump to pack a denser air-fuel charge into the cylinders. Because the density of the air-fuel charge is greater, the following occurs:

- The weight of the air-fuel charge is higher.
- Power is increased because it is directly related to the weight of an air-fuel charge consumed within a given time period.

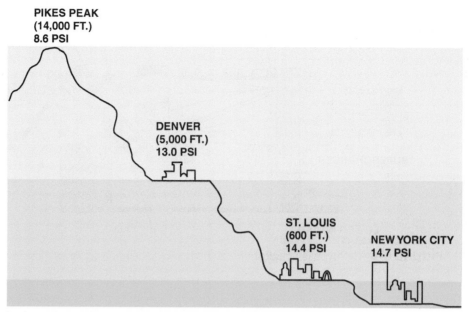

**FIGURE 9–4** Atmospheric pressure decreases with increases in altitude.

| FINAL COMPRESSION RATIO CHART AT VARIOUS BOOST LEVELS | | | | | | | | | | |
|---|---|---|---|---|---|---|---|---|---|---|
| | BLOWER BOOST (PSI) | | | | | | | | | |
| Comp Ratio | 2 | 4 | 6 | 8 | 10 | 12 | 14 | 16 | 18 | 20 |
| 6.5 | 7.4 | 8.3 | 9.2 | 10 | 10.9 | 11.8 | 12.7 | 13.6 | 14.5 | 15.3 |
| 7 | 8 | 8.9 | 9.9 | 10.8 | 11.8 | 12.7 | 13.6 | 14.5 | 15.3 | 16.2 |
| 7.5 | 8.5 | 9.5 | 10.6 | 11.6 | 12.6 | 13.6 | 14.6 | 15.7 | 16.7 | 17.8 |
| 8 | 9.1 | 10.2 | 11.3 | 12.4 | 13.4 | 14.5 | 15.6 | 16.7 | 17.8 | 18.9 |
| 8.5 | 9.7 | 10.8 | 12 | 13.1 | 14.3 | 15.4 | 16.6 | 17.8 | 18.9 | 19.8 |
| 9 | 10.2 | 11.4 | 12.7 | 13.9 | 15.1 | 16.3 | 17.6 | 18.8 | 20 | 21.2 |
| 9.5 | 10.8 | 12.1 | 13.4 | 14.7 | 16 | 17.3 | 18.5 | 19.8 | 21.1 | 22.4 |
| 10 | 11.4 | 12.7 | 14.1 | 15.4 | 16.8 | 18.2 | 19.5 | 20.9 | 22.2 | 23.6 |

**CHART 9–1**

The effective compression ratio compared to the boost pressure.

the engine. The higher the boost pressure, the greater the compression ratio. This means that any engine that uses a supercharger or turbocharger must use all of the following engine components:

- Forged pistons to withstand the increased combustion pressures
- Stronger-than-normal connecting rods
- Piston oil squirters that direct a stream of oil to the underneath part of the piston to keep piston temperatures under control
- Lower compression ratio compared to a naturally aspirated engine

● **SEE CHART 9–1.**

# SUPERCHARGERS

**INTRODUCTION** A **supercharger** is an engine-driven air pump that supplies more than the normal amount of air into the intake manifold and boosts engine torque and power. A supercharger provides an instantaneous increase in power without any delay. However, a supercharger, because it is driven by the engine, requires horsepower to operate and is not as efficient as a turbocharger.

**PARTS AND OPERATION** Gears, shafts, chains, or belts from the crankshaft can all be used to turn the pump. This means that the air pump or supercharger pumps air in direct relation to engine speed.

**FIGURE 9–5**

A roots-type super-charger uses two lobes to force the air around the outside of the housing and into the intake manifold.

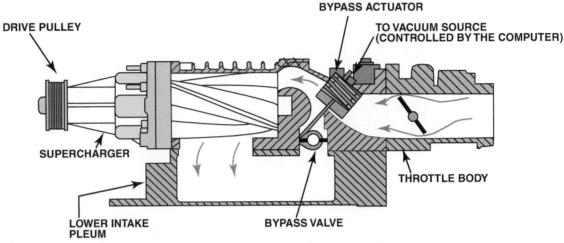

**FIGURE 9–6** The bypass actuator opens the bypass valve to control boost pressure.

## TYPES OF SUPERCHARGERS
There are two general types of superchargers:

- **Roots type.** Named for Philander and Francis Roots, two brothers from Connersville, Indiana, the **roots supercharger** was patented in 1860 as a type of water pump to be used in mines. Later, it was used to move air and is used today on two-stroke-cycle Detroit diesel engines and other supercharged engines. The roots-type supercharger is called a **positive displacement** design because all of the air that enters is forced through the unit. Examples of a roots-type supercharger include the GMC 6-71 (used originally on GMC diesel engines that had 6 cylinders each with 71 cu. in.). Eaton used the roots design for the supercharger on the 3800 V-6 GM engine. ● **SEE FIGURE 9–5.**

- **Centrifugal supercharger.** A centrifugal supercharger is similar to a turbocharger but is mechanically driven by the engine instead of being powered by the hot exhaust gases. A centrifugal supercharger is not a positive displacement pump, and all of the air that enters is not forced through the unit. Air enters a centrifugal supercharger housing in the center and exits at the outer edges of the compressor wheels at a much higher speed because of centrifugal force. The speed of the blades has to be higher than engine speed, so a smaller pulley is used on the supercharger, compared to the engine crankshaft which overdrives the impeller through an internal gear box, achieving about seven times the speed of the engine. Examples of centrifugal superchargers include Vortech and Paxton.

## SUPERCHARGER BOOST CONTROL
Many factory installed superchargers are equipped with a **bypass valve** that allows intake air to flow directly into the intake manifold, bypassing the supercharger. The computer controls the bypass valve actuator. ● **SEE FIGURE 9–6.**

**TECH TIP**

### Faster Moves More Air
One of the high-performance measures that can be used to increase horsepower on a supercharged engine is to install a smaller diameter pulley. The smaller the pulley diameter, the faster the supercharger will rotate and the higher the potential boost pressure will be. The change will require a shorter belt, and the extra boost could cause serious engine damage.

The airflow is directed around the supercharger whenever any of the following conditions occur:

- The boost pressure, as measured by the MAP sensor, indicates that the intake manifold pressure is reaching the predetermined boost level.

- During deceleration, to prevent excessive pressure buildup in the intake.

- Reverse gear is selected.

- When the engine is at idle speed.

## SUPERCHARGER SERVICE
Superchargers are usually lubricated with synthetic engine oil inside the unit. This oil level should be checked and replaced as specified by the vehicle or supercharger manufacturer. The drive belt should also be inspected and replaced as necessary. The air filter should be replaced regularly, and always use the filter specified for a supercharged engine. Many factory supercharger systems use a separate cooling system for the air charge cooler located under the supercharger. Check service information for the exact service procedures to follow. ● **SEE FIGURE 9–7.**

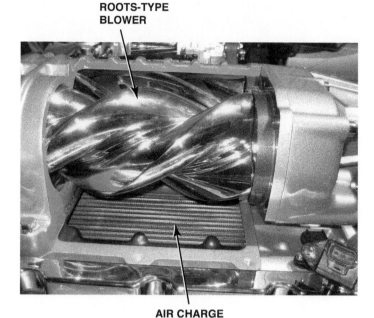

FIGURE 9–7 A Ford supercharger cutaway display showing the roots-type blower and air charge cooler (intercooler). The air charge cooler is used to reduce the temperature of the compressed air before it enters the engine to increase the air charge density.

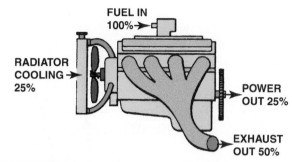

FIGURE 9–8 A turbocharger uses some of the heat energy that would normally be wasted.

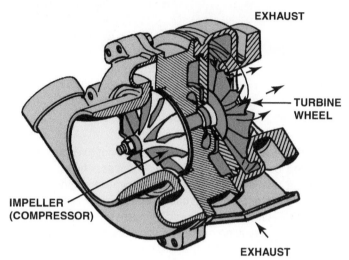

FIGURE 9–9 A turbine wheel is turned by the expanding exhaust gases.

# TURBOCHARGERS

**INTRODUCTION** The major disadvantage of a supercharger is it takes some of the engine power to drive the unit. In some installations, as much as 20% of the engine power is used by a mechanical supercharger. A **turbocharger** uses the heat of the exhaust to power a turbine wheel and therefore does not directly reduce engine power. In a naturally aspirated engine, about half of the heat energy contained in the fuel goes out the exhaust system. As much as 50% of the heat is lost to the exhaust system. Some of this lost energy is regained by using a turbocharger that uses the normally wasted combustion heat energy to perform useful work. Another 25% is lost through radiator cooling. Only about 25% is actually converted to mechanical power. A mechanically driven pump uses some of this mechanical output, but a turbocharger gets its energy from the exhaust gases, converting more of the fuel's heat energy into useful mechanical energy. ● **SEE FIGURE 9–8.**

**OPERATION** A turbocharger turbine looks much like a typical centrifugal pump used for supercharging.

Hot exhaust gases flow from the combustion chamber to the *turbine wheel.* The gases are heated and expanded as they leave the engine. It is not the speed of force of the exhaust gases that forces the turbine wheel to turn, as is commonly thought, but the expansion of hot gases against the turbine wheel's blades.

A turbocharger consists of two chambers connected with a center housing. The two chambers contain a turbine wheel and an *impeller* (compressor) *wheel* connected by a shaft that passes through the center housing. ● **SEE FIGURE 9–9.**

To take full advantage of the exhaust heat that provides the rotating force, a turbocharger must be positioned as close as possible to the exhaust manifold. This allows the hot exhaust to pass directly into the unit with minimal heat loss. As exhaust gas enters the turbocharger, it rotates the turbine blades. The turbine wheel and compressor wheel are on the same shaft so that they turn at the same speed. Rotation of the compressor wheel draws air in through a central inlet, and centrifugal force pumps it through an outlet at the edge of the housing. A pair of bushings in the center housing supports the turbine and compressor wheel shaft and is lubricated by engine oil. ● **SEE FIGURE 9–10.**

Both the turbine and the compressor wheels must operate with extremely close clearances to minimize possible leakage around their blades. Any leakage around the turbine blades causes a dissipation of the heat energy required for compressor rotation. Leakage around the compressor blades prevents the turbocharger from developing its full boost pressure.

**TURBOCHARGER OPERATION** When the engine is started and runs at low speed, both exhaust heat and pressure are low, and the turbine runs at a low speed (approximately

FIGURE 9–10 The exhaust drives the turbine wheel on the left, which is connected to the impeller wheel on the right through a shaft. The bushings that support the shaft are lubricated with engine oil under pressure.

FIGURE 9–11 Engine oil is fed to the center of the turbocharger to lubricate the bushings and returns to the oil pan through a return line.

1,000 RPM). Because the compressor does not turn fast enough to develop boost pressure, air simply passes through it, and the engine works like any naturally aspirated engine. As the engine runs faster or load increases, both exhaust heat and flow increase, causing the turbine and compressor wheels to rotate faster. Since there is no brake and very little rotating resistance on the turbocharger shaft, the turbine and compressor wheels accelerate as the exhaust heat energy increases. When an engine is running at full power, the typical turbocharger rotates at speeds between 100,000 and 150,000 RPM. The turbocharger is lubricated by engine oil through an oil line to the center bushing assembly. ● SEE FIGURE 9–11.

Engine deceleration from full power to idle requires only a second or two because of its internal friction, pumping resistance, and drivetrain load. The turbocharger, however, has no such load on its shaft and is already turning many times faster than the engine at top speed. As a result, it can take as much as a minute or more after the engine has returned to idle speed before the turbocharger also has returned to idle. If the engine is decelerated to idle and then shut off immediately, engine lubrication stops flowing to the center housing bushings while the turbocharger is still spinning at thousands of RPM. The oil in the center housing is then subjected to extreme heat and can gradually "coke" or oxidize. The coked oil can clog passages and will reduce the life of the turbocharger.

The high rotating speeds and extremely close clearances of the turbine and compressor wheels in their housings require equally critical bushing clearances. The bushings must keep radial clearances of 0.003 to 0.006 inches (0.08 to 0.15 mm). Axial clearance (endplay) must be maintained at 0.001 to 0.003 inches (0.025 to 0.08 mm). If properly maintained, the turbocharger also is a trouble-free device. However, to prevent problems, the following conditions must be met:

- The turbocharger bushings must be constantly lubricated with clean engine oil. Turbocharged engines usually have specified oil changes at more frequent intervals than nonturbocharged engines. Always use the specified engine oil, which is likely to be vehicle specific and synthetic.

- Dirt particles and other contamination must be kept out of the intake and exhaust housings.

- Whenever a basic engine bearing (crankshaft or camshaft) has been damaged, the turbocharger must be flushed with clean engine oil after the bearing has been replaced.

- If the turbocharger is damaged, the engine oil must be drained and flushed and the oil filter replaced as part of the repair procedure.

Late-model turbochargers all have liquid-cooled center bushings to prevent heat damage. In a liquid-cooled turbocharger, engine coolant is circulated through passages cast in the center housing to draw off the excess heat. This allows the bushings to run cooler and minimizes the probability of oil coking when the engine is shut down.

**TURBOCHARGER SIZE AND RESPONSE TIME** A time lag occurs between an increase in engine speed and the increase in the speed of the turbocharger. This delay between acceleration and turbo boost is called **turbo lag.** Like any material, moving exhaust gas has inertia. Inertia also is present in the turbine and compressor wheels as well as the intake airflow. Unlike a supercharger, the turbocharger cannot supply an adequate amount of boost at low speed.

Turbocharger response time is directly related to the size of the turbine and compressor wheels. Small wheels accelerate rapidly; large wheels accelerate slowly. While small wheels would seem to have an advantage over larger ones, they may not have enough airflow capacity for an engine. To minimize turbo lag, the intake and exhaust breathing capacities of an engine must be matched to the exhaust and intake airflow capabilities of the turbocharger.

## BOOST CONTROL

**PURPOSE AND FUNCTION** Both supercharged and turbocharged systems are designed to provide a pressure greater than atmospheric pressure in the intake manifold. This increased pressure forces additional amounts of air into the combustion chamber over what would normally be forced in by atmospheric pressure. This increased charge increases engine power. The amount of "boost" (or pressure in the intake manifold) is measured in pounds per square inch (PSI), in inches of mercury (in. Hg), in bars, or in atmospheres. The following values will vary, depending on altitude and weather conditions (barometric pressure):

> 1 atmosphere = 14.7 PSI
> 1 atmosphere = 29.50 in. Hg
> 1 atmosphere = 1 bar
> 1 bar = 14.7 PSI

**BOOST CONTROL FACTORS** The higher the level of boost (pressure), the greater the horsepower output potential. However, other factors must be considered when increasing boost pressure:

1. As boost pressure increases, the temperature of the air also increases.

2. As the temperature of the air increases, combustion temperatures also increase, as does the possibility of detonation.

3. Power can be increased by cooling the compressed air after it leaves the turbocharger. *The power can be increased about 1% per 10°F by which the air is cooled.* A typical cooling device is called an **intercooler.** It is similar to a radiator, wherein outside air can pass through, cooling the pressurized heated air. An intercooler is located between the turbocharger and the intake manifold. ● **SEE FIGURE 9–12.** Some intercoolers use engine coolant to cool the hot compressed air that flows from the turbocharger to the intake.

4. As boost pressure increases, combustion temperature and pressures increase, which, if not limited, can do severe engine damage. The maximum exhaust gas temperature must be 1,550°F (840°C). Higher temperatures decrease the durability of the turbocharger *and* the engine.

**WASTEGATE** Turbochargers use exhaust gases to increase boost, which causes the engine to make more exhaust gases, which in turn increases the boost from the turbocharger. To prevent overboost and severe engine damage, most turbocharger systems use a wastegate. A **wastegate** is a valve similar to a door that can open and close. It is a bypass valve at the exhaust inlet to the turbine, which allows all of the exhaust into the

**FIGURE 9–12** The unit on top of this Subaru that looks like a radiator is the intercooler, which cools the air after it has been compressed by the turbocharger.

 **TECH TIP**

**Boost Is the Result of Restriction**

The boost pressure of a turbocharger (or supercharger) is commonly measured in pounds per square inch. If a cylinder head is restricted because of small valves and ports, the turbocharger will quickly provide boost. Boost results when the air being forced into the cylinder heads cannot flow into the cylinders fast enough and "piles up" in the intake manifold, increasing boost pressure. If an engine had large valves and ports, the turbocharger could provide a much greater *amount* of air into the engine at the same boost pressure as an identical engine with smaller valves and ports. Therefore, by increasing the size of the valves, a turbocharged or supercharged engine will be capable of producing much greater power.

turbine, or it can route part of the exhaust past the turbine to the exhaust system. If the valve is closed, all of the exhaust travels to the turbocharger. When a predetermined amount of boost pressure develops in the intake manifold, the wastegate valve is opened. As the valve opens, most of the exhaust flows directly out the exhaust system, bypassing the turbocharger. With less exhaust flowing across the vanes of the turbocharger, the turbocharger decreases in speed, and boost pressure is reduced. When the boost pressure drops, the wastegate valve closes to direct the exhaust over the turbocharger vanes to again allow the boost pressure to rise. Wastegate operation is a continuous process to control boost pressure.

**FIGURE 9–13** A wastegate is used on many turbocharged engines to control maximum boost pressure. The wastegate is controlled by a computer-controlled valve.

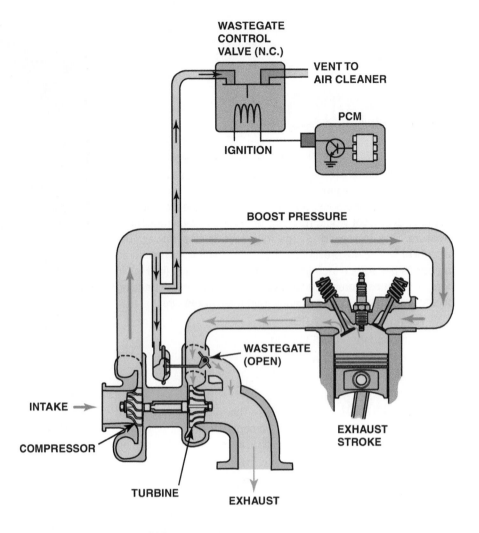

The wastegate is the pressure control valve of a turbocharger system. It is usually controlled by the engine control computer through a boost control solenoid, also called a wastegate control valve. ● **SEE FIGURE 9–13.**

**RELIEF VALVES** A wastegate controls the exhaust side of the turbocharger. A relief valve controls the intake side. A relief valve vents pressurized air from the connecting pipe between the outlet of the turbocharger and the throttle whenever the throttle is closed during boost, such as during shifts. If the pressure is not released, the turbocharger turbine wheel will slow down, creating a lag when the throttle is opened again after a shift has been completed. There are two basic types of relief valves:

1. **Compressor bypass valve (CBV).** This type of relief valve routes the pressurized air to the inlet side of the turbocharger for reuse and is quiet during operation.

2. **Blow-off valve (BOV).** Also called a **dump valve** or **vent valve,** the BOV features an adjustable spring design that keeps the valve closed until a sudden release of the throttle. The resulting pressure increase opens the valve and vents the pressurized air directly into the atmosphere. This type of relief valve is noisy in operation and creates a whooshing sound when the valve opens. ● **SEE FIGURE 9–14.**

**TECH TIP**

**If One Is Good, Two Are Better**

A turbocharger uses the exhaust from the engine to spin a turbine, which is connected to an impeller inside a turbocharger. This impeller then forces air into the engine under pressure, higher than is normally achieved without a turbocharger. The more air that can be forced into an engine, the greater the power potential. A V-type engine has two exhaust manifolds, so two small turbochargers can be used to help force greater quantities of air into an engine, as shown in ● **FIGURE 9–15.**

## TURBOCHARGER FAILURES

**SYMPTOMS OF FAILURE** When turbochargers fail to function correctly, a noticeable drop in power occurs. To restore proper operation, the turbocharger must be rebuilt,

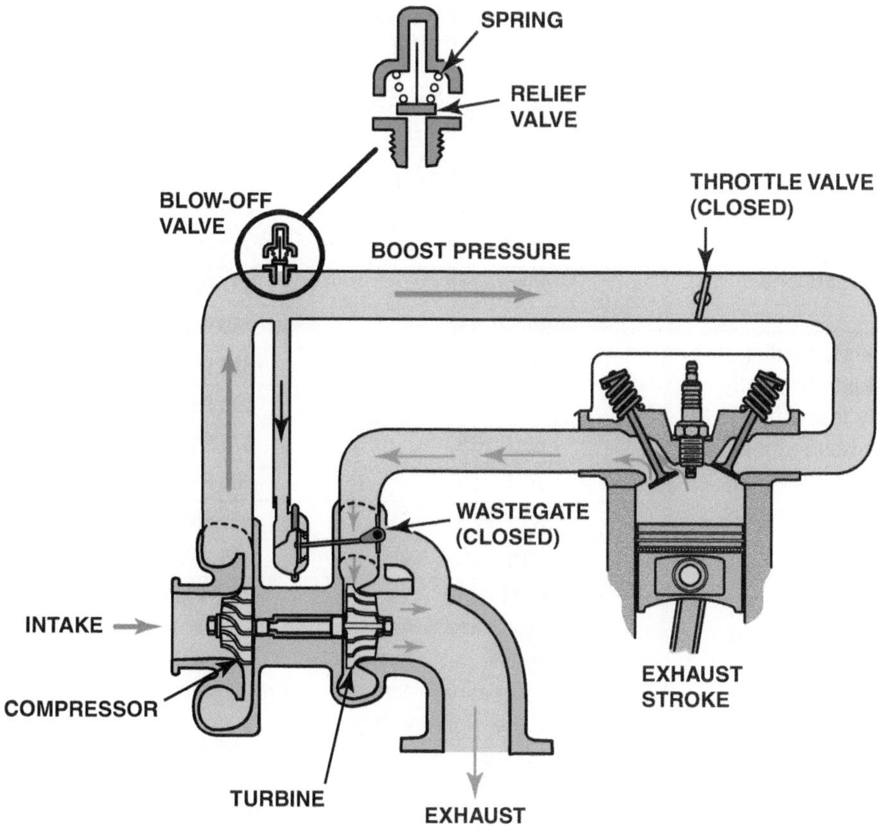

RELIEF VALVE

BLOW-OFF VALVE

THROTTLE VALVE (CLOSED)

BOOST PRESSURE

**FIGURE 9–14** A blow-off valve is used in some turbocharged systems to relieve boost pressure during deceleration.

WASTEGATE (CLOSED)

INTAKE

COMPRESSOR

EXHAUST STROKE

TURBINE

EXHAUST

**FIGURE 9–15** A dual turbocharger system installed on a small block Chevrolet V-8 engine.

repaired, or replaced. It is not possible to simply remove the turbocharger, seal any openings, and maintain decent drive-ability. Bushing failure is a common cause of turbocharger failure, and replacement bushings are usually available only to rebuilders. Another common turbocharger problem is excessive and continuous oil consumption resulting in blue exhaust smoke. Turbochargers use small rings similar to piston rings

on the shaft to prevent exhaust (combustion gases) from entering the central bushings. Because there are no seals to keep oil in, excessive oil consumption is usually caused by the following:

1. Plugged positive crankcase ventilation (PCV) system, resulting in excessive crankcase pressures forcing oil into the air inlet (This failure is not related to the turbocharger, but the turbocharger is often blamed.)

2. Clogged air filter, which causes a low-pressure area in the inlet, drawing oil past the turbo shaft rings and into the intake manifold.

3. Clogged oil return (drain) line from the turbocharger to the oil pan (sump), which can cause the engine oil pressure to force oil past the turbocharger's shaft rings and into the intake *and* exhaust manifolds (Obviously, oil being forced into both the intake and exhaust would create lots of smoke.)

**PREVENTING TURBOCHARGER FAILURES** To help prevent turbocharger failures, the wise vehicle owner should follow the vehicle manufacturer's recommended routine service procedures. The most critical of these services include the following:

■ Regular oil changes (synthetic oil would be best)

■ Regular air filter replacement intervals

■ Performing any other inspections and services recommended, such as cleaning the intercooler

# NITROUS OXIDE

**INTRODUCTION** Nitrous oxide is used for racing or high-performance only and is not used from the factory on any vehicle. This system is a relatively inexpensive way to get additional power from an engine but can cause serious engine damage if not used correctly or in excess amounts or without proper precautions.

**PRINCIPLES** Nitrous oxide ($N_2O$) is a colorless, nonflammable gas. It was discovered by a British chemist, Joseph Priestly (1733–1804), who also discovered oxygen. Priestly found that if a person breathed in nitrous oxide, it caused light-headedness, and so the gas soon became known as *laughing gas*. Nitrous oxide was used in dentistry during tooth extractions to reduce the pain and cause the patient to forget the experience.

Nitrous oxide has two nitrogen atoms and one oxide atom. About 36% of the molecule weight is oxygen. Nitrous oxide is a manufactured gas because, even though both nitrogen and oxygen are present in our atmosphere, they are not combined into one molecule and require heat and a catalyst to be combined.

**ENGINE POWER ADDER** A **power adder** is a device or system added to an engine, such as a supercharger, turbocharger, or nitrous oxide, to increase power. When nitrous oxide is injected into an engine along with gasoline, engine power is increased. The addition of $N_2O$ supplies the needed oxygen for the extra fuel. $N_2O$ by itself does not burn but provides the oxygen for additional fuel that is supplied along with the $N_2O$ to produce more power.

**NOTE: Nitrous oxide was used as a power adder in World War II on some fighter aircraft. Having several hundred more horsepower for a short time saved many lives.**

**PRESSURE AND TEMPERATURE** It requires about 11 pounds of pressure per degree Fahrenheit to condense nitrous oxide gas into liquid nitrous oxide. For example, at 70°F, it requires a pressure of about 770 PSI to condense $N_2O$ into a liquid. To change $N_2O$ from a liquid under pressure to a gas, all that is needed is to lower its pressure below the pressure it takes to cause it to become a liquid.

The temperature also affects the pressure of $N_2O$. ● **SEE CHART 9–2.**

Nitrous oxide is stored in a pressurized storage container and installed at an angle so the pickup tube is in the liquid. The front or discharge end of the storage bottle should be toward the front of the vehicle. ● **SEE FIGURE 9–16.**

**WET AND DRY SYSTEM** There are two different types of $N_2O$ systems that depend on whether additional fuel (gasoline) is supplied at the same time as when the nitrous oxide is squirted:

- The **wet system** involves additional fuel being injected. It is identified as having both a red and a blue nozzle, with the red flowing gasoline and the blue flowing nitrous oxide.

| TEMPERATURE (°F/°C) | PRESSURE (PSI/KPA) |
|---|---|
| −30°F/−34°C | 67 PSI/468 kPa |
| −20°F/−29°C | 203 PSI/1,400 kPa |
| −10°F/−23°C | 240 PSI/1,655 kPa |
| 0°F/−18°C | 283 PSI/1,950 kPa |
| 10°F/−12°C | 335 PSI/2,310 kPa |
| 20°F/−7°C | 387 PSI/2,668 kPa |
| 30°F/−1°C | 460 PSI/3,172 kPa |
| 40°F/4°C | 520 PSI/3,585 kPa |
| 50°F/10°C | 590 PSI/4,068 kPa |
| 60°F/16°C | 675 PSI/4,654 kPa |
| 70°F/21°C | 760 PSI/5,240 kPa |
| 80°F/27°C | 865 PSI/5,964 kPa |
| 90°F/32°C | 985 PSI/6,792 kPa |
| 100°F/38°C | 1,120 PSI/7,722 kPa |

**CHART 9–2**

Temperature/pressure relation for nitrous oxide: The higher the temperature, the higher the pressure.

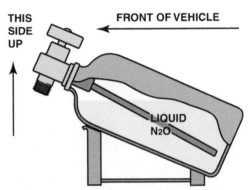

**FIGURE 9–16** Nitrous bottles have to be mounted at an angle to ensure that the pickup tube is in the liquid $N_2O$.

- In a **dry system,** such as an engine using port fuel injection, only nitrous oxide needs to be injected because the PCM can be commanded to provide more fuel when the $N_2O$ is being sprayed. As a result, the intake manifold contains only air and the injected gaseous $N_2O$.

 **TECH TIP**

**Increase Bottle Pressure**

To increase the pressure of the nitrous oxide in a bottle, an electrical warming blanket can be used, as seen in ● **FIGURE 9–17.** The higher the temperature, the higher the pressure and the greater the amount of $N_2O$ flow when energized.

**FIGURE 9-17** An electrical heating mat is installed on the bottle of nitrous oxide to increase the pressure of the gas inside.

**ENGINE CHANGES NEEDED FOR N₂O** If nitrous oxide is going to be used to increase horsepower more than 50 hp, the engine must be designed and built to withstand the greater heat and pressure that will occur in the combustion chambers. For example, the following items should be considered if adding a turbocharger, supercharger, or nitrous oxide system:

- Forged pistons are best able to withstand the pressure and temperature when using nitrous oxide or other power adder.

- Cylinder-to-wall clearance should be increased. Because of the greater amount of heat created by the extra fuel and N₂O injection, the piston temperature will be increased. Although using forged pistons will help, most experts recommend using increased cylinder-to-wall clearance.

- Using forged crankshaft and connecting rods.

Check the instructions from the nitrous oxide supplier for details and other suggested changes.

**CAUTION: The use of a nitrous oxide injection system can cause catastrophic engine damage. Always follow the instructions that come with the kit and be sure that all of the internal engine parts meet the standard specified to help avoid severe engine damage.**

**SYSTEM INSTALLATION AND CALIBRATION** Nitrous oxide systems are usually purchased as a kit with all of the needed components included. The kit also includes one or more sizes of nozzle(s) that are calibrated to control the flow of nitrous oxide into the intake manifold.

The sizes of the nozzles are often calibrated in horsepower that can be gained by their use. Commonly sized nozzles include the following:

- 50 hp
- 100 hp
- 150 hp

Installation of a nitrous oxide kit also includes the installation of an on off switch and a switch on or near the throttle, which is used to activate the system only when the throttle is fully opened (WOT).

## SUMMARY

1. Volumetric efficiency is a comparison of the actual volume of air-fuel mixture drawn into the engine to the theoretical maximum volume that can be drawn into the cylinder.

2. A supercharger operates from the engine by a drive belt, and, although it consumes some engine power, it forces a greater amount of air into the cylinders for even more power.

3. There are two types of superchargers: roots type and centrifugal.

4. A turbocharger uses the normally wasted heat energy of the exhaust to turn an impeller at high speed. The impeller is linked to a turbine wheel on the same shaft and is used to force air into the engine.

5. A bypass valve is used to control the boost pressure on most factory-installed superchargers.

6. An intercooler is used on many turbocharged and some supercharged engines to reduce the temperature of air entering the engine for increased power.

7. A wastegate is used on most turbocharger systems to limit and control boost pressures, as well as a relief valve, to keep the speed of the turbine wheel from slowing down during engine deceleration.

8. Nitrous oxide injection can be used as a power adder but only with extreme caution.

## REVIEW QUESTIONS

1. What are the reasons why supercharging increases engine power?

2. How does the bypass valve work on a supercharged engine?

3. What are the advantages and disadvantages of supercharging?

4. What are the advantages and disadvantages of turbocharging?

5. What turbocharger control valves are needed for proper engine operation?

## CHAPTER QUIZ

1. Boost pressure is generally measured in _____.
   a. in. Hg
   b. PSI
   c. in. $H_2O$
   d. in. lb

2. Two types of superchargers include _____.
   a. Rotary and reciprocating
   b. Roots-type and centrifugal
   c. Double and single acting
   d. Turbine and piston

3. Which valve is used on a factory supercharger to limit boost?
   a. Bypass valve
   b. Wastegate
   c. Blow-off valve
   d. Air valve

4. How are most superchargers lubricated?
   a. By engine oil under pressure through lines from the engine
   b. By an internal oil reservoir
   c. By greased bearings
   d. No lubrication is needed because the incoming air cools the supercharger

5. How are most turbochargers lubricated?
   a. By engine oil under pressure through lines from the engine
   b. By an internal oil reservoir
   c. By greased bearings
   d. No lubrication is needed because the incoming air cools the supercharger

6. Two technicians are discussing the term *turbo lag*. Technician A says that it refers to the delay between when the exhaust leaves the cylinder and when it contacts the turbine blades of the turbocharger. Technician B says that it refers to the delay in boost pressure that occurs when the throttle is first opened. Which technician is correct?
   a. Technician A only
   b. Technician B only
   c. Both Technicians A and B
   d. Neither Technician A nor B

7. What is the purpose of an intercooler?
   a. To reduce the temperature of the air entering the engine
   b. To cool the turbocharger
   c. To cool the engine oil on a turbocharged engine
   d. To cool the exhaust before it enters the turbocharger

8. Which type of relief valve used on a turbocharged engine is noisy?
   a. Bypass valve
   b. BOV
   c. Dump valve
   d. Both b and c

9. Technician A says that a stuck open wastegate can cause the engine to burn oil. Technician B says that a clogged PCV system can cause the engine to burn oil. Which technician is correct?
   a. Technician A only
   b. Technician B only
   c. Both Technicians A and B
   d. Neither Technician A nor B

10. What service operation is *most* important on engines equipped with a turbocharger?
    a. Replacing the air filter regularly
    b. Replacing the fuel filter regularly
    c. Regular oil changes
    d. Regular exhaust system maintenance

## chapter 10

# ENGINE CONDITION DIAGNOSIS

**OBJECTIVES:** **After studying Chapter 10, the reader should be able to:** • Prepare for ASE Engine Performance (A8) certification test content area "A" (General Engine Diagnosis). • List the visual checks to determine engine condition. • Discuss engine noise and its relation to engine condition. • Describe how to perform a dry and a wet compression test. • Explain how to perform a cylinder leakage test. • Explain how to perform a power balance test. • Describe vacuum testing results. • Describe what various colors of exhaust mean.

**KEY TERMS:** Back pressure 147 • compression test 140 • cranking vacuum test 144 • cylinder leakage test 143 • dynamic compression test 142 • idle vacuum test 144 • inches of mercury (in. Hg) 144 • paper test 141 • power balance test 144 • restricted exhaust 146 • running compression test 142 • vacuum test 144 • wet compression test 142

If there is an engine operation problem, then the cause could be any one of many items, including the engine itself. The condition of the engine should be tested anytime the operation of the engine is not satisfactory.

## TYPICAL ENGINE-RELATED COMPLAINTS

Many driveability problems are *not* caused by engine mechanical problems. A thorough inspection and testing of the ignition and fuel systems should be performed before testing for mechanical engine problems.

Typical engine mechanical-related complaints include the following:

- Excessive oil consumption
- Engine misfiring
- Loss of power
- Smoke from the engine or exhaust
- Engine noise

## ENGINE SMOKE DIAGNOSIS

The color of engine exhaust smoke can indicate what engine problem might exist.

| Typical Exhaust Smoke Color | Possible Causes |
| --- | --- |
| Blue | Blue exhaust indicates that the engine is burning oil. Oil is getting into the combustion chamber either past the piston rings or past the valve stem seals. Blue smoke only after start-up is usually due to defective valve stem seals. ● **SEE FIGURE 10–1.** |
| Black | Black exhaust smoke is due to excessive fuel being burned in the combustion chamber. Typical causes include a defective or misadjusted throttle body, leaking fuel injector, or excessive fuel-pump pressure. |
| White (steam) | White smoke or steam from the exhaust is normal during cold weather and represents condensed steam. Every engine creates about 1 gallon of water for each gallon of gasoline burned. If the steam from the exhaust is excessive, then water (coolant) is getting into the combustion chamber. Typical causes include a defective cylinder head gasket, a cracked cylinder head, or in severe cases a cracked block. ● **SEE FIGURE 10–2.** |

**Note:** White smoke can also be created when automatic transmission fluid (ATF) is burned. A common source of ATF getting into the engine is through a defective vacuum modulator valve on older automatic transmissions.

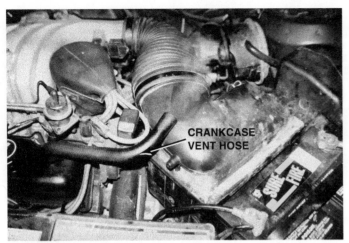

**FIGURE 10–1** Blowby gases coming out of the crankcase vent hose. Excessive amounts of combustion gases flow past the piston rings and into the crankcase.

**FIGURE 10–2** White steam is usually an indication of a blown (defective) cylinder head gasket that allows engine coolant to flow into the combustion chamber where it is turned to steam.

### TECH TIP

**Your Nose Knows**

Whenever diagnosing any vehicle, try to use all senses including the smell. Some smells and their cause include the following:

- **Gasoline.** If the exhaust smells like gasoline or unburned fuel, then a fault with the ignition system is a likely cause. Unburned fuel due to lean air–fuel mixture causing a lean misfire is also possible.
- **Sweet smell.** A coolant leak often gives off a sweet smell, especially if the leaking coolant flows onto the hot exhaust.
- **Exhaust smell.** Check for an exhaust leak, including a possible cracked exhaust manifold, which can be difficult to find because it often does not make noise.

## THE DRIVER IS YOUR BEST RESOURCE

The driver of the vehicle knows a lot about the vehicle and how it is driven. *Before* diagnosis is started, always ask the following questions:

- When did the problem first occur?
- Under what conditions does it occur?
  1. Cold or hot?
  2. Acceleration, cruise, or deceleration?
  3. How far was it driven?

After the nature and scope of the problem are determined, the complaint should be verified before further diagnostic tests are performed.

## VISUAL CHECKS

The first and most important "test" that can be performed is a careful visual inspection.

**OIL LEVEL AND CONDITION** The first area for visual inspection is oil level and condition.

1. Oil level—oil should be to the proper level
2. Oil condition
   a. Using a match or lighter, try to light the oil on the dipstick; if the oil flames up, gasoline is present in the engine oil.
   b. Drip some of the engine oil from the dipstick onto the hot exhaust manifold. If the oil bubbles or boils, there is coolant (water) in the oil.
   c. Check for grittiness by rubbing the oil between your fingers.

**COOLANT LEVEL AND CONDITION** Most mechanical engine problems are caused by overheating. The proper operation of the cooling system is critical to the life of any engine.

**NOTE: Check the coolant level in the radiator only if the radiator is cool. If the radiator is hot and the radiator cap is removed, the drop in pressure above the coolant will cause the coolant to boil immediately and can cause severe burns when the coolant explosively expands upward and outward from the radiator opening.**

1. The coolant level in the coolant recovery container should be within the limits indicated on the overflow bottle. If this level is too low or the coolant recovery container is empty, then check the level of coolant in the radiator (only when cool) and also check the operation of the pressure cap.

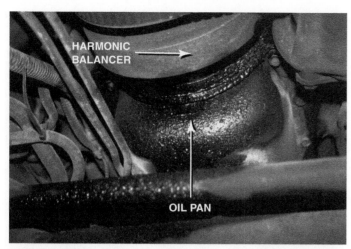

FIGURE 10–3 What looks like an oil pan gasket leak can be a rocker cover gasket leak. Always look up and look for the highest place you see oil leaking; that should be repaired first.

2. The coolant should be checked with a hydrometer for boiling and freezing temperature. This test indicates if the concentration of the antifreeze is sufficient for proper protection.

3. Pressure test the cooling system and look for leakage. Coolant leakage can often be seen around hoses or cooling system components because it will often cause the following:
   a. A grayish white stain
   b. A rusty color stain
   c. Dye stains from antifreeze (greenish or yellowish depending on the type of coolant)

4. Check for cool areas of the radiator indicating clogged sections.

5. Check operation and condition of the fan clutch, electric fan and water pump drive belt.

**OIL LEAKS** Oil leaks can lead to severe engine damage if the resulting low oil level is not corrected. Besides causing an oily mess where the vehicle is parked, the oil leak can cause blue smoke to occur under the hood as leaking oil drips on the exhaust system. *Finding* the location of the oil leak can often be difficult. ● **SEE FIGURES 10–3 AND 10–4.** To help find the source of oil leaks, follow these steps:

**STEP 1** Clean the engine or area around the suspected oil leak. Use a high-powered hot-water spray to wash the engine. While the engine is running, spray the entire engine and the engine compartment. Avoid letting the water come into direct contact with the air inlet and ignition distributor or ignition coil(s).

> **NOTE: If the engine starts to run rough or stalls when the engine gets wet, then the secondary ignition wires (spark plug wires) or distributor cap may be defective or have weak insulation. Be certain to wipe all wires and the distributor cap dry with a soft, dry cloth if the engine stalls.**

FIGURE 10–4 The transmission and flexplate (flywheel) were removed to check the exact location of this oil leak. The rear main seal and/or the oil pan gasket could be the cause of this leak.

**TECH TIP**

**What's Leaking?**

The color of the leaks observed under a vehicle can help the technician determine and correct the cause. Some leaks, such as condensate (water) from the air-conditioning system, are normal, whereas a brake fluid leak is very dangerous. The following are colors of common leaks:

| Sooty Black | Engine Oil |
| --- | --- |
| Yellow, green, blue, or orange | Antifreeze (coolant) |
| Red | Automatic transmission fluid |
| Murky brown | Brake or power steering fluid or very neglected antifreeze (coolant) |
| Clear | Air-conditioning condensate (water) (normal) |

An alternative method is to spray a degreaser on the engine, then start and run the engine until warm. Engine heat helps the degreaser penetrate the grease and dirt. Use a water hose to rinse off the engine and engine compartment.

**FIGURE 10-5** Using a black light to spot leaks after adding dye to the oil.

**FIGURE 10-6** An accessory belt tensioner. Most tensioners have a mark that indicates normal operating location. If the belt has stretched, this indicator mark will be outside of the normal range. Anything wrong with the belt or tensioner can cause noise.

 **TECH TIP**

**The Foot Powder Spray Trick**

The source of an oil or other fluid leak is often difficult to determine. A quick and easy method that works is the following. First, clean the entire area. This can best be done by using a commercially available degreaser to spray the entire area. Let it soak to loosen all accumulated oil and greasy dirt. Clean off the degreaser with a water hose. Let the area dry. Start the engine and, using spray foot powder or other aerosol powder product, spray the entire area. The leak will turn the white powder dark. The exact location of any leak can be quickly located.

**NOTE: Most oil leaks appear at the bottom of the engine due to gravity. Look for the highest, most forward location for the source of the leak.**

**STEP 2** If the oil leak is not visible or oil seems to be coming from "everywhere," use a white talcum powder. The leaking oil will show as a dark area on the white powder. See the Tech Tip, "The Foot Powder Spray Trick."

**STEP 3** Fluorescent dye can be added to the engine oil. Add about 1/2 ounce (15 cc) of dye per 5 quarts of engine oil. Start the engine and allow it to run about 10 minutes to thoroughly mix the dye throughout the engine. A black light can then be shown around every suspected oil leak location. The black light will easily show all oil leak locations because the dye will show as a bright yellow/green area. ● **SEE FIGURE 10-5.**

**NOTE: Fluorescent dye works best with clean oil.**

## ENGINE NOISE DIAGNOSIS

An engine knocking noise is often difficult to diagnose. Several items that can cause a deep engine knock include the following:

- **Valves clicking.** This can happen because of lack of oil to the lifters. This noise is most noticeable at idle when the oil pressure is the lowest.

- **Torque converter.** The attaching bolts or nuts may be loose on the flex plate. This noise is most noticeable at idle or when there is no load on the engine.

- **Cracked flex plate.** The noise of a cracked flex plate is often mistaken for a rod- or main-bearing noise.

- **Loose or defective drive belts or tensioners.** If an accessory drive belt is loose or defective, the flopping noise often sounds similar to a bearing knock. ● **SEE FIGURE 10-6.**

- **Piston pin knock.** This knocking noise is usually not affected by load on the cylinder. If the clearance is too great, a double knock noise is heard when the engine idles. If all cylinders are grounded out one at a time and the noise does not change, a defective piston pin could be the cause.

- **Piston slap.** A piston slap is usually caused by an undersized or improperly shaped piston or oversized cylinder bore. A piston slap is most noticeable when the engine is cold and tends to decrease or stop making noise as the piston expands during engine operation.

- **Timing chain noise.** An excessively loose timing chain can cause a severe knocking noise when the chain hits the timing chain cover. This noise can often sound like a rod-bearing knock.

| Typical Noises | Possible Causes |
|---|---|
| Clicking noise—like the clicking of a ballpoint pen | 1. Loose spark plug<br>2. Loose accessory mount (for air-conditioning compressor, alternator, power steering pump, etc.)<br>3. Loose rocker arm<br>4. Worn rocker arm pedestal<br>5. Fuel pump (broken mechanical fuel pump return spring)<br>6. Worn camshaft<br>7. Exhaust leak ● SEE FIGURE 10–7. |
| Clacking noise—like tapping on metal | 1. Worn piston pin<br>2. Broken piston<br>3. Excessive valve clearance<br>4. Timing chain hitting cover |
| Knock—like knocking on a door | 1. Rod bearing(s)<br>2. Main bearing(s)<br>3. Thrust bearing(s)<br>4. Loose torque converter<br>5. Cracked flex plate (drive plate) |
| Rattle—like a baby rattle | 1. Manifold heat control valve<br>2. Broken harmonic balancer<br>3. Loose accessory mounts<br>4. Loose accessory drive belt or tensioner |
| Clatter—like rolling marbles | 1. Rod bearings<br>2. Piston pin<br>3. Loose timing chain |
| Whine—like an electric motor running | 1. Alternator bearing<br>2. Drive belt<br>3. Power steering<br>4. Belt noise (accessory or timing) |
| Clunk—like a door closing | 1. Engine mount<br>2. Drive axle shaft U-joint or constant velocity (CV) joint |

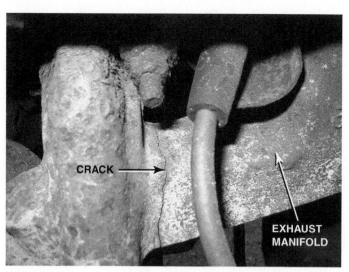

**FIGURE 10–7** A cracked exhaust manifold on a Ford V-8.

**TECH TIP**

**Engine Noise and Cost**

A light ticking noise often heard at one-half engine speed and associated with valve train noise is a less serious problem than many deep-sounding knocking noises. Generally, the deeper the sound of the engine noise, the more the owner will have to pay for repairs. A light "tick tick tick," though often not cheap, is usually far less expensive than a deep "knock knock knock" from the engine.

## OIL PRESSURE TESTING

Proper oil pressure is very important for the operation of any engine. *Low oil pressure can cause engine wear, and engine wear can cause low oil pressure.*

If main thrust or rod bearings are worn, oil pressure is reduced because of leakage of the oil around the bearings. Oil pressure testing is usually performed with the following steps:

**STEP 1** Operate the engine until normal operating temperature is achieved.

**STEP 2** With the engine off, remove the oil pressure sending unit or sender, usually located near the oil filter. Thread an oil pressure gauge into the threaded hole. ● SEE FIGURE 10–8.

NOTE: An oil pressure gauge can be made from another gauge, such as an old air-conditioning gauge and a flexible brake hose. The threads are often the same as those used for the oil pressure sending unit.

■ **Rod-bearing noise.** The noise from a defective rod bearing is usually load sensitive and changes in intensity as the load on the engine increases and decreases. A rod-bearing failure can often be detected by grounding out the spark plugs one cylinder at a time. If the knocking noise decreases or is eliminated when a particular cylinder is grounded (disabled), then the grounded cylinder is the one from which the noise is originating.

■ **Main-bearing knock.** A main-bearing knock often cannot be isolated to a particular cylinder. The sound can vary in intensity and may disappear at times depending on engine load.

Regardless of the type of loud knocking noise, after the external causes of the knocking noise have been eliminated, the engine should be disassembled and carefully inspected to determine the exact cause.

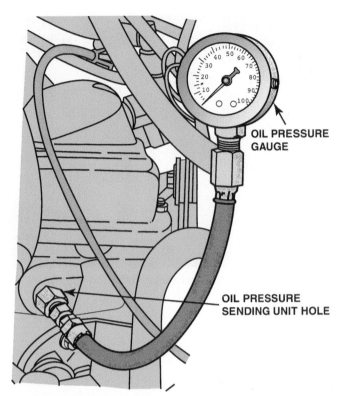

**FIGURE 10–8** To measure engine oil pressure, remove the oil pressure sending (sender) unit usually located near the oil filter. Screw the pressure gauge into the oil pressure sending unit hole.

**STEP 3** Start the engine and observe the gauge. Record the oil pressure at idle and at 2,500 RPM. Most vehicle manufacturers recommend a minimum oil pressure of 10 PSI per 1,000 RPM. Therefore, at 2,500 RPM, the oil pressure should be at least 25 PSI. Always compare your test results with the manufacturer's recommended oil pressure.

Besides engine bearing wear, other possible causes for low oil pressure include the following:

- Low oil level
- Diluted oil
- Stuck oil pressure relief valve

# OIL PRESSURE WARNING LAMP

The red oil pressure warning lamp in the dash usually lights when the oil pressure is less than 4 to 7 PSI, depending on vehicle and engine. The oil light should not be on during driving. If the oil warning lamp is on, stop the engine immediately. Always confirm oil pressure with a reliable mechanical gauge before performing engine repairs. The sending unit or circuit may be defective.

**TECH TIP**

**Use the KISS Test Method**

Engine testing is done to find the cause of an engine problem. All the simple things should be tested first. Just remember KISS–"keep it simple, stupid." A loose alternator belt or loose bolts on a torque converter can sound just like a lifter or rod bearing. A loose spark plug can make the engine perform as if it had a burned valve. Some simple items that can cause serious problems include the following:

**Oil Burning**

- Low oil level
- Clogged PCV valve or system, causing blowby and oil to be blown into the air cleaner
- Clogged drainback passages in the cylinder head
- Dirty oil that has not been changed for a long time (Change the oil and drive for about 1,000 miles [1,600 kilometers] and change the oil and filter again.)

**Noises**

- Carbon on top of the piston(s) can sound like a bad rod bearing (often called a carbon knock)
- Loose torque-to-flex plate bolts (or nuts), causing a loud knocking noise

  **NOTE: Often this problem will cause noise only at idle; the noise tends to disappear during driving or when the engine is under load.**

- A loose and/or defective drive belt, which may cause a rod- or main-bearing knocking noise (A loose or broken mount for the generator [alternator], power steering pump, or air-conditioning compressor can also cause a knocking noise.)

# COMPRESSION TEST

An engine **compression test** is one of the fundamental engine diagnostic tests that can be performed. For smooth engine operation, all cylinders must have equal compression. An engine can lose compression by leakage of air through one or more of only three routes:

- Intake or exhaust valve
- Piston rings (or piston, if there is a hole)
- Cylinder head gasket

For best results, the engine should be warmed to normal operating temperature before testing. An accurate compression test should be performed as follows:

**STEP 1** Remove all spark plugs. This allows the engine to be cranked to an even speed. Be sure to label all spark plug wires.

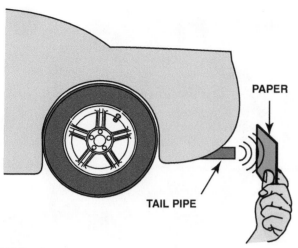

TAIL PIPE

PAPER

**FIGURE 10–9** The paper test involves holding a piece of paper near the tailpipe of an idling engine. A good engine should produce even, outward puffs of exhaust. If the paper is sucked in toward the tailpipe, a burned valve is a possibility.

---

🔧 **TECH TIP**

**The Paper Test**

A soundly running engine should produce even and steady exhaust at the tailpipe. You can test this with the **paper test.** Hold a piece of paper or a 3″ × 5″ index card (even a dollar bill works) within 1 inch (25 mm) of the tailpipe with the engine running at idle. ● **SEE FIGURE 10–9.**

The paper should blow out evenly without "puffing." If the paper is drawn *toward* the tailpipe at times, the exhaust valves in one or more cylinders could be burned. Other reasons why the paper might be sucked toward the tailpipe include the following:

1. The engine could be misfiring because of a lean condition that could occur normally when the engine is cold.
2. Pulsing of the paper toward the tailpipe could also be caused by a hole in the exhaust system. If exhaust escapes through a hole in the exhaust system, air could be drawn in during the intervals between the exhaust puffs from the tailpipe to the hole in the exhaust, causing the paper to be drawn toward the tailpipe.
3. Ignition fault causing misfire.

---

**STEP 2**   Block open the throttle. This permits the maximum amount of air to be drawn into the engine. This step also ensures consistent compression test results.

CAUTION: Disable the ignition system by disconnecting the primary leads from the ignition coil or module or by grounding the coil wire after

---

**FIGURE 10–10** A two-piece compression gauge set. The threaded hose is screwed into the spark plug hole after removing the spark plug. The gauge part is then snapped onto the end of the hose.

removing it from the center of the distributor cap. Also disable the fuel-injection system to prevent the squirting of fuel into the cylinder.

**STEP 3**   Thread a compression gauge into one spark plug hole and crank the engine. ● **SEE FIGURE 10–10.**

Continue cranking the engine through *four* compression strokes. Each compression stroke makes a puffing sound.

NOTE: Note the reading on the compression gauge after the first puff. This reading should be at least one-half the final reading. For example, if the final, highest reading is 150 PSI, then the reading after the first puff should be higher than 75 PSI. A low first-puff reading indicates possible weak piston rings. Release the pressure on the gauge and repeat for the other cylinders.

**STEP 4**   Record the highest readings and compare the results. Most vehicle manufacturers specify the minimum compression reading and the maximum allowable variation among cylinders. Most manufacturers specify a maximum difference of 20% between the highest reading and the lowest reading. An example follows:

| If the high reading is | 150 PSI |
|---|---|
| Subtract 20% | −30 PSI |
| Lowest allowable compression is | 120 PSI |

NOTE: To make the math quick and easy, think of 10% of 150, which is 15 (move the decimal point to the left one place). Now double it: 15 × 2 = 30. This represents 20%.

NOTE: During cranking, the oil pump cannot maintain normal oil pressure. Extended engine cranking, such as that which occurs during a compression test, can cause hydraulic lifters to collapse. When the engine starts, loud valve clicking noises may be heard. This should be considered normal after performing a compression test, and the noise should stop after the vehicle has been driven a short distance.

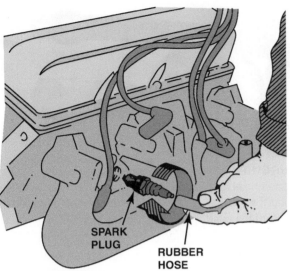

**FIGURE 10–11** Use a vacuum or fuel line hose over the spark plug to install it without danger of cross-threading the cylinder head.

SPARK PLUG

RUBBER HOSE

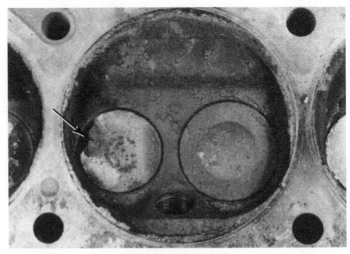

**FIGURE 10–12** Badly burned exhaust valve. A compression test could have detected a problem, and a cylinder leakage test (leak-down test) could have been used to determine the exact problem.

 **TECH TIP**

**The Hose Trick**

Installing spark plugs can be made easier by using a rubber hose on the end of the spark plug. The hose can be a vacuum hose, fuel line, or even an old spark plug wire end. ● **SEE FIGURE 10–11.**

The hose makes it easy to start the threads of the spark plug into the cylinder head. After starting the threads, continue to thread the spark plug for several turns. Using the hose eliminates the chance of cross-threading the plug. This is especially important when installing spark plugs in aluminum cylinder heads.

# WET COMPRESSION TEST

If the compression test reading indicates low compression on one or more cylinders, add three squirts of oil to the cylinder and retest. This is called a **wet compression test** when oil is used to help seal around the piston rings.

CAUTION: Do not use more oil than three squirts from a hand-operated oil squirt can. Too much oil can cause a hydrostatic lock, which can damage or break pistons or connecting rods or even crack a cylinder head.

Perform the compression test again and observe the results. If the first-puff readings greatly improve and the readings are much higher than without the oil, the cause of the low compression is worn or defective piston rings. If the compression

readings increase only slightly (or not at all), then the cause of the low compression is usually defective valves. ● **SEE FIGURE 10–12.**

NOTE: During both the dry and wet compression tests, be sure that the battery and starting system are capable of cranking the engine at normal cranking speed.

# RUNNING (DYNAMIC) COMPRESSION TEST

A compression test is commonly used to help determine engine condition and is usually performed with the engine cranking.

What is the RPM of a cranking engine? An engine idles at about 600 to 900 RPM, and the starter motor obviously cannot crank the engine as fast as the engine idles. Most manufacturers' specifications require the engine to crank at 80 to 250 cranking RPM. Therefore, a check of the engine's compression at cranking speed determines the condition of an engine that does not run at such low speeds.

But what should be the compression of a running engine? Some would think that the compression would be substantially higher because the valve overlap of the cam is more effective at higher engine speeds, which would tend to increase the compression.

A **running compression test,** also called a **dynamic compression test,** is a compression test done with the engine running rather than during engine cranking as is done in a regular compression test.

Actually, the compression pressure of a running engine is much *lower* than cranking compression pressure. This results from the volumetric efficiency. The engine is revolving faster, and therefore there is less *time* for air to enter the combustion

**FIGURE 10–13** A typical handheld cylinder leakage tester.

**FIGURE 10–14** A whistle stop used to find top dead center. Remove the spark plug and install the whistle stop, then rotate the engine by hand. When the whistle stops making a sound, the piston is at the top.

chamber. With less air to compress, the compression pressure is lower. Typically, the higher the engine RPM, the lower the running compression. For most engines, the value ranges are as follows:

- Compression during cranking:     125 to 160 PSI
- Compression at idle:     60 to 90 PSI
- Compression at 2,000 RPM:     30 to 60 PSI

As with cranking compression, the running compression of all cylinders should be equal. Therefore, a problem is likely to be detected not by single compression values but by *variations* in running compression values among the cylinders. Broken valve springs, worn valve guides, bent pushrods, and worn cam lobes are some items that would be indicated by a low running compression test reading on one or more cylinders.

**PERFORMING A RUNNING COMPRESSION TEST**   To perform a running compression test, remove just one spark plug at a time. With one spark plug removed from the engine, use a jumper wire to *ground* the spark plug wire to a good engine ground. This prevents possible ignition coil damage. Start the engine, push the pressure release on the gauge, and read the compression. Increase the engine speed to about 2,000 RPM and push the pressure release on the gauge again. Read the gauge. Stop the engine, reinstall the spark plug, reattach the spark plug wire, and repeat the test for each of the remaining cylinders. Just like the cranking compression test, the running compression test can inform a technician of the *relative* compression of all the cylinders.

## CYLINDER LEAKAGE TEST

One of the best tests that can be used to determine engine condition is the **cylinder leakage test.** This test involves injecting air under pressure into the cylinders one at a time. The amount and location of any escaping air helps the technician determine the condition of the engine. The air is injected into the cylinder through a cylinder leakage gauge into the spark plug hole. ● **SEE FIGURE 10–13.** To perform the cylinder leakage test, take the following steps:

**STEP 1**   For best results, the engine should be at normal operating temperature (upper radiator hose hot and pressurized).

**STEP 2**   The cylinder being tested must be at top dead center (TDC) of the compression stroke. ● **SEE FIGURE 10–14.**

> **NOTE: The greatest amount of wear occurs at the top of the cylinder because of the heat generated near the top of the cylinders. The piston ring flex also adds to the wear at the top of the cylinder.**

**STEP 3**   Calibrate the cylinder leakage unit as per manufacturer's instructions.

**STEP 4**   Inject air into the cylinders one at a time, rotating the engine as necessitated by firing order to test each cylinder at TDC on the compression stroke.

**STEP 5**   Evaluate the results:
Less than 10% leakage: good
Less than 20% leakage: acceptable
Less than 30% leakage: poor
More than 30% leakage: definite problem

> **NOTE: If leakage seems unacceptably high, repeat the test, being certain that it is being performed correctly and that the cylinder being tested is at TDC on the compression stroke.**

**STEP 6**   Check the source of air leakage.
   **a.** If air is heard escaping from the oil filler cap, the *piston rings* are worn or broken.
   **b.** If air is observed bubbling out of the radiator, there is a possible blown *head gasket* or cracked *cylinder head.*
   **c.** If air is heard coming from the throttle body or air inlet on fuel injection-equipped engines, there is a defective *intake valve(s).*
   **d.** If air is heard coming from the tailpipe, there is a defective *exhaust valve(s).*

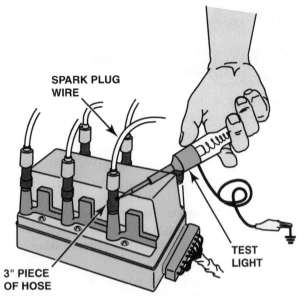

SPARK PLUG
WIRE

TEST
LIGHT

3" PIECE
OF HOSE

**FIGURE 10–15** Using a vacuum hose and a test light to ground one cylinder at a time on a distributorless ignition system. This works on all types of ignition systems and provides a method for grounding out one cylinder at a time without fear of damaging any component. Do not short out a cylinder for longer than 15 seconds to prevent possible damage to the catalytic converter.

## CYLINDER POWER BALANCE TEST

Most large engine analyzers and scan tools have a cylinder power balance feature. The purpose of a cylinder **power balance test** is to determine if all cylinders are contributing power equally. It determines this by shorting out one cylinder at a time. If the engine speed (RPM) does not drop as much for one cylinder as for other cylinders of the same engine, then the shorted cylinder must be weaker than the other cylinders. An example follows:

| Cylinder Number | RPM Drop When Ignition Is Shorted |
|:---:|:---:|
| 1 | 75 |
| 2 | 70 |
| 3 | 15 |
| 4 | 65 |
| 5 | 75 |
| 6 | 70 |

Cylinder #3 is the weak cylinder.

**NOTE: Most automotive test equipment uses automatic means for testing cylinder balance. Be certain to correctly identify the offending cylinder. Cylinder #3 as identified by the equipment may be the third cylinder in the firing order instead of the actual cylinder #3.**

## POWER BALANCE TEST PROCEDURE

When point-type ignition was used on all vehicles, the common method for determining which, if any, cylinder was weak was to remove a spark plug wire from one spark plug at a time while watching a tachometer and a vacuum gauge. This method is not recommended on any vehicle with any type of electronic ignition. If any of the spark plug wires are removed from a spark plug with the engine running, the ignition coil tries to supply increasing levels of voltage attempting to jump the increasing gap as the plug wires are removed. This high voltage could easily track the ignition coil, damage the ignition module, or both.

The acceptable method of canceling cylinders, which will work on all types of ignition systems, including distributorless, is to *ground* the secondary current for each cylinder. ● **SEE FIGURE 10–15.** The cylinder with the least RPM drop is the cylinder not producing its share of power.

## VACUUM TESTS

Vacuum is pressure below atmospheric pressure and is measured in **inches** (or millimeters) **of mercury (in. Hg).** An engine in good mechanical condition will run with high manifold vacuum. Manifold vacuum is developed by the pistons as they move down on the intake stroke to draw the charge from the throttle body and intake manifold. Air to refill the manifold comes past the throttle plate into the manifold. Vacuum will increase anytime the engine turns faster or has better cylinder sealing while the throttle plate remains in a fixed position. Manifold vacuum will decrease when the engine turns more slowly or when the cylinders no longer do an efficient job of pumping. **Vacuum tests** include testing the engine for **cranking vacuum, idle vacuum,** and vacuum at 2,500 RPM.

**CRANKING VACUUM TEST** Measuring the amount of manifold vacuum during cranking is a quick and easy test to determine if the piston rings and valves are properly sealing. (For accurate results, the engine should be warm and the throttle closed.) To perform the cranking vacuum test, take the following steps:

**STEP 1** Disable the ignition or fuel injection.

**STEP 2** Connect the vacuum gauge to a manifold vacuum source.

**STEP 3** Crank the engine while observing the vacuum gauge.

Cranking vacuum should be higher than 2.5 in. Hg. (Normal cranking vacuum is 3 to 6 in. Hg.) If it is lower than 2.5 in. Hg, then the following could be the cause:

- Too slow a cranking speed
- Worn piston rings

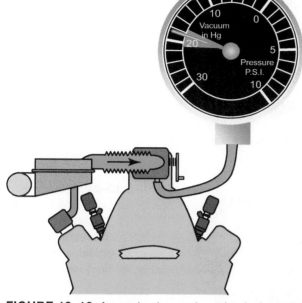

FIGURE 10–16 An engine in good mechanical condition should produce 17 to 21 in. Hg of vacuum at idle at sea level.

FIGURE 10–17 A steady but low reading could indicate retarded valve or ignition timing.

FIGURE 10–18 A gauge reading with the needle fluctuating 3 to 9 in. Hg below normal often indicates a vacuum leak in the intake system.

FIGURE 10–19 A leaking head gasket can cause the needle to vibrate as it moves through a range from below to above normal.

FIGURE 10–20 An oscillating needle 1 or 2 in. Hg below normal could indicate an incorrect air–fuel mixture (either too rich or too lean).

- Leaking valves
- Excessive amounts of air bypassing the throttle plate (This could give a false low vacuum reading. Common sources include a throttle plate partially open or a high-performance camshaft with excessive overlap.)

## IDLE VACUUM TEST
An engine in proper condition should idle with a steady vacuum between 17 and 21 in. Hg. ● SEE FIGURE 10–16.

NOTE: Engine vacuum readings vary with altitude. A reduction of 1 in. Hg per 1,000 feet (300 m) of altitude should be subtracted from the expected values if testing a vehicle above 1,000 feet (300 m).

## LOW AND STEADY VACUUM
If the vacuum is lower than normal yet the gauge reading is steady, the most common causes include the following:

- Retarded ignition timing
- Retarded cam timing (check timing chain for excessive slack or timing belt for proper installation)
  ● SEE FIGURE 10–17.

## FLUCTUATING VACUUM
If the needle drops, then returns to a normal reading, then drops again, and again returns, this indicates a sticking valve. A common cause of sticking valves is lack of lubrication of the valve stems. ● SEE FIGURES 10–18 THROUGH 10–26. If the vacuum gauge fluctuates above and below a center point, burned valves or weak valve springs may be indicated. If the fluctuation is slow and steady, unequal fuel mixture could be the cause.

**FIGURE 10–21** A rapidly vibrating needle at idle that becomes steady as engine speed is increased indicates worn valve guides.

**FIGURE 10–22** If the needle drops 1 or 2 in. Hg from the normal reading, one of the engine valves is burned or not seating properly.

**FIGURE 10–23** Weak valve springs will produce a normal reading at idle, but as engine speed increases, the needle will fluctuate rapidly between 12 and 24 in. Hg.

**FIGURE 10–24** A steady needle reading that drops 2 or 3 in. Hg when the engine speed is increased slightly above idle indicates that the ignition timing is retarded.

**FIGURE 10–25** A steady needle reading that rises 2 or 3 in. Hg when the engine speed is increased slightly above idle indicates that the ignition timing is advanced.

**FIGURE 10–26** A needle that drops to near zero when the engine is accelerated rapidly and then rises slightly to a reading below normal indicates an exhaust restriction.

**NOTE:** A common trick that some technicians use is to squirt some automatic transmission fluid (ATF) down the throttle body or into the air inlet of a warm engine. Often the idle quality improves, and normal vacuum gauge readings are restored. The use of ATF does create excessive exhaust smoke for a short time, but it should not harm oxygen sensors or catalytic converters.

## EXHAUST RESTRICTION TEST

If the exhaust system is restricted, the engine will be low on power yet smooth. Common causes of **restricted exhaust** include the following:

- **Clogged catalytic converter.** Always check the ignition and fuel-injection systems for faults that could cause excessive amounts of unburned fuel to be exhausted. Excessive unburned fuel can overheat the catalytic converter and cause the beads or structure of the converter to fuse together, creating the restriction. A defective fuel delivery system could also cause excessive unburned fuel to be dumped into the converter.
- **Clogged or restricted muffler.** This can cause low power. Often a defective catalytic converter will shed particles that can clog a muffler. Broken internal baffles can also restrict exhaust flow.
- **Damaged or defective piping.** This can reduce the power of any engine. Some exhaust pipe is constructed with double walls, and the inside pipe can collapse and form a restriction that is not visible on the outside of the exhaust pipe.

**FIGURE 10–27** A technician-made adapter used to test exhaust system back pressure.

**FIGURE 10–28** A tester that uses a blue liquid to check for exhaust gases in the exhaust, which would indicate a head gasket leak problem.

## TESTING BACK PRESSURE WITH A VACUUM GAUGE

A vacuum gauge can be used to measure manifold vacuum at a high idle (2,000 to 2,500 RPM). If the exhaust system is restricted, pressure increases in the exhaust system. This pressure is called **back pressure.** Manifold vacuum will drop gradually if the engine is kept at a constant speed if the exhaust is restricted.

The reason the vacuum will drop is that all exhaust leaving the engine at the higher engine speed cannot get through the restriction. After a short time (within 1 minute), the exhaust tends to "pile up" above the restriction and eventually remains in the cylinder of the engine at the end of the exhaust stroke. Therefore, at the beginning of the intake stroke, when the piston traveling downward should be lowering the pressure (raising the vacuum) in the intake manifold, the extra exhaust in the cylinder *lowers* the normal vacuum. If the exhaust restriction is severe enough, the vehicle can become undriveable because cylinder filling cannot occur except at idle.

## TESTING BACK PRESSURE WITH A PRESSURE GAUGE

Exhaust system back pressure can be measured directly by installing a pressure gauge into an exhaust opening. This can be accomplished in one of the following ways:

- **With an oxygen sensor.** Use a back pressure gauge and adapter or remove the inside of an old, discarded oxygen sensor and thread in an adapter to convert to a vacuum or pressure gauge.

**NOTE: An adapter can be easily made by inserting a metal tube or pipe. A short section of brake line works great. The pipe can be brazed to the oxygen sensor housing or it can be glued in with epoxy. An 18-millimeter compression gauge adapter can also be adapted to fit into the oxygen sensor opening.** ● **SEE FIGURE 10–27.**

- **With the exhaust gas recirculation (EGR) valve.** Remove the EGR valve and fabricate a plate to connect to a pressure gauge.

- **With the air-injection reaction (AIR) check valve.** Remove the check valve from the exhaust tubes leading down to the exhaust manifold. Use a rubber cone with a tube inside to seal against the exhaust tube. Connect the tube to a pressure gauge.

At idle, the maximum back pressure should be less than 1.5 PSI (10 kPa), and it should be less than 2.5 PSI (15 kPa) at 2,500 RPM.

## DIAGNOSING HEAD GASKET FAILURE

Several items can be used to help diagnose a head gasket failure:

- **Exhaust gas analyzer.** With the radiator cap removed, place the probe from the exhaust analyzer above the radiator filler neck. If the HC reading increases, the exhaust (unburned hydrocarbons) is getting into the coolant from the combustion chamber.

- **Chemical test.** A chemical tester using blue liquid is also available. The liquid turns yellow if combustion gases are present in the coolant. ● **SEE FIGURE 10–28.**

- **Bubbles in the coolant.** Remove the coolant pump belt to prevent pump operation. Remove the radiator cap and start the engine. If bubbles appear in the coolant before it begins to boil, a defective head gasket or cracked cylinder head is indicated.
- **Excessive exhaust steam.** If excessive water or steam is observed coming from the tailpipe, this means that coolant is getting into the combustion chamber from a defective head gasket or a cracked head. If there is leakage between cylinders, the engine usually misfires and a power balancer test and/or compression test can be used to confirm the problem.

If any of the preceding indicators of head gasket failure occur, remove the cylinder head(s) and check all of the following:

1. Head gasket
2. Sealing surfaces—for warpage
3. Castings—for cracks

**NOTE: A leaking thermal vacuum valve can cause symptoms similar to those of a defective head gasket. Most thermal vacuum valves thread into a coolant passage, and they often leak only after they get hot.**

## DASH WARNING LIGHTS

Most vehicles are equipped with several dash warning lights often called "telltale" or "idiot" lights. These lights are often the only warning a driver receives that there may be engine problems. A summary of typical dash warning lights and their meanings follows.

**OIL (ENGINE) LIGHT**    The red oil light indicates that the engine oil pressure is too low (usually lights when oil pressure is 4 to 7 PSI [20 to 50 kPa]). Normal oil pressure should be 10 to 60 PSI (70 to 400 kPa) or 10 PSI per 1,000 engine RPM.

When this light comes on, the driver should shut off the engine immediately and check the oil level and condition for possible dilution with gasoline caused by a fuel system fault. If the oil level is okay, then there is a possible serious engine problem or a possible defective oil pressure sending (sender) unit. The automotive technician should always check the oil pressure using a reliable mechanical oil pressure gauge if low oil pressure is suspected.

**NOTE: Some automobile manufacturers combine the dash warning lights for oil pressure and coolant temperature into one light, usually labeled "engine." Therefore, when the engine light comes on, the technician should check for possible coolant temperature and/or oil pressure problems.**

**COOLANT TEMPERATURE LIGHT**    Most vehicles are equipped with a coolant temperature gauge or dash warning light. The warning light may be labeled "coolant," "hot," or "temperature." If the coolant temperature warning light comes on during driving, this usually indicates that the coolant temperature is above a safe level, or above about 250°F (120°C). Normal coolant temperature should be about 200° to 220°F (90° to 105°C).

If the coolant temperature light comes on during driving, the following steps should be followed to prevent possible engine damage:

1. Turn off the air conditioning and turn on the heater. The heater will help get rid of some of the heat in the cooling system.
2. Raise the engine speed in neutral or park to increase the circulation of coolant through the radiator.
3. If possible, turn the engine off and allow it to cool (this may take over an hour).
4. Do not continue driving with the coolant temperature light on (or the gauge reading in the red warning section or above 260°F), or serious engine damage may result.

**NOTE: If the engine does not feel or smell hot, it is possible that the problem is a faulty coolant temperature sensor or gauge.**

 **TECH TIP**

**Misfire Diagnosis**
If a misfire goes away with propane added to the air inlet, suspect a lean injector.

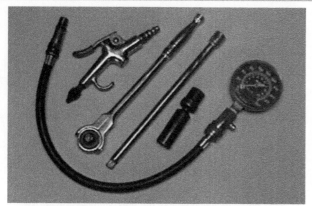

**1** The tools and equipment needed to perform a compression test include a compression gauge, an air nozzle, and the socket ratchets and extensions that may be necessary to remove the spark plugs from the engine.

**2** To prevent ignition and fuel-injection operation while the engine is being cranked, remove both the fuel-injection fuse and the ignition fuse. If the fuses cannot be removed, disconnect the wiring connectors for the injectors and the ignition system.

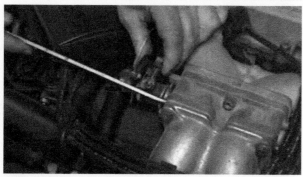

**3** Block open the throttle (and choke if the engine is equipped with a carburetor). Here a screwdriver is being used to wedge the throttle linkage open. Keeping the throttle open ensures that enough air will be drawn into the engine so that the compression test results will be accurate.

**4** Before removing the spark plugs, use an air nozzle to blow away any dirt that may be around the spark plug. This step helps prevent debris from getting into the engine when the spark plugs are removed.

**5** Remove all of the spark plugs. Be sure to mark the spark plug wires so that they can be reinstalled onto the correct spark plugs after the compression test has been performed.

**6** Select the proper adapter for the compression gauge. The threads on the adapter should match those on the spark plug.

CONTINUED ▶

**7** If necessary, connect a battery charger to the battery before starting the compression test. It is important that consistent cranking speed be available for each cylinder being tested.

**8** Make a note of the reading on the gauge after the first "puff," which indicates the first compression stroke that occurred on that cylinder as the engine was being rotated. If the first puff reading is low and the reading gradually increases with each puff, weak or worn piston rings may be indicated.

**9** After the engine has been cranked for four "puffs," stop cranking the engine and observe the compression gauge.

**10** Record the first puff and this final reading for each cylinder. The final readings should all be within 20% of each other.

**11** If a cylinder(s) is lower than most of the others, use an oil can and squirt two squirts of engine oil into the cylinder and repeat the compression test. This is called performing a wet compression test.

**12** If the gauge reading is now much higher than the first test results, then the cause of the low compression is due to worn or defective piston rings. The oil in the cylinder temporarily seals the rings which causes the higher reading.

## SUMMARY

1. The first step in diagnosing engine condition is to perform a thorough visual inspection, including a check of oil and coolant levels and condition.

2. Oil leaks can be found by using a white powder or a fluorescent dye and a black light.

3. Many engine-related problems make a characteristic noise.

4. A compression test can be used to test the condition of valves and piston rings.

5. A cylinder leakage test fills the cylinder with compressed air, and the gauge indicates the percentage of leakage.

6. A cylinder balance test indicates whether all cylinders are working equally.

7. Testing engine vacuum is another procedure that can help the service technician determine engine condition.

## REVIEW QUESTIONS

1. Describe the visual checks that should be performed on an engine if a mechanical malfunction is suspected.

2. List three simple items that could cause excessive oil consumption.

3. List three simple items that could cause engine noises.

4. Describe how to perform a compression test and how to determine what is wrong with an engine based on a compression test result.

5. Describe the cylinder leakage test.

6. Describe how a vacuum gauge would indicate if the valves were sticking in their guides.

7. Describe the test procedure for determining if the exhaust system is restricted (clogged) using a vacuum gauge.

## CHAPTER QUIZ

1. Technician A says that the paper test could detect a burned valve. Technician B says that a grayish white stain on the engine could be a coolant leak. Which technician is correct?
   a. Technician A only
   b. Technician B only
   c. Both Technicians A and B
   d. Neither Technician A nor B

2. Two technicians are discussing oil leaks. Technician A says that an oil leak can be found using a fluorescent dye in the oil with a black light to check for leaks. Technician B says that a white spray powder can be used to locate oil leaks. Which technician is correct?
   a. Technician A only
   b. Technician B only
   c. Both Technicians A and B
   d. Neither Technician A nor B

3. Which of the following is the *least likely* to cause an engine noise?
   a. Carbon on the pistons
   b. Cracked exhaust manifold
   c. Loose accessory drive belt
   d. Vacuum leak

4. A good engine should produce how much compression during a running (dynamic) compression test at idle?
   a. 150–200 PSI
   b. 100–150 PSI
   c. 60–90 PSI
   d. 30–60 PSI

5. A smoothly operating engine depends on _____.
   a. High compression on most cylinders
   b. Equal compression between cylinders
   c. Cylinder compression levels above 100 PSI (700 kPa) and within 70 PSI (500 kPa) of each other
   d. Compression levels below 100 PSI (700 kPa) on most cylinders

6. A good reading for a cylinder leakage test would be _____.
   a. Within 20% between cylinders
   b. All cylinders below 20% leakage
   c. All cylinders above 20% leakage
   d. All cylinders above 70% leakage and within 7% of each other

7. Technician A says that during a power balance test, the cylinder that causes the biggest RPM drop is the weak cylinder. Technician B says that if one spark plug wire is grounded out and the engine speed does not drop, a weak or dead cylinder is indicated. Which technician is correct?
   a. Technician A only
   b. Technician B only
   c. Both Technicians A and B
   d. Neither Technician A nor B

8. *Cranking* vacuum should be _____.
   a. 2.5 in. Hg or higher
   b. Over 25 in. Hg
   c. 17 to 21 in. Hg
   d. 6 to 16 in. Hg

9. Technician A says that a leaking head gasket can be tested for using a chemical tester. Technician B says that leaking head gasket can be found using an exhaust gas analyzer.
   a. Technician A only
   b. Technician B only
   c. Both Technicians A and B
   d. Neither Technician A nor B

10. The low oil pressure warning light usually comes on _____.
   a. Whenever an oil change is required
   b. Whenever oil pressure drops dangerously low (4 to 7 PSI)
   c. Whenever the oil filter bypass valve opens
   d. Whenever the oil filter antidrainback valve opens

# ON-BOARD DIAGNOSIS

**OBJECTIVES:** **After studying Chapter 11, the reader should be able to:** • Prepare for ASE Engine Performance (A8) certification test content area "D" (Emissions Control Systems Diagnosis and Repair (Including OBD-II)). • Explain the purpose and function of onboard diagnosis. • List the various duties of the diagnostic executive (task master). • List five continuous monitors. • List five noncontinuous monitors.

**KEY TERMS:** California Air Resources Board (CARB) 153 • Component identification (CID) 160 • Comprehensive component monitor (CCM) 154 • Diagnostic executive 154 • Enable criteria 156 • Exponentially weighted moving average (EWMA) monitor 156 • Federal Test Procedure (FTP) 154 • Freeze-frame 154 • Functionality 155 • Malfunction indicator lamp (MIL) 153 • On-board diagnosis (OBD) 153 • Parameter identification (PID) 160 • Rationality 155 • Society of Automotive Engineers (SAE) 157 • Test identification (TID) 160 • Task manager 154

## ON-BOARD DIAGNOSTICS GENERATION-II (OBD-II) SYSTEMS

**PURPOSE AND FUNCTION OF OBD II** During the 1980s, most manufacturers began equipping their vehicles with full-function control systems capable of alerting the driver of a malfunction and of allowing the technician to retrieve codes that identify circuit faults. These early diagnostic systems were meant to reduce emissions and speed up vehicle repair.

The automotive industry calls these systems **On-board Diagnostics (OBDs)**. The **California Air Resources Board (CARB)** developed the first regulation requiring manufacturers selling vehicles in that state to install OBD. OBD Generation I (OBD I) applies to all vehicles sold in California beginning with the 1988 model year. It specifies the following requirements:

1. An instrument panel warning lamp able to alert the driver of certain control system failures, now called a **malfunction indicator lamp (MIL).** ● **SEE FIGURE 11–1.**

2. The system's ability to record and transmit diagnostic trouble codes (DTCs) for emission-related failures.

3. Electronic system monitoring of the HO2S, EGR valve, and evaporative purge solenoid. Although not U.S. EPA required, during this time most manufacturers also equipped vehicles sold outside of California with OBD I.

By failing to monitor the catalytic converter, the evaporative system for leaks, and the presence of engine misfire, OBD I

**FIGURE 11–1** A typical malfunction indicator lamp (MIL) often labeled "check engine" or "service engine soon" (SES).

did not do enough to lower automotive emissions. This led the CARB and the EPA to develop OBD Generation II (OBD II).

**OBD-II OBJECTIVES** Generally, the CARB defines an OBD-II-equipped vehicle by its ability to do the following:

1. Detect component degradation or a faulty emission-related system that prevents compliance with federal emission standards.

2. Alert the driver of needed emission-related repair or maintenance.

3. Use standardized DTCs and accept a generic scan tool.

These requirements apply to all 1996 and later model light-duty vehicles. The Clean Air Act of 1990 directed the EPA to develop new regulations for OBD. The primary purpose of OBD II is emission related, whereas the primary purpose of OBD I (1988) was to detect faults in sensors or sensor circuits. OBD-II regulations require that not only sensors be tested but also all exhaust emission control devices and that they be verified for proper operation.

All new vehicles must pass the **Federal Test Procedure (FTP)** for exhaust emissions while being tested for 1874 seconds on dynamometer rollers that simulate the urban drive cycle around downtown Los Angeles.

**NOTE: IM 240 is simply a shorter 240-second version of the 1874-second federal test procedure.**

The regulations for OBD-II vehicles state that the vehicle computer must be capable of testing for, and determining, if the exhaust emissions are within 1.5 times the FTP limits. To achieve this goal, the computer must do the following:

1. Test all exhaust emission system components for correct operation.
2. Actively operate the system and measure the results.
3. Continuously monitor all aspects of the engine operation to be certain that the exhaust emissions do not exceed 1.5 times the FTP limit.
4. Check engine operation for misfire.
5. Turn on the MIL (check engine) if the computer senses a fault in a circuit or system.
6. Record a **freeze-frame,** which is a snapshot of all key engine data at the time the DTC was set.
7. Flash the MIL if an engine misfire occurs that could damage the catalytic converter.

## DIAGNOSTIC EXECUTIVE AND TASK MANAGER

On OBD-II systems, the powertrain control module (PCM) incorporates a special segment of software. On Ford and GM systems, this software is called the **diagnostic executive.** On Chrysler systems, it is called the **task manager.** This software program is designed to manage the operation of all OBD-II monitors by controlling the sequence of steps necessary to execute the diagnostic tests and monitors.

## MONITORS

A monitor is an organized method of testing a specific part of the system. Monitors are simply tests that the computer performs to evaluate components and systems. If a component or system failure is detected while a monitor is running, a DTC will

be stored and the MIL illuminated during the second trip. The two types of monitors are continuous and noncontinuous.

**CONTINUOUS MONITORS** As required conditions are met, continuous monitors begin to run. These continuous monitors will run for the remainder of the vehicle drive cycle. The three continuous monitors are as follows:

- **Comprehensive component monitor (CCM).** This monitor watches the sensors and actuators in the OBD-II system. Sensor values are constantly compared with known-good values stored in the PCM's memory.

  The CCM is an internal program in the PCM designed to monitor a failure in any electronic component or circuit (including emission-related and non–emission-related circuits) that provide input or output signals to the PCM. The PCM considers that an input or output signal is inoperative when a failure exists because of an open circuit or out-of-range value or if an onboard rationality check fails. If an emission-related fault is detected, the PCM will set a code and activate the MIL (requires two consecutive trips).

  Many PCM sensors and output devices are tested at key-on or immediately after engine start-up. However, some devices are tested by the CCM only after the engine meets certain engine conditions. The number of times the CCM must detect a fault before it will activate the MIL depends upon the manufacturer, but most require two consecutive trips to activate the MIL. The components tested by the CCM include the following:

  Four-wheel-drive low switch

  Brake switch

  Camshaft (CMP) and crankshaft (CKP) sensors

  Clutch switch (manual transmissions/transaxles only)

  Cruise servo switch

  Engine coolant temperature (ECT) sensor

  EVAP purge sensor or switch

  Fuel composition sensor

  Intake air temperature (IAT) sensor

  Knock sensor (KS)

  Manifold absolute pressure (MAP) sensor

  Mass airflow (MAF) sensor

  Throttle-position (TP) sensor

  Transmission temperature sensor

  Transmission turbine speed sensor

  Vacuum sensor

  Vehicle speed (VS) sensor

  EVAP canister purge and EVAP purge vent solenoid

  Idle air control (IAC)

  Ignition control system

  Transmission torque converter clutch solenoid

  Transmission shift solenoids

- **Misfire monitor.** This monitor looks at engine misfire. The PCM uses the information received from the crankshaft position sensor (CKP) to calculate the time between the edges of the reluctor as well as the rotational speed and acceleration. By comparing the acceleration of each firing event, the PCM can determine if a cylinder is not firing correctly.

**Misfire type A.** Upon detection of a misfire type A (200 revolutions), which would cause catalyst damage, the MIL will blink once per second during the actual misfire, and a DTC will be stored.

**Misfire type B.** Upon detection of a misfire type B (1,000 revolutions), which will exceed 1.5 times the EPA federal test procedure (FTP) standard or cause a vehicle to fail an inspection and maintenance tailpipe emissions test, the MIL will illuminate, and a DTC will be stored.

The DTC associated with multiple cylinder misfire for a type A or type B misfire is DTC P0300. The DTCs associated with an individual cylinder misfire for a type A or type B misfire are DTCs P0301, P0302, P0303, P0304, P0305, P0306, P0307, P0308, P0309, and P0310.

■ **Fuel trim monitor.** The PCM continuously monitors short- and long-term fuel trim. Constantly updated adaptive fuel tables are stored in long-term memory (KAM) and used by the PCM for compensation due to wear and aging of the fuel system components. The MIL will illuminate when the PCM determines the fuel trim values have reached and stayed at their limits for too long a period of time.

**NONCONTINUOUS MONITORS** Noncontinuous monitors run (at most) once per vehicle drive cycle. The noncontinuous monitors are as follows:

O2S monitor

O2S heater monitor

Catalyst monitor

EGR monitor

EVAP monitor

Secondary AIR monitor

Transmission monitor

PCV system monitor

Thermostat monitor

Once a noncontinuous monitor has run to completion, it will not be run again until the conditions are met during the next vehicle drive cycle. Also, after a noncontinuous monitor has run to completion, the readiness status on your scan tool will show "complete" or "done" for that monitor. Monitors that have not run to completion will show up on your scanner as "incomplete."

## OBD-II MONITOR INFORMATION

**COMPREHENSIVE COMPONENT MONITOR** The circuits and components covered by the comprehensive component monitor (CCM) do not include those directly monitored by another monitor.

However, OBD-II also requires that inputs from powertrain components to the PCM be tested for **rationality** and that outputs to powertrain components from the PCM be tested for **functionality.** Both inputs and outputs are to be checked electrically. Rationality checks refer to a PCM comparison of input value to values from other sensors to determine if they make sense and are normal (rational):

**Example:**

| | |
|---|---|
| TPS | 3 V |
| MAP | 18 in. Hg |
| RPM | 700 RPM |
| PRNDL | Park |

**NOTE: Comprehensive component monitors are continuous. Therefore, enabling conditions do not apply.**

■ Monitor runs continuously.

■ Monitor includes sensors, switches, relays, solenoids, and PCM hardware.

■ All are checked for opens, shorts-to-ground, and shorts-to-voltage.

■ Inputs are checked for rationality.

■ Outputs are checked for functionality.

■ Most are one-trip DTCs.

■ Freeze-frame is priority 3.

■ Three consecutive good trips are used to extinguish the MIL.

■ Forty warm-up cycles are required to self-erase DTC and freeze-frame.

■ Two minutes run time without reoccurrence of the fault constitutes a "good trip."

**CONTINUOUS RUNNING MONITORS** Continuous monitors run continuously and only stop if they fail and include:

■ Fuel system: rich/lean.

■ Misfire: catalyst damaging/FTP (emissions).

■ Two-trip faults (except early generation catalyst damaging misfire).

■ MIL, DTC, freeze-frame after two consecutive faults.

■ Freeze-frame is priority 2 on first trip.

■ Freeze-frame is priority 4 on maturing trip.

■ Three consecutive good trips in a similar condition window are used to extinguish the MIL.

■ Forty warm-up cycles are used to erase DTC and freeze-frame (80 to erase one-trip failure if similar conditions cannot be met).

**ONCE PER TRIP MONITORS**

■ Monitor runs once per trip, pass or fail.

■ O$_2$ response, O$_2$ heaters, EGR, purge flow EVAP leak, secondary air, catalyst.

■ Two-trip DTCs.

- MIL, DTC, freeze-frame after two consecutive faults.
- Freeze-frame is priority 1 on first trip.
- Freeze-frame is priority 3 on maturing trip.
- Three consecutive good trips are used to extinguish the MIL.
- Forty warm-up cycles are used to erase DTC and freeze-frame.

## EXPONENTIALLY WEIGHTED MOVING AVERAGE (EWMA) MONITORS

The **exponentially weighted moving average (EWMA) monitor** is a mathematical method used to determine performance. This method smooths out any variables in the readings over time and results in a running average. This method is used by some vehicle manufacturers for two monitors.

1. Catalyst monitor.
2. EGR monitor.

## ENABLING CRITERIA

With so many different tests (monitors) to run, the PCM needs an internal director to keep track of when each monitor should run. As mentioned, different manufacturers have different names for this director, such as the diagnostic executive or the task manager. Each monitor has enabling criteria. These criteria are a set of conditions that must be met before the task manager will give the go-ahead for each monitor to run. Most enabling criteria follow simple logic, such as follows:

- The task manager will not authorize the start of the $O_2S$ monitor until the engine has reached operating temperature and the system has entered closed loop.

- The task manager will not authorize the start of the EGR monitor when the engine is at idle because the EGR is always closed at this time.

Because each monitor is responsible for testing a different part of the system, the enabling criteria can differ greatly from one monitor to the next. The task manager must decide when each monitor should run, and in what order, to avoid confusion.

There may be a conflict if two monitors were to run at the same time. The results of one monitor might also be tainted if a second monitor were to run simultaneously. In such cases, the task manager decides which monitor has a higher priority. Some monitors also depend on the results of other monitors before they can run.

A monitor may be classified as pending if a failed sensor or other system fault is keeping it from running on schedule.

The task manager may suspend a monitor if the conditions are not correct to continue. For example, if the catalyst monitor is running during a road test and the PCM detects a misfire, the catalyst monitor will be suspended for the duration of the misfire.

### What is a Drive Cycle?

A drive cycle is a vehicle being driven under specified speed and times that will allow all monitors to run. In other words, the powertrain control module (PCM) is looking at a series of data points representing speed and time and determines from these data points when the conditions are right to perform a monitor or a test of a component. These data points, and therefore the drive cycle, are vehicle specific and are not the same for each vehicle. Some common conditions for a drive cycle to successfully run all of the monitors include:

1. Cold start intake air temperature (IAT) and engine coolant temperature (ECT) close to each other indicating that the engine has cooled to the temperature of the surrounding air temperature.
2. Fuel level within a certain range usually between 15% and 85%.
3. Vehicle speed within a certain speed range for an certain amount of time usually 4 to 12 minutes.
4. Stop and idle for a certain time.

Each monitor requires its own set of parameters needed to run the test and sometimes these conditions cannot be met. For example, some evaporate emissions control (EVAP) systems require a temperature that may not be possible in winter months in a cold climatic area.

A typical universal drive cycle that works for many vehicles includes the following steps.

MIL must be off.

No DTCs present.

Fuel fill between 15% and 85%.

Cold start—Preferred = 8-hour soak at 68°F to 86°F.

Alternative = ECT below 86°F.

**STEP 1** With the ignition off, connect scan tool.
**STEP 2** Start engine and drive between 20 and 30 mph for 22 minutes, allowing speed to vary.
**STEP 3** Stop and idle for 40 seconds, gradually accelerate to 55 mph.
**STEP 4** Maintain 55 mph for 4 minutes using a steady throttle input.
**STEP 5** Stop and idle for 30 seconds, then accelerate to 30 mph.
**STEP 6** Maintain 30 mph for 12 minutes.
**STEP 7** Repeat steps 4 and 5 four times.

Using scan tool, check readiness. Always check service information for the exact drive cycle conditions for the vehicle being serviced for best results.

**TRIP** A trip is defined as a key-on condition that contains the necessary conditions for a particular test to be performed followed by a key-off. These conditions are called the **enable criteria**. For example, for the EGR test to be performed, the engine must be at normal operating temperature and decelerating for a minimum amount of time. Some tests are performed when the engine is cold, whereas others require that the vehicle be cruising at a steady highway speed.

**WARM-UP CYCLE** Once a MIL is deactivated, the original code will remain in memory until 40 warm-up cycles are completed without the fault reappearing. A warm-up cycle is defined as a trip with an engine temperature increase of at least 40°F and where engine temperature reaches at least 160°F (71°C).

**MIL CONDITION: OFF** This condition indicates that the PCM has not detected any faults in an emissions-related component or system or that the MIL circuit is not working.

**MIL CONDITION: ON STEADY** This condition indicates a fault in an emissions-related component or system that could affect the vehicle emission levels.

**MIL CONDITION: FLASHING** This condition indicates a misfire or fuel control system fault that could damage the catalytic converter.

**NOTE: In a misfire condition with the MIL on steady, if the driver reaches a vehicle speed and load condition with the engine misfiring at a level that could cause catalyst damage, the MIL would start flashing. It would continue to flash until engine speed and load conditions caused the level of misfire to subside. Then the MIL would go back to the on-steady condition. This situation might result in a customer complaint of a MIL with an intermittent flashing condition.**

**MIL: OFF** The PCM will turn off the MIL if any of the following actions or conditions occur:

- The codes are cleared with a scan tool.
- Power to the PCM is removed at the battery or with the PCM power fuse for an extended period of time (may be up to several hours or longer).
- A vehicle is driven on three consecutive trips with a warm-up cycle and meets all code set conditions without the PCM detecting any faults.

The PCM will set a code if a fault is detected that could cause tailpipe emissions to exceed 1.5 times the FTP standard; however, the PCM will not deactivate the MIL until the vehicle has been driven on three consecutive trips with vehicle conditions similar to actual conditions present when the fault was detected. This is not merely three vehicle start-ups and trips. It means three trips during which certain engine operating conditions are met so that the OBD-II monitor that found the fault can run again and pass the diagnostic test.

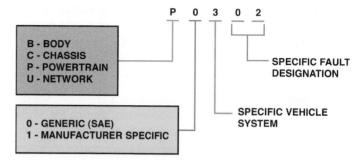

**EXAMPLE: P0302 = CYLINDER #2 MISFIRE DETECTED**

**FIGURE 11–2** OBD-II DTC identification format.

## OBD-II DTC NUMBERING DESIGNATION

A scan tool is required to retrieve DTCs from an OBD-II vehicle. Every OBD-II scan tool will be able to read all generic **Society of Automotive Engineers (SAE)** DTCs from any vehicle. ● **SEE FIGURE 11–2** for definitions and explanations of OBD alphanumeric DTCs. The diagnostic trouble codes (DTCs) are grouped into major categories, depending on the location of the fault on the system involved:

Pxxx codes—powertrain DTCs (engine, transmission-related faults)

Bxxx codes—body DTCs (accessories, interior-related faults)

Cxxx codes—chassis DTCs (suspension and steering-related faults)

Uxxx codes—network DTCs (module communication-related faults)

**DTC NUMBERING EXPLANATION** The number in the hundredth position indicates the specific vehicle system or subgroup that failed. This position should be consistent for P0xxx and P1xxx type codes. The following numbers and systems were established by SAE:

- P0100—Air metering and fuel system fault
- P0200—Fuel system (fuel injector only) fault
- P0300—Ignition system or misfire fault
- P0400—Emission control system fault
- P0500—Idle speed control, vehicle speed (VS) sensor fault
- P0600—Computer output circuit (relay, solenoid, etc.) fault
- P0700—Transaxle, transmission faults

**NOTE: The tens and ones numbers indicate the part of the system at fault.**

**TYPES OF DTCS** Not all OBD-II DTCs are of the same importance for exhaust emissions. Each type of DTC has different requirements for it to set, and the computer will turn on the MIL only for emissions-related DTCs.

**TYPE A CODES** A type A DTC is emission related and will cause the MIL to be turned on the first trip if the computer has detected a problem. Engine misfire or a very rich or lean air–fuel ratio, for example, would cause a type A DTC. These codes alert the driver to an emission problem that may cause damage to the catalytic converter.

**TYPE B CODES** A type B code will be stored, and the MIL will be turned on during the second consecutive trip, alerting the driver to the fact that a diagnostic test was performed and failed.

**NOTE: Type A and B codes are emission-related codes that will cause the lighting of the malfunction indicator lamp (MIL), usually labeled "check engine" or "service engine soon."**

**TYPE C AND D CODES** Type C and D codes are for use with non–emission-related diagnostic tests; they will cause the lighting of a "service" lamp (if the vehicle is so equipped). Type C codes are also called type C1 codes, and D codes are also called type C0 codes.

## DIAGNOSTIC TROUBLE CODE PRIORITY CARB has also mandated that all diagnostic trouble codes (DTCs) be stored according to individual priority. DTCs with a higher priority overwrite those with a lower priority. The OBD-II System DTC Priority is listed here:

Priority 0—Non–emission-related codes

Priority 1—One-trip failure of two-trip fault for non fuel, non misfire codes

Priority 2—One-trip failure of two-trip fault for fuel or misfire codes

Priority 3—Two-trip failure or matured fault of non fuel, non misfire codes

Priority 4—Two-trip failure or matured fault for fuel or misfire codes

## OBD-II FREEZE-FRAME

To assist the service technician, OBD II requires the computer to take a "snapshot" or freeze-frame of all data at the instant an emission-related DTC is set. A scan tool is required to retrieve this data.

**NOTE: Although OBD-II requires that just one freeze-frame of data be stored, the instant an emission-related DTC is set, vehicle manufacturers usually provide expanded data about the DTC beyond that required such as General Motors's *failure recorders*. However, retrieving this enhanced data usually requires the use of the vehicle-specific scan tool.**

Freeze-frame items include the following:

- Calculated load value
- Engine speed (RPM)
- Short-term and long-term fuel trim percent
- Fuel system pressure (on some vehicles)
- Vehicle speed (mph)

- Engine coolant temperature
- Intake manifold pressure
- Closed-open-loop status
- Fault code that triggered the freeze-frame
- If a misfire code is set, identify which cylinder is misfiring

A DTC should not be cleared from the vehicle computer memory unless the fault has been corrected and the technician is so directed by the diagnostic procedure. If the problem that caused the DTC to be set has been corrected, the computer will automatically clear the DTC after 40 consecutive warm-up cycles with no further faults detected (misfire and excessively rich or lean condition codes require 80 warm-up cycles). The codes can also be erased by using a scan tool. ● **SEE CHART 11–1.**

**NOTE: Disconnecting the battery may not erase OBD-II DTCs or freeze-frame data. Most vehicle manufacturers recommend using a scan tool to erase DTCs rather than disconnecting the battery because the memory for the radio, seats, and learned engine operating parameters is lost if the battery is disconnected.**

## ENABLING CONDITIONS

These are the exact engine operating conditions required for a diagnostic monitor to run:

**Example:**

Specific RPM
Specific ECT, MAP, run time, etc.

**PENDING** Under some situations the PCM will not run a monitor if the MIL is illuminated and a fault is stored from another monitor. In these situations, the PCM postpones monitors pending a resolution of the original fault. The PCM does not run the test until the problem is remedied.

For example, when the MIL is illuminated for an oxygen sensor fault, the PCM does not run the catalyst monitor until the oxygen sensor fault is remedied. Since the catalyst monitor is based on signals from the oxygen sensor, running the test would produce inaccurate results.

| MONITOR NAME | MONITOR TYPE (HOW OFTEN IT COMPLETES) | NUMBER OF FAULTS ON SEPARATE TRIPS TO SET A PENDING DTC | NUMBER OF SEPARATE CONSECUTIVE TRIPS TO LIGHT MIL, STORE A DTC | NUMBER OF TRIPS WITH NO FAULTS TO ERASE A MATURING DTC | NUMBER OF TRIPS WITH NO FAULT TO TURN THE MIL OFF | NUMBER OF WARM-UP CYCLES TO ERASE DTC AFTER MIL IS TURNED OFF |
|---|---|---|---|---|---|---|
| CCM | Continuous (when trip conditions allow it) | 1 | 2 | 1 | 3–Trips | 40 |
| Catalyst | Once per drive cycle | 1 | 3 | 1 | 3–OBD-II drive cycle | 40 |
| Misfire type A | Continuous | | 1 | | 3–Similar conditions | 80 |
| Misfire type B | Continuous | 1 | 2 | 1 | 3–Similar conditions | 80 |
| Fuel system | Continuous | 1 | 2 | 1 | 3–Similar conditions | 80 |
| Oxygen sensor | Once per trip | 1 | 2 | 1 | 3–Trips | 40 |
| EGR | Once per trip | 1 | 2 | 1 | 3–Trips | 40 |
| EVAP | Once per trip | 1 | 1 | 1 | 3–Trips | 40 |
| AIR | Once per trip | 1 | 2 | 1 | 3–Trips | 40 |

**CHART 11–1**

PCM Determination of Faults Chart

**CONFLICT**   There are also situations when the PCM does not run a monitor if another monitor is in progress. In these situations, the effects of another monitor running could result in an erroneous failure. If this conflict is present, the monitor is not run until the conflicting condition passes. Most likely, the monitor will run later after the conflicting monitor has passed.

For example, if the fuel system monitor is in progress, the PCM does not run the EGR monitor. Since both tests monitor changes in air–fuel ratio and adaptive fuel compensation, the monitors conflict with each other.

**SUSPEND**   Occasionally, the PCM may not allow a two-trip fault to mature. The PCM will suspend the maturing fault if a condition exists that may induce erroneous failure. This prevents illuminating the MIL for the wrong fault and allows more precise diagnosis.

For example, if the PCM is storing a one-trip fault for the oxygen sensor and the EGR monitor, the PCM may still run the EGR monitor but will suspend the results until the oxygen sensor monitor either passes or fails. At that point, the PCM can determine if the EGR system is actually failing or if an oxygen sensor is failing.

## PCM TESTS

**RATIONALITY TEST**   While input signals to the PCM are constantly being monitored for electrical opens and shorts, they are also tested for rationality. This means that the input signal is compared against other inputs and information to see if it makes sense under the current conditions.

PCM sensor inputs that are checked for rationality include the following:

- MAP sensor
- O$_2$ sensor
- ECT
- Camshaft position sensor (CMP)
- VS sensor
- Crankshaft position sensor (CKP)
- IAT sensor
- TP sensor
- Ambient air temperature sensor
- Power steering switch
- O$_2$ sensor heater
- Engine controller
- Brake switch
- P/N switch (range switch)
- Transmission controls

**FUNCTIONALITY TEST**   A functionality test refers to PCM inputs checking the operation of the outputs:

**Example:**

PCM commands IAC to increase engine speed
PCM monitors engine RPM
Functionality test fails if engine speed does not increase

PCM outputs that are checked for functionality include the following:

- EVAP canister purge solenoid
- EVAP purge vent solenoid
- Cooling fan
- Idle air control solenoid
- Ignition control system
- Transmission torque converter clutch solenoid
- Transmission shift solenoids (A, B, 1–2, etc.)

**ELECTRICAL TEST** Refers to the PCM check of both input and outputs for the following:

- Open
- Shorts
- Ground

### Example:

ECT

Shorted high (input to PCM) above capable voltage; that is, 5-volt sensor with 12-volt input to PCM would indicate a short to voltage.

| Monitor Type | Conditions to Set DTC and Illuminate MIL | Extinguish MIL | Clear DTC Criteria | Applicable DTC |
|---|---|---|---|---|
| Continuous 1-trip monitor | (See note below) Input and output failure—rationally, functionally, electrically | 3 consecutive pass trips | 40 warm-up cycles | P0123 |

**NOTE: The number of times the comprehensive component monitor must detect a fault depends on the vehicle manufacturer. On some vehicles, the comprehensive component monitor will activate the MIL as soon as it detects a fault. On other vehicles, the comprehensive component monitor must fail two times in a row.**

- Freeze-frame captured on first-trip failure.
- Enabling conditions: Many PCM sensors and output devices are tested at key-on or immediately after engine start-up. However, some devices (ECT, idle speed control) are tested by the CCM only after the engine meets particular engine conditions.
- Pending: No pending condition
- Conflict: No conflict conditions
- Suspend: No suspend conditions

## GLOBAL OBD-II

All OBD-II vehicles must be able to display data on a global (also called *generic*) scan tool under nine different modes of operation. These modes include the following:

**Mode One** Current power train data (**parameter identification** display or **PID**)

**Mode Two** Freeze-frame data

**Mode Three** Diagnostic trouble codes

**Mode Four** Clear and reset diagnostic trouble codes (DTCs), freeze-frame data, and readiness status monitors for noncontinuous monitors only

**Mode Five** Oxygen sensor monitor test results

**Mode Six** Onboard monitoring of test results for non-continuously monitored systems

**Mode Seven** Onboard monitoring of test results for continuously monitored systems

**Mode Eight** Bidirectional control of onboard systems

**Mode Nine** Module identification

The global (generic) data is used by most state emission programs. Global OBD-II displays often use hexadecimal numbers, which use 16 numbers instead of 10. The numbers 0 to 9 (zero counts as a number) make up the first 10 and then capital letters A to F complete the 16 numbers. To help identify the number as being in a hexadecimal format, a dollar sign ($) is used in front of the number or letter. See the following conversion chart:

| Decimal Number | Hexadecimal Code |
|:---:|:---:|
| 0 | $0 |
| 1 | $1 |
| 2 | $2 |
| 3 | $3 |
| 4 | $4 |
| 5 | $5 |
| 6 | $6 |
| 7 | $7 |
| 8 | $8 |
| 9 | $9 |
| 10 | $A |
| 11 | $B |
| 12 | $C |
| 13 | $D |
| 14 | $E |
| 15 | $F |

Hexadecimal coding is also used to identify tests (**test identification [TID]** and **component identification [CID]**).

  **FREQUENTLY ASKED QUESTION**

**How Can You Tell Generic from Factory?**

When using a scan tool on an OBD-II-equipped vehicle, if the display asks for make, model, and year, then the factory or enhanced part of the PCM is being accessed. If the generic or global part of the PCM is being scanned, then there is no need to know the vehicle identification details.

# DIAGNOSING PROBLEMS USING MODE SIX

Mode six information can be used to diagnose faults by following three steps:

1. Check the monitor status before starting repairs. This step will show how the system failed.

2. Look at the component or parameter that triggered the fault. This step will help pin down the root cause of the failure.

3. Look to the monitor enable criteria, which will show what it takes to fail or pass the monitor.

Many scan tools display all of the parameters and information needed so that additional mode $06 data is not needed. Many vehicle manufacturers post mode $06 information on the service information websites. This information is often free, unlike other service information. Refer to the National Automotive Service Task Force (NASTF) website for the website address of all vehicle manufacturers' service information sites (*www.NASTF.org*). Two examples include: *http://service.gm.com* (free access to mode $06 information) *www.motorcraftservice.com* (search for mode $06 free access)

## SUMMARY

1. If the MIL is on, retrieve the DTC and follow the manufacturer's recommended procedure to find the root cause of the problem.

2. All monitors must have the enable criteria achieved before a test is performed.

3. OBD-II vehicles use common generic DTCs.

4. OBD-II includes generic (SAE) as well as vehicle manufacturer-specific DTCs and data display.

## REVIEW QUESTIONS

1. What does the PCM do during a trip to test emission-related components?

2. What is the difference between a type A and type B OBD-II DTC?

3. What is the difference between a trip and a warm-up cycle?

4. What could cause the MIL to flash?

## CHAPTER QUIZ

1. A freeze-frame is generated on an OBD-II vehicle _____.
   a. When a type C or D diagnostic trouble code is set
   b. When a type A or B diagnostic trouble code is set
   c. Every other trip
   d. When the PCM detects a problem with the O2S

2. An ignition misfire or fuel mixture problem is an example of what type of DTC?
   a. Type A           c. Type C
   b. Type B           d. Type D

3. The comprehensive component monitor checks computer-controlled devices for _____.
   a. Opens            c. Shorts-to-ground
   b. Rationality      d. All of the above

4. OBD-II has been on all passenger vehicles in the United States since _____.
   a. 1986             c. 1996
   b. 1991             d. 2000

5. Which is a continuous monitor?
   a. Fuel system monitor    c. Oxygen sensor monitor
   b. EGR monitor            d. Catalyst monitor

6. DTC P0302 is a _____.
   a. Generic DTC
   b. Vehicle manufacturer–specific DTC
   c. Idle speed–related DTC
   d. Transmission/transaxle-related DTC

7. Global (generic) OBD-II contains some data in what format?
   a. Plain English          c. Roman numerals
   b. Hexadecimal            d. All of the above

8. By looking at the way diagnostic trouble codes are formatted, which DTC could indicate that the gas cap is loose or defective?
   a. P0221            c. P0442
   b. P1301            d. P1603

9. The computer will automatically clear a DTC if there are no additional detected faults after _____.
   a. Forty consecutive warm-up cycles
   b. Eighty warm-up cycles
   c. Two consecutive trips
   d. Four key-on/key-off cycles

10. A pending code is set when a fault is detected on _____.
    a. A one-trip fault item
    b. The first fault of a two-trip failure
    c. The catalytic converter efficiency
    d. Thermostat problem (too long to closed-loop status)

# CAN AND NETWORK COMMUNICATIONS

**OBJECTIVES: After studying Chapter 12, the reader should be able to:** • Prepare for ASE Electrical/Electronic Systems (A6) certification test content area "A" (General Electrical/Electronic Systems Diagnosis). • Describe the types of networks and serial communications used on vehicles. • Discuss how the networks connect to the data link connector and to other modules. • Explain how to diagnose module communication faults.

**KEY TERMS:** Breakout box (BOB) 173 • BUS 165 • CAN 165 • Chrysler Collision Detection (CCD) 169 • Class 2 165 • E & C 165 • GMLAN 165 • Keyword 165 • Multiplexing 162 • Network 162 • Node 162 • Plastic optical fiber (POF) 173 • Programmable controller interface (PCI) 170 • Protocol 165 • Serial communications interface (SCI) 170 • Serial data 162 • Splice pack 163 • Standard corporate protocol (SCP) 168 • State of health (SOH) 174 • SWCAN 166 • Terminating resistors 174 • Twisted pair 162 • UART 165 • UART-based protocol (UBP) 168

## MODULE COMMUNICATIONS AND NETWORKS

**NEED FOR NETWORK** Since the 1990s, vehicles have used modules to control the operation of most electrical components. A typical vehicle will have 10 or more modules and they communicate with each other over data lines or hard wiring, depending on the application.

**ADVANTAGES** Most modules are connected together in a network because of the following advantages:

- A decreased number of wires are needed, thereby saving weight and cost, as well as helping with installation at the factory and decreased complexity, making servicing easier.

- Common sensor data can be shared with those modules that may need the information, such as vehicle speed, outside air temperature, and engine coolant temperature.
  ● **SEE FIGURE 12–1.**

## NETWORK FUNDAMENTALS

**MODULES AND NODES** Each module, also called a **node,** must communicate to other modules. For example, if the driver depresses the window-down switch, the power window switch sends a window-down message to the body control module. The body control module then sends the request to the driver's side window module. This module is responsible for actually performing the task by supplying power and ground to the window lift motor in the current polarity to cause the window to go down. The module also contains a circuit that monitors the current flow through the motor and will stop and/or reverse the window motor if an obstruction causes the window motor to draw more than the normal amount of current.

**TYPES OF COMMUNICATION** The types of communications include the following:

- **Differential.** In the differential form of module communication, a difference in voltage is applied to two wires, which are twisted to help reduce electromagnetic interference (EMI). These transfer wires are called a **twisted pair.**

- **Parallel.** In the parallel type of module communication, the send and receive signals are on different wires.

- **Serial data.** The **serial data** is data transmitted over one wire by a series of rapidly changing voltage signals pulsed from low to high or from high to low.

- **Multiplexing.** The process of **multiplexing** involves the sending of multiple signals of information at the same time over a signal wire and then separating the signals at the receiving end.

This system of intercommunication of computers or processors is referred to as a **network.** ● **SEE FIGURE 12–2.**

By connecting the computers together on a communications network, they can easily share information back and forth. This multiplexing has the following advantages:

- Elimination of redundant sensors and dedicated wiring for these multiple sensors

- Reduction of the number of wires, connectors, and circuits

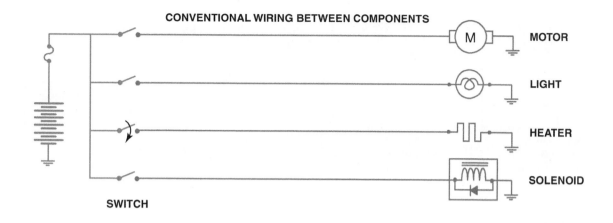

**CONVENTIONAL WIRING BETWEEN COMPONENTS**

MOTOR

LIGHT

HEATER

SOLENOID

SWITCH

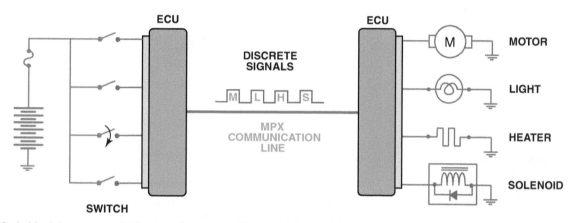

ECU ECU

DISCRETE SIGNALS

MPX COMMUNICATION LINE

MOTOR

LIGHT

HEATER

SOLENOID

SWITCH

**FIGURE 12–1** Module communications makes controlling multiple electrical devices and accessories easier by utilizing simple low-current switches to signal another module, which does the actual switching of the current to the device.

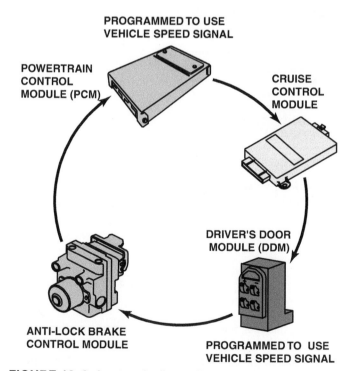

PROGRAMMED TO USE VEHICLE SPEED SIGNAL

POWERTRAIN CONTROL MODULE (PCM)

CRUISE CONTROL MODULE

DRIVER'S DOOR MODULE (DDM)

ANTI-LOCK BRAKE CONTROL MODULE

PROGRAMMED TO USE VEHICLE SPEED SIGNAL

**FIGURE 12–2** A network allows all modules to communicate with other modules.

- Addition of more features and option content to new vehicles
- Weight reduction due to fewer components, wires, and connectors, thereby increasing fuel economy
- Changeable features with software upgrades versus component replacement

## MODULE COMMUNICATIONS CONFIGURATION

The three most common types of networks used on vehicles are the following:

1. **Ring link networks.** In a ring-type network, all modules are connected to each other by a serial data line (in a line) until all are connected in a ring. ● **SEE FIGURE 12–3.**

2. **Star link networks.** In a star link network, a serial data line attaches to each module, and then each is connected to a central point. This central point is called a **splice pack**, abbreviated SP, such as in "SP 306." The splice pack uses a bar to splice all of the serial lines together. Some GM vehicles use two or more splice packs to tie the modules

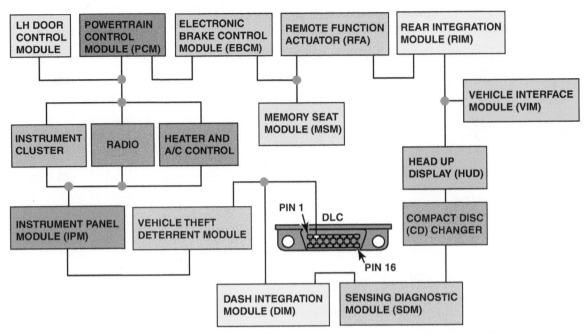

**FIGURE 12–3** A ring link network reduces the number of wires it takes to interconnect all of the modules.

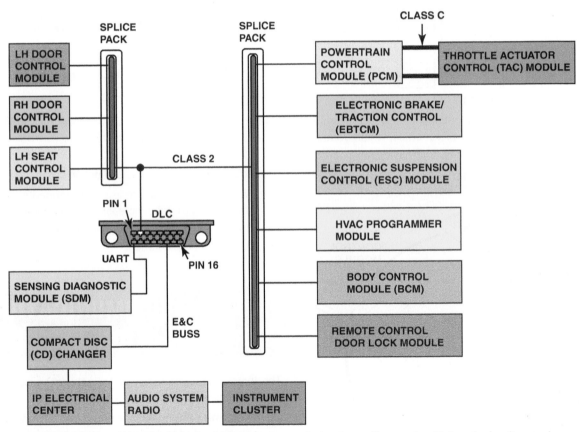

**FIGURE 12–4** In a star link network, all of the modules are connected using splice packs. Network circuits can be easily tested by separating the circuits at the splice packs.

together. When more than one splice pack is used, a serial data line connects one splice pack to the others. In most applications, the BUS bar used in each splice pack can be removed. When the BUS bar is removed, a special tool (J 42236) can be installed in place of the removed BUS bar.

Using this tool, the serial data line for each module can be isolated and tested for a possible problem. Using the special tool at the splice pack makes diagnosing this type of network easier than many others. ● **SEE FIGURE 12–4.**

3. **Ring/star hybrid.** In a ring/star network, the modules are connected using both types of network configurations. Check service information (SI) for details on how this network is connected on the vehicle being diagnosed and always follow the recommended diagnostic steps.

# NETWORK COMMUNICATIONS CLASSIFICATIONS

The Society of Automotive Engineers (SAE) standards include the following three categories of in-vehicle network communications.

**CLASS A** Low-speed networks, meaning less than 10,000 bits per second (bps, or 10 Kbs), are generally used for trip computers, entertainment, and other convenience features.

**CLASS B** Medium-speed networks, meaning 10,000 to 125,000 bps (10 to 125 Kbs), are generally used for information transfer among modules, such as instrument clusters, temperature sensor data, and other general uses.

**CLASS C** High-speed networks, meaning 125,000 to 1,000,000 bps, are generally used for real-time powertrain and vehicle dynamic control. High-speed BUS communication systems now use a **controller area network (CAN).** ● SEE FIGURE 12–5.

# GENERAL MOTORS COMMUNICATIONS PROTOCOLS

**UART** General Motors and others use UART communications for some electronic modules or systems. **UART** is a serial data communications protocol that stands for **universal asynchronous receive and transmit.** UART uses a master control module connected to one or more remote modules. The master

control module is used to control message traffic on the data line by poling all of the other UART modules. The remote modules send a response message back to the master module.

UART uses a fixed pulse-width switching between 0 and 5-V. The UART data BUS operates at a baud rate of 8,192 bps. ● SEE FIGURE 12–6.

## ENTERTAINMENT AND COMFORT COMMUNICATION

The GM **entertainment and comfort (E & C)** serial data is similar to UART but uses a 0- to 12-V toggle. Like UART, the E & C serial data uses a master control module connected to other remote modules, which could include the following:

- Compact disc (CD) player
- Instrument panel (IP) electrical center
- Audio system (radio)
- Heating, ventilation, and air-conditioning (HVAC) programmer and control head
- Steering wheel controls
  ● SEE FIGURE 12–7.

**CLASS 2 COMMUNICATIONS** **Class 2** is a serial communications system that operates by toggling between 0 and 7 V at a transfer rate of 10.4 Kbs. Class 2 is used for most high-speed communications between the powertrain control module (PCM) and other control modules, plus to the scan tool. ● SEE FIGURE 12–8.

**KEYWORD COMMUNICATION** **Keyword** 81, 82, and 2000 serial data are also used for some module-to-module communication on GM vehicles. Keyword data BUS signals are toggled from 0 to 12 V when communicating. The voltage or the data stream is zero volts when not communicating. Keyword serial communication is used by the seat heater module and others but is not connected to the data link connector (DLC). ● SEE FIGURE 12–9.

**GMLAN** General Motors, like all vehicle manufacturers, must use high-speed serial data to communicate with scan tools on all vehicles effective with the 2008 model year. As mentioned, the standard is called controller area network (CAN), which General Motors calls **GMLAN,** which stands for **GM local area network.**

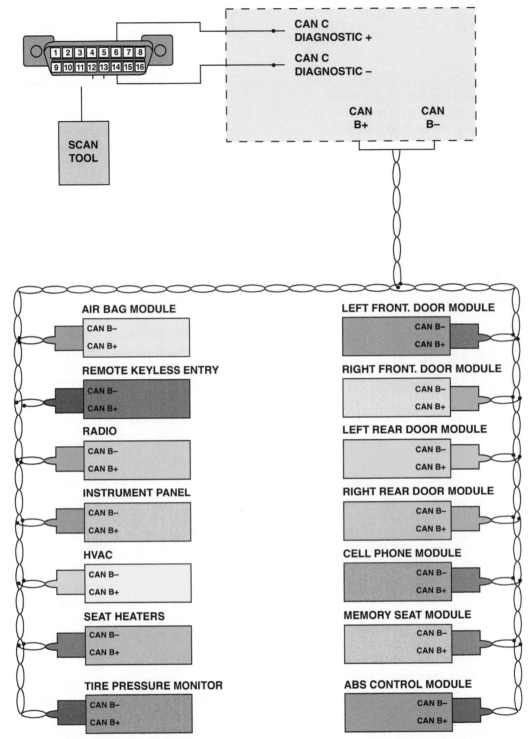

**FIGURE 12–5** A typical BUS system showing module CAN communications and twisted pairs of wire.

General Motors uses two versions of GMLAN.

- **Low-speed GMLAN.** The low-speed version is used for driver-controlled functions such as power windows and door locks. The baud rate for low-speed GMLAN is 33,300 bps. The GMLAN low-speed serial data is not connected directly to the data link connector and uses one wire. The voltage toggles between 0 and 5 V after an

initial 12-V spike, which indicates to the modules to turn on or wake up and listen for data on the line. Low-speed GMLAN is also known as **single-wire CAN,** or **SWCAN.**

- **High-speed GMLAN.** The baud rate is almost real time at 500 Kbs. This serial data method uses a two-twisted-wire circuit that is connected to the data link connector on pins 6 and 14. ● **SEE FIGURE 12–10.**

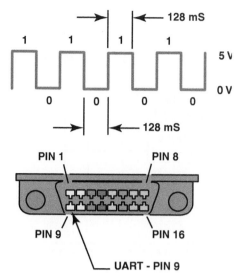

FIGURE 12–6 UART serial data master control module is connected to the data link connector at pin 9.

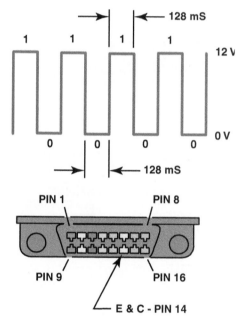

FIGURE 12–7 The E & C serial data is connected to the data link connector (DLC) at pin 14.

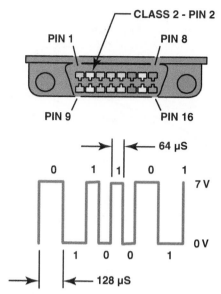

FIGURE 12–8 Class 2 serial data communication is accessible at the data link connector (DLC) at pin 2.

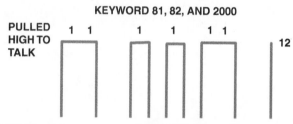

FIGURE 12–9 Keyword 82 operates at a rate of 8,192 bps, similar to UART, and keyword 2000 operates at a baud rate of 10,400 bps (the same as a Class 2 communicator).

## ? FREQUENTLY ASKED QUESTION

### Why Is a Twisted Pair Used?

A twisted pair is where two wires are twisted to prevent electromagnetic radiation from affecting the signals passing through the wires. By twisting the two wires about once every inch (9 to 16 times per foot), the interference is canceled by the adjacent wire.

● SEE FIGURE 12–11.

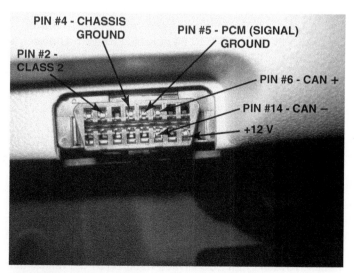

FIGURE 12–10 GMLAN uses pins at terminals 6 and 14.

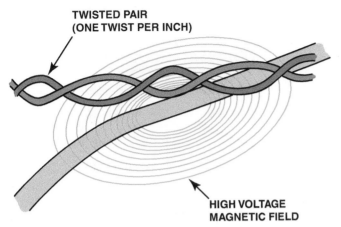

FIGURE 12–11 A twisted pair is used by several different network communications protocols to reduce interference that can be induced in the wiring from nearby electromagnetic sources.

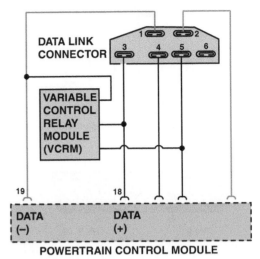

FIGURE 12–13 A Ford OBD-I diagnostic link connector showing that SCP communication uses terminals in cavities 1 (upper left) and 3 (lower left).

FIGURE 12–12 A CANDi module will flash the green LED rapidly if communication is detected.

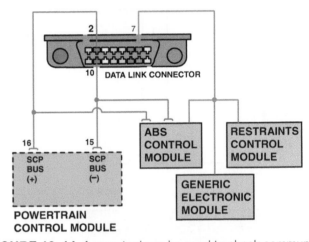

FIGURE 12–14 A scan tool can be used to check communications with the SCP BUS through terminals 2 and 10 and to the other modules connected to terminal 7 of the data link connector (DLC).

A CANDi (CAN diagnostic interface) module is required to be used with the Tech 2 to be able to connect a GM vehicle equipped with GMLAN. ● SEE FIGURE 12–12.

# FORD NETWORK COMMUNICATIONS PROTOCOLS

**STANDARD CORPORATE PROTOCOL** Only a few Fords had scan tool data accessible through the OBD-I data link connector. To identify an OBD-I (1988–1995) on a Ford vehicle that is equipped with **standard corporate protocol (SCP)** and be

able to communicate through a scan tool, look for terminals in cavities 1 and 3 of the DLC. ● SEE FIGURE 12–13.

SCP uses the J-1850 protocol and is active with the key on. The SCP signal is from 4 V negative to 4.3 V positive, and a scan tool does not have to be connected for the signal to be detected on the terminals. OBD-II (EECV) Ford vehicles use terminals 2 (positive) and 10 (negative) of the 16-pin data link connector (DLC) for network communication, using the SCP module communications.

**UART-BASED PROTOCOL** Newer Fords use the CAN for scan tool diagnosis but still retain SCP and **UART-based protocol (UBP)** for some modules. ● SEE FIGURES 12–14 AND 12–15.

### What Are U Codes?

The U diagnostic trouble codes were at first "undefined" but are now network-related codes. Use the network codes to help pinpoint the circuit or module that is not working correctly.

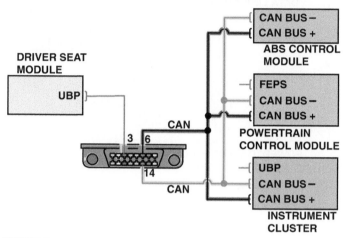

**FIGURE 12–15** Many Fords use UBP module communications along with CAN.

# CHRYSLER COMMUNICATIONS PROTOCOLS

**CCD** Since the late 1980s, the **Chrysler Collision Detection (CCD)** multiplex network is used for scan tool and module communications. It is a differential-type communication and uses a twisted pair of wires. The modules connected to the network apply a bias voltage on each wire. CCD, signals are divided into plus and minus (CCD+ and CCD−), and the voltage difference does not exceed 0.02 V. The baud rate is 7,812.5 bps.

**NOTE: The "collision" in the Chrysler Collision detection BUS communications refers to the program that avoids conflicts of information exchange within the BUS and does not refer to airbags or other accident-related circuits of the vehicle.**

The circuit is active without a scan tool command. ● **SEE FIGURE 12–16.**

The modules on the CCD BUS apply a bias voltage on each wire by using termination resistors. ● **SEE FIGURE 12–17.**

The difference in voltage between CCD+ and CCD− is less than 20 mV. For example, using a digital meter with the

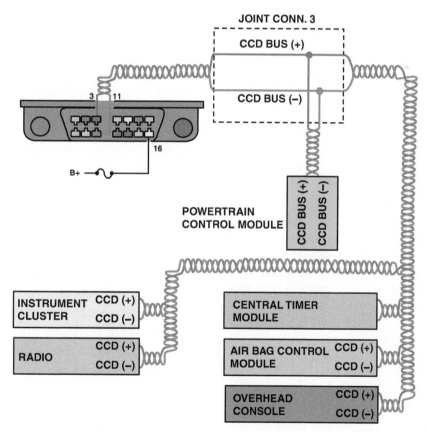

**FIGURE 12–16** CCD signals are labeled plus and minus and use a twisted pair of wires. Notice that terminals 3 and 11 of the data link connector are used to access the CCD BUS from a scan tool. Pin 16 is used to supply 12 volts to the scan tool.

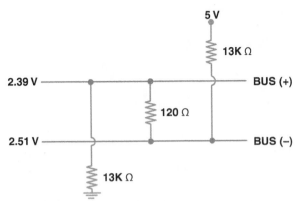

FIGURE 12–17 The differential voltage for the CCD BUS is created by using resistors in a module.

black meter lead attached to ground and the red meter lead attached at the data link connector (DLC), a normal reading could include the following:

- Terminal 3 = 2.45 volts
- Terminal 11 = 2.47 volts

This is an acceptable reading because the readings are 20 mV (0.020 volt) of each other. If both had been exactly 2.5 volts, then this could indicate that the two data lines are shorted together. The module providing the bias voltage is usually the body control module on passenger cars and the front control module on Jeeps and trucks.

## PROGRAMMABLE CONTROLLER INTERFACE
The Chrysler **programmable controller interface (PCI)** is a one-wire communication protocol that connects at the OBD-II DLC at terminal 2. The PCI BUS is connected to all modules on the BUS in a star configuration and operates at a baud rate of 10,200 bps. The voltage signal toggles between 7.5 and 0 V. If this voltage is checked at terminal 2 of the OBD-II DLC, a voltage of about 1 V indicates the average voltage and means that the BUS is functioning and is not shorted-to-ground. PCI and CCD are often used in the same vehicle. ● **SEE FIGURE 12–18.**

## SERIAL COMMUNICATIONS INTERFACE
Chrysler used **serial communications interface (SCI)** for most scan tool and flash reprogramming functions until it was replaced with CAN. SCI is connected at the OBD-II diagnostic link connector (DLC) at terminals 6 (SCI receive) and 7 (SCI transmit). A scan tool must be connected to test the circuit.

## CONTROLLER AREA NETWORK

**BACKGROUND** Robert Bosch Corporation developed the CAN protocol, which was called CAN 1.2, in 1993. The CAN protocol was approved by the Environmental Protection Agency (EPA)

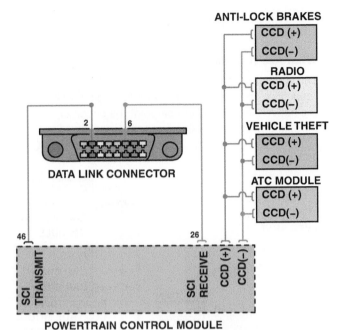

FIGURE 12–18 Many Chrysler vehicles use both SCI and CCD for module communication.

for 2003 and newer vehicle diagnostics and a legal requirement for all vehicles by 2008. The CAN diagnostic systems use pins 6 and 14 in the standard 16 pin OBD-II (J-1962) connector. Before CAN, the scan tool protocol had been manufacturer specific.

**CAN FEATURES** The CAN protocol offers the following features:

- Faster than other BUS communication protocols
- Cost effective because it is an easier system than others to use
- Less effected by electromagnetic interference (Data is transferred on two wires that are twisted together, called twisted pair, to help reduce EMI interference.)
- Message based rather than address based, making it easier to expand
- No wake-up needed because it is a two-wire system
- Supports up to15 modules plus a scan tool
- Uses a 120-ohm resistor at the ends of each pair to reduce electrical noise
- Applies 2.5 volts on both wires:
  H (high) goes to 3.5 volts when active
  L (low) goes to 1.5 volts when active
  ● **SEE FIGURE 12–19.**

**CAN CLASS A, B, AND C** There are three classes of CAN. and they operate at different speeds. The CAN A, B, and C networks can all be linked using a gateway within the same vehicle. The gateway is usually one of the many modules in the vehicle.

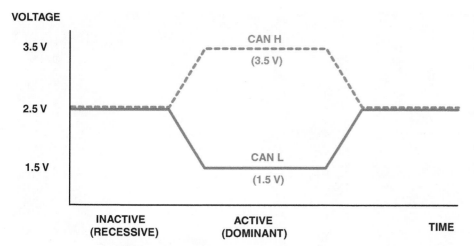

**FIGURE 12–19** CAN uses a differential type of module communication where the voltage on one wire is the equal but opposite voltage on the other wire. When no communication is occurring, both wires have 2.5 volts applied. When communication is occurring, CAN H (high) goes up 1 volt to 3.5 volts, and CAN L (low) goes down 1 volt to 1.5 volts.

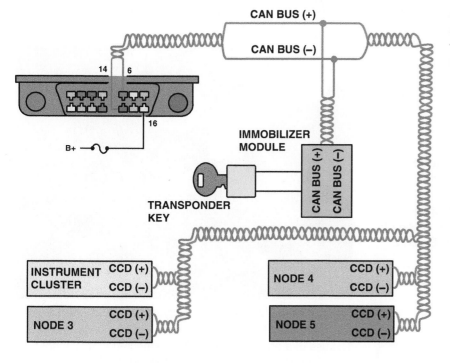

**FIGURE 12–20** A typical (generic) system showing how the CAN BUS is connected to various electrical accessories and systems in the vehicle.

▪ **CAN A.** This class operates on only one wire at slow speeds and is therefore less expensive to build. CAN A operates a data transfer rate of 33.33 Kbs in normal mode and up to 83.33 Kbs during reprogramming mode. CAN A uses the vehicle ground as the signal return circuit.

▪ **CAN B.** This class operates on a two-wire network and does not use the vehicle ground as the signal return circuit. CAN B uses a data transfer rate of 95.2 Kbs. Instead, CAN B (and CAN C) uses two network wires for differential signaling. This means that the two data signal voltages are opposite to each other and used for error detection by constantly being compared. In this case, when the signal voltage at one of the CAN data wires goes high (CAN H), the other one goes low (CAN L), hence the name *differential signaling*. Differential signaling is also used for redundancy in case one of the signal wires shorts out.

▪ **CAN C.** This class is the highest speed CAN protocol with speeds up to 500 Kbs. Beginning with 2008 models, all vehicles sold in the United States must use CAN BUS for scan tool communications. Most vehicle manufacturers started using CAN in older models, and it is easy to determine if a vehicle is equipped with CAN. The CAN BUS communicates to the scan tool through terminals 6 and 14 of the DLC, indicating that the vehicle is equipped with CAN. ● **SEE FIGURE 12–20.**

The total voltage remains constant at all times, and the electromagnetic field effects of the two data BUS lines cancel each other out. The data BUS line is protected against received radiation and is virtually neutral in sending radiation.

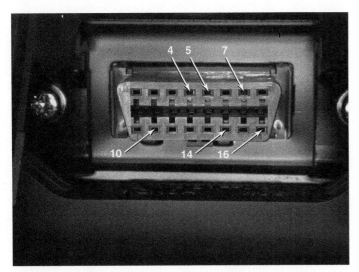

**FIGURE 12–21** A DLC from a pre-CAN Acura. It shows terminals in cavities 4, 5 (grounds), 7, 10, 14, and 16 (B+).

| Code | Status | Description |
|------|--------|-------------|
| BZ107 | Active | Ignition Switch Sense Input Circuit/Performance |
| U0184 | Stored | Lost Communication With Radio |
| U0141 | Stored | Lost Communication With Front Control Module |

**FIGURE 12–22** A Honda scan display showing a B and two U codes, all indicating a BUS-related problem(s).

## HONDA/TOYOTA COMMUNICATIONS

The primary BUS communications on pre-CAN-equipped vehicles is ISO 9141-2 using terminals 7 and 15 at the OBD-II DLC. ● **SEE FIGURE 12–21.**

A factory scan tool or an aftermarket scan tool equipped with enhanced original equipment (OE) software is needed to access many of the BUS messages. ● **SEE FIGURE 12–22.**

## EUROPEAN BUS COMMUNICATIONS

**FIGURE 12–23** A typical 38-cavity diagnostic connector as found on many BMW and Mercedes vehicles under the hood. The use of a breakout box (BOB) connected to this connector can often be used to gain access to module BUS information.

**UNIQUE DIAGNOSTIC CONNECTOR** Many different types of module communications protocols are used on European vehicles such as Mercedes and BMW.

Most of these communication BUS messages cannot be accessed through the data link connector (DLC). To check the operation of the individual modules, a scan tool equipped with factory-type software will be needed to communicate with the module through the gateway module. ● **SEE FIGURE 12–23** for an alternative access method to the modules.

**MEDIA ORIENTED SYSTEM TRANSPORT BUS** The media-oriented system transport (MOST) BUS uses fiber optics for module-to-module communications in a ring or star configuration. This BUS system is currently being used for entertainment equipment data communications for videos, CDs, and other media systems in the vehicle.

**MOTOROLA INTERCONNECT BUS** Motorola interconnect (MI) is a single-wire serial communications protocol, using one master control module and many slave modules. Typical application of the MI BUS protocol is with power and memory mirrors, seats, windows, and headlight levelers.

**DISTRIBUTED SYSTEM INTERFACE BUS** Distributed system interface (DSI) BUS protocol was developed by Motorola and uses a two-wire serial BUS. This BUS protocol is currently being used for safety-related sensors and components.

**BOSCH-SIEMANS-TEMIC BUS** The Bosch-Siemans-Temic (BST) BUS is another system that is used for safety-related components and sensors in a vehicle, such as airbags. The BST BUS is a two-wire system and operates up to 250,000 bps.

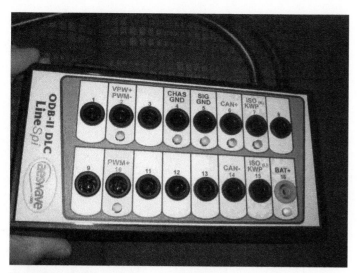

**FIGURE 12–24** A breakout box (BOB) used to access the BUS terminals while using a scan tool to activate the modules. This breakout box is equipped with LEDs that light when circuits are active.

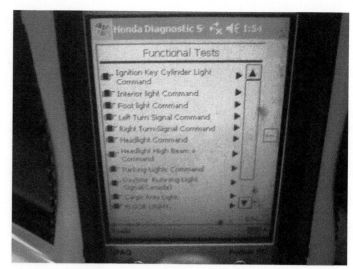

**FIGURE 12–25** This Honda scan tool allows the technician to turn on individual lights and operate individual power windows and other accessories that are connected to the BUS system.

---

**? FREQUENTLY ASKED QUESTION**

**How Do You Know What System Is Used?**

Use service information to determine which network communication protocol is used. However, because of the various systems on some vehicles, it may be easier to look at the data link connection to determine the system. All OBD-II vehicles have terminals in the following cavities:

Terminal 4: chassis ground

Terminal 5: computer (signal) ground

Terminal 16: 12 V positive

The terminals in cavities 6 and 14 mean that this vehicle is equipped with CAN as the only module communication protocol available at the DLC. To perform a test of the BUS, use a **breakout box (BOB)** to gain access to the terminals while connecting to the vehicle, using a scan tool. ● **SEE FIGURE 12–24** or a typical OBD-II connector breakout box.

**BYTEFLIGHT BUS** The byteflight BUS is used in safety critical systems, such as airbags, and uses the time division multiple access (TDMA) protocol, which operates at 10 million bps using a **plastic optical fiber (POF).**

**FLEXRAY BUS** FlexRay BUS is a version of byteflight and is a high-speed serial communication system for in-vehicle networks. FlexRay is commonly used for steer-by-wire and brake-by-wire systems.

**DOMESTIC DIGITAL BUS** The domestic digital BUS, commonly designated D2B, is an optical BUS system connecting audio, video, computer, and telephone components in a single-ring structure with a speed of up to 5,600,000 bps.

**LOCAL INTERCONNECT NETWORK BUS** Local interconnect network (LIN) is a BUS protocol used between intelligent sensors and actuators and has a BUS speed of 19,200 bps.

## NETWORK COMMUNICATIONS DIAGNOSIS

**STEPS TO FINDING A FAULT** When a network communications fault is suspected, perform the following steps:

**STEP 1** **Check everything that does and does not work.** Often accessories that do not seem to be connected can help identify which module or BUS circuit is at fault.

**STEP 2** **Perform module status test.** Use a factory-level scan tool or an aftermarket scan tool equipped with enhanced software that allows OE-like functions. Check if the components or systems can be operated through the scan tool. ● **SEE FIGURE 12–25.**

■ **Ping modules.** Start the Class 2 diagnosis by using a scan tool and select *diagnostic circuit check*. If no diagnostic trouble codes (DTCs) are shown, there could be a communication problem. Select

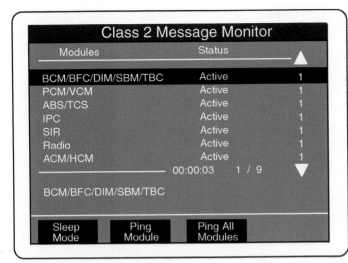

FIGURE 12–26 Modules used in a General Motors vehicle can be "pinged" using a Tech 2 scan tool.

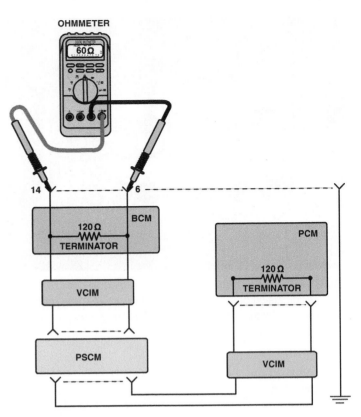

FIGURE 12–27 Checking the terminating resistors using an ohmmeter at the DLC.

### TECH TIP

**No Communication? Try Bypass Mode.**

If a Tech 2 scan tool shows "no communication," try using the bypass mode to see what should be on the data display. To enter bypass mode, perform the following steps:

**STEP 1** Select tool option (F3).

**STEP 2** Set communications to bypass (F5).

**STEP 3** Select enable.

**STEP 4** Input make/model and year of vehicle.

**STEP 5** Note all parameters that should be included, as shown. The values will not be shown.

*message monitor,* which will display the status of all of the modules on the Class 2 BUS circuit. The modules that are awake will be shown as active and the scan tool can be used to ping individual modules or command all modules. The ping command should change the status from "active" to "inactive." ● **SEE FIGURE 12–26.**

NOTE: If an excessive parasitic draw is being diagnosed, use a scan tool to ping the modules in one way to determine if one of the modules is not going to sleep and causing the excessive battery drain.

■ **Check state of health.** All modules on the Class 2 BUS circuit have at least one other module responsible for reporting **state of health (SOH).** If a module fails to send a state of health message within five seconds, the companion module will set a diagnostic trouble code for the module that did not respond. The defective module is not capable of sending this message.

**STEP 3** **Check the resistance of the terminating resistors.** Most high-speed BUS systems use resistors at each end, called **terminating resistors.** These resistors are used to help reduce interference into other systems in the vehicle. Usually two 120-ohm resistors are installed at each end and are therefore connected electrically in parallel. Two 120-ohm resistors connected in parallel would measure 60 ohms if being tested using an ohmmeter. ● **SEE FIGURE 12–27.**

**STEP 4** **Check data BUS for voltages.** Use a digital multimeter set to DC volts to monitor communications and check the BUS for proper operation. Some BUS conditions and possible causes include the following:

■ **Signal is zero volt all of the time.** Check for short-to-ground by unplugging modules one at a time to check if one module is causing the problem.

■ **Signal is high or 12 volts all of the time.** The BUS circuit could be shorted to 12 V. Check with the customer to see if any service or body repair work was done recently. Try unplugging each module one at a time to pin down which module is causing the communications problem.

■ **A variable voltage usually indicates that messages are being sent and received.** CAN and Class 2 can be identified by looking at the data link connector (DLC) for a terminal in cavity number 2. Class 2 is active all of the time the ignition is on, and therefore voltage variation between 0 and 7 V can be measured using a DMM set to read DC volts. ● **SEE FIGURE 12–28.**

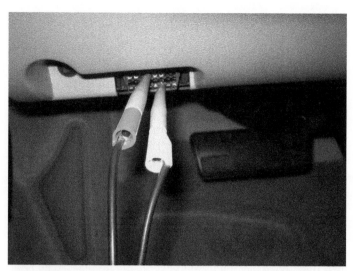

**FIGURE 12–28** Use front-probe terminals to access the data link connector. Always follow the specified back-probe and front-probe procedures as found in service information.

**STEP 5** **Use a digital storage oscilloscope to monitor the waveforms of the BUS circuit.** Using a scope on the data line terminals can show if communication is being transmitted. Typical faults and their causes include the following:

- **Normal operation.** Normal operation shows variable voltage signals on the data lines. It is impossible to know what information is being transmitted, but if there is activity with short sections of inactivity, this indicates normal data line transmission activity. ● **SEE FIGURE 12–29.**
- **High voltage.** If there is a constant high-voltage signal without any change, this indicates that the data line is shorted to voltage.
- **Zero or low voltage.** If the data line voltage is zero or almost zero and not showing any higher voltage signals, then the data line is short-to-ground.

**STEP 6** **Follow factory service information instructions to isolate the cause of the fault.** This step often involves disconnecting one module at a time to see if it is the cause of a short-to-ground or an open in the BUS circuit.

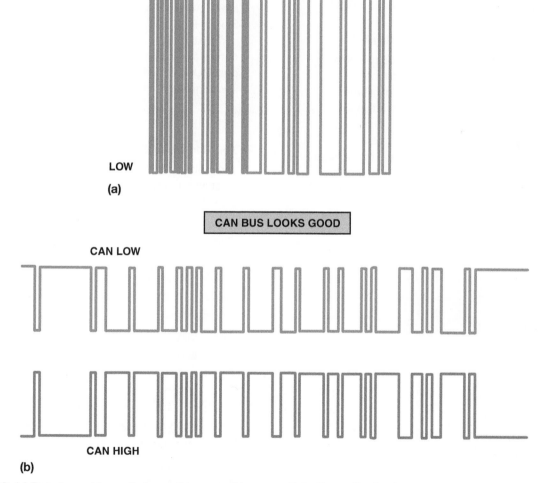

**FIGURE 12–29** (a) Data is sent in packets, so it is normal to see activity then a flat line between messages. (b) A CAN BUS should show voltages that are opposite when there is normal communications. CAN H (high) circuit should go from 2.5 volts at rest to 3.5 volts when active. The CAN L (low) circuit goes from 2.5 volts at rest to 1.5 volts when active.

## REAL WORLD FIX

### The Radio Caused No-Start Story

A 2005 Chevrolet Cobalt did not start. A technician checked with a subscription-based helpline service and discovered that a fault with the Class 2 data circuit could prevent the engine from starting. The advisor suggested that a module should be disconnected one at a time to see if one of them was taking the data line to ground. The two most common components on the Class 2 serial data line that have been known to cause a lack of communication and become shorted-to-ground are the radio and electronic brake control module (EBCM). The first one the technician disconnected was the radio. The engine started and ran. Apparently the Class 2 serial data line was shorted-to-ground inside the radio, which took the entire BUS down. When BUS communication is lost, the PCM is not able to energize the fuel pump, ignition, or fuel injectors so the engine would not start. The radio was replaced to solve the no-start condition.

## ? FREQUENTLY ASKED QUESTION

### Which Module Is the Gateway Module?

The gateway module is responsible for communicating with other modules and acts as the main communications module for scan tool data. Most General Motors vehicles use the body control module (BCM) or the instrument panel control (IPC) module as the gateway. To verify which module is the gateway, check the schematic and look for one that has voltage applied during all of the following conditions:

• Key on, engine off
• Engine cranking
• Engine running

## OBD-II DATA LINK CONNECTOR

All OBD-II vehicles use a 16-pin connector that includes the following:

Pin 4 = chassis ground
Pin 5 = signal ground
Pin 16 = battery power (4 A max)
● SEE FIGURE 12–30.

### GENERAL MOTORS VEHICLES

■ SAE J-1850 (VPW, Class 2, 10.4 Kbs) standard, which uses pins 2, 4, 5, and 16 but not 10

---

| PIN NO. | ASSIGNMENTS |
|---|---|
| 1. | MANUFACTURER'S DISCRETION |
| 2. | BUS + LINE, SAE J1850 |
| 3. | MANUFACTURER'S DISCRETION |
| 4. | CHASSIS GROUND |
| 5. | SIGNAL GROUND |
| 6. | MANUFACTURER'S DISCRETION |
| 7. | K LINE, ISO 9141 |
| 8. | MANUFACTURER'S DISCRETION |
| 9. | MANUFACTURER'S DISCRETION |
| 10. | BUS – LINE, SAE J1850 |
| 11. | MANUFACTURER'S DISCRETION |
| 12. | MANUFACTURER'S DISCRETION |
| 13. | MANUFACTURER'S DISCRETION |
| 14. | MANUFACTURER'S DISCRETION |
| 15. | L LINE, ISO 9141 |
| 16. | VEHICLE BATTERY POSITIVE (4A MAX) |

**OBD-II DLC**

**FIGURE 12–30** A 16-pin OBD-II DLC with terminals identified. Scan tools use the power pin (16) and ground pin (4) for power so that a separate cigarette lighter plug is not necessary on OBD-II vehicles.

## 🔧 TECH TIP

### Check Computer Data Line Circuit Schematic

Many General Motors vehicles use more than one type of BUS communications protocol. Check service information (SI) and look at the schematic for computer data line circuits, which should show all of the data BUSes and their connectors to the diagnostic link connector (DLC). ● SEE FIGURE 12–31.

■ GM Domestic OBD-II

Pin 1 and 9: CCM (comprehensive component monitor) slow baud rate, 8,192 UART
Pins 2 and 10: OEM enhanced, fast rate, 40,500 baud rate
Pins 7 and 15: generic OBD-II, ISO 9141, 10,400 baud rate
Pins 6 and 14: GMLAN

## ASIAN, CHRYSLER, AND EUROPEAN VEHICLES

■ ISO 9141-2 standard, which uses pins 4, 5, 7, 15, and 16
■ Chrysler Domestic Group OBD-II

Pins 2 and 10: CCM
Pins 3 and 14: OEM enhanced, 60,500 baud rate
Pins 7 and 15: generic OBD-II, ISO 9141, 10,400 baud rate

## FORD VEHICLES

■ SAE J-1850 (PWM, 41.6 Kbs) standard, which uses pins 2, 4, 5, 10, and 16
■ Ford Domestic OBD-II

Pins 2 and 10: CCM
Pins 6 and 14: OEM enhanced, Class C, 40,500 baud rate
Pins 7 and 15: generic OBD-II, ISO 9141, 10,400 baud rate

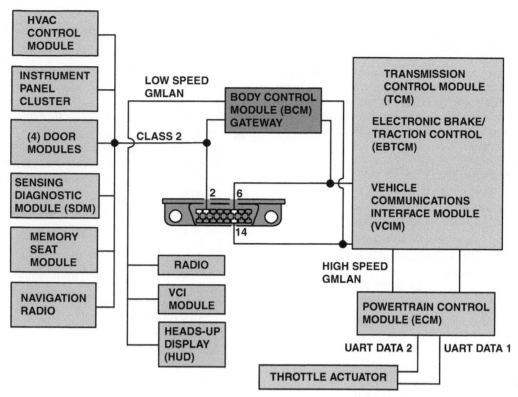

**FIGURE 12–31** This schematic of a Chevrolet Equinox shows that the vehicle uses a GMLAN BUS (DLC pins 6 and 14), plus a Class 2 (pin 2) and UART.

## SUMMARY

1. The use of a network for module communications reduces the number of wires and connections needed.

2. Module communication configurations include ring link, star link, and ring/star hybrid systems.

3. The SAE communication classifications for vehicle communications systems include Class A (low speed), Class B (medium speed), and Class C (high speed).

4. Various module communications used on General Motors vehicles include UART, E & C, Class 2, keyword communications, and GMLAN (CAN).

5. Types of module communications used on Ford vehicles include SCP, UBP, and CAN.

6. Chrysler brand vehicles use SCI, CCD, PCI, and CAN communications protocols.

7. Many European vehicles use an underhood electrical connector that can be used to access electrical components and modules using a breakout box (BOB) or special tester.

8. Diagnosis of network communications includes checking the terminating resistors and checking for changing voltage signals at the DLC.

## REVIEW QUESTIONS

1. Why is a communication network used?

2. Why are the two wires twisted if used for network communications?

3. Why is a gateway module used?

4. What are U codes?

1. Technician A says that module communications networks are used to reduce the number of wires in a vehicle. Technician B says that a communications network is used to share data from sensors, which can be used by many different modules. Which technician is correct?
   a. Technician A only
   b. Technician B only
   c. Both Technicians A and B
   d. Neither Technician A nor B

2. A module is also known as a _____.
   a. BUS
   b. Node
   c. Terminator
   d. Resistor pack

3. A high-speed CAN BUS communicates with a scan tool through which terminal(s)?
   a. 6 and 14
   b. 2
   c. 7 and 15
   d. 4 and 16

4. UART uses a(n) _____ signal that toggles 0 V.
   a. 5-V
   b. 7-V
   c. 8-V
   d. 12-V

5. GM Class 2 communication toggles between _____.
   a. 5 and 7 V
   b. 0 and 12 V
   c. 7 and 12 V
   d. 0 and 7 V

6. Which terminal of the data link connector does General Motors use for Class 2 communication?
   a. 1
   b. 2
   c. 3
   d. 4

7. GMLAN is the General Motors term for which type of module communication?
   a. UART
   b. Class 2
   c. High-speed CAN
   d. Keyword 2000

8. CAN H and CAN L operate how?
   a. CAN H is at 2.5 volts when not transmitting.
   b. CAN L is at 2.5 volts when not transmitting.
   c. CAN H goes to 3.5 volts when transmitting.
   d. All of the above

9. Which terminal of the OBD-II data link connector is the signal ground for all vehicles?
   a. 1
   b. 3
   c. 4
   d. 5

10. Terminal 16 of the OBD-II data link connector is used for what?
    a. Chassis ground
    b. 12 V positive
    c. Module (signal ground)
    d. Manufacturer's discretion

# chapter 13

# TEMPERATURE SENSORS

**OBJECTIVES:** **After studying Chapter 13, the reader should be able to:** • Prepare for ASE Engine Performance (A8) certification test content area "E" (Computerized Engine Controls Diagnosis and Repair). • Explain the purpose and function of the ECT and IAT temperature sensors. • Describe how to test temperature sensors. • Discuss how automatic fluid temperature sensor values can affect transmission operation.

**KEY TERMS:** Cylinder head temperature (CHT) 187 • Engine coolant temperature (ECT) 179 • Engine fuel temperature (EFT) 187 • Negative temperature coefficient (NTC) 179 • Throttle-body temperature (TBT) 185 • Transmission fluid temperature (TFT) 186

## ENGINE COOLANT TEMPERATURE SENSORS

**PURPOSE AND FUNCTION** Computer-equipped vehicles use an **engine coolant temperature (ECT)** sensor. When the engine is cold, the fuel mixture must be richer to prevent stalling and engine stumble. When the engine is warm, the fuel mixture can be leaner to provide maximum fuel economy with the lowest possible exhaust emissions. Because the computer controls spark timing and fuel mixture, it will need to know the engine temperature. An engine coolant temperature (ECT) sensor screwed into the engine coolant passage will provide the computer with this information. ● **SEE FIGURE 13–1.** This will be the most important (high-authority) sensor while the engine is cold. The ignition timing can also be tailored to engine (coolant) temperature. A hot engine cannot have the spark timing as far advanced as can a cold engine. The ECT sensor is also used as an important input for the following:

- Idle air control (IAC) position
- Oxygen sensor closed-loop status
- Canister purge on/off times
- Idle speed

**ECT SENSOR CONSTRUCTION** Engine coolant temperature sensors are constructed of a semiconductor material that decreases in resistance as the temperature of the sensor increases. Coolant sensors have very high resistance when the coolant is cold and low resistance when the coolant is hot. This is referred to as having a **negative temperature coefficient (NTC),** which is opposite to the situation with most other electrical components. ● **SEE FIGURE 13–2.** Therefore, if the coolant sensor has a poor connection (high resistance) at the wiring connector,

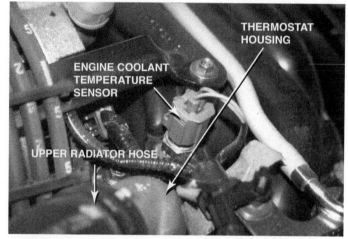

**FIGURE 13–1** A typical engine coolant temperature (ECT) sensor. ECT sensors are located near the thermostat housing on most engines.

the computer will supply a richer-than-normal fuel mixture based on the resistance of the coolant sensor. Poor fuel economy and a possible-rich code can be caused by a defective sensor or high resistance in the sensor wiring. If the sensor was shorted or defective and had too low a resistance, a leaner-than-normal fuel mixture would be supplied to the engine. A too-lean fuel mixture can cause driveability problems and a possible-lean computer code.

**STEPPED ECT CIRCUITS** Some vehicle manufacturers use a step-up resistor to effectively broaden the range of the ECT sensor. Chrysler and General Motors vehicles use the same sensor as a nonstepped ECT circuit but instead apply the sensor voltage through two different resistors:

- When the temperature is cold, usually below 120°F (50°C), the ECT sensor voltage is applied through a high-value resistor inside the PCM.

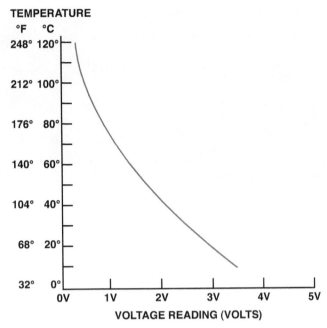

**FIGURE 13–2** A typical ECT sensor temperature versus voltage curve.

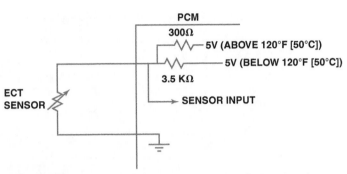

**FIGURE 13–3** A typical two-step ECT circuit showing that when the coolant temperature is low, the PCM applies a 5-volt reference voltage to the ECT sensor through a higher resistance compared to when the temperature is higher.

- When the temperature is warm, usually above 120°F (50°C), the ECT sensor voltage is applied through a much lower resistance value inside the PCM. ● **SEE FIGURE 13–3.**

The purpose of this extra circuit is to give the PCM a more accurate reading of the engine coolant temperature compared to the same sensor with only one circuit. ● **SEE FIGURE 13–4.**

## TESTING THE ENGINE COOLANT TEMPERATURE SENSOR

**TESTING THE ENGINE COOLANT TEMPERATURE BY VISUAL INSPECTION** The correct functioning of the engine coolant temperature (ECT) sensor depends on the following items that should be checked or inspected:

- **Properly filled cooling system.** Check that the radiator reservoir bottle is full and that the radiator itself is filled to the top.

  CAUTION: Be sure that the radiator is cool before removing the radiator cap to avoid being scalded by hot coolant.

  The ECT sensor must be submerged in coolant to be able to indicate the proper coolant temperature.

- **Proper pressure maintained by the radiator cap.** If the radiator cap is defective and cannot allow the cooling system to become pressurized, air pockets could develop. These air pockets could cause the engine to operate at a hotter-than-normal temperature and prevent proper temperature measurement, especially if the air pockets occur around the sensor.

- **Proper antifreeze–water mixture.** Most vehicle manufacturers recommend a 50/50 mixture of antifreeze and water as the best compromise between freezing protection and heat transfer ability.

- **Proper operation of the cooling fan.** If the cooling fan does not operate correctly, the engine may overheat.

**TESTING THE ECT USING A MULTIMETER** Both the resistance (in ohms) and the voltage drop across the sensor can be measured and compared with specifications. ● **SEE FIGURE 13–5.** See the following charts showing examples of typical engine coolant temperature sensor specifications. Some vehicles use the PCM to attach another resistor in the ECT circuit to provide a more accurate measure of the engine temperature. ● **SEE FIGURE 13–6.**

If resistance values match the approximate coolant temperature and there is still a coolant sensor trouble code, the problem is generally in the wiring between the sensor and the computer. Always consult the manufacturer's recommended procedures for checking this wiring. If the resistance values do not match, the sensor may need to be replaced.

| General Motors ECT Sensor with Pull-Up Resistor | | | |
|---|---|---|---|
| °F | °C | Ohms | Voltage Drop Across Sensor |
| −40 | −40 | 100,000+ | 4.95 |
| 18 | −8 | 14,628 | 4.68 |
| 32 | 0 | 9,420 | 4.52 |
| 50 | 10 | 5,670 | 4.25 |
| 68 | 20 | 3,520 | 3.89 |
| 86 | 30 | 2,238 | 3.46 |
| 104 | 40 | 1,459 | 2.97 |
| 122 | 50 | 973 | 2.47 |
| 140 | 60 | 667 | 2.00 |
| 158 | 70 | 467 | 1.59 |
| 176 | 80 | 332 | 1.25 |
| 194 | 90 | 241 | 0.97 |
| 212 | 100 | 177 | 0.75 |

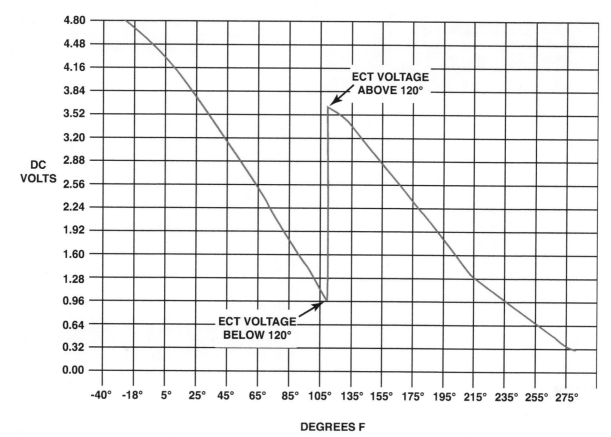

**DEGREES F**

**FIGURE 13-4** The transition between steps usually occurs at a temperature that would not interfere with cold engine starts or the cooling fan operation. In this example, the switch point between the two resistors occurs when the sensor voltage is about 1 volt and rises to about 3.6 volts.

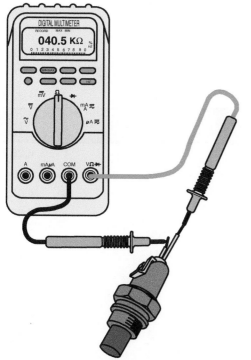

**FIGURE 13-5** Measuring the resistance of the ECT sensor. The resistance measurement can then be compared with specifications.

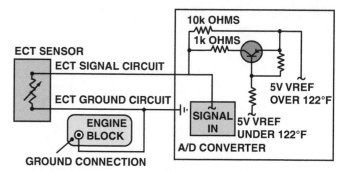

**FIGURE 13-6** When the voltage drop reaches approximately 1.2 volts, the PCM turns on a transistor. The transistor connects a 1-k resistor in parallel with the 10-k resistor. Total circuit resistance now drops to around 909 ohms. This function allows the PCM to have full control at cold temperatures up to approximately 122°F and a second full control at temperatures greater than 122°F.

| General Motors ECT Sensor Without Pull-Up Resistor | | | |
|---|---|---|---|
| °F | °C | Ohms | Voltage Drop Across Sensor |
| −40 | −40 | 100,000 | 5 |
| −22 | −30 | 53,000 | 4.78 |
| −4 | −20 | 29,000 | 4.34 |
| 14 | −10 | 16,000 | 3.89 |
| 32 | 0 | 9,400 | 3.45 |
| 50 | 10 | 5,700 | 3.01 |
| 68 | 20 | 3,500 | 2.56 |
| 86 | 30 | 2,200 | 1.80 |
| 104 | 40 | 1,500 | 1.10 |
| 122 | 50 | 970 | 3.25 |
| 140 | 60 | 670 | 2.88 |
| 158 | 70 | 470 | 2.56 |
| 176 | 80 | 330 | 2.24 |
| 194 | 90 | 240 | 1.70 |
| 212 | 100 | 177 | 1.42 |
| 230 | 110 | 132 | 1.15 |
| 248 | 120 | 100 | .87 |

| Ford ECT Sensor | | | |
|---|---|---|---|
| °F | °C | Resistance ( ) | Voltage (V) |
| 50 | 10 | 58,750 | 3.52 |
| 68 | 20 | 37,300 | 3.06 |
| 86 | 30 | 24,270 | 2.26 |
| 104 | 40 | 16,150 | 2.16 |
| 122 | 50 | 10,970 | 1.72 |
| 140 | 60 | 7,600 | 1.35 |
| 158 | 70 | 5,370 | 1.04 |
| 176 | 80 | 3,840 | 0.80 |
| 194 | 90 | 2,800 | 0.61 |
| 212 | 100 | 2,070 | 0.47 |
| 230 | 110 | 1,550 | 0.36 |
| 248 | 120 | 1,180 | 0.28 |

| Chrysler ECT Sensor Without Pull-Up Resistor | | |
|---|---|---|
| °F | °C | Voltage (V) |
| 130 | 54 | 3.77 |
| 140 | 60 | 3.60 |
| 150 | 66 | 3.40 |
| 160 | 71 | 3.20 |
| 170 | 77 | 3.02 |
| 180 | 82 | 2.80 |
| 190 | 88 | 2.60 |
| 200 | 93 | 2.40 |
| 210 | 99 | 2.20 |
| 220 | 104 | 2.00 |
| 230 | 110 | 1.80 |
| 240 | 116 | 1.62 |
| 250 | 121 | 1.45 |

| Chrysler ECT Sensor with Pull-Up Resistor | | |
|---|---|---|
| °F | °C | Volts |
| −20 | −29 | 4.70 |
| −10 | −23 | 4.57 |
| 0 | −18 | 4.45 |
| 10 | −12 | 4.30 |
| 20 | −7 | 4.10 |
| 30 | −1 | 3.90 |
| 40 | 4 | 3.60 |
| 50 | 10 | 3.30 |
| 60 | 16 | 3.00 |
| 70 | 21 | 2.75 |
| 80 | 27 | 2.44 |
| 90 | 32 | 2.15 |
| 100 | 38 | 1.83 |

| | | Pull-Up Resistor Switched by PCM |
|---|---|---|
| 110 | 43 | 4.20 |
| 120 | 49 | 4.10 |
| 130 | 54 | 4.00 |
| 140 | 60 | 3.60 |
| 150 | 66 | 3.40 |
| 160 | 71 | 3.20 |
| 170 | 77 | 3.02 |
| 180 | 82 | 2.80 |
| 190 | 88 | 2.60 |
| 200 | 93 | 2.40 |
| 210 | 99 | 2.20 |
| 220 | 104 | 2.00 |
| 230 | 110 | 1.80 |
| 240 | 116 | 1.62 |
| 250 | 121 | 1.45 |

| Nissan ECT Sensor | | |
|---|---|---|
| °F | °C | Resistance () |
| 14 | −10 | 7,000–11,400 |
| 68 | 20 | 2,100–2,900 |
| 122 | 50 | 680–1,000 |
| 176 | 80 | 260–390 |
| 212 | 100 | 180–200 |

| Mercedes ECT | | |
|---|---|---|
| °F | °C | Voltage (DCV) |
| 60 | 20 | 3.5 |
| 86 | 30 | 3.1 |
| 104 | 40 | 2.7 |
| 122 | 50 | 2.3 |
| 140 | 60 | 1.9 |
| 158 | 70 | 1.5 |
| 176 | 80 | 1.2 |
| 194 | 90 | 1.0 |
| 212 | 100 | 0.8 |

| European Bosch ECT Sensor | | |
|---|---|---|
| °F | °C | Resistance () |
| 32 | 0 | 6,500 |
| 50 | 10 | 4,000 |
| 68 | 20 | 3,000 |
| 86 | 30 | 2,000 |
| 104 | 40 | 1,500 |
| 122 | 50 | 900 |
| 140 | 60 | 650 |
| 158 | 70 | 500 |
| 176 | 80 | 375 |
| 194 | 90 | 295 |
| 212 | 100 | 230 |

| Honda ECT Sensor (Resistance Chart) | | |
|---|---|---|
| °F | °C | Resistance () |
| 0 | −18 | 15,000 |
| 32 | 0 | 5,000 |
| 68 | 20 | 3,000 |
| 104 | 40 | 1,000 |
| 140 | 60 | 500 |
| 176 | 80 | 400 |
| 212 | 100 | 250 |

| Honda ECT Sensor (Voltage Chart) | | |
|---|---|---|
| °F | °C | Voltage (V) |
| 0 | −18 | 4.70 |
| 10 | −12 | 4.50 |
| 20 | −7 | 4.29 |
| 30 | −1 | 4.10 |
| 40 | 4 | 3.86 |
| 50 | 10 | 3.61 |
| 60 | 16 | 3.35 |
| 70 | 21 | 3.08 |
| 80 | 27 | 2.81 |
| 90 | 32 | 2.50 |
| 100 | 38 | 2.26 |
| 110 | 43 | 2.00 |
| 120 | 49 | 1.74 |
| 130 | 54 | 1.52 |
| 140 | 60 | 1.33 |
| 150 | 66 | 1.15 |
| 160 | 71 | 1.00 |
| 170 | 77 | 0.88 |
| 180 | 82 | 0.74 |
| 190 | 88 | 0.64 |
| 200 | 93 | 0.55 |
| 210 | 99 | 0.47 |

Normal operating temperature varies with vehicle make and model. Some vehicles are equipped with a thermostat with an opening temperature of 180°F (82°C), whereas other vehicles use a thermostat that is 195°F (90°C) or higher. Before replacing the ECT sensor, be sure that the engine is operating at the temperature specified by the manufacturer. Most manufacturers recommend checking the ECT sensor after the cooling fan has cycled twice, indicating a fully warmed engine. To test for voltage at the ECT sensor, select DC volts on a digital meter and carefully back probe the sensor wire and read the voltage. ● SEE FIGURE 13–7.

NOTE: Many manufacturers install another resistor in parallel inside the computer to change the voltage drop across the ECT sensor. This is done to expand the scale of the ECT sensor and to make the sensor more sensitive. Therefore, if measuring *voltage* at the ECT sensor, check with the service manual for the proper voltage at each temperature.

## TESTING THE ECT SENSOR USING A SCAN TOOL
Follow the scan tool manufacturer's instructions and connect a scan tool to the data link connector (DLC) of the vehicle. Comparing the temperature of the engine coolant as displayed on a scan tool with the actual temperature of the engine is an excellent method to test an engine coolant temperature sensor:

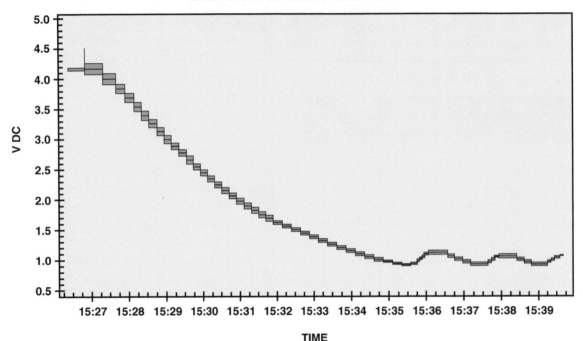

REMARKS: ECT Voltage
2001 Jeep Wrangler Warm-up Cycle
AUTO 202 - Fuel and Emissions Systems

FORM SAVED TIME: 2/18/04 4:11:55 PM
UPLOAD TIME: 2/18/04 4:09:05 PM
METER ID: FLUKE 189 V2.02 0085510089

SHOW DATA: ALL GRAPH VIEW: ALL

**FIGURE 13–7** An ECT sensor being tested using a digital meter set to DC volts and in record mode. A chart showing the voltage decrease of the ECT sensor as the temperature increases from a cold start. The bumps at the bottom of the waveform represent temperature decreases when the thermostat opens and is controlling coolant temperature.

1. Record the scan tool temperature of the coolant (ECT).
2. Measure the actual temperature of the coolant using an infrared pyrometer or contact-type temperature probe.

**NOTE: Often the coolant temperature gauge in the dash of the vehicle can be used to compare with the scan tool temperature. Although not necessarily accurate, it may help to diagnose a faulty sensor, especially if the temperature shown on the scan tool varies greatly from the temperature indicated on the dash gauge.**

The maximum difference between the two readings should be 10°F (5°C). If the actual temperature varies by more than 10°F from the temperature indicated on the scan tool, check the ECT sensor wiring and connector for damage or corrosion. If the connector and wiring are okay, check the sensor with a DVOM for resistance and compare to the actual engine temperature chart. If that checks out okay, check the computer.

**NOTE: Some manufacturers use two coolant sensors, one for the dash gauge and another one for the computer.**

## INTAKE AIR TEMPERATURE SENSOR

**PURPOSE AND FUNCTION** The intake air temperature (IAT) sensor is a negative temperature coefficient (NTC) thermistor that decreases in resistance as the temperature of the sensor increases. The IAT sensor can be located in one of the following locations:

- In the air cleaner housing
- In the air duct between the air filter and the throttle body, as shown in ● **FIGURE 13–8**
- Built into the mass airflow (MAF) or airflow sensor
- Screwed into the intake manifold, where it senses the temperature of the air entering the cylinders

**NOTE: An IAT installed in the intake manifold is the most likely to suffer damage because of an engine backfire, which can often destroy the sensor.**

The purpose and function of the intake air temperature sensor is to provide the engine computer (PCM) the temperature

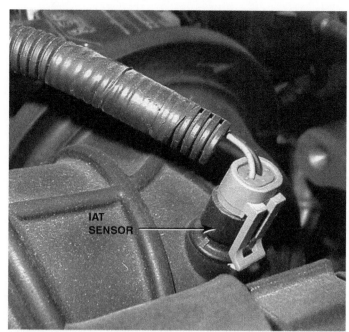

FIGURE 13–8 The IAT sensor on this General Motors 3800 V-6 engine is in the air passage duct between the air cleaner housing and the throttle body.

of the air entering the engine. The IAT sensor information is used for fuel control (adding or subtracting fuel) and spark timing, depending on the temperature of incoming air:

- If the air temperature is cold, the PCM will modify the amount of fuel delivery and add fuel.
- If the air temperature is hot, the PCM will subtract the calculated amount of fuel.
- Spark timing is also changed, depending on the temperature of the air entering the engine. The timing is advanced if the temperature is cold and retarded from the base-programmed timing if the temperature is hot.
- Cold air is more dense, contains more oxygen, and therefore requires a richer mixture to achieve the proper air-fuel mixture. Air at 32°F (0°C) is 14% denser than air at 100°F (38°C).
- Hot air is less dense, contains less oxygen, and therefore requires less fuel to achieve the proper air-fuel mixture.

The IAT sensor is a low-authority sensor and is used by the computer to modify the amount of fuel and ignition timing as determined by the engine coolant temperature sensor.

The IAT sensor is used by the PCM as a backup in the event that the ECT sensor is determined to be inoperative.

NOTE: Some engines use a **throttle-body temperature (TBT)** sensor to sense the temperature of the air entering the engine, instead of an intake air temperature sensor.

Engine temperature is most accurately determined by looking at the engine coolant temperature (ECT) sensor. In certain conditions, the IAT has an effect on performance and drive-

**TECH TIP**

**Quick and Easy ECT Test**

To check that the wiring and the computer are functioning, regarding the ECT sensor, connect a scan tool and look at the ECT temperature display:

STEP 1  Unplug the connector from the ECT sensor. The temperature displayed on the scan tool should read about −40.

NOTE: −40° Celsius is also −40° Fahrenheit. This is the point where both temperature scales meet.

STEP 2  With the connector still removed from the ECT sensor, use a fused jumper lead and connect the two terminals of the connector together. The scan tool should display about 285°F (140°C).

This same test procedure will work for the IAT and most other temperature sensors.

**TECH TIP**

**Poor Fuel Economy? Black Exhaust Smoke? Look at the IAT**

If the intake air temperature sensor is defective, it may be signaling the computer that the intake air temperature is extremely cold when in fact it is warm. In such a case the computer will supply a mixture that is much richer than normal.

If a sensor is physically damaged or electrically open, the computer will often set a diagnostic trouble code (DTC). This DTC is based on the fact that the sensor temperature did not change for a certain amount of time, usually about eight minutes. If, however, the wiring or the sensor itself has excessive resistance, a DTC will not be set and the result will be lower-than-normal fuel economy and, in serious cases, black exhaust smoke from the tailpipe during acceleration.

ability. One such condition is a warm engine being stopped in very cold weather. In this case, when the engine is restarted, the ECT may be near normal operating temperature such as 200°F (93°C), yet the air temperature could be −20°F (−30°C). In this case, the engine requires a richer mixture because of the cold air than the ECT would seem to indicate.

# TESTING THE INTAKE AIR TEMPERATURE SENSOR

If the intake air temperature sensor circuit is damaged or faulty, a diagnostic trouble code (DTC) is set, and the malfunction indicator lamp (MIL) may or may not turn on, depending on the condition and the type and model of the vehicle. To diagnose the IAT sensor follow these steps:

**STEP 1** After the vehicle has been allowed to cool for several hours, use a scan tool, observe the IAT, and compare it to the engine coolant temperature (ECT). The two temperatures should be within 5°F of each other.

**STEP 2** Perform a thorough visual inspection of the sensor and the wiring. If the IAT is screwed into the intake manifold, remove the sensor and check for damage.

**STEP 3** Check the voltage and compare to the following chart.

| Intake Air Temperature Sensor Temperature Versus Resistance and Voltage Drop (Approximate) | | | |
|---|---|---|---|
| °F | °C | Ohms | Voltage Drop Across the Sensor |
| −40 | −40 | 100,000 | 4.95 |
| +18 | −8 | 15,000 | 4.68 |
| 32 | 0 | 9,400 | 4.52 |
| 50 | 10 | 5,700 | 4.25 |
| 68 | 20 | 3,500 | 3.89 |
| 86 | 30 | 2,200 | 3.46 |
| 104 | 40 | 1,500 | 2.97 |
| 122 | 50 | 1,000 | 2.47 |
| 140 | 60 | 700 | 2.00 |
| 158 | 70 | 500 | 1.59 |
| 176 | 80 | 300 | 1.25 |
| 194 | 90 | 250 | 0.97 |
| 212 | 100 | 200 | 0.75 |

# TRANSMISSION FLUID TEMPERATURE SENSOR

The **transmission fluid temperature (TFT),** also called *transmission oil temperature (TOT),* sensor is an important sensor for the proper operation of the automatic transmission. A TFT sensor is a negative temperature coefficient (NTC) thermistor that decreases in resistance as the temperature of the sensor increases.

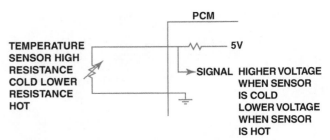

FIGURE 13–9 A typical temperature sensor circuit.

**?** FREQUENTLY ASKED QUESTION

**What Exactly Is an NTC Sensor?**

A negative temperature coefficient (NTC) thermistor is a semiconductor whose resistance decreases as the temperature increases. In other words, the sensor becomes more electrically conductive as the temperature increases. Therefore, when a voltage is applied, typically 5 volts, the signal voltage is high when the sensor is cold because the sensor has a high resistance and little current flows through to ground. ● **SEE FIGURE 13–9.**

However, when the temperature increases, the sensor becomes more electrically conductive and takes more of the 5 volts to ground, resulting in a lower signal voltage as the sensor warms.

| General Motors Transaxle Sensor—Temperature to Resistance (approximate) | | |
|---|---|---|
| °F | °C | Resistance Ohms |
| 32 | 0 | 7,987–10,859 |
| 50 | 10 | 4,934–6,407 |
| 68 | 20 | 3,106–3,923 |
| 86 | 30 | 1,991–2,483 |
| 104 | 40 | 1,307–1,611 |
| 122 | 50 | 878–1,067 |
| 140 | 60 | 605–728 |
| 158 | 70 | 425–507 |
| 176 | 80 | 304–359 |
| 194 | 90 | 221–259 |
| 212 | 100 | 163–190 |

| Chrysler Sensor Resistance (Ohms)—Transmission Temperature Sensor | | |
|---|---|---|
| °F | °C | Resistance Ohms |
| −40 | −40 | 291,490–381,710 |
| −4 | −20 | 85,850–108,390 |
| 14 | −10 | 49,250–61,430 |
| 32 | 0 | 29,330–35,990 |
| 50 | 10 | 17,990–21,810 |
| 68 | 20 | 11,370–13,610 |
| 77 | 25 | 9,120–10,880 |
| 86 | 30 | 7,370–8,750 |
| 104 | 40 | 4,900–5,750 |
| 122 | 50 | 3,330–3,880 |
| 140 | 60 | 2,310–2,670 |
| 158 | 70 | 1,630–1,870 |
| 176 | 80 | 1,170–1,340 |
| 194 | 90 | 860–970 |
| 212 | 100 | 640–720 |
| 230 | 110 | 480–540 |
| 248 | 120 | 370–410 |

| Ford Transmission Fluid Temperature | | |
|---|---|---|
| °F | °C | Resistance Ohms |
| −40 to −4 | −40 to −20 | 967K–284K |
| −3 to 31 | −19 to −1 | 284K–100K |
| 32 to 68 | 0 to 20 | 100K–37K |
| 69 to 104 | 21 to 40 | 37K–16K |
| 105 to 158 | 41 to 70 | 16K–5K |
| 159 to 194 | 71 to 90 | 5K–2.7K |
| 195 to 230 | 91 to 110 | 2.7K–1.5K |
| 231 to 266 | 111 to 130 | 1.5K–0.8K |
| 267 to 302 | 131 to 150 | 0.8K–0.54K |

The transmission fluid temperature signal is used by the powertrain control module (PCM) to perform certain strategies based on the temperature of the automatic transmission fluid. For example:

- If the temperature of the automatic transmission fluid is low (typically below 32°F [0°C]), the shift points may be delayed and overdrive disabled. The torque converter clutch also may not be applied to assist in the heating of the fluid.

- If the temperature of the automatic transmission fluid is high (typically above 260°F [130°C]), the overdrive is disabled and the torque converter clutch is applied to help reduce the temperature of the fluid.

NOTE: Check service information for the exact shift strategy based on high and low transmission fluid temperatures for the vehicle being serviced.

## CYLINDER HEAD TEMPERATURE SENSOR

Some vehicles are equipped with **cylinder head temperature (CHT)** sensors:

**VW Golf**

$$14°F (−10°C) = 11,600$$
$$68°F (20°C) = 2,900$$
$$176°F (80°C) = 390$$

## ENGINE FUEL TEMPERATURE (EFT) SENSOR

Some vehicles, such as many Ford vehicles that are equipped with an electronic returnless type of fuel injection, use an **engine fuel temperature (EFT)** sensor to give the PCM information regarding the temperature and, therefore, the density of the fuel.

## EXHAUST GAS RECIRCULATION (EGR) TEMPERATURE SENSOR

Some engines, such as Toyota, are equipped with exhaust gas recirculation (EGR) temperature sensors. EGR is a well-established method for reduction of $NO_x$ emissions in internal combustion engines. The exhaust gas contains unburned hydrocarbons, which are recirculated in the combustion process. Recirculation is controlled by valves, which operate as a function of exhaust gas speed, load, and temperature. The gas reaches a temperature of about 850°F (450°C) for which a special heavy-duty glass-encapsulated NTC sensor is available.

The PCM monitors the temperature in the exhaust passage between the EGR valve and the intake manifold. If the temperature increases when the EGR is commanded on, the PCM can determine that the valve or related components are functioning.

# ENGINE OIL TEMPERATURE SENSOR

Engine oil temperature sensors are used on many General Motors vehicles and are used as an input to the oil life monitoring system. The computer program inside the PCM calculates engine oil life based on run time, engine RPM, and oil temperature.

# TEMPERATURE SENSOR DIAGNOSTIC TROUBLE CODES

The OBD-II diagnostic trouble codes that relate to temperature sensors include both high- and low-voltage codes as well as intermittent codes.

| Diagnostic Trouble Code | Description | Possible Causes |
|---|---|---|
| P0112 | IAT sensor low voltage | • IAT sensor internally shorted-to-ground<br>• IAT sensor wiring shorted-to-ground<br>• IAT sensor damaged by backfire (usually associated with IAT sensors that are mounted in the intake manifold)<br>• Possible defective PCM |
| P0113 | IAT sensor high voltage | • IAT sensor internally (electrically) open<br>• IAT sensor signal, circuit, or ground circuit open<br>• Possible defective PCM |
| P0117 | ECT sensor low voltage | • ECT sensor internally shorted-to-ground<br>• The ECT sensor circuit wiring shorted-to-ground<br>• Possible defective PCM |
| P0118 | ECT sensor high voltage | • ECT sensor internally (electrically) open<br>• ECT sensor signal, circuit, or ground circuit open<br>• Engine operating in an overheated condition<br>• Possible defective PCM |

# SUMMARY

1. The ECT sensor is a high-authority sensor at engine start-up and is used for closed-loop control as well as idle speed.
2. All temperature sensors decrease in resistance as the temperature increases. This is called negative temperature coefficient (NTC).
3. The ECT and IAT sensors can be tested visually as well as by using a digital multimeter or a scan tool.
4. Some vehicle manufacturers use a stepped ECT circuit inside the PCM to broaden the accuracy of the sensor.
5. Other temperature sensors include transmission fluid temperature (TFT), engine fuel temperature (EFT), exhaust gas recirculation (EGR) temperature, and engine oil temperature.

# REVIEW QUESTIONS

1. How does a typical NTC temperature sensor work?
2. What is the difference between a stepped and a nonstepped ECT circuit?
3. What temperature should be displayed on a scan tool if the ECT sensor is unplugged with the key on, engine off?
4. What are the three ways that temperature sensors can be tested?
5. If the transmission fluid temperature (TFT) sensor were to fail open (as if it were unplugged), what would the PCM do to the transmission shifting points?

1. The sensor that most determines fuel delivery when a fuel-injected engine is first started is the _____.
   a. O2S
   b. ECT sensor
   c. Engine MAP sensor
   d. IAT sensor

2. What happens to the voltage measured at the ECT sensor when the thermostat opens?
   a. Increases slightly
   b. Increases about 1 volt
   c. Decreases slightly
   d. Decreases about 1 volt

3. Two technicians are discussing a stepped ECT circuit. Technician A says that the sensor used for a stepped circuit is different than one used in a nonstepped circuit. Technician B says that a stepped ECT circuit uses different internal resistance inside the PCM. Which technician is correct?
   a. Technician A only
   b. Technician B only
   c. Both Technicians A and B
   d. Neither Technician A nor B

4. When testing an ECT sensor on a vehicle, a digital multimeter can be used and the signal wire tested with the connector attached the ignition on (engine off). What setting should the technician use to test the sensor?
   a. AC volts
   b. DC volts
   c. Ohms
   d. Hz (hertz)

5. When testing the ECT sensor with the connector disconnected, the technician should select what position on the DMM?
   a. AC volts
   b. DC volts
   c. Ohms
   d. Hz (hertz)

6. When checking the ECT sensor with a scan tool, about what temperature should be displayed if the connector is removed from the sensor with the key on, engine off?
   a. 284°F (140°C)
   b. 230°F (110°C)
   c. 120°F (50°C)
   d. −40°F (−40°C)

7. Two technicians are discussing the IAT sensor. Technician A says that the IAT sensor is more important to the operation of the engine (higher authority) than the ECT sensor. Technician B says that the PCM will add fuel if the IAT indicates that the incoming air temperature is cold. Which technician is correct?
   a. Technician A only
   b. Technician B only
   c. Both Technicians A and B
   d. Neither Technician A nor B

8. A typical IAT or ECT sensor reads about 3,000 ohms when tested using a DMM. This resistance represents a temperature of about _____.
   a. −40°F (−40°C)
   b. 70°F (20°C)
   c. 120°F (50°C)
   d. 284°F (140°C)

9. If the transmission fluid temperature (TFT) sensor indicates cold automatic transmission fluid temperature, what would the PCM do to the shifts?
   a. Normal shifts and normal operation of the torque converter clutch
   b. Disable torque converter clutch; normal shift points
   c. Delayed shift points and torque converter clutch disabled
   d. Normal shifts, but overdrive will be disabled

10. A P0118 DTC is being discussed. Technician A says that the ECT sensor could be shorted internally. Technician B says that the signal wire could be open. Which technician is correct?
    a. Technician A only
    b. Technician B only
    c. Both Technicians A and B
    d. Neither Technician A nor B

# chapter 14

# THROTTLE POSITION SENSORS

**OBJECTIVES:** **After studying Chapter 14, the reader should be able to:** • Prepare for ASE Engine Performance (A8) certification test content area "E" (Computerized Engine Controls Diagnosis and Repair). • Discuss how throttle position (TP) sensors work. • List the methods that can be used to test TP sensors. • Describe the symptoms of a failed TP sensor. • List how the operation of the TP sensor affects vehicle operation. • Discuss TP sensor rationality tests.

**KEY TERMS:** Potentiometer 190 • Skewed 193 • Throttle position (TP) sensor 190

## THROTTLE POSITION SENSOR CONSTRUCTION

Most computer-equipped engines use a **throttle position (TP) sensor** to signal to the computer the position of the throttle.
● **SEE FIGURE 14–1.** The TP sensor consists of a **potentiometer,** a type of variable resistor.

**POTENTIOMETERS** A potentiometer is a variable-resistance sensor with three terminals. One end of the resistor receives reference voltage, while the other end is grounded. The third terminal is attached to a movable contact that slides across the resistor to vary its resistance. Depending on whether the contact is near the supply end or the ground end of the resistor, return voltage is high or low. ● **SEE FIGURE 14–2.**

Throttle position (TP) sensors are among the most common potentiometer-type sensors. The computer uses their input to determine the amount of throttle opening and the rate of change.

A typical sensor has three wires:

- A 5-volt reference feed wire from the computer
- Signal return (a ground wire back to the computer)
- A voltage signal wire back to the computer; as the throttle is opened, the voltage to the computer changes

Normal throttle position voltage on most vehicles is about 0.5 volt at idle (closed throttle) and 4.5 volts at wide-open throttle (WOT).

**NOTE: The TP sensor voltage at idle is usually about 10% of the TP sensor voltage when the throttle is wide open but can vary from as low as 0.3 volt to 1.2 volts, depending on the make and model of vehicle.**

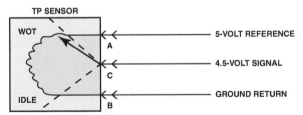

**FIGURE 14–1** A typical TP sensor mounted on the throttle plate of this port-injected engine.

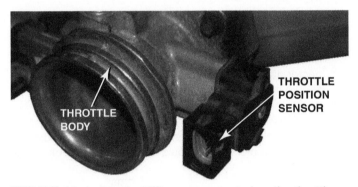

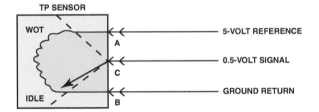

**FIGURE 14–2** The signal voltage from a throttle position increases as the throttle is opened because the wiper arm is closer to the 5-volt reference. At idle, the resistance of the sensor winding effectively reduces the signal voltage output to the computer.

# TP SENSOR COMPUTER INPUT FUNCTIONS

- The computer senses any change in throttle position and changes the fuel mixture and ignition timing. The actual change in fuel mixture and ignition timing is also partly determined by the other sensors, such as the manifold pressure (engine vacuum), engine RPM, the coolant temperature, and oxygen sensor(s). Some throttle position sensors are adjustable and should be set according to the exact engine manufacturer's specifications.

- The throttle position (TP) sensor used on fuel-injected vehicles acts as an "electronic accelerator pump." This means that the computer will pulse additional fuel from the injectors when the throttle is depressed. Because the air can quickly flow into the engine when the throttle is opened, additional fuel must be supplied to prevent the air-fuel mixture from going lean, causing the engine to hesitate when the throttle is depressed. If the TP sensor is unplugged or defective, the engine may still operate satisfactorily but hesitate upon acceleration.

- The PCM supplies the TP sensor with a regulated voltage that ranges from 4.8 to 5.1 volts. This reference voltage is usually referred to as a 5-volt reference or "Vref." The TP output signal is an input to the PCM, and the TP sensor ground also flows through the PCM.

See the Ford throttle position (TP) sensor chart for an example of how sensor voltage changes with throttle angle.

| Ford Throttle Position (TP) Sensor Chart | |
|---|---|
| Throttle Angle (Degrees) | Voltage (V) |
| 0 | 0.50 |
| 10 | 0.97 |
| 20 | 1.44 |
| 30 | 1.90 |
| 40 | 2.37 |
| 50 | 2.84 |
| 60 | 3.31 |
| 70 | 3.78 |
| 80 | 4.24 |

NOTE: Generally, any reading higher than 80% represents wide-open throttle to the computer.

# PCM USES FOR THE TP SENSOR

The TP sensor is used by the powertrain control module (PCM) for the following reasons.

**CLEAR FLOOD MODE**  If the throttle is depressed to the floor during engine cranking, the PCM will either greatly reduce or entirely eliminate any fuel-injector pulses to aid in cleaning a flooded engine. If the throttle is depressed to the floor and the engine is not flooded with excessive fuel, the engine may not start.

**TORQUE CONVERTER CLUTCH ENGAGEMENT AND RELEASE**  The torque converter clutch will be released if the PCM detects rapid acceleration to help the transmission deliver maximum torque to the drive wheels. The torque converter clutch is also disengaged when the accelerator pedal is released with the vehicle moving to help engine braking.

**RATIONALITY TESTING FOR MAP AND MAF SENSORS**
As part of the rationality tests for the MAP and/or MAF sensor, the TP sensor signal is compared to the reading from other sensors to determine if they match. For example, if the throttle position sensor is showing wide-open throttle (WOT), the MAP and/or MAF reading should also indicate that this engine is under a heavy load. If not, a diagnostic trouble code could be set for the TP, as well as the MAP and/or MAF sensors.

**AUTOMATIC TRANSMISSION SHIFT POINTS**  The shift points are delayed if the throttle is opened wide to allow the engine speed to increase, thereby producing more power and aiding in the acceleration of the vehicle. If the throttle is barely open, the shift point occurs at the minimum speed designed for the vehicle.

**TARGET IDLE SPEED (IDLE CONTROL STRATEGY)**
When the TP sensor voltage is at idle, the PCM then controls idle speed using the idle air control (IAC) and/or spark timing variation to maintain the commanded idle speed. If the TP sensor indicates that the throttle has moved off idle, fuel delivery and spark timing are programmed for acceleration. Therefore, if the throttle linkage is stuck or binding, the idle speed may not be correct.

**AIR-CONDITIONING COMPRESSOR OPERATION**  The TP sensor is also used as an input sensor for air-conditioning compressor operation. If the PCM detects that the throttle is at or close to wide open, the air-conditioning compressor is disengaged.

**BACKS UP OTHER SENSORS**  The TP sensor is used as a backup to the MAP sensor and/or MAF in the event the PCM detects that one or both are not functioning correctly. The PCM then calculates fuel needs and spark timing based on the engine speed (RPM) and throttle position.

**FIGURE 14-3** A meter lead connected to a T-pin that was gently pushed along the signal wire of the TP sensor until the point of the pin touched the metal terminal inside the plastic connector.

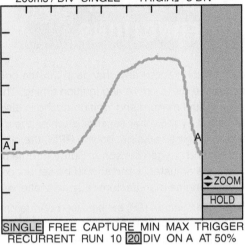

A 1V DC 1:1 PROBE  B 200mV OFF 1:1 PROBE
200ms / DIV  SINGLE      TRIG:A⌐-3 DIV

SINGLE FREE CAPTURE MIN MAX TRIGGER
RECURRENT RUN 10 20 DIV ON A AT 50%

**FIGURE 14-4** A typical waveform of a TP sensor signal as recorded on a DSO when the accelerator pedal was depressed with the ignition switch on (engine off). Clean transitions and the lack of any glitches in this waveform indicate a good sensor. *(Courtesy of Fluke Corporation)*

# TESTING THE THROTTLE POSITION SENSOR

A TP sensor can be tested using one or more of the following tools:

- A digital voltmeter with three test leads connected in series between the sensor and the wiring harness connector or back probing using T-pins or other recommended tool that will not cause harm to the connector or wiring.
- A scan tool or a specific tool recommended by the vehicle manufacturer.
- A breakout box that is connected in series between the computer and the wiring harness connector(s). A typical breakout box includes test points at which TP voltages can be measured with a digital voltmeter.
- An oscilloscope.

Use jumper wires, T-pins to back-probe the wires, or a breakout box to gain electrical access to the wiring to the TP sensor. ● **SEE FIGURE 14-3.**

**NOTE: The procedure that follows is the method used by many manufacturers. Always refer to service information for the exact recommended procedure and specifications for the vehicle being tested.**

The procedure for testing the sensor using a digital multimeter is as follows:

1. Turn the ignition switch on (engine off).
2. Set the digital meter to read to DC volts and measure the voltage between the signal wire and ground (reference low) wire. The voltage should be about 0.5 volt.

**NOTE: Consult the service information for exact wire colors or locations.**

3. With the engine still not running (but with the ignition still on), slowly increase the throttle opening. The voltage signal from the TP sensor should also increase. Look for any "dead spots" or open circuit readings as the throttle is increased to the wide-open position. ● **SEE FIGURE 14-4** for an example of how a good TP sensor would look when tested with a digital storage oscilloscope (DSO).

**NOTE: Use the accelerator pedal to depress the throttle because this applies the same forces on the TP sensor as the driver does during normal driving. Moving the throttle by hand under the hood may not accurately test the TP sensor.**

4. With the voltmeter still connected, slowly return the throttle down to the idle position. The voltage from the TP sensor should also decrease evenly on the return to idle.

The TP sensor voltage at idle should be within the acceptable range as specified by the manufacturer. Some TP sensors can be adjusted by loosening their retaining screws and moving the sensor in relation to the throttle opening. This movement changes the output voltage of the sensor.

All TP sensors should also provide a smooth transition voltage reading from idle to WOT and back to idle. Replace the TP sensor if erratic voltage readings are obtained or if the correct setting at idle cannot be obtained.

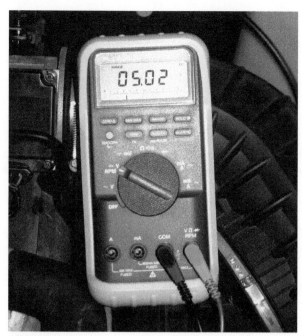

FIGURE 14–5 Checking the 5-volt reference from the computer being applied to the TP sensor with the ignition switch on (engine off). The reading for this vehicle (5.02 volts DC) is within the normal range for the reference voltage of 4.9 to 5.1 volts.

 TECH TIP

**Check Power and Ground Before Condemning a Bad Sensor**

Most engine sensors use a 5-volt reference and a ground. If the 5 volts to the sensor is too high (shorted to voltage) or too low (high resistance), then the sensor output will be **skewed** or out of range. Before replacing the sensor that did not read correctly, measure both the 5-volt reference and ground. To measure the ground, simply turn the ignition on (engine off) and touch one test lead of a DMM set to read DC volts to the sensor ground and the other to the negative terminal of the battery. Any reading higher than 0.2 volt (200 mV) represents a poor ground. ● **SEE FIGURES 14–5 AND 14–6.**

# TESTING A TP SENSOR USING THE MIN/MAX FUNCTION

Many digital multimeters are capable of recording voltage readings over time and then displaying the minimum, maximum, and average readings. To perform a MIN/MAX test of the TP sensor, manually set the meter to read higher than 4 volts:

FIGURE 14–6 Checking the voltage drop between the TP sensor ground and a good engine ground with the ignition on (engine off). A reading of greater than 0.2 volt (200 mV) represents a bad computer ground.

STEP 1   Connect the red meter lead to the signal wire and the black meter lead to a good ground or the ground return wire at the TP sensor.

STEP 2   With the ignition on, engine off, slowly depress and release the accelerator pedal from inside the vehicle.

STEP 3   Check the minimum and maximum voltage reading on the meter display. Any 0-volt or 5-volt reading would indicate a fault or short in the TP sensor.

# TESTING THE TP SENSOR USING A SCAN TOOL

A scan tool can be used to check for proper operation of the throttle position sensor using the following steps:

STEP 1   With the key on, engine off, the TP sensor voltage display should be about 0.5 volt but can vary from as low as 0.3 volt to as high as 1.2 volts.

STEP 2   Check the scan tool display for the percentage of throttle opening. The reading should be zero and gradually increase in percentage as the throttle is depressed.

STEP 3   The idle air control (IAC) counts should increase as the throttle is opened and decrease as the throttle is closed. Start the engine and observe the IAC counts as the throttle is depressed.

STEP 4   Start the engine and observe the TP sensor reading. Use a wedge at the throttle stop to increase the throttle opening slightly. The throttle percentage reading should increase. Shut off and restart the engine. If the percentage of throttle opening returns to 0%, the PCM determines that the increased throttle opening is now the new minimum and resets the idle position of the TP sensor. Remove the wedge and cycle the ignition key. The throttle position sensor should again read 0%.

NOTE: Some engine computers are not capable of resetting the throttle position sensor.

# TP SENSOR DIAGNOSTIC TROUBLE CODES

The diagnostic trouble codes (DTCs) associated with the throttle position sensor include the following:

| Diagnostic Trouble Code | Description | Possible Causes |
| --- | --- | --- |
| P0122 | TP sensor low voltage | • TP sensor internally shorted-to-ground<br>• TP sensor wiring shorted-to-ground<br>• TP sensor or wiring open |
| P0123 | TP sensor high voltage | • TP sensor internally shorted to 5-volt reference<br>• TP sensor ground open<br>• TP sensor wiring shorted-to-voltage |
| P0121 | TP sensor signal does not agree with MAP | • Defective TP sensor<br>• Incorrect vehicle-speed (VS) sensor signal<br>• MAP sensor out-of-calibration or defective |

## SUMMARY

1. A throttle position (TP) sensor is a three-wire variable resistor called a potentiometer.

2. The three wires on the TP sensor include a 5-volt reference voltage from the PCM, plus the signal wire to the PCM, and a ground, which also goes to the PCM.

3. The TP sensor is used by the PCM for clear flood mode, torque converter engagement and release, and automotive transmission shift points as well as rationality testing for the MAP and MAF sensors.

4. The TP sensor signal voltage should be about 0.5 volt at idle and increase to about 4.5 volts at wide-open throttle (WOT).

5. A TP sensor can be tested using a digital multimeter, a digital storage oscilloscope (DSO), or a scan tool.

## REVIEW QUESTIONS

1. What is the purpose of each of the three wires on a typical TP sensor?

2. What all does the PCM do with the TP sensor signal voltage?

3. What is the procedure to follow when checking the 5-volt reference and TP sensor ground?

4. How can a TP sensor be diagnosed using a scan tool?

## CHAPTER QUIZ

1. Which sensor is generally considered to be the electronic accelerator pump of a fuel-injected engine?
   - **a.** O2S
   - **b.** ECT sensor
   - **c.** Engine MAP sensor
   - **d.** TP sensor

2. Typical TP sensor voltage at idle is about _____.
   - **a.** 2.5 to 2.8 volts
   - **b.** 0.5 volt or 10% of WOT TP sensor voltage
   - **c.** 1.5 to 2.8 volts
   - **d.** 13.5 to 15 volts

3. A TP sensor is what type of sensor?
   - **a.** Rheostat
   - **b.** Voltage generating
   - **c.** Potentiometer
   - **d.** Piezoelectric

4. Most TP sensors have how many wires?
   - **a.** One
   - **b.** Two
   - **c.** Three
   - **d.** Four

5. Which sensor does the TP sensor back up if the PCM determines that a failure has occurred?
   a. Oxygen sensor
   b. MAF sensor
   c. MAP sensor
   d. Either b or c

6. Which wire on a TP sensor should be back-probed to check the voltage signal to the PCM?
   a. 5-volt reference (Vref)
   b. Signal
   c. Ground
   d. Meter should be connected between the 5-volt reference and the ground

7. After a TP sensor has been tested using the MIN/MAX function on a DMM, a reading of 0 volts is displayed. What does this reading indicate?
   a. The TP sensor is open at one point during the test.
   b. The TP sensor is shorted.
   c. The TP sensor signal is shorted to 5-volt reference.
   d. Both b and c are possible.

8. After a TP sensor has been tested using the MIN/MAX function on a DMM, a reading of 5 volts is displayed. What does this reading indicate?
   a. The TP sensor is open at one point during the test.
   b. The TP sensor is shorted.
   c. The TP sensor signal is shorted to 5-volt reference.
   d. Both b and c are possible.

9. A technician attaches one lead of a digital voltmeter to the ground terminal of the TP sensor and the other meter lead to the negative terminal of the battery. The ignition is switched to on, engine off, and the meter displays 37.3 mV. Technician A says that this is the signal voltage and is a little low. Technician B says that the TP sensor ground circuit has excessive resistance. Which technician is correct?
   a. Technician A only
   b. Technician B only
   c. Both Technicians A and B
   d. Neither Technician A nor B

10. A P0122 DTC is retrieved using a scan tool. This DTC means _____.
   a. The TP sensor voltage is low
   b. The TP sensor could be shorted-to-ground
   c. The TP sensor signal circuit could be shorted-to-ground
   d. All of the above

# chapter 15

# MAP/BARO SENSORS

**OBJECTIVES:** After studying Chapter 15, the reader should be able to: • Prepare for ASE Engine Performance (A8) certification test content area "E" (Computerized Engine Controls Diagnosis and Repair). • Discuss how MAP sensors work. • List the methods that can be used to test MAP sensors. • Describe the symptoms of a failed MAP sensor. • List how the operation of the MAP sensor affects vehicle operation. • Discuss MAP sensor rationality tests. • Describe how the BARO sensor is used to determine altitude.

**KEY TERMS:** Barometric manifold absolute pressure (BMAP) sensor 201 • Barometric pressure (BARO) sensor 201 • Manifold absolute pressure (MAP) sensor 196 • Piezoresistivity 198 • Pressure differential 196 • Speed density 199 • Vacuum 196

## AIR PRESSURE—HIGH AND LOW

Think of an internal combustion engine as a big air pump. As the pistons move up and down in the cylinders, they pump in air and fuel for combustion and pump out exhaust gases. They do this by creating a difference in air pressure. The air outside an engine has weight and exerts pressure, as does the air inside an engine.

As a piston moves down on an intake stroke with the intake valve open, it creates a larger area inside the cylinder for the air to fill. This lowers the air pressure within the engine. Because the pressure inside the engine is lower than the pressure outside, air flows into the engine to fill the low-pressure area and equalize the pressure.

The low pressure within the engine is called **vacuum.** Vacuum causes the higher-pressure air on the outside to flow into the low-pressure area inside the cylinder. The difference in pressure between the two areas is called a **pressure differential.** ● SEE FIGURE 15–1.

## PRINCIPLES OF PRESSURE SENSORS

Intake manifold pressure changes with changing throttle positions. At wide-open throttle, manifold pressure is almost the same as atmospheric pressure. On deceleration or at idle, manifold pressure is below atmospheric pressure, thus creating a vacuum. In cases where turbo- or supercharging is used, under part- or full-load condition, intake manifold pressure rises above

atmospheric pressure. Also, oxygen content and barometric pressure change with differences in altitude, and the computer must be able to compensate by making changes in the flow of fuel entering the engine. To provide the computer with changing airflow information, a fuel-injection system may use the following:

■ Manifold absolute pressure (MAP) sensor

■ Manifold absolute pressure (MAP) sensor plus barometric absolute pressure (BARO) sensor

■ Barometric and manifold absolute pressure sensors combined (BMAP)

The **manifold absolute pressure (MAP) sensor** may be a ceramic capacitor diaphragm, an aneroid bellows, or a piezoresistive crystal. It has a sealed vacuum reference input on one side; the other side is connected (vented) to the intake manifold. This sensor housing also contains signal conditioning circuitry. ● SEE FIGURE 15–2. Pressure changes in the manifold cause the sensor to deflect, varying its analog or digital return signal to the computer. As the air pressure increases, the MAP sensor generates a higher voltage or frequency return signal to the computer.

## CONSTRUCTION OF MAP SENSORS

The MAP sensor is used by the engine computer to sense engine load. The typical MAP sensor consists of a ceramic or silicon wafer sealed on one side with a perfect vacuum and exposed to intake manifold vacuum on the other side. As the

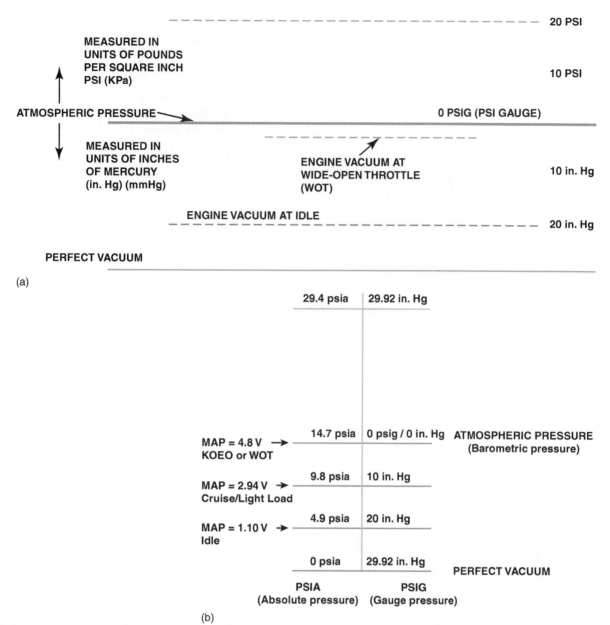

(a)

(b)

**FIGURE 15–1** (a) As an engine is accelerated under a load, the engine vacuum drops. This drop in vacuum is actually an increase in absolute pressure in the intake manifold. A MAP sensor senses all pressures greater than that of a perfect vacuum. (b) The relationship between absolute pressure, vacuum, and gauge pressure.

**FIGURE 15–2** A clear plastic MAP sensor used for training purposes showing the electronic circuit board and electrical connections.

engine vacuum changes, the pressure difference on the wafer changes the output voltage or frequency of the MAP sensor.

A MAP sensor is used on many engines for the PCM to determine the load on the engine. The relationship among barometer pressure, engine vacuum, and MAP sensor voltage includes the following:

- Absolute pressure is equal to barometric pressure minus intake manifold vacuum.

- A decrease in manifold vacuum means an increase in manifold pressure.

- The MAP sensor compares manifold vacuum to a perfect vacuum.

- Barometric pressure minus MAP sensor reading equals intake manifold vacuum. Normal engine vacuum is 17 to 21 in. Hg.

- Supercharged and turbocharged engines require a MAP sensor that is calibrated for pressures above atmospheric as well as for vacuum.

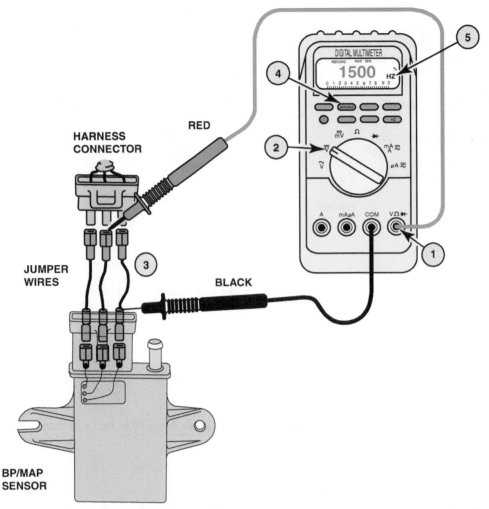

**FIGURE 15–3** MAP sensors use three wires: 1. 5-volt reference from the PCM 2. Sensor signal (output signal) 3. Ground. A DMM set to test a MAP sensor. (1) Connect the red meter lead to the V meter terminal and the black meter lead to the COM meter terminal. (2) Select DC volts. (3) Connect the test leads to the sensor signal wire and the ground wire. (4) Select hertz (Hz) if testing a MAP sensor whose output is a varying frequency; otherwise, keep it on DC volts. (5) Read the change of voltage (frequency) as the vacuum is applied to the sensor. Compare the vacuum reading and the frequency (or voltage) reading to the specifications. *(Courtesy of Fluke Corporation)*

## SILICON-DIAPHRAGM STRAIN GAUGE MAP SENSOR

This is the most commonly used design for a MAP sensor, and the output is a DC analog (variable) voltage. One side of a silicon wafer is exposed to engine vacuum, and the other side is exposed to a perfect vacuum.

There are four resistors attached to the silicon wafer, which changes in resistance when strain is applied to the wafer. This change in resistance due to strain is called **piezoresistivity.** The resistors are electrically connected to a Wheatstone bridge circuit and then to a differential amplifier, which creates a voltage in proportion to the vacuum applied.

A typical General Motors MAP sensor voltage varies from 0.88 to 1.62 at engine idle:

- 17 in. Hg is equal to about 1.62 volts.
- 21 in. Hg is equal to about 0.88 volts.

Therefore, a good reading should be about 1 volt from the MAP sensor on a sound engine at idle speed. See the following chart that shows engine load, engine vacuum, and MAP.

| Engine Load | Manifold Vacuum | Manifold Absolute Pressure | MAP Sensor Volt Signal |
|---|---|---|---|
| Heavy (WOT) | Low (almost 0 in. Hg) | High (almost atmospheric) | High (4.6–4.8 V) |
| Light (idle) | High (17–21 in. Hg) | Low (lower than atmospheric) | Low (0.8–1.6 V) |

**CAPACITOR-CAPSULE MAP SENSOR** A capacitor-capsule is a type of MAP sensor used by Ford which uses two ceramic (alumina) plates with an insulating washer spacer in the center to create a capacitor. Changes in engine vacuum cause the plates to deflect, which changes the capacitance. The electronics in the sensor then generate a varying digital frequency output signal, which is proportional to the engine vacuum. ● **SEE FIGURE 15–3.** ● **SEE FIGURE 15–4** for a scope waveform of a digital MAP sensor. Also see the Ford MAP sensor chart.

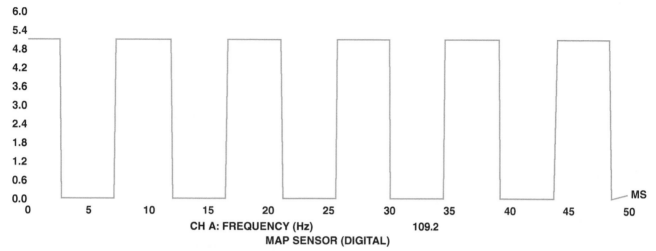

**FIGURE 15–4** A waveform of a typical digital MAP sensor.

**FIGURE 15–5** Shown is the electronic circuit inside a ceramic disc MAP sensor used on many Chrysler engines. The black areas are carbon resistors that are applied to the ceramic, and lasers are used to cut lines into these resistors during testing to achieve the proper operating calibration.

| Ford MAP Sensor Chart | | |
|---|---|---|
| MAP Sensor Output | Engine Operating Conditions | Intake Manifold Vacuum |
| 156–159 Hz | Key on, engine off | 0 in. Hg |
| 102–109 Hz | Engine at idle (sea level) | 17–21 in. Hg |
| 156–159 Hz | Engine at wide-open throttle (WOT) | About 0 in. Hg |

**CERAMIC DISC MAP SENSOR** The ceramic disc MAP sensor is used by Chrysler and it converts manifold pressure into a capacitance discharge. The discharge controls the amount of voltage delivered by the sensor to the PCM. The output is the same as the previously used strain gauge/Wheatstone bridge design and is interchangeable. ● **SEE FIGURE 15–5.** See the Chrysler MAP sensor chart.

| Chrysler MAP Sensor Chart | |
|---|---|
| Vacuum (in. Hg) | MAP Sensor Signal Voltage (V) |
| 0.5 | 4.8 |
| 1.0 | 4.6 |
| 3.0 | 4.1 |
| 5.0 | 3.8 |
| 7.0 | 3.5 |
| 10.0 | 2.9 |
| 15.0 | 2.1 |
| 20.0 | 1.2 |
| 25.0 | 0.5 |

## PCM USES OF THE MAP SENSOR

The PCM uses the MAP sensor to determine the following:

- **Load on the engine.** The MAP sensor is used on a **speed density**-type fuel-injection system to determine engine load, and therefore the amount of fuel needed. On engines equipped with a mass airflow (MAF) sensor, the

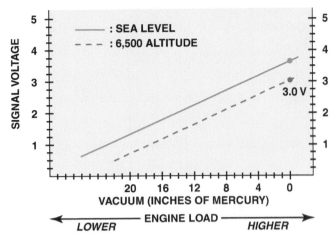

FIGURE 15–6 Altitude affects the MAP sensor voltage.

MAP is used as a backup to the MAF, for diagnosis of other sensors, and systems such as the EGR system.

- **Altitude, fuel, and spark control calculations.** At key on, the MAP sensor determines the altitude (acts as a BARO sensor) and adjusts the fuel delivery and spark timing accordingly:

  - If the altitude is high, generally over 5,000 feet (1,500 m), the PCM will reduce fuel delivery and advance the ignition timing.

  - The altitude is also reset when the engine is accelerated to wide-open throttle and the MAP sensor is used to reset the altitude reading. ● **SEE FIGURE 15–6.**

- **EGR system operation.** As part of the OBD-II standards, the exhaust gas recirculation (EGR) system must be checked for proper operation. One method used by many vehicle manufacturers is to command the EGR valve on and then watch the MAP sensor signal. The opening of the EGR pintle should decrease engine vacuum. If the MAP sensor does not react with the specified drop in manifold vacuum (increase in manifold pressure), an EGR flow rate problem diagnostic trouble code is set.

- **Detect deceleration (vacuum increases).** The engine vacuum rises when the accelerator is released, which changes the MAP sensor voltage. When deceleration is detected by the PCM, fuel is either stopped or greatly reduced to improve exhaust emissions.

- **Monitor engine condition.** As an engine wears, the intake manifold vacuum usually decreases. The PCM is programmed to detect the gradual change in vacuum and is able to keep the air-fuel mixture in the correct range. If the PCM were not capable of making adjustments for engine wear, the lower vacuum could be interpreted as increased load on the engine, resulting in too much

 **TECH TIP**

**Use the MAP Sensor as a Vacuum Gauge**

A MAP sensor measures the pressure inside the intake manifold compared with absolute zero (perfect vacuum). For example, an idling engine that has 20 in. Hg of vacuum has a lower pressure inside the intake manifold than when the engine is under a load and the vacuum is at 10 in. Hg. A decrease in engine vacuum results in an increase in manifold pressure. A normal engine should produce between 17 and 21 in. Hg at idle. Comparing the vacuum reading with the voltage reading output of the MAP sensor indicates that the reading should be between 1.62 and 0.88 volt or 109 to 102 Hz or lower on Ford MAP sensors. Therefore, a digital multimeter (DMM), scan tool, or scope can be used to measure the MAP sensor voltage and be used instead of a vacuum gauge.

NOTE: This chart was developed by testing a MAP sensor at a location about 600 feet above sea level. For best results, a chart based on your altitude should be made by applying a known vacuum, and reading the voltage of a known-good MAP sensor. Vacuum usually drops about 1 inch per 1,000 feet of altitude.

| Vacuum (in. Hg) | GM (DC volts) | Ford (Hz) |
|---|---|---|
| 0 | 4.80 | 156–159 |
| 1 | 4.52 | |
| 2 | 4.46 | |
| 3 | 4.26 | |
| 4 | 4.06 | |
| 5 | 3.88 | 141–143 |
| 6 | 3.66 | |
| 7 | 3.50 | |
| 8 | 3.30 | |
| 9 | 3.10 | |
| 10 | 2.94 | 127–130 |
| 11 | 2.76 | |
| 12 | 2.54 | |
| 13 | 2.36 | |
| 14 | 2.20 | |
| 15 | 2.00 | 114–117 |
| 16 | 1.80 | |
| 17 | 1.62 | |
| 18 | 1.42 | 108–109 |
| 19 | 1.20 | |
| 20 | 1.10 | 102–104 |
| 21 | 0.88 | |
| 22 | 0.66 | |

fuel being injected, thereby reducing fuel economy and increasing exhaust emissions.

- **Load detection for returnless-type fuel injection.** On fuel delivery systems that do not use a return line back to the fuel tank, the engine load calculation for the fuel needed is determined by the signals from the MAP sensor.

- **Altitude and MAP sensor values.** On an engine equipped with a speed density-type fuel injection, the MAP sensor is the most important sensor needed to determine injection pulse width. Changes in altitude change the air density as well as weather conditions. Barometric pressure and altitude are inversely related:

  - As altitude increases, barometric pressure decreases.

  - As altitude decreases, barometric pressure increases.

As the ignition switch is turned from off to the start position, the PCM reads the MAP sensor value to determine atmospheric and air pressure conditions. This barometric pressure reading is updated every time the engine is started and whenever wide-open throttle is detected. The barometric pressure reading at that time is updated. See the chart that compares altitude to MAP sensor voltage.

| Altitude and MAP Sensor Voltage | |
|---|---|
| **Altitude** | **MAP Sensor Voltage (key on, engine off)** |
| Sea level | 4.6 to 4.8 volts |
| 2,500 ft (760 m) | 4.0 volts |
| 5,000 ft (1,520 m) | 3.7 volts |
| 7,500 ft (2,300 m) | 3.35 volts |
| 10,000 ft (3,050 m) | 3.05 volts |
| 12,500 ft (3,800 m) | 2.80 volts |
| 15,000 ft (4,600 m) | 2.45 volts |

# BAROMETRIC PRESSURE SENSOR

A **barometric pressure (BARO) sensor** is similar in design, but senses more subtle changes in barometric absolute pressure (atmospheric air pressure). It is vented directly to the atmosphere. The **barometric manifold absolute pressure (BMAP) sensor** is actually a combination of a BARO and MAP sensor in the same housing. The BMAP sensor has individual circuits to measure barometric and manifold pressure. This input not

**REAL WORLD FIX**

**The Cavalier Convertible Story**

The owner of a Cavalier convertible stated to a service technician that the "check engine" (MIL) was on. The technician found a diagnostic trouble code (DTC) for a MAP sensor. The technician removed the hose at the MAP sensor and discovered that gasoline had accumulated in the sensor and dripped out of the hose as it was being removed. The technician replaced the MAP sensor and test-drove the vehicle to confirm the repair. Almost at once the check engine light came on with the same MAP sensor code. After several hours of troubleshooting without success in determining the cause, the technician decided to start over again. Almost at once, the technician discovered that no vacuum was getting to the MAP sensor where a vacuum gauge was connected with a T-fitting in the vacuum line to the MAP sensor. The vacuum port in the base of the throttle body was clogged with carbon. After a thorough cleaning and clearing the DTC, the Cavalier again performed properly, and the check engine light did not come on again. The technician had assumed that if gasoline was able to reach the sensor through the vacuum hose, surely vacuum could reach the sensor. The technician learned to stop assuming when diagnosing a vehicle and concentrate more on testing the simple things first.

only allows the computer to adjust for changes in atmospheric pressure due to weather but also is the primary sensor used to determine altitude.

**NOTE: A MAP sensor and a BARO sensor are usually the same sensor, but the MAP sensor is connected to the manifold and a BARO sensor is open to the atmosphere. The MAP sensor is capable of reading barometric pressure just as the ignition switch is turned to the on position before the engine starts. Therefore, altitude and weather changes are available to the computer. During mountainous driving, it may be an advantage to stop and then restart the engine so that the engine computer can take another barometric pressure reading and recalibrate fuel delivery based on the new altitude. See the Ford/BARO altitude chart for an example of how altitude affects intake manifold pressure. The computer on some vehicles will monitor the throttle position sensor and use the MAP sensor reading at wide-open throttle (WOT) to update the BARO sensor if it has changed during driving.**

| Ford MAP/BARO Altitude Chart | |
|---|---|
| Altitude (ft) | Volts (V) |
| 0 | 1.59 |
| 1,000 | 1.56 |
| 2,000 | 1.53 |
| 3,000 | 1.50 |
| 4,000 | 1.47 |
| 5,000 | 1.44 |
| 6,000 | 1.41 |
| 7,000 | 1.39 |

NOTE: Some older Chrysler brand vehicles were equipped with a combination BARO and IAT sensor. The sensor was mounted on the bulkhead (firewall) and sensed the underhood air temperature.

## TESTING THE MAP SENSOR

Most pressure sensors operate on 5 volts from the computer and return a signal (voltage or frequency) based on the pressure (vacuum) applied to the sensor. If a MAP sensor is being tested, make certain that the vacuum hose and hose fittings are sound and making a good, tight connection to a manifold vacuum source on the engine.

Four different types of test instruments can be used to test a pressure sensor:

1. A digital voltmeter with three test leads connected in series between the sensor and the wiring harness connector or back-probe the terminals
2. A scope connected to the sensor output, power, and ground
3. A scan tool or a specific tool recommended by the vehicle manufacturer
4. A breakout box connected in series between the computer and the wiring harness connection(s) (A typical breakout box includes test points at which pressure sensor values can be measured with a digital voltmeter set on DC volts— or frequency counter, if a frequency-type MAP sensor is being tested.)

NOTE: Always check service information for the exact testing procedures and specifications for the vehicle being tested.

### TESTING THE MAP SENSOR USING A DMM OR SCOPE

Use jumper wires, T-pins to back-probe the connector, or a breakout box to gain electrical access to the wiring to the pressure sensor. Most pressure sensors use three wires:

1. A 5-volt wire from the computer
2. A variable-signal wire back to the computer
3. A ground or reference low wire

TECH TIP

**Visual Check of the MAP Sensor**

A defective vacuum hose to a MAP sensor can cause a variety of driveability problems including poor fuel economy, hesitation, stalling, and rough idle. A small air leak (vacuum leak) around the hose can cause these symptoms and often set a trouble code in the vehicle computer. When working on a vehicle that uses a MAP sensor, make certain that the vacuum hose travels consistently *downward* on its route from the sensor to the source of manifold vacuum. Inspect the hose, especially if another technician has previously replaced the factory-original hose. It should not be so long that it sags down at any point. Condensed fuel and/or moisture can become trapped in this low spot in the hose and cause all types of driveability problems and MAP sensor codes.

When checking the MAP sensor, if anything comes out of the sensor itself, it should be replaced. This includes water, gasoline, or any other substance.

The procedure for testing the sensor is as follows:

1. Turn the ignition on (engine off).
2. Measure the voltage (or frequency) of the sensor output.
3. Using a hand-operated vacuum pump (or other variable vacuum source), apply vacuum to the sensor.

A good pressure sensor should change voltage (or frequency) in relation to the applied vacuum. If the signal does not change or the values are out of range according to the manufacturer's specifications, the sensor must be replaced.

### TESTING THE MAP SENSOR USING A SCAN TOOL   A scan tool can be used to test a MAP sensor by monitoring the injector pulse width (in milliseconds) when vacuum is being applied to the MAP sensor using a hand-operated vacuum pump. ● SEE FIGURE 15–7.

STEP 1   Apply about 20 in. Hg of vacuum to the MAP sensor and start the engine.

STEP 2   Observe the injector pulse width. On a warm engine, the injector pulse width will normally be 1.5 to 3.5 ms.

STEP 3   Slowly reduce the vacuum to the MAP sensor and observe the pulse width. A lower vacuum to the MAP sensor indicates a heavier load on the engine, and the injector pulse width should increase.

NOTE: If 23 in. Hg or more vacuum is applied to the MAP sensor with the engine running, this high vacuum will often stall the engine. The engine stalls because the high vacuum is interpreted by the PCM to indicate that the engine is being decelerated, which shuts off the fuel. During engine deceleration, the PCM shuts off the fuel injectors to reduce exhaust emissions and increase fuel economy.

**FIGURE 15–7** A typical hand-operated vacuum pump.

## FUEL-RAIL PRESSURE SENSOR

A fuel-rail pressure (FRP) sensor is used on some vehicles such as Fords that are equipped with electronic returnless fuel injection. This sensor provides fuel pressure information to the PCM for fuel-injection pulse-width calculations.

## MAP/BARO DIAGNOSTIC TROUBLE CODES

The diagnostic trouble codes (DTCs) associated with the MAP and BARO sensors include the following:

| Diagnostic Trouble Code | Description | Possible Causes |
| --- | --- | --- |
| P0106 | BARO sensor out-of-range at key on | • MAP sensor fault<br>• MAP sensor O-ring damaged or missing |
| P0107 | MAP sensor low voltage | • MAP sensor fault<br>• MAP sensor signal circuit shorted-to-ground<br>• MAP sensor 5-volt supply circuit open |
| P0108 | Map sensor high voltage | • MAP sensor fault<br>• MAP sensor O-ring damaged or missing<br>• MAP sensor signal circuit shorted-to-voltage |

## SUMMARY

1. Pressure below atmospheric pressure is called vacuum and is measured in inches of mercury.
2. A manifold absolute pressure sensor uses a perfect vacuum (zero absolute pressure) in the sensor to determine the pressure.
3. Three types of MAP sensors include the following:
   • Silicon-diaphragm strain gauge
   • Capacitor-capsule design
   • Ceramic disc design
4. A heavy engine load results in low intake manifold vacuum and a high MAP sensor signal voltage.
5. A light engine load results in high intake manifold vacuum and a low MAP sensor signal voltage.
6. A MAP sensor is used to detect changes in altitude as well as check other sensors and engine systems.
7. A MAP sensor can be tested by visual inspection, testing the output using a digital meter or scan tool.

## REVIEW QUESTIONS

1. What is the relationship among atmospheric pressure, vacuum, and boost pressure in PSI?
2. What are two types (construction) of MAP sensors?
3. What is the MAP sensor signal voltage or frequency at idle on a typical General Motors, Chrysler, and Ford engine?
4. What are three uses of a MAP sensor by the PCM?

1. As the load on an engine increases, the manifold vacuum decreases and the manifold absolute pressure _____.
   a. Increases
   b. Decreases
   c. Changes with barometric pressure only (altitude or weather)
   d. Remains constant (absolute)

2. A typical MAP sensor compares the vacuum in the intake manifold to _____.
   a. Atmospheric pressure
   b. A perfect vacuum
   c. Barometric pressure
   d. The value of the IAT sensor

3. Which statement is *false?*
   a. Absolute pressure is equal to barometric pressure plus intake manifold vacuum.
   b. A decrease in manifold vacuum means an increase in manifold pressure.
   c. The MAP sensor compares manifold vacuum to a perfect vacuum.
   d. Barometric pressure minus the MAP sensor reading equals intake manifold vacuum.

4. Which design of MAP sensor produces a frequency (digital) output signal?
   a. Silicon-diaphragm strain gauge
   b. Piezoresistivity design
   c. Capacitor-capsule
   d. Ceramic disc

5. The frequency output of a digital MAP sensor is reading 114 Hz. What is the approximate engine vacuum?
   a. Zero
   b. 5 in. Hg
   c. 10 in. Hg
   d. 15 in. Hg

6. Which is *not* a purpose or function of the MAP sensor?
   a. Measures the load on the engine
   b. Measures engine speed
   c. Calculates fuel delivery based on altitude
   d. Helps diagnose the EGR system

7. When measuring the output signal of a MAP sensor on a General Motors vehicle, the digital multimeter should be set to read _____.
   a. DC V
   b. AC V
   c. Hz
   d. DC A

8. Two technicians are discussing testing MAP sensors. Technician A says that the MAP sensor voltage on a General Motors vehicle at idle should be about 1 volt. Technician B says that the MAP sensor frequency on a Ford vehicle at idle should be about 105 to 108 Hz. Which technician is correct?
   a. Technician A only
   b. Technician B only
   c. Both Technicians A and B
   d. Neither Technician A nor B

9. Technician A says that MAP sensors use a 5-volt reference voltage from the PCM. Technician B says that the MAP sensor voltage will be higher at idle at high altitudes compared to when the engine is operating at near sea level. Which technician is correct?
   a. Technician A only
   b. Technician B only
   c. Both Technicians A and B
   d. Neither Technician A nor B

10. A P0107 DTC is being discussed. Technician A says that a defective MAP sensor could be the cause. Technician B says that a MAP sensor signal wire shorted-to-ground could be the cause. Which technician is correct?
    a. Technician A only
    b. Technician B only
    c. Both Technicians A and B
    d. Neither Technician A nor B

# chapter 16

# MASS AIRFLOW SENSORS

**OBJECTIVES:** **After studying Chapter 16, the reader should be able to:** • Prepare for ASE Engine Performance (A8) certification test content area "E" (Computerized Engine Controls Diagnosis and Repair). • Discuss how mass airflow (MAF) sensors work. • List the methods that can be used to test MAF sensors. • Describe the symptoms of a failed MAF sensor. • List how the operation of the MAF sensor affects vehicle operation. • Discuss MAF sensor rationality tests.

**KEY TERMS:** False air 209 • Mass airflow (MAF) sensor 206 • Speed density 205 • Tap test 208 • Vane airflow (VAF) sensor 205

## AIRFLOW SENSORS

Electronic fuel injection systems that do not use the "speed density" system for fuel calculation measure the airflow volume delivered to the engine. Older systems use a movable vane in the intake stream called a vane airflow (VAF) sensor. The vane is part of the **vane airflow (VAF) sensor.** The vane is deflected by intake airflow. ● SEE FIGURE 16–1.

The VAF sensor used in Bosch L-Jetronic, Ford, and most Japanese electronic port fuel-injection systems is a

movable vane connected to a laser-calibrated potentiometer. The vane is mounted on a pivot pin and is deflected by intake airflow proportionate to air velocity. As the vane moves, it also moves the potentiometer. This causes a change in the signal voltage supplied to the computer. ● **SEE FIGURE 16–2.** For example, if the reference voltage is 5 volts, the potentiometer's signal to the computer will vary from a zero voltage signal (no airflow) to almost a 5-volt signal (maximum airflow). In this way, the potentiometer provides the information the computer needs to vary the injector pulse width proportionate to airflow. There is a special "dampening chamber" built into the VAF to smooth out vane pulsations that would be created by intake manifold air-pressure fluctuations caused by the valve opening and closing. Many VAF sensors include a switch to energize the electric fuel pump. This is a safety feature that prevents the operation of the fuel pump if the engine stalls.

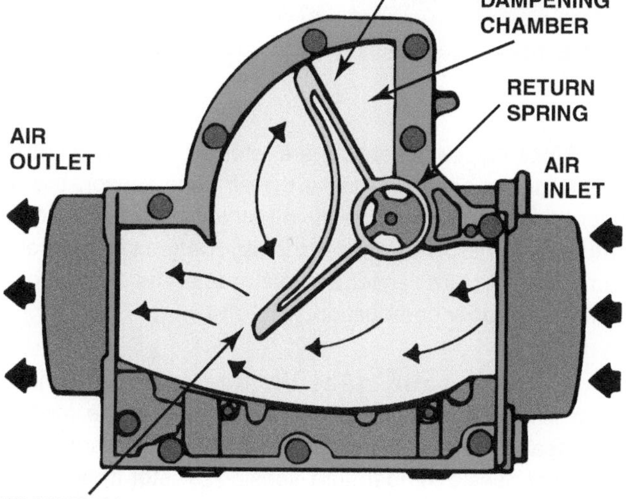

FIGURE 16–1 A vane airflow (VAF) sensor.

## MASS AIRFLOW SENSOR TYPES

Most newer fuel injection systems use a **Mass Air Flow (MAF)** sensor to calculate the amount of air volume delivered to the engine.

There are several types of mass airflow sensors.

**HOT FILM SENSOR**   The hot film sensor uses a temperature-sensing resistor (thermistor) to measure the temperature of the incoming air. Through the electronics within the sensor, a

**FIGURE 16–2** A typical air vane sensor with the cover removed. The movable arm contacts a carbon resistance path as the vane opens. Many air vane sensors also have contacts that close to supply voltage to the electric fuel pump as the air vane starts to open when the engine is being cranked and air is being drawn into the engine.

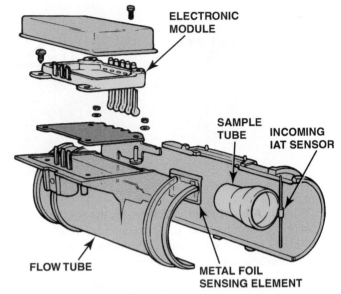

**FIGURE 16–3** This five-wire mass airflow sensor consists of a metal foil sensing unit, an intake air temperature (IAT) sensor, and the electronic module.

 **FREQUENTLY ASKED QUESTION**

**What Is the Difference Between an Analog and a Digital MAF Sensor?**

Some MAF sensors produce a digital DC voltage signal whose frequency changes with the amount of airflow through the sensor. The frequency range also varies with the make of sensor and can range from 0 to 300 Hz for older General Motors MAF sensors to 1,000 to 9,000 Hz for most newer designs.

Some MAF sensors, such as those used by Ford and others, produce a changing DC voltage rather than frequency and range from 0 to 5 volts DC.

**FIGURE 16–4** The sensing wire in a typical hot wire mass airflow sensor.

conductive film is kept at a temperature 70°C above the temperature of the incoming air. ● **SEE FIGURE 16–3.**

Because both the amount and the density of the air tend to contribute to the cooling effect as the air passes through the sensor, this type of sensor can actually produce an output based on the mass of the airflow. Mass equals volume times density. For example, cold air is denser than warm air, so a small amount of cold air may have the same mass as a larger amount of warm air. Therefore, a mass airflow sensor is designed to measure the mass, not the volume, of the air entering the engine.

The output of this type of sensor is usually a frequency based on the amount of air entering the sensor. The more air that enters the sensor, the more the hot film is cooled. The electronics inside the sensor, therefore, increase the current flow through the hot film to maintain the 70°C temperature differential between the air temperature and the temperature of the hot film. This change in current flow is converted to a frequency output that the computer can use as a measurement of airflow.

Most of these types of sensors are referred to as **mass airflow (MAF) sensors** because, unlike the air vane sensor, the MAF sensor takes into account relative humidity, altitude, and temperature of the air. The denser the air, the greater the cooling effect on the hot film sensor and the greater the amount of fuel required for proper combustion.

**HOT WIRE SENSOR** The hot wire sensor is similar to the hot film type but uses a hot wire to sense the mass airflow instead of the hot film. Like the hot film sensor, the hot wire sensor uses a temperature-sensing resistor (thermistor) to measure the temperature of the air entering the sensor. ● **SEE FIGURE 16–4.** The electronic circuitry within the sensor keeps the temperature of the wire at 70°C above the temperature of the incoming air.

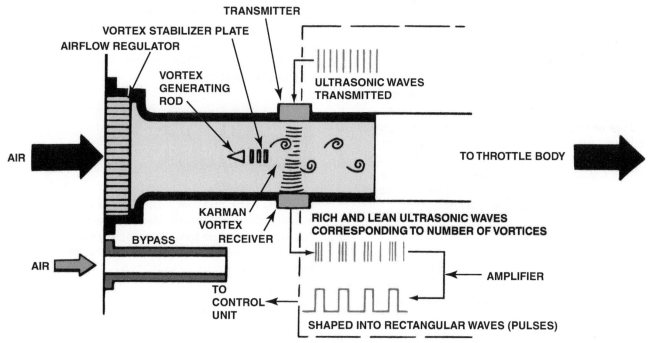

**FIGURE 16–5** A Karman vortex airflow sensor uses a triangle-shaped rod to create vortexes as the air flows through the sensor. The electronics in the sensor itself converts these vortexes to a digital square wave signal.

Both designs operate in essentially the same way. A resistor wire or screen installed in the path of intake airflow is heated to a constant temperature by electric current provided by the computer. Air flowing past the screen or wire cools it. The degree of cooling varies with air velocity, temperature, density, and humidity. These factors combine to indicate the mass of air entering the engine. As the screen or wire cools, more current is required to maintain the specified temperature. As the screen or wire heats up, less current is required. The operating principle can be summarized as follows:

- More intake air volume = cooler sensor, more current
- Less intake air volume = warmer sensor, less current

The computer constantly monitors the change in current and translates it into a voltage signal that is used to determine injector pulse width.

**BURN-OFF CIRCUIT.** Some hot wire-type MAF sensors use a burn-off circuit to keep the sensing wire clean of dust and dirt. A high current is passed through the sensing wire for a short time but long enough to cause the wire to glow because of the heat. The burn-off circuit is turned on when the ignition switch is switched off after the engine has been operating long enough to achieve normal operating temperature.

## KARMAN VORTEX SENSORS

In 1912, a Hungarian scientist named Theodore Van Karman observed that vortexes were created when air passed over a pointed surface. This type of sensor sends a sound wave

through the turbulence created by incoming air passing through the sensor. Air mass is calculated based on the time required for the sound waves to cross the turbulent air passage.

There are two basic designs of Karman vortex airflow sensors:

- **Ultrasonic.** This type of sensor uses ultrasonic waves to detect the vortexes that are produced and produces a digital (on-and-off) signal where frequency is proportional to the amount of air passing through the sensor. ● **SEE FIGURE 16–5.**
- **Pressure type.** Chrysler uses a pressure-type Karman vortex sensor that uses a pressure sensor to detect the vortexes. As the airflow through the sensor increases, so do the number of pressure variations. The electronics in the sensor convert these pressure variations to a square wave (digital DC voltage) signal, whose frequency is in proportion to the airflow through the sensor.

## PCM USES FOR AIRFLOW SENSORS

The PCM uses the information from the airflow sensor for the following purposes:

- Airflow sensors are used mostly to determine the amount of fuel needed and base pulse-width numbers. The greater the mass of the incoming air, the longer the injectors are pulsed on.

### The Dirty MAF Sensor Story

The owner of a Buick Park Avenue equipped with a 3800 V-6 engine complained that the engine would hesitate during acceleration, showed lack of power, and seemed to surge or miss at times. A visual inspection found everything to be like new, including a new air filter. There were no stored diagnostic trouble codes (DTCs). A look at the scan data showed airflow to be within the recommended 3 to 7 g per second. A check of the frequency output showed the problem:

**Idle frequency = 2.177 kHz (2,177 Hz)**

Normal frequency at idle speed should be 2.37 to 2.52 kHz. Cleaning the hot wire of the MAF sensor restored proper operation. The sensor wire was covered with what looked like fine fibers, possibly from the replacement air filter.

**NOTE: Older GM MAF sensors operated at a lower frequency of 32 to 150 Hz, with 32 Hz being the average reading at idle and 150 Hz for wide-open throttle.**

### FREQUENTLY ASKED QUESTION

### What Is Meant by a "High-Authority Sensor"?

A high-authority sensor is a sensor that has a major influence over the amount of fuel being delivered to the engine. For example, at engine start-up, the engine coolant temperature (ECT) sensor is a high-authority sensor, and the oxygen sensor (O2S) is a low-authority sensor. However, as the engine reaches operating temperature, the oxygen sensor becomes a high-authority sensor and can greatly affect the amount of fuel being supplied to the engine. See the chart.

| High-Authority Sensors | Low-Authority Sensors |
|---|---|
| ECT (especially when the engine starts and is warming up) | IAT (intake air temperature) sensors modify and back up the ECT |
| O2S (after the engine reaches closed-loop operation) | TFT (transmission fluid temperature) |
| MAP | PRNDL (shift position sensor) |
| MAF | KS (knock sensor) |
| TP (high authority during acceleration and deceleration) | EFT (engine fuel temperature) |

- Airflow sensors back up the TP sensor in the event of a loss of signal or an inaccurate throttle position sensor signal. If the MAF sensor fails, then the PCM will calculate the fuel delivery needs of the engine based on throttle position and engine speed (RPM).

## TESTING MASS AIRFLOW SENSORS

**VISUAL INSPECTION**   Start the testing of a MAF sensor by performing a thorough visual inspection. Look at all the hoses that direct and send air, especially between the MAF sensor and the throttle body. Also check the electrical connector for the following:

- Corrosion
- Terminals that are bent or pushed out of the plastic connector
- Frayed wiring

**MAF SENSOR OUTPUT TEST**   MAF sensors calculate air mass by weight in a given amount of time usually in grams per second (gm/sec). A digital multimeter, set to read DC volts on the signal wire circuit, can be used to check the MAF sensor. See the chart that shows the voltage output compared with the grams per second of airflow through the sensor. Normal airflow is 3 to 7 g per second.

| Analog MAF Sensor Grams per Second/Voltage Chart | |
|---|---|
| Grams per Second | Sensor Voltage |
| 0 | 0.2 |
| 2 | 0.7 |
| 4 | 1.0 (typical idle value) |
| 8 | 1.5 |
| 15 | 2.0 |
| 30 | 2.5 |
| 50 | 3.0 |
| 80 | 3.5 |
| 110 | 4.0 |
| 150 | 4.5 |
| 175 | 4.8 |

**TAP TEST**   With the engine running at idle speed, gently tap the MAF sensor with the fingers of an open hand. If the engine stumbles or stalls, the MAF sensor is defective. This test is commonly called the **tap test.**

**DIGITAL METER TEST OF A MAF SENSOR**   A digital multimeter can be used to measure the frequency (Hz) output of the sensor and compare the reading with specifications.

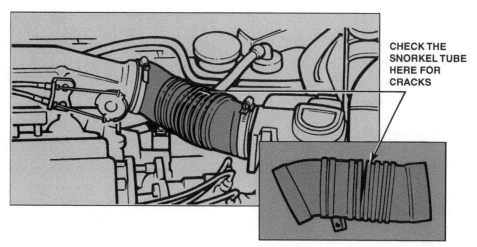

**CHECK THE SNORKEL TUBE HERE FOR CRACKS**

**FIGURE 16–6** Carefully check the hose between the MAF sensor and the throttle body assembly for cracks or splits that could create extra (false) air into the engine that is not measured by the MAF sensor.

---

 **FREQUENTLY ASKED QUESTION**

**What Is False Air?**

Airflow sensors and mass airflow (MAF) sensors are designed to measure *all* the air entering the engine. If an air hose between the MAF sensor and the throttle body was loose or had a hole, extra air could enter the engine without being measured. This extra air is often called **false air**. ● **SEE FIGURE 16–6.** Because this extra air is unmeasured, the computer does not provide enough fuel delivery, and the engine operates too lean, especially at idle. A small hole in the air inlet hose would represent a fairly large percentage of false air at idle but would represent a very small percentage of extra air at highway speeds.

To diagnose for false air, look at long-term fuel trim numbers at idle and at 3,000 RPM.

**NOTE: If the engine runs well in reverse yet runs terrible in any forward gear, carefully look at the inlet hose for air leaks that would open when the engine torque moves the engine slightly on its mounts.**

---

**TECH TIP**

**The Unplug-It Test**

If a sensor is defective yet still produces a signal to the computer, the computer will often accept the reading and make the required changes in fuel delivery and spark advance. If, however, the sensor is not reading correctly, the computer will process this wrong information and perform an action assuming that information being supplied is accurate. For example, if a mass airflow (MAF) sensor is telling the computer that 12 g of air per second is going into the engine, the computer will then pulse the injector for 6.4 ms or whatever figure it is programmed to provide. However, if the air going into the engine is actually 14 g per second, the amount of fuel supplied by the injectors will not be enough to provide proper engine operation. If the MAF sensor is unplugged, the computer knows that the sensor is not capable of supplying airflow information, so it defaults to a fixed amount of fuel based on the values of other sensors, such as the TP and MAP sensors. "If in doubt, take it out."

If the engine operates better with a sensor unplugged, then suspect that the sensor is defective. A sensor that is not supplying the correct information is said to be skewed. The computer will not set a diagnostic trouble code for this condition because the computer can often not detect that the sensor is supplying wrong information.

---

The frequency output and engine speed in RPM can also be plotted on a graph to check to see if the frequency and RPM are proportional, resulting in a straight line on the graph.

## MAF SENSOR CONTAMINATION

Dirt, oil, silicon, or even spiderwebs can coat the sensing wire. Because it tends to insulate the sensing wire at low airflow rates, a contaminated sensor often overestimates the amount of air entering the engine at idle and therefore causes the fuel system to go rich. At higher engine speeds near wide-open throttle (WOT), the contamination can cause the sensor to underestimate the amount of air entering the engine. As a result, the fuel system will go lean, causing spark knock and lack of power concerns. To check for contamination, check the fuel trim numbers.

**The Rich-Running Toyota**

A Toyota failed an enhanced emission test for excessive carbon monoxide, which is caused by a rich (too much fuel) air-fuel ratio problem. After checking all of the basics and not finding any fault in the fuel system, the technician checked the archives of the International Automotive Technicians Network (www.iatn.net) and discovered that a broken spring inside the airflow sensor was a possible cause. The sensor was checked, and a broken vane return spring was discovered. Replacing the airflow sensor restored the engine to proper operating conditions, and it passed the emission test.

If the fuel trim is negative (removing fuel) at idle yet is positive (adding fuel) at higher engine speeds, a contaminated MAF sensor is a likely cause. Other tests for a contaminated MAF sensor include the following:

- At WOT, the grams per second, as read on a scan tool, should exceed 100 g.
- At WOT, the voltage, as read on a digital voltmeter, should exceed 4 volts for an analog sensor.
- At WOT, the frequency, as read on a meter or scan tool, should exceed 7 kHz for a digital sensor.

If the readings do not exceed these values, then the MAF sensor is contaminated.

# MAF-RELATED DIAGNOSTIC TROUBLE CODES

The diagnostic trouble codes (DTCs) associated with the mass airflow and air vane sensors include the following:

| Diagnostic Trouble Code | Description | Possible Causes |
|---|---|---|
| P0100 | Mass or volume airflow circuit problems | • Open or short in mass airflow circuit<br>• Defective MAF sensor |
| P0101 | Mass airflow circuit range problems | • Defective MAF sensor (check for false air) |
| P0102 | Mass airflow circuit low output | • Defective MAF sensor<br>• MAF sensor circuit open or shorted-to-ground<br>• Open 12-volt supply voltage circuit |
| P0103 | Mass airflow circuit high output | • Defective MAF sensor<br>• MAF sensor circuit shorted-to-voltage |

# SUMMARY

1. A mass airflow sensor actually measures the density and amount of air flowing into the engine, which results in accurate engine control.

2. An air vane sensor measures the volume of the air, and the intake air temperature sensor is used by the PCM to calculate the mass of the air entering the engine.

3. A hot wire MAF sensor uses the electronics in the sensor itself to heat a wire 70°C above the temperature of the air entering the engine.

# REVIEW QUESTIONS

1. How does a hot film MAF sensor work?
2. What type of voltage signal is produced by a MAF?
3. What change in the signal will occur if engine speed is increased?
4. How is a MAF sensor tested?
5. What is the purpose of a MAF sensor?
6. What are the types of airflow sensors?

1. A fuel-injection system that does not use a sensor to measure the amount (or mass) of air entering the engine is usually called a(n) _____ type of system.
   a. Air vane-controlled
   b. Speed density
   c. Mass airflow
   d. Hot wire

2. Which type of sensor uses a burn-off circuit?
   a. Hot wire MAF sensor
   b. Hot film MAF sensor
   c. Vane-type airflow sensor
   d. Both a and b

3. Which sensor has a switch that controls the electric fuel pump?
   a. VAF
   b. Hot wire MAF
   c. Hot filter MAF
   d. Karman vortex sensor

4. Two technicians are discussing Karman vortex sensors. Technician A says that they contain a burn-off circuit to keep them clean. Technician B says that they contain a movable vane. Which technician is correct?
   a. Technician A only
   b. Technicians B only
   c. Both Technicians A and B
   d. Neither Technician A nor B

5. The typical MAF reading on a scan tool with the engine at idle speed and normal operating temperature is _____.
   a. 1 to 3 g per second
   b. 3 to 7 g per second
   c. 8 to 12 g per second
   d. 14 to 24 g per second

6. Two technicians are diagnosing a poorly running engine. There are no diagnostic trouble codes. When the MAF sensor is unplugged, the engine runs better. Technician A says that this means that the MAF is supplying incorrect airflow information to the PCM. Technician B says that this indicates that the PCM is defective. Which technician is correct?
   a. Technician A only
   b. Technician B only
   c. Both Technicians A and B
   d. Neither Technician A nor B

7. A MAF sensor on a General Motors 3800 V-6 is being tested for contamination. Technician A says that the sensor should show over 100 g per second on a scan tool display when the accelerator is depressed to WOT on a running engine. Technician B says that the output frequency should exceed 7,000 Hz when the accelerator pedal is depressed to WOT on a running engine. Which technician is correct?
   a. Technician A only
   b. Technician B only
   c. Both Technicians A and B
   d. Neither Technician A nor B

8. Which airflow sensor has a dampening chamber?
   a. Vane airflow
   b. Hot film MAF
   c. Hot wire MAF
   d. Karman vortex

9. Air that enters the engine without passing through the airflow sensor is called _____.
   a. Bypass air
   b. Dirty air
   c. False air
   d. Measured air

10. A P0102 DTC is being discussed. Technician A says that a sensor circuit shorted-to-ground can be the cause. Technician B says that an open sensor voltage supply circuit could be the cause. Which technician is correct?
   a. Technician A only
   b. Technician B only
   c. Both Technicians A and B
   d. Neither Technician A nor B

# chapter 17

# OXYGEN SENSORS

**OBJECTIVES:** **After studying Chapter 17, the reader should be able to:** • Prepare for ASE Engine Performance (A8) certification test content area "E" (Computerized Engine Controls Diagnosis and Repair). • Discuss how oxygen sensors (O2S) work. • List the methods that can be used to test oxygen sensors. • Describe the symptoms of a failed O2S. • List how the operation of the O2S affects vehicle operation.

**KEY TERMS:** Bias voltage 215 • Closed-loop operation 214 • Cross counts 217 • False lean indication 223 • False rich indication 225 • Open-loop operation 214 • Oxygen sensor (O2S) 212

## OXYGEN SENSORS

**PURPOSE AND FUNCTION** Automotive computer systems use a sensor in the exhaust system to measure the oxygen content of the exhaust. These sensors are called **oxygen sensors (O2S).** The oxygen sensor is installed in the exhaust manifold or located downstream from the manifold in the exhaust pipe. ● **SEE FIGURE 17–1.** The oxygen sensor is directly in the path of the exhaust gas stream, where it monitors oxygen level in both the exhaust stream and the ambient air. In a zirconia oxygen sensor, the tip contains a thimble made of zirconium dioxide ($ZrO_2$), an electrically conductive material capable of generating a small voltage in the presence of oxygen. The oxygen sensor is used by the PCM to control fuel delivery.

**CONSTRUCTION AND OPERATION** Exhaust from the engine passes through the end of the sensor, where the gases contact the outer side of the thimble. Atmospheric air enters through the other end of the sensor or through the wire of the sensor and contacts the inner side of the thimble. The inner and outer surfaces of the thimble are plated with platinum. The inner surface becomes a negative electrode; the outer surface is a positive electrode. The atmosphere contains a relatively constant 21% of oxygen. Rich exhaust gases contain little oxygen. Exhaust from a lean mixture contains more oxygen.

Negatively charged oxygen ions are drawn to the thimble, where they collect on both the inner and outer surfaces. ● **SEE FIGURE 17–2.** Because the percentage of oxygen present in the atmosphere exceeds that in the exhaust gases, the atmosphere side of the thimble draws more negative oxygen ions than the exhaust side. The difference between the two sides creates an electrical potential, or voltage. When the concentration

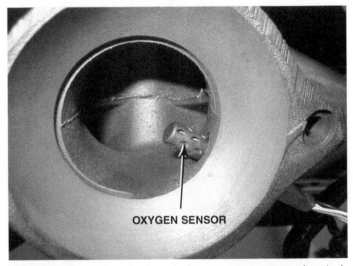

**OXYGEN SENSOR**

**FIGURE 17–1** Many fuel-control oxygen sensors are located in the exhaust manifold near its outlet so that the sensor can detect the presence or absence of oxygen in the exhaust stream for all cylinders that feed into the manifold.

of oxygen on the exhaust side of the thimble is low (rich exhaust), a high voltage (0.6 to 1 volt) is generated between the electrodes. As the oxygen concentration on the exhaust side increases (lean exhaust), the voltage generated drops low (0.0 to 0.3 volt). ● **SEE FIGURE 17–3.**

This voltage signal is sent to the computer, where it passes through the input conditioner for amplification. The computer interprets a high-voltage signal (low-oxygen content) as a rich air-fuel ratio and a low-voltage signal (high-oxygen content) as a lean air-fuel ratio. Based on the O2S signal (above or below 0.45 volt), the computer compensates by making the mixture either leaner or richer as required to continually vary close to a 14.7:1 air-fuel ratio to satisfy the needs of the three-way catalytic converter.

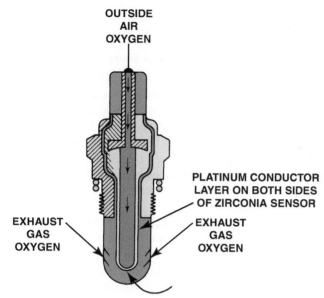

**FIGURE 17–2** A cross-sectional view of a typical zirconia oxygen sensor.

OXYGEN SENSOR ELEMENT

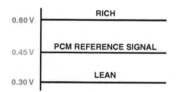

**FIGURE 17–3** A difference in oxygen content between the atmosphere and the exhaust gases enables an O2S to generate voltage.

The O2S is the key sensor of an electronically controlled fuel metering system for emission control.

An O2S does not send a voltage signal until its tip reaches a temperature of about 572°F (300°C). Also, oxygen sensors provide their fastest response to mixture changes at about 1,472°F (800°C). When the engine starts and the O2S is cold, the computer runs the engine in the open-loop mode, drawing on prerecorded data in the PROM for fuel control on a cold engine or when O2S output is not within certain limits.

If the exhaust contains very little oxygen (O2S), the computer assumes that the intake charge is rich (too much fuel) and reduces fuel delivery. ● **SEE FIGURE 17–4.** However, when the oxygen level is high, the computer assumes that the intake

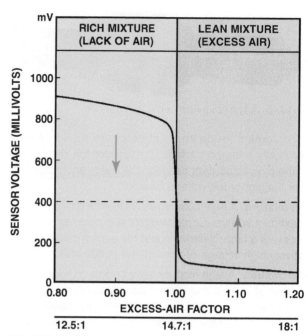

**FIGURE 17–4** The oxygen sensor provides a quick response at the stoichiometric air-fuel ratio of 14.7:1.

charge is lean (not enough fuel) and increases fuel delivery. There are several different designs of oxygen sensors, including the following:

- **One-wire oxygen sensor.** The single wire of a one-wire oxygen sensor is the O2S signal wire. The ground for the O2S is through the shell and threads of the sensor and through the exhaust manifold.
- **Two-wire oxygen sensor.** The two-wire sensor has a signal wire and a ground wire for the O2S.
- **Three-wire oxygen sensor.** The three-wire sensor design uses an electric resistance heater to help get the O2S up to temperature more quickly and to help keep the sensor at operating temperature even at idle speeds. The three wires include the O2S signal, the power, and ground for the heater.
- **Four-wire oxygen sensor.** The four-wire sensor is a heated O2S (HO2S) that uses an O2S signal wire and signal ground. The other two wires are the power and ground for the heater.

## ZIRCONIA OXYGEN SENSORS

The most common type of oxygen sensor is made from zirconia (zirconium dioxide). It is usually constructed using powder that is pressed into a thimble shape and coated with porous platinum material that acts as electrodes. All zirconia sensors use 18-mm-diameter threads with a washer. ● **SEE FIGURE 17–5.**

Zirconia oxygen sensors are constructed so that oxygen ions flow through the sensor when there is a difference between

**FIGURE 17–5** A typical zirconia oxygen sensor.

the oxygen content inside and outside of the sensor. An ion is an electrically charged particle. The greater the differences between the oxygen content between the inside and outside of the sensor the higher the voltage created:

- **Rich mixture.** A rich mixture results in little oxygen in the exhaust stream. Compared to the outside air, this represents a large difference and the sensor creates a relatively high voltage of about 1 volt (1,000 mV).

- **Lean mixture.** A lean mixture leaves some oxygen in the exhaust stream that did not combine with the fuel. This leftover oxygen reduces the difference between the oxygen content of the exhaust compared to the oxygen content of the outside air. As a result, the sensor voltage is low or almost zero volts.

- **O2S voltage above 450 mV.** This is produced by the sensor when the oxygen content in the exhaust is low. This is interpreted by the engine computer (PCM) as being a rich exhaust.

- **O2S voltage below 450 mV.** This is produced by the sensor when the oxygen content is high. This is interpreted by the engine computer (PCM) as being a lean exhaust.

## TITANIA OXYGEN SENSOR

The titania (titanium dioxide) oxygen sensor does not produce a voltage but rather changes in resistance with the presence of oxygen in the exhaust. All titania oxygen sensors use a four-terminal variable-resistance unit with a heating element. A titania sensor samples exhaust air only and uses a reference voltage from the PCM. Titania oxide oxygen sensors use a 14-mm thread and are not interchangeable with zirconia oxygen sensors. One volt is applied to the sensor, and the changing resistance of the titania oxygen sensor changes the voltage of the sensor circuit. As with a zirconia oxygen sensor, the voltage signal is above 450 mV when the exhaust is rich and low (below 450 mV) when the exhaust is lean.

## CLOSED LOOP AND OPEN LOOP

The amount of fuel delivered to an engine is determined by the powertrain control module (PCM) based on inputs from the engine coolant temperature (ECT), throttle position (TP)

sensor, and others until the oxygen sensor is capable of supplying a usable signal. When the PCM alone (without feedback) is determining the amount of fuel needed, it is called **open-loop operation.** As soon as the oxygen sensor is capable of supplying rich and lean signals, adjustments by the computer can be made to fine-tune the correct air-fuel mixture. This checking and adjusting by the computer is called **closed-loop operation.**

## PCM USES OF THE OXYGEN SENSOR

**FUEL CONTROL** The upstream oxygen sensors are among the high-authority sensors used for fuel control while operating in closed loop. Before the oxygen sensors are hot enough to give accurate exhaust oxygen information to the computer, fuel control is determined by other sensors and the anticipated injector pulse width determined by those sensors. After the control system achieves closed-loop status, the oxygen sensor provides feedback with actual exhaust gas oxygen content.

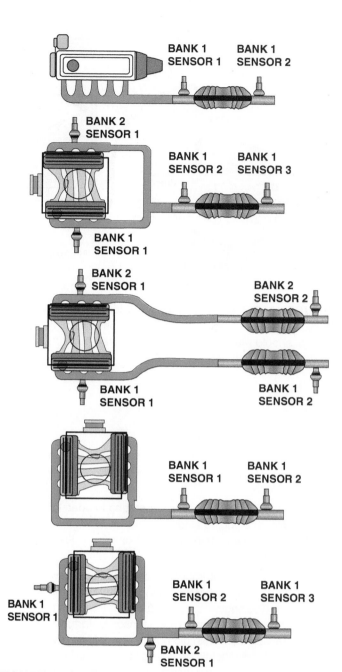

**FIGURE 17–6** Number and label designations for oxygen sensors. Bank 1 is the bank where cylinder number 1 is located.

**FUEL TRIM** Fuel trim is a computer program that is used to compensate for a too rich or a too lean air-fuel exhaust as detected by the oxygen sensor(s). Fuel trim is necessary to keep the air-fuel mixture within limits to allow the catalytic converter to operate efficiently. If the exhaust is too lean or too rich for a long time, the catalytic converter can be damaged. The fuel trim numbers are determined from the signals from the oxygen sensor(s). If the engine has been operating too lean, short-term and long-term fuel time programming inside the PCM can cause an increase in the commanded injector pulse width to bring the air-fuel mixture back into the proper range. Fuel trim can be negative (subtracting fuel) or positive (adding fuel).

**?** FREQUENTLY ASKED QUESTION

### What Happens to the Bias Voltage?

Some vehicle manufacturers such as General Motors Corporation have the computer apply 450 mV (0.450 V) to the O2S signal wire. This voltage is called the **bias voltage** and represents the threshold voltage for the transition from rich to lean.

This bias voltage is displayed on a scan tool when the ignition switch is turned on with the engine off. When the engine is started, the O2S becomes warm enough to produce a usable voltage, and bias voltage "disappears" as the O2S responds to a rich and lean mixture. What happened to the bias voltage that the computer applied to the O2S? The voltage from the O2S simply overcame the very weak voltage signal from the computer. This bias voltage is so weak that even a 20-megohm impedance DMM will affect the strength enough to cause the voltage to drop to 426 mV. Other meters with only 10 megohms of impedance will cause the bias voltage to read less than 400 mV.

Therefore, even though the O2S voltage is relatively low powered, it is more than strong enough to override the very weak bias voltage the computer sends to the O2S.

## OXYGEN SENSOR DIAGNOSIS

The oxygen sensors are used for diagnosis of other systems and components. For example, the exhaust gas recirculation (EGR) system is tested by the PCM by commanding the valve to open during the test. Some PCMs determine whether enough exhaust gas flows into the engine by looking at the oxygen sensor response (fuel trim numbers). The upstream and downstream oxygen sensors are also used to determine the efficiency of the catalytic converter. ● **SEE FIGURE 17–7.**

**TESTING AN OXYGEN SENSOR USING A DIGITAL VOLTMETER** The oxygen sensor can be checked for proper operation using a digital high-impedance voltmeter:

1. With the engine off, connect the red lead of the meter to the oxygen sensor signal wire and the black meter lead to a good engine ground. ● **SEE FIGURE 17–8.**

2. Start the engine and allow it to reach closed-loop operation.

3. In closed-loop operation, the oxygen sensor voltage should be constantly changing as the fuel mixture is being controlled.

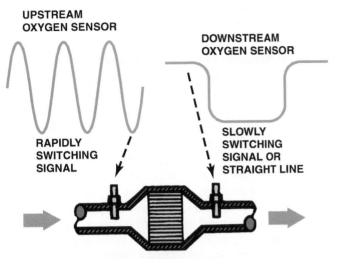

**FIGURE 17–7** The OBD-II catalytic converter monitor compares the signals of the upstream and downstream oxygen sensor to determine converter efficiency.

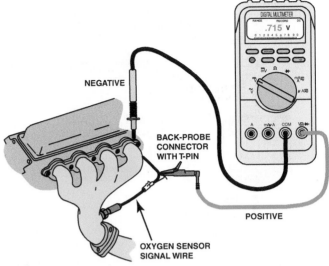

**FIGURE 17–8** Testing an oxygen sensor using a DMM set on DC volts. With the engine operating in closed loop, the oxygen voltage should read over 800 mV and lower than 200 mV and be constantly fluctuating.

---

### REAL WORLD FIX

**The Oxygen Sensor Is Lying to You**

A technician was trying to solve a driveability problem with an older V-6 passenger car. The car idled roughly, hesitated, and accelerated poorly. A thorough visual inspection did not indicate any possible problems, and there were no diagnostic trouble codes stored.

A check was made on the oxygen sensor activity using a DMM. The voltage stayed above 600 mV most of the time. If a large vacuum hose was removed, the oxygen sensor voltage would temporarily drop to below 450 mV and then return to a reading of over 600 mV. Remember the following:

- High O2S readings = rich exhaust (low $O_2$ content in the exhaust)
- Low O2S readings = lean exhaust (high $O_2$ content in the exhaust)

As part of a thorough visual inspection, the technician removed and inspected the spark plugs. All the spark plugs were white, indicating a lean mixture, not the rich mixture that the oxygen sensor was indicating. The high O2S reading signaled the computer to reduce the amount of fuel, resulting in an excessively lean operation.

After replacing the oxygen sensor, the engine ran great. But what killed the oxygen sensor? The technician finally learned from the owner that the head gasket had been replaced over a year ago. The phosphate and silicate additives in the antifreeze coolant had coated the oxygen sensor. Because the oxygen sensor was coated, the oxygen content of the exhaust could not be detected—the result: a false rich signal from the oxygen sensor.

---

### REAL WORLD FIX

**The Missing Ford Escort**

A Ford Escort was being analyzed for poor engine operation. The engine ran perfectly during the following conditions:

1. With the engine cold or operating in open loop
2. With the engine at idle
3. With the engine operating at or near wide-open throttle

After hours of troubleshooting, the cause was found to be a poor ground connection for the oxygen sensor. The engine ran okay during times when the computer ignored the oxygen sensor. Unfortunately, the service technician did not have a definite plan during the diagnostic process and as a result checked and replaced many unnecessary parts. An oxygen sensor test early in the diagnostic procedure would have indicated that the oxygen (O2S) signal was not correct. The poor ground caused the oxygen sensor voltage level to be too high, indicating to the computer that the mixture was too rich. The computer then subtracted fuel, which caused the engine to miss and run rough as the result of the now too lean air-fuel mixture.

The results should be interpreted as follows:

- If the oxygen sensor fails to respond and its voltage remains at about 450 mV, the sensor may be defective and require replacement. Before replacing the oxygen sensor, check the manufacturer's recommended procedures.
- If the oxygen sensor reads high all the time (above 550 mV), the fuel system could be supplying too rich a

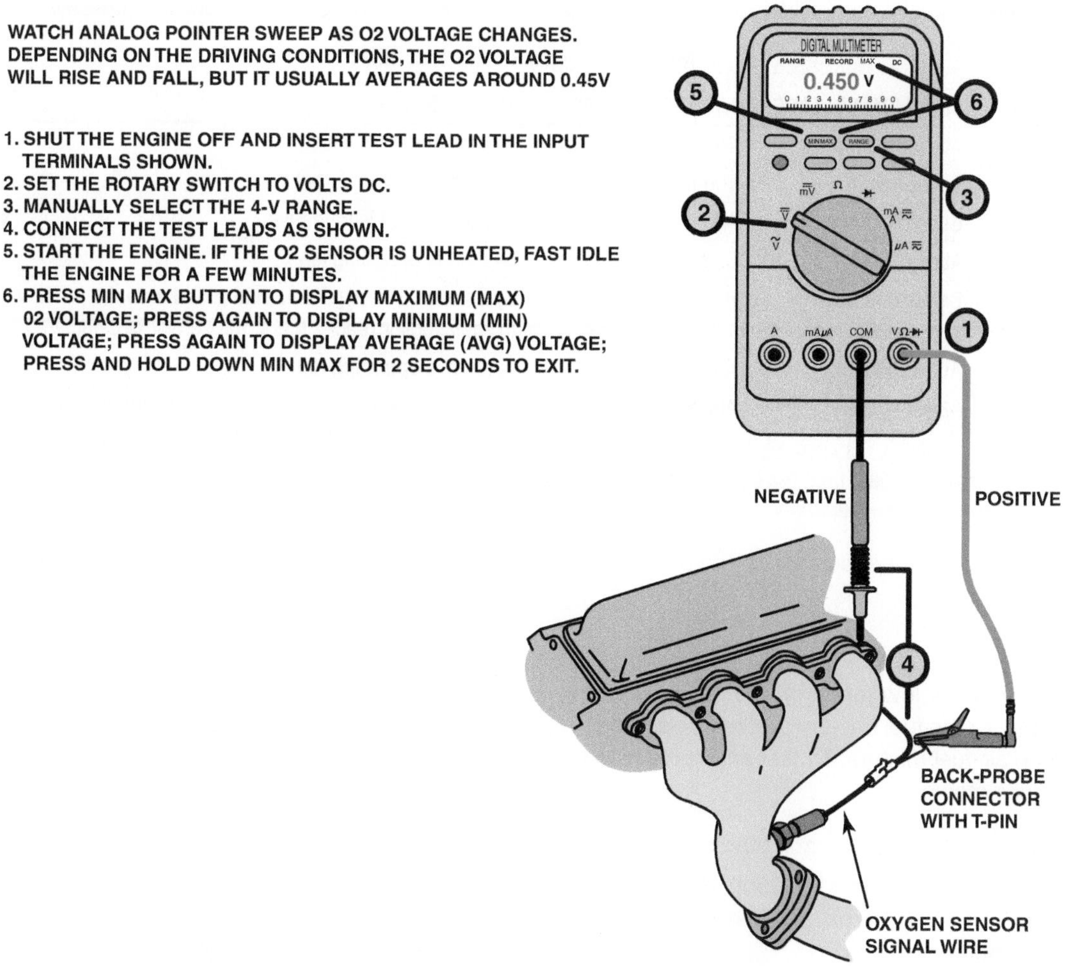

WATCH ANALOG POINTER SWEEP AS O2 VOLTAGE CHANGES.
DEPENDING ON THE DRIVING CONDITIONS, THE O2 VOLTAGE
WILL RISE AND FALL, BUT IT USUALLY AVERAGES AROUND 0.45V

1. SHUT THE ENGINE OFF AND INSERT TEST LEAD IN THE INPUT
   TERMINALS SHOWN.
2. SET THE ROTARY SWITCH TO VOLTS DC.
3. MANUALLY SELECT THE 4-V RANGE.
4. CONNECT THE TEST LEADS AS SHOWN.
5. START THE ENGINE. IF THE O2 SENSOR IS UNHEATED, FAST IDLE
   THE ENGINE FOR A FEW MINUTES.
6. PRESS MIN MAX BUTTON TO DISPLAY MAXIMUM (MAX)
   02 VOLTAGE; PRESS AGAIN TO DISPLAY MINIMUM (MIN)
   VOLTAGE; PRESS AGAIN TO DISPLAY AVERAGE (AVG) VOLTAGE;
   PRESS AND HOLD DOWN MIN MAX FOR 2 SECONDS TO EXIT.

NEGATIVE    POSITIVE

BACK-PROBE
CONNECTOR
WITH T-PIN

OXYGEN SENSOR
SIGNAL WIRE

**FIGURE 17–9** Using a digital multimeter to test an oxygen sensor using the MIN/MAX record function of the meter.

**FREQUENTLY ASKED QUESTION**

### Why Does the Oxygen Sensor Voltage Read 5 Volts on Many Chrysler Vehicles?

Many Chrysler vehicles apply a 5-volt reference to the signal wire of the oxygen sensor. The purpose of this voltage is to allow the computer to detect if the oxygen sensor signal circuit is open or grounded:

- If the voltage on the signal wire is 4.5 volts or more, the computer assumes that the sensor is open.
- If the voltage on the signal wire is zero, the computer assumes that the sensor is shorted-to-ground.

If either condition exists, the computer can set a diagnostic trouble code (DTC).

fuel mixture, or the oxygen sensor may be contaminated.

- If the oxygen sensor voltage remains low (below 350 mV), the fuel system could be supplying too lean a fuel mixture. Check for a vacuum leak or partially clogged fuel injector(s). Before replacing the oxygen sensor, check the manufacturer's recommended procedures.

**TESTING THE OXYGEN SENSOR USING THE MIN/ MAX METHOD** A digital meter set on DC volts can be used to record the minimum and maximum voltage with the engine running. A good oxygen sensor should be able to produce a value of less than 300 mV and a maximum voltage above 800 mV. Replace any oxygen sensor that fails to go above 700 mV or lower than 300 mV. ● **SEE FIGURE 17–9 AND CHART 17–1.**

**TESTING AN OXYGEN SENSOR USING A SCAN TOOL** A good oxygen sensor should be able to sense the oxygen content and change voltage outputs rapidly. How fast an oxygen sensor switches from high (above 450 mV) to low (below 350 mV) is measured in oxygen sensor **cross counts.** Cross counts are the number of times an oxygen sensor changes voltage from high to low (from low to high voltage is not counted) in 1 second (or 1.25 seconds, depending on scan tool and computer speed).

**NOTE: On a fuel-injected engine at 2,000 engine RPM, 8 to 10 cross counts is normal.**

Oxygen sensor cross counts can be determined only by using a scan tool or other suitable tester that reads computer data.

| MIN/MAX Oxygen Sensor Test Chart | | | |
|---|---|---|---|
| **MINIMUM VOLTAGE** | **MAXIMUM VOLTAGE** | **AVERAGE VOLTAGE** | **TEST RESULTS** |
| Below 200 mV | Above 800 mV | 400 to 500 mV | Oxygen sensor is okay. |
| Above 200 mV | Any reading | 400 to 500 mV | Oxygen sensor is defective. |
| Any reading | Below 800 mV | 400 to 500 mV | Oxygen sensor is defective. |
| Below 200 mV | Above 800 mV | Below 400 mV | System is operating lean.* |
| Below 200 mV | Below 800 mV | Below 400 mV | System is operating lean. (Add propane to the intake air to see if the oxygen sensor reacts. If not, the sensor is defective.) |
| Below 200 mV | Above 800 mV | Above 500 mV | System is operating rich. |
| Above 200 mV | Above 800 mV | Above 500 mV | System is operating rich. (Remove a vacuum hose to see if the oxygen sensor reacts. If not, the sensor is defective.) |
| *Check for an exhaust leak upstream from the O2S or ignition misfire that can cause a false lean indication before further diagnosis. | | | |

**CHART 17–1**

Use this chart to check for proper operation of the oxygen sensors and fuel system after checking them using a multimeter set to read MIN/MAX.

If the cross counts are low (or zero), the oxygen sensor may be contaminated, or the fuel delivery system is delivering a constant rich or lean air-fuel mixture. To test an engine using a scan tool, follow these steps:

1. Connect the scan tool to the DLC and start the engine.
2. Operate the engine at a fast idle (2500 RPM) for two minutes to allow time for the oxygen sensor to warm to operating temperature.
3. Observe the oxygen sensor activity on the scan tool to verify closed-loop operation. Select "snapshot" mode and hold the engine speed steady and start recording.
4. Play back snapshot and place a mark beside each range of oxygen sensor voltage for each frame of the snapshot.

A good oxygen sensor and computer system should result in most snapshot values at both ends (0 to 300 mV and 600 to 1,000 mV). If most of the readings are in the middle, the oxygen sensor is not working correctly.

## TESTING AN OXYGEN SENSOR USING A SCOPE

An oscilloscope (scope) can also be used to test an oxygen sensor. Connect the scope to the signal wire and ground for the sensor (if it is so equipped). ● **SEE FIGURE 17–10.** With the engine operating in closed loop, the voltage signal of the sensor should be constantly changing. ● **SEE FIGURE 17–11.** Check for rapid switching from rich to lean and lean to rich and change between once every two seconds and five times per second (0.5 to 5 Hz). ● **SEE FIGURES 17–12, 17–13, AND 17–14.**

**NOTE: General Motors warns not to base the diagnosis of an oxygen sensor problem solely on its scope pattern. The varying voltage output of an oxygen sensor can easily be mistaken for a fault in the sensor itself rather than a fault in the fuel delivery system.**

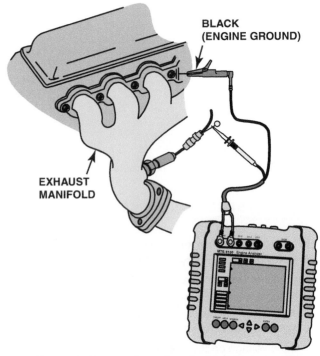

**FIGURE 17–10** Connecting a handheld digital storage oscilloscope to an oxygen sensor signal wire. Check the instructions for the scope as some require the use of a filter to be installed in the test lead to reduce electromagnetic interference that can affect the oxygen sensor waveform.

## OXYGEN SENSOR WAVEFORM ANALYSIS

As the O2S sensor warms up, the sensor voltage begins to rise. When the sensor voltage rises above 450 mV, the PCM determines that the sensor is up to operating temperature, takes

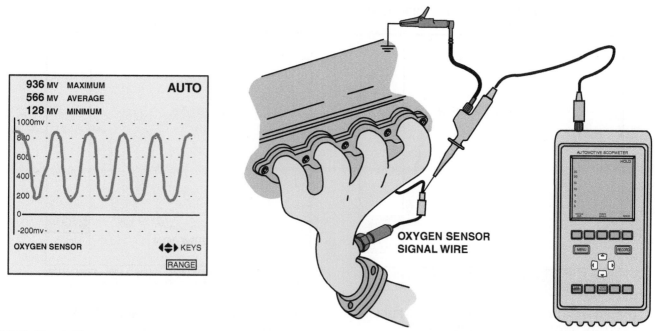

**FIGURE 17–11** The waveform of a good oxygen sensor as displayed on a digital storage oscilloscope (DSO). Note that the maximum reading is above 800 mV and that the minimum reading is less than 200 mV.

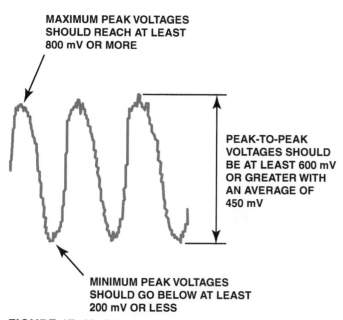

**FIGURE 17–12** A typical good oxygen sensor waveform as displayed on a digital storage oscilloscope. Look for transitions that occur between once every two seconds at idle and five times per second at higher engine speeds (0.5 and 5 Hz). (*Courtesy of Fluke Corporation*)

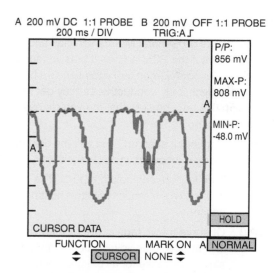

ONCE YOU'VE ACTIVATED "PEAK-TO-PEAK," "MAX-PEAK," AND "MIN-PEAK," FRAME THE WAVEFORM WITH CURSORS. LOOK FOR THE MINIMUM AND MAXIMUM VOLTAGES AND THE DIFFERENCE BETWEEN THEM IN THE RIGHT DISPLAY.

**FIGURE 17–13** Using the cursors on the oscilloscope, the high- and low-oxygen sensor values can be displayed on the screen. (*Courtesy of Fluke Corporation*)

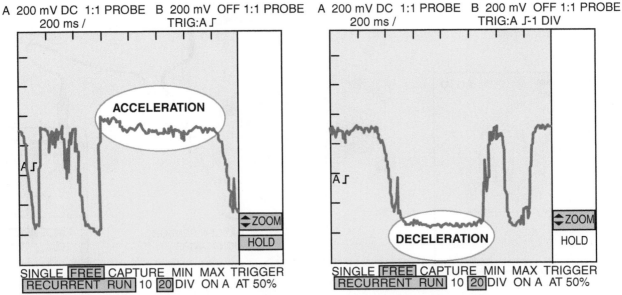

**UNDER HARD ACCELERATION, THE AIR–FUEL MIXTURE SHOULD BECOME RICH - THE VOLTAGE SHOULD STAY FAIRLY HIGH**

**WHILE DECELERATING, MIXTURES BECOME LEAN. LOOK FOR LOW VOLTAGE LEVELS.**

**FIGURE 17–14** When the air-fuel mixture rapidly changes such as during a rapid acceleration, look for a rapid response. The transition from low to high should be less than 100 ms. (*Courtesy of Fluke Corporation*)

---

🔧 **TECH TIP**

**The Key On, Engine Off Oxygen Sensor Test**

This test works on General Motors vehicles and may work on others if the PCM applies a bias voltage to the oxygen sensors. Zirconia oxygen sensors become more electrically conductive as they get hot. To perform this test, be sure that the vehicle has not run for several hours:

**STEP 1** Connect a scan tool and get the display ready to show oxygen sensor data.

**STEP 2** Turn key on, engine off (KOEO). The heater in the oxygen sensor will start heating the sensor.

**STEP 3** Observe the voltage of the oxygen sensor. The applied bias voltage of 450 mV should slowly decrease for all oxygen sensors as they become more electrically conductive and other bias voltage is flowing to ground.

**STEP 4** A good oxygen sensor should indicate a voltage of less than 100 mV after three minutes. Any sensor that displays a higher-than-usual voltage or seems to stay higher longer than the others could be defective or skewed high.

🔧 **TECH TIP**

**The Propane Oxygen Sensor Test**

Adding propane to the air inlet of a running engine is an excellent way to check if the oxygen sensor is able to react to changes in air-fuel mixture. Follow these steps in performing the propane trick:

1. Connect a digital storage oscilloscope to the oxygen sensor signal wire.
2. Start and operate the engine until up to operating temperature and in closed-loop fuel control.
3. While watching the scope display, add some propane to the air inlet. The scope display should read full rich (over 800 mV), as shown in ● **FIGURE 17–15.**
4. Shut off the propane. The waveform should drop to less than 200 mV (0.200 V), as shown in ● **FIGURE 17–16.**
5. Quickly add some propane while the oxygen sensor is reading low and watch for a rapid transition to rich. The transition should occur in less than 100 milliseconds (ms).

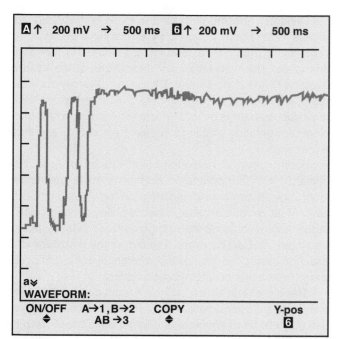

FIGURE 17–15 Adding propane to the air inlet of an engine operating in closed loop with a working oxygen sensor causes the oxygen sensor voltage to read high.

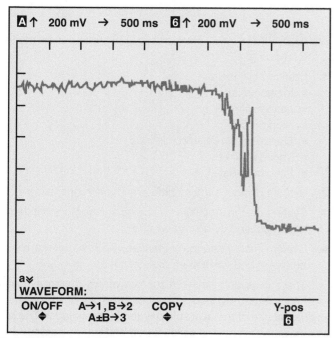

FIGURE 17–16 When the propane is shut off, the oxygen sensor should read below 200 mV.

control of the fuel mixture, and begins to cycle rich and lean. At this point, the system is considered to be in closed loop. ● **SEE FIGURE 17–17.**

**FREQUENCY** The frequency of the O2S is important in determining the condition of the fuel control system. The higher the frequency, the better, but the frequency must not exceed

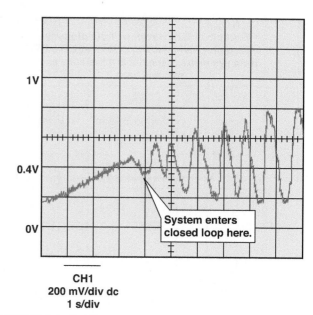

CH1
200 mV/div dc
1 s/div

FIGURE 17–17 When the O2S voltage rises above 450 mV, the PCM starts to control the fuel mixture based on oxygen sensor activity.

6 Hz. For its OBD-II standards, the government has stated that a frequency greater than 6 Hz represents a misfire.

**THROTTLE-BODY FUEL-INJECTION SYSTEMS.** Normal TBI system rich/lean switching frequencies are from about 0.5 Hz at idle to about 3 Hz at 2500 RPM. Additionally, because of the TBI design limitations, fuel distribution to individual cylinders may not always be equal (due to unequal intake runner length etc.). This may be normal unless certain other conditions are present at the same time.

**PORT FUEL-INJECTION SYSTEMS.** Specification for port fuel-injection systems is 0.5 Hz at idle to 5 Hz at 2,500 RPM. ● **SEE FIGURE 17–18.** Port fuel-injection systems have more rich/lean O2S voltage transitions (cross counts) for a given amount of time than any other type of system because of the greatly improved system design compared to TBI units.

Port fuel-injection systems take the least amount of time to react to the fuel adaptive command (for example, changing injector pulse width).

**BACKGROUND INFORMATION** Hash on the O2S waveform is defined as a series of high-frequency spikes, or the fuzz (or noise) viewed on some O2S waveforms, or, more specifically, oscillation frequencies higher than those created by the PCM normal feedback operation (normal rich/lean oscillations).

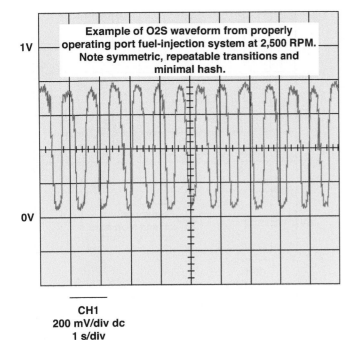

Example of O2S waveform from properly operating port fuel-injection system at 2,500 RPM. Note symmetric, repeatable transitions and minimal hash.

1V

0V

CH1
200 mV/div dc
1 s/div

**FIGURE 17–18** Normal oxygen sensor frequency is from about one to five times per second.

Hash is the critical indicator of reduced combustion efficiency. Hash on the O2S waveform can warn of reduced performance in individual engine cylinders. Hash also impedes proper operation of the PCM feedback fuel control program. The feedback program is the active software program that interprets the O2S voltage and calculates a corrective mixture control command.

Generally, the program for the PCM is not designed to process O2S signal frequencies efficiently that result from events other than normal system operation and fuel control commands. The high-frequency oscillations of the hash can cause the PCM to lose control. This, in turn, has several effects. When the operating strategy of the PCM is adversely affected, the air-fuel ratio drifts out of the catalyst window, which affects converter operating efficiency, exhaust emissions, and engine performance.

Hash on the O2S waveform indicates an exhaust charge imbalance from one cylinder to another, or, more specifically, a higher oxygen content sensed from an individual combustion event. Most oxygen sensors, when working properly, can react fast enough to generate voltage deflections corresponding to a single combustion event. The bigger the amplitude of the deflection (hash), the greater the differential in oxygen content sensed from a particular combustion event.

There are vehicles that will have hash on their O2S waveforms and are operating perfectly normal. Small amounts of hash may not be of concern, and larger amounts of hash may be all important. A good rule concerning hash is, if engine performance is good, there are no vacuum leaks, and if exhaust (HC) hydrocarbon and oxygen levels are okay while hash is present on the O2S waveform, then the hash is nothing to worry about.

**CAUSES OF HASH** Hash on the O2S signal can be caused by the following:

1. Misfiring cylinders
   - Ignition misfire
   - Lean misfire
   - Rich misfire
   - Compression-related misfire
   - Vacuum leaks
   - Injector imbalance

2. System design, such as different intake runner length

3. System design amplified by engine and component degradation caused by aging and wear

4. System manufacturing variances, such as intake runner blockage and valve stem mismachining

The spikes and hash on the waveform during a misfire event are created by incomplete combustion, which results in only partial use of the available oxygen in the cylinder. The leftover oxygen goes out the exhaust port and travels past the oxygen sensor. When the oxygen sensor "sees" the oxygen-filled exhaust charge, it quickly generates a low voltage, or spike. A series of these high-frequency spikes make up what we are calling "hash."

## CLASSIFICATIONS OF HASH

**CLASS 1: AMPLIFIED AND SIGNIFICANT HASH.** Amplified hash is the somewhat unimportant hash that is often present between 300 and 600 mV on the O2S waveform. This type of hash is usually not important for diagnosis. That is because amplified hash is created largely as a result of the electrochemical

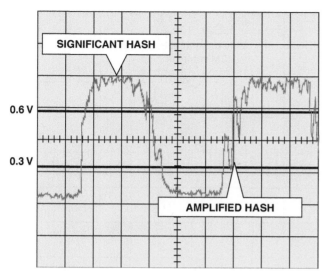

**FIGURE 17–19** Significant hash can be caused by faults in one or more cylinders, whereas amplified hash is not as important for diagnosis.

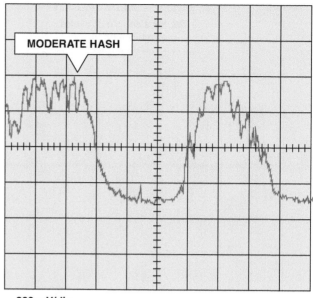

200 mV/div
1 s/div

**FIGURE 17–20** Moderate hash may or may not be significant for diagnosis.

properties of the O2S itself and many times not an engine or other unrelated problem. Hash between 300 and 600 mV is not particularly conclusive, so for all practical purposes it is insignificant. ● **SEE FIGURE 17–19.**

Significant hash is defined as the hash that occurs above 600 mV and below 300 mV on the O2S waveform. This is the area of the waveform that the PCM is watching to determine the fuel mixture. Significant hash is important for diagnosis because it is caused by a combustion event. If the waveform exhibits class 1 hash, the combustion event problem is probably occurring in only one of the cylinders. If the event happens in a greater number of the cylinders, the waveform will become class 3 or be fixed lean or rich the majority of the time.

**CLASS 2: MODERATE HASH.** Moderate hash is defined as spikes shooting downward from the top arc of the waveform as the waveform carves its arc through the rich phase. Moderate hash spikes are not greater than 150 mV in amplitude. They may get as large as 200 mV in amplitude as the O2S waveform goes through 450 mV. Moderate hash may or may not be significant to a particular diagnosis. ● **SEE FIGURE 17–20.** For instance, most vehicles will exhibit more hash on the O2S waveform at idle. Additionally, the engine family or type of O2S could be important factors when considering the significance of moderate hash on the O2S waveform.

**CLASS 3: SEVERE HASH.** Severe hash is defined as hash whose amplitude is greater than 200 mV. Severe hash may even cover the entire voltage range of the sensor for an extended period of operation. Severe hash on the DSO display appears as spikes that shoot downward, over 200 mV from the top of the operating range of the sensor, or as far as to the bottom of the sensor's operating range. ● **SEE FIGURE 17–21.** If severe hash is present for several seconds during a steady-state engine operating mode, say 2,500 RPM, it is almost always significant to the diagnosis of any vehicle. Severe hash of this nature is almost never caused by a normal system design. It is caused by cylinder misfire or mixture imbalance.

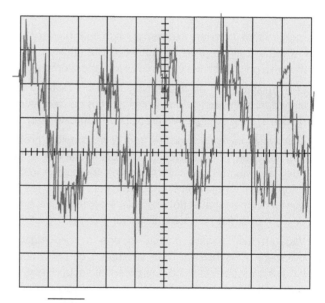

CH1
200 mV/div dc
500 ms/div

**FIGURE 17–21** Severe hash is almost always caused by cylinder misfire conditions.

## HASH INTERPRETATION

### TYPES OF MISFIRES THAT CAN CAUSE HASH

1. Ignition misfire caused by a bad spark plug, spark plug wire, distributor cap, rotor, ignition coil, or ignition primary problem. Usually an engine analyzer is used to eliminate these possibilities or confirm these problems. ● **SEE FIGURE 17–22.**

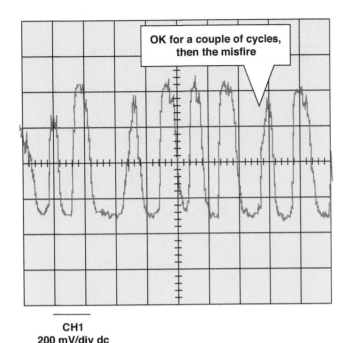

CH1
200 mV/div dc
500 ms/div

**FIGURE 17–22** An ignition- or mixture-related misfire can cause hash on the oxygen sensor waveform.

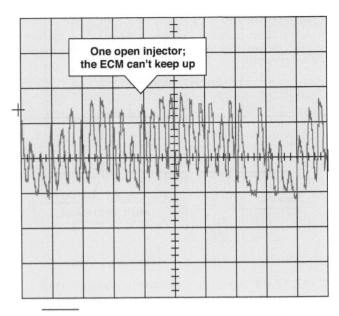

Memory 4
200 mV/div
200 ms/div

**FIGURE 17–23** An injector imbalance can cause a lean or a rich misfire.

2. Rich misfire from an excessively rich fuel delivery to an individual cylinder (various potential root causes). Air-fuel ratio in a given cylinder ventured below approximately 13:1.

3. Lean misfire from an excessively lean fuel delivery to an individual cylinder (various potential root causes). Air-fuel ratio in a given cylinder ventured above approximately 17:1.

4. Compression-related misfire from a mechanical problem that reduces compression to the point that not enough heat is generated from compressing the air-fuel mixture prior to ignition, preventing combustion. This raises O2S content in the exhaust (for example, a burned valve, broken or worn ring, flat cam lobe, or sticking valve).

5. Vacuum leak misfire unique to one or two individual cylinders. This possibility is eliminated or confirmed by inducing propane around any potential vacuum leak area (intake runners, intake manifold gaskets, vacuum hoses, etc.) while watching the DSO to see when the signal goes rich and the hash changes from ingesting the propane. Vacuum leak misfires are caused when a vacuum leak unique to one cylinder or a few individual cylinders causes the air-fuel ratio in the affected cylinder(s) to venture above approximately 17:1, causing a lean misfire.

6. Injector imbalance misfire (on port fuel-injected engines only); one cylinder has a rich or lean misfire because of an individual injector(s) delivering the wrong quantity of fuel. Injector imbalance misfires are caused when an injector on one cylinder or a few individual cylinders causes the air-fuel ratio in its cylinder(s) to venture above approximately 17:1, causing a lean misfire, or

below approximately 13.7:1, causing a rich misfire. ● **SEE FIGURE 17–23.**

**OTHER RULES CONCERNING HASH ON THE O2S WAVEFORM** If there is significant hash on the O2S signal that is not normal for that type of system, it will usually be accompanied by a repeatable and generally detectable engine miss at idle (for example, a thump, thump, thump every time the cylinder fires). Generally, if the hash is significant, the engine miss will correlate in time with individual spikes seen on the waveform.

Hash that may be difficult to get rid of (and is normal in some cases) will not be accompanied by a significant engine miss that corresponds with the hash. When the individual spikes that make up the hash on the waveform do not correlate in time with an engine miss, less success can usually be found in getting rid of them by performing repairs.

A fair rule of thumb is that if you are sure there are no intake vacuum leaks, the exhaust gas HC (hydrocarbon) and oxygen levels are normal, and the engine does not run or idle rough, the hash is probably acceptable or normal.

## NEGATIVE O2S VOLTAGE

When testing O2S waveforms, some oxygen sensors will exhibit some negative voltage. The acceptable amount of negative O2S voltage is −0.75 mV, provided that the maximum

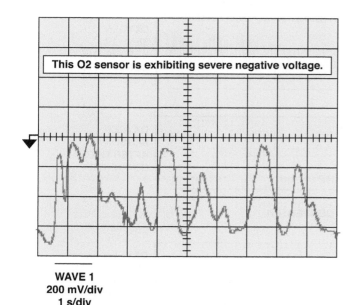

**WAVE 1**
**200 mV/div**
**1 s/div**

**FIGURE 17–24** Negative reading oxygen sensor voltage can be caused by several problems.

---

🔧 **TECH TIP**

**Look for Missing Shield**

In rare (very rare) instances, the metal shield on the exhaust side of the oxygen sensor (the shield over the zirconia thimble) may be damaged (or missing) and may create hash on the O2S waveform that could be mistaken for bad injectors or other misfires, vacuum leaks, or compression problems. After you have checked everything and possibly replaced the injectors, pull the O2S to check for rare situations.

---

voltage peak exceeds 850 mV. ● **SEE FIGURE 17–24.** Testing has shown that negative voltage signals from an oxygen sensor have usually been caused by the following:

1. Chemical poisoning of sensing element (silicon, oil, etc.)
2. Overheated engines
3. Mishandling of new oxygen sensors (dropped and banged around, resulting in a cracked insulator)
4. Poor oxygen sensor ground

## LOW O2S READINGS

An oxygen sensor reading that is low could be due to other things besides a lean air-fuel mixture. Remember, an O2S senses oxygen, not unburned gas, even though a high reading generally indicates a rich exhaust (lack of oxygen) and a low reading indicates a lean mixture (excess oxygen).

**FALSE LEAN** If an oxygen sensor reads low as a result of a factor besides a lean mixture, it is often called a **false lean indication.**

False lean indications (low O2S readings) can be attributed to the following:

1. **Ignition misfire.** An ignition misfire due to a defective spark plug wire, fouled spark plug, and so forth causes no burned air and fuel to be exhausted past the O2S. The O2S "sees" the oxygen (not the unburned gasoline), and the O2S voltage is low.
2. **Exhaust leak in front of the O2S.** An exhaust leak between the engine and the oxygen sensor causes outside oxygen to be drawn into the exhaust and past the O2S. This oxygen is "read" by the O2S and produces a lower-than-normal voltage. The computer interrupts the lower-than-normal voltage signal from the O2S as meaning that the air-fuel mixture is lean. The computer will cause the fuel system to deliver a richer air-fuel mixture.
3. **A spark plug misfire represents a false lean signal to the oxygen sensor.** The computer does not know that the extra oxygen going past the oxygen sensor is not due to a lean air-fuel mixture. The computer commands a richer mixture, which could cause the spark plugs to foul, increasing the rate of misfirings.

## HIGH O2S READINGS

An oxygen sensor reading that is high could be due to other things beside a rich air-fuel mixture. When the O2S reads high as a result of other factors besides a rich mixture, it is often called a **false rich indication.**

False rich indication (high O2S readings) can be attributed to the following:

1. Contaminated O2S due to additives in the engine coolant or due to silicon poisoning
2. A stuck-open EGR valve (especially at idle)
3. A spark plug wire too close to the oxygen sensor signal wire, which can induce a higher-than-normal voltage in the signal wire, thereby indicating to the computer a false rich condition
4. A loose oxygen sensor ground connection, which can cause a higher-than-normal voltage and a false rich signal
5. A break or contamination of the wiring and its connectors, which could prevent reference oxygen from reaching the oxygen sensor, resulting in a false rich indication (All oxygen sensors require an oxygen supply inside the sensor itself for reference to be able to sense exhaust gas oxygen.)

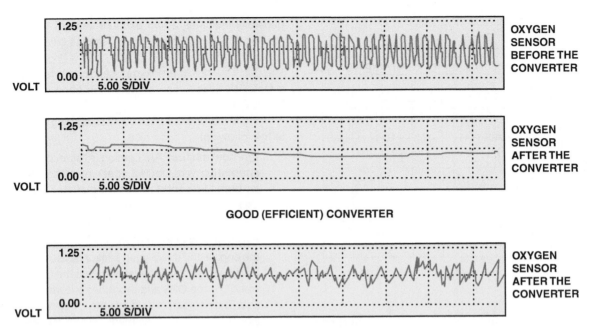

VOLT  1.25  0.00  5.00 S/DIV — OXYGEN SENSOR BEFORE THE CONVERTER

VOLT  1.25  0.00  5.00 S/DIV — OXYGEN SENSOR AFTER THE CONVERTER

**GOOD (EFFICIENT) CONVERTER**

VOLT  1.25  0.00  5.00 S/DIV — OXYGEN SENSOR AFTER THE CONVERTER

**BAD (INEFFICIENT) CONVERTER**

**FIGURE 17–25** The post-catalytic converter oxygen sensor should display very little activity if the catalytic converter is efficient.

## POST-CATALYTIC CONVERTER OXYGEN SENSOR TESTING

The oxygen sensor located behind the catalytic converter is used on OBD-II vehicles to monitor converter efficiency. A changing air-fuel mixture is required for the most efficient operation of the converter. If the converter is working correctly, the oxygen content after the converter should be fairly constant. ● **SEE FIGURE 17–25.**

## OXYGEN SENSOR VISUAL INSPECTION

Whenever an oxygen sensor is replaced, the old sensor should be carefully inspected to help determine the cause of the failure. This is an important step because if the cause of the failure is not discovered, it could lead to another sensor failure.

Inspection may reveal the following:

1. **Black sooty deposits** usually indicate a rich air-fuel mixture.

**What Is Lambda?**

An oxygen sensor is also called a lambda sensor because the voltage changes at the air-fuel ratio of 14.7:1, which is the stoichiometric rate for gasoline. If this mixture of gasoline and air is burned, all of the gasoline is burned and uses all of the oxygen in the mixture. This exact ratio represents a lambda of 1.0. If the mixture is richer (more fuel or less air), the number is less than 1.0, such as 0.850. If the mixture is leaner than 14.7:1 (less fuel or more air), the lambda number is higher than 1.0, such as 1.130. Often, the target lambda is displayed on a scan tool. ● **SEE FIGURE 17–26.**

2. **White chalky deposits** are characteristic of silica contamination. Usual causes for this type of sensor failure include silica deposits in the fuel or a technician having used the wrong type of silicone sealant during the servicing of the engine.

3. **White sandy or gritty deposits** are characteristic of antifreeze (ethylene glycol) contamination. A defective cylinder head or intake manifold gasket could be the cause, as could a cracked cylinder head or engine block. Antifreeze

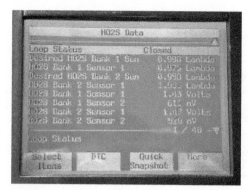

**FIGURE 17–26** The target lambda on this vehicle is slightly lower than 1.0, indicating that the PCM is attempting to supply the engine with an air-fuel mixture that is slightly richer than stoichiometric. Multiply the lambda number by 14.7 to find the actual air-fuel ratio.

may also cause the oxygen sensor to become green as a result of the dye used in antifreeze.

4. **Dark brown deposits** are an indication of excessive oil consumption. Possible causes include a defective positive crankcase ventilation (PCV) system or a mechanical engine problem, such as defective valve stem seals or piston rings.

CAUTION: Do not spray any silicone spray near the engine where the engine vacuum could draw the fumes into the engine. This can also cause silica damage to the oxygen sensor. Also be sure that the silicone sealer used for gaskets is rated oxygen-sensor safe.

## O2S-RELATED DIAGNOSTIC TROUBLE CODES

Diagnostic trouble codes (DTCs) associated with the oxygen sensor include the following:

| Diagnostic Trouble Code | Description | Possible Causes |
|---|---|---|
| P0131 | Upstream HO2S grounded | • Exhaust leak upstream of HO2S (bank 1)<br>• Extremely lean air-fuel mixture<br>• HO2S defective or contaminated<br>• HO2S signal wire shorted-to-ground |
| P0132 | Upstream HO2S shorted | • Upstream HO2S (bank 1) shorted<br>• Defective HO2S<br>• Fuel-contaminated HO2S |
| P0133 | Upstream HO2S slow response | • Open or short in heater circuit<br>• Defective or fuel-contaminated HO2S<br>• EGR or fuel-system fault |

## SUMMARY

1. An oxygen sensor produces a voltage output signal based on the oxygen content of the exhaust stream.
2. If the exhaust has little oxygen, the voltage of the oxygen sensor will be close to 1 volt (1,000 mV) and close to zero if there is high oxygen content in the exhaust.
3. Oxygen sensors can have one, two, three, four, or more wires, depending on the style and design.
4. The oxygen sensor signal determines fuel trim, which is used to tailor the air-fuel mixture for the catalytic converter.
5. Conditions can occur that cause the oxygen sensor to be fooled and give a false lean or false rich signals to the PCM.
6. Oxygen sensors can be tested using a digital meter, a scope, or a scan tool.

## REVIEW QUESTIONS

1. How does an oxygen sensor detect oxygen levels in the exhaust?
2. What are four basic designs of oxygen sensors, and how many wires may be used for each?
3. What is the difference between open-loop and closed-loop engine operation?
4. What are three ways oxygen sensors can be tested?
5. How can the oxygen sensor be fooled and provide the wrong information to the PCM?

1. The sensor that must be warmed and functioning before the engine management computer will go to closed loop is the _____.
   a. O2S
   b. ECT sensor
   c. Engine MAP sensor
   d. BARO sensor

2. The voltage output of a zirconia oxygen sensor when the exhaust stream is lean (excess oxygen) is _____.
   a. Relatively high (close to 1 volt)
   b. About in the middle of the voltage range
   c. Relatively low (close to zero volt)
   d. Either a or b, depending on atmospheric pressure

3. Where is sensor 1, bank 1 located on a V-type engine?
   a. On the same bank where number 1 cylinder is located
   b. In the exhaust manifold
   c. On the bank opposite cylinder number 1
   d. Both a and b

4. A heated zirconia oxygen sensor will have how many wires?
   a. Two
   b. Three
   c. Four
   d. Either b or c

5. A high O2S voltage could be due to a _____.
   a. Rich exhaust
   b. Lean exhaust
   c. Defective spark plug wire
   d. Both a and c

6. A low O2S voltage could be due to a _____.
   a. Rich exhaust
   b. Lean exhaust
   c. Defective spark plug wire
   d. Both b and c

7. An oxygen sensor is being tested with digital multimeter (DMM), using the MIN/MAX function. The readings are minimum = 78 mV, maximum = 932 mV, and average = 442 mV. Technician A says that the engine is operating correctly. Technician B says that the oxygen sensor is skewed too rich. Which technician is correct?
   a. Technician A only
   b. Technician B only
   c. Both Technicians A and B
   d. Neither Technician A nor B

8. An oxygen sensor is being tested using a digital storage oscilloscope (DSO). A good oxygen sensor should display how many switches per second?
   a. 1 to 5
   b. 5 to 10
   c. 10 to 15
   d. 15 to 20

9. When testing an oxygen sensor using a digital storage oscilloscope (DSO), how quickly should the voltage change when either propane is added to the intake stream or a vacuum leak is created?
   a. Less than 50 ms
   b. 1 to 3 seconds
   c. Less than 100 ms
   d. 450 to 550 ms

10. A P0133 DTC is being discussed. Technician A says that a defective heater circuit could be the cause. Technician B says that a contaminated sensor could be the cause. Which technician is correct?
    a. Technician A only
    b. Technician B only
    c. Both Technicians A and B
    d. Neither Technician A nor B

# chapter 18

# WIDE-BAND OXYGEN SENSORS

**OBJECTIVES:** After studying Chapter 18, the reader should be able to: • Prepare for ASE Engine Performance (A8) certification test content area "E" (Computerized Engine Controls Diagnosis and Repair). • Describe the difference between a two-band and a wide-band oxygen sensor. • Explain the difference between a thimble design and a planar design. • Discuss the operation of a wide-band oxygen sensor. • List the test procedure for testing a dual cell and a single-cell wide-band oxygen sensor.

**KEY TERMS:** Air-fuel ratio sensor 234 • Air reference chamber 232 • Ambient air electrode 231 • Ambient side electrode 231 • Cup design 231 • Diffusion chamber 232 • Dual cell 232 • Exhaust side electrode 231 • Finger design 231 • Lean air-fuel (LAF) sensor 229 • Light-off time (LOT) 231 • Nernst cell 232 • Planar design 231 • Pump cell 232 • Reference electrode 231 • Reference voltage 232 • Signal electrode 231 • Single-cell 234 • Thimble design 231

## TERMINOLOGY

Honda was the first manufacturer to use wide band oxygen sensors beginning in 1992. Wide-band oxygen sensors are used by most vehicle manufacturers to ensure that the exhaust emissions can meet the current standard. Wide-band oxygen sensors are also called by various names, depending on the vehicle and/or oxygen sensor manufacturer. The terms used include the following:

- **Wide-band oxygen sensor**
- **Broadband oxygen sensor**
- **Wide-range oxygen sensor**
- **Air-fuel ratio (AFR) sensor**
- **Wide-range air-fuel (WRAF) sensor**
- **Lean air-fuel (LAF) sensor**
- **Air-fuel (AF) sensor**

Wide-band oxygen sensors are also manufactured in dual-cell and single-cell designs.

## NEED FOR WIDE-BAND SENSORS

**INTRODUCTION** A conventional zirconia oxygen sensor reacts to an air-fuel mixture that is either richer or leaner than 14.7:1. This means that the sensor cannot be used to detect the exact air-fuel mixture. ● **SEE FIGURE 18–1.**

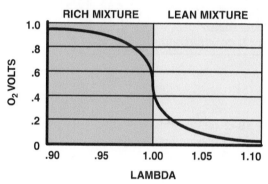

**FIGURE 18–1** A conventional zirconia oxygen sensor can only reset to exhaust mixtures that are richer or leaner than 14.7:1 (lambda 1.00).

The need for more stringent exhaust emission standards such as the natural low-emission vehicle (NLEV) plus the ultra low-emission vehicle (ULEV) and the super ultra low-emission vehicle (SULEV) require more accurate fuel control than can be provided by a traditional oxygen sensor.

**PURPOSE AND FUNCTION** A wide-band oxygen sensor is capable of supplying air-fuel ratio information to the PCM over a much broader range. The use of a wide-band oxygen sensor compared with a conventional zirconia oxygen sensor differs as follows:

1. Able to detect exhaust air-fuel ratio from as rich as 10:1 and as lean as 23:1 in some cases
2. Cold-start activity within as little as 10 seconds

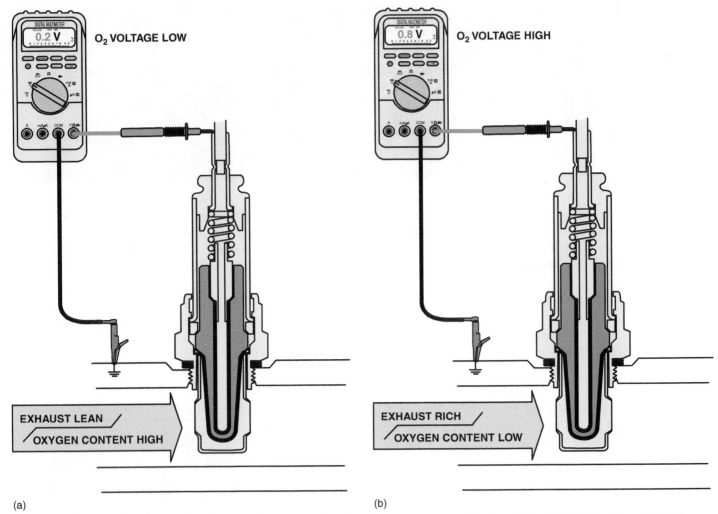

O₂ VOLTAGE LOW

O₂ VOLTAGE HIGH

EXHAUST LEAN / OXYGEN CONTENT HIGH

EXHAUST RICH / OXYGEN CONTENT LOW

(a)

(b)

**FIGURE 18–2** (a) When the exhaust is lean, the output of a zirconia oxygen sensor is below 450 mV. (b) When the exhaust is rich, the output of a zirconia oxygen sensor is above 450 mV.

 **FREQUENTLY ASKED QUESTION**

**How Quickly Can a Wide-Band Oxygen Sensor Achieve Closed Loop?**

In a Toyota Highlander hybrid electric vehicle, the operation of the gasoline engine is delayed for a short time when the vehicle is first driven. During this time of electric operation, the oxygen sensor heaters are turned on in readiness for the gasoline engine starting. The gasoline engine often achieves closed-loop operation during *cranking* because the oxygen sensors are fully warm and ready to go at the same time the engine is started. Having the gasoline engine achieve closed loop quickly allows it to meet the stringent SULEV standards.

# CONVENTIONAL O2S REVIEW

**NARROW BAND** A conventional zirconia oxygen sensor (O2S) is only able to detect if the exhaust is richer or leaner than 14.7:1. A conventional oxygen sensor is therefore referred to as follows:

- **2-step sensor**—either rich or lean
- **Narrow band sensor**—informs the PCM whether the exhaust is rich or lean only

The voltage value where a zirconia oxygen sensor switches from rich to lean or from lean to rich is 0.450 V (450 mV):

- Above 0.450 V = rich
- Below 0.450 V = lean
- **SEE FIGURE 18–2.**

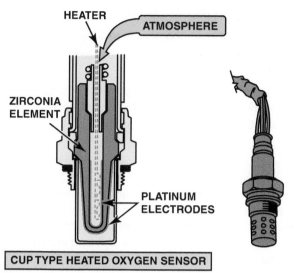

**CUP TYPE HEATED OXYGEN SENSOR**

**FIGURE 18–3** Most conventional zirconia oxygen sensors and some wide-band oxygen sensors use the cup-type design.

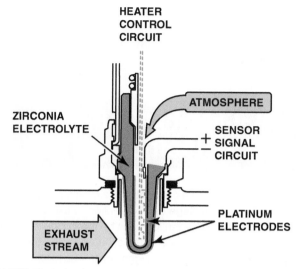

**FIGURE 18–4** A typical heated zirconia oxygen sensor, showing the sensor signal circuit that uses the outer (exhaust) electrode as negative and the ambient air side electrode as the positive.

## CONSTRUCTION

A typical zirconia oxygen sensor has the sensing element in the shape of a thimble and is often referred to as follows:

- **Thimble design**
- **Cup design**
- **Finger design**
    - ● **SEE FIGURE 18–3.**

A typical zirconia oxygen sensor has a heater inside the thimble and does not touch the inside of the sensor. The sensor is similar to a battery that has two electrodes and an electrolyte. The electrolyte is solid and is the zirconia (zirconium dioxide). There are also two porous platinum electrodes, which have the following functions:

- **Exhaust side electrode**—This electrode is exposed to the exhaust stream.
- **Ambient side electrode**—This electrode is exposed to outside (ambient) air and is the **signal electrode,** also called the **reference electrode** or **ambient air electrode.**
    - ● **SEE FIGURE 18–4.**

The electrolyte (zirconia) is able to conduct electrons as follows:

- If the exhaust is rich, $O_2$ from the reference (inner) electrode wants to flow to the exhaust side electrode, which results in the generation of a voltage.
- If the exhaust is lean, $O_2$ flow is not needed, and, as a result, there is little, if any, electron movement, and therefore no voltage is being produced.

## HEATER CIRCUITS

The heater circuit on conventional oxygen sensors requires 0.8 to 2 amperes, and it keeps the sensor at about 600°F (315°C).

A wide-band oxygen sensor operates at a higher temperature than a conventional HO2S from 1,200°F to 1,400°F (650°C to 760°C). The amount of electrical current needed for a wide-band oxygen sensor is about 8 to 10 amperes.

## PLANAR DESIGN

In 1998, Bosch introduced a wide-band oxygen sensor that is flat and thin (1.5 mm, or 0.006 in.), known as a planar design and not in the shape of a thimble, as previously constructed. Now several manufacturers produce a similar planar design wide-band oxygen sensor. Because it is thin, it is easier to heat than older styles of oxygen sensors and as a result can achieve closed loop in less than 10 seconds. This fast heating, called **light-off time (LOT),** helps improve fuel economy and reduces cold-start exhaust emissions. The type of construction is not noticed by the technician, nor does it affect the testing procedures.

A conventional oxygen sensor can be constructed using a **planar design** instead of the thimble-type design. A planar design has the following features:

- The elements including the zirconia electrolyte and the two electrodes and heater are stacked together in a flat-type design.
- The planar design allows faster warm-up because the heater is in direct contact with the other elements.
- Planar oxygen sensors are the most commonly used. Some planar designs are used as a conventional narrow-band oxygen sensor.

The sandwich-type design of the planar style of oxygen sensor has the same elements and operates the same but is stacked in the following way from the exhaust side to the ambient air side:

Exhaust stream

Outer electrode

Zirconia ($ZiO_2$) (electrolyte)

Inner electrode (reference or signal)

Outside (ambient) air

Heater

● **SEE FIGURE 18–5**

NOTE: Another name for a conventional oxygen sensor is a **Nernst cell.** The Nernst cell is named for Walther Nernst, 1864–1941, a German physicist known for his work in electrochemistry.

# DUAL-CELL PLANAR WIDE-BAND SENSOR OPERATION

**CONSTRUCTION** In a conventional zirconia oxygen sensor, a bias or **reference voltage** can be applied to the two platinum electrodes, and then oxygen ions can be forced (pumped) from the ambient reference air side to the exhaust side of the sensor. If the polarity is reversed, the oxygen ion can be forced to travel in the opposite direction.

A **dual cell** planar-type wide-band oxygen sensor is made like a conventional planar O2S and is labeled Nernst cell. Above the Nernst cell is another zirconia layer with two electrodes, which is called the **pump cell.** The two cells share a common ground, which is called the reference.

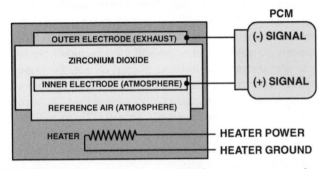

**FIGURE 18–5** A planar design zirconia oxygen sensor places all of the elements together, which allows the sensor to reach operating temperature quickly.

There are two internal chambers:

- The **air reference chamber** is exposed to ambient air.
- The **diffusion chamber** is exposed to the exhaust gases.

Platinum electrodes are on both sides of the zirconia electrolyte elements, which separate the air reference chamber and the exhaust-exposed diffusion chamber.

**OPERATION** The basic principle of operation of a typical wide-band oxygen sensor is that it uses a positive or negative voltage signal to keep a balance between two sensors. Oxygen sensors do not measure the quantity of free oxygen in the exhaust. Instead, oxygen sensors produce a voltage that is based on the ion flow between the platinum electrodes of the sensor to maintain a stoichiometric balance.

An example follows:

- If there is a lean exhaust, there is oxygen in the exhaust, and the ion flow from the ambient side to the exhaust side is low.
- If there were rich exhaust, the ion flow is increased to help maintain balance between the ambient air side and the exhaust side of the sensor.

The PCM can apply a small current to the pump cell electrodes, which causes oxygen ions through the zirconia into or out of the diffusion chamber. The PCM pumps $O_2$ ions in and out of the diffusion chamber to bring the voltage back to 0.45, using the pump cell.

The operation of a wide-band oxygen sensor is best described by looking at what occurs when the exhaust is stoichiometric, rich, and lean. ● **SEE FIGURE 18–6.**

## STOICHIOMETRIC

- When the exhaust is at stoichiometric (14.7:1 air-fuel ratio), the voltage of the Nernst cell is 450 mV (0.450 V).

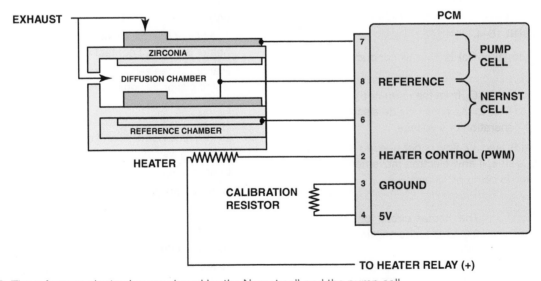

**FIGURE 18–6** The reference electrodes are shared by the Nernst cell and the pump cell.

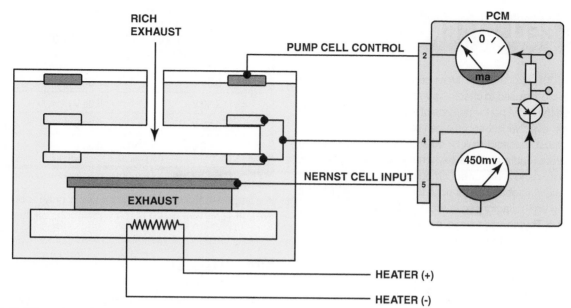

**FIGURE 18–7** When the exhaust is rich, the PCM applies a negative current into the pump cell.

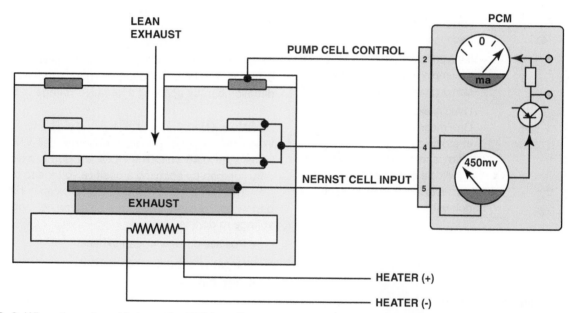

**FIGURE 18–8** When the exhaust is lean, the PCM applies a positive current into the pump cell.

- The voltage between the diffusion chamber and the air reference chamber changes from 0.45 V. This voltage will be as follows:

  - Higher if the exhaust is rich
  - Lower if the exhaust is lean

  The reference voltage remains constant, usually at 2.5 volts, but can vary depending on the year, make, and model of vehicle and the type of sensor. Typical reference voltages include the following:

  - 2.2
  - 2.5
  - 2.7

  - 3.3
  - 3.6

**RICH EXHAUST.** When the exhaust is rich, the voltage between the common (reference) electrode and the Nernst cell electrode that is exposed to ambient air is higher than 0.45 V. The PCM applies a negative current in milliamperes to the pump cell electrode to bring the circuit back into balance. ● **SEE FIGURE 18–7.**

**LEAN EXHAUST.** When the exhaust is lean, the voltage between the common (reference) electrode and the Nernst cell electrode is lower than 0.45 V. The PCM applies a positive current in milliamperes to the pump cell to bring the circuit back into balance. ● **SEE FIGURE 18–8.**

## DUAL-CELL DIAGNOSIS

**SCAN TOOL DIAGNOSIS** Most service information specifies that a scan tool be used to check the wide-band oxygen sensor. This is because the PCM performs tests of the unit and can identify faults. However, even wide-band oxygen sensors can be fooled if there is an exhaust manifold leak or other fault that could lead to false or inaccurate readings. If the oxygen sensor reading is false, the PCM will command an incorrect amount of fuel. The scan data shown on a generic (global) OBD-II scan tool will often be different than the reading on the factory scan tool. ● **SEE CHART 18–1** for an example of a Toyota wide-band oxygen sensor being tested using a factory scan tool and a generic OBD-II scan tool.

**SCAN TOOL DATA (PID)** The following information will be displayed on a scan tool when looking at data for a wide-band oxygen sensor:

| | |
|---|---|
| HO2S1 = _____ mA | If the current is positive, this means that the PCM is pumping current in the diffusion gap because of a rich exhaust. |
| | If the current is negative, the PCM is pumping current out of the diffusion gap because of a lean exhaust. |
| Air-fuel ratio = _____ | Usually expressed in lambda. One means that the exhaust is at stoichiometric (14.7:1 air-fuel ratio), and numbers higher than 1 indicate a lean exhaust, and numbers lower than 1 indicate a rich exhaust. |

## DIGITAL MULTIMETER TESTING

When testing a wide-band oxygen sensor for proper operation, perform the following steps:

**STEP 1** Check service information and determine the circuit and connector terminal identification.

**STEP 2** Measure the calibration resistor. While the value of this resistor can vary widely, depending on the type of sensor, the calibrating resistor should still be checked for opens and shorts.

> **NOTE: The calibration resistor is usually located within the connector itself.**

- If open, the ohmmeter will read OL (infinity ohms).
- If shorted, the ohmmeter will read zero or close to zero.

| MASTER TECH TOYOTA (FACTORY SCAN TOOL) | OBD-II SCAN TOOL | AIR-FUEL RATIO |
|---|---|---|
| 2.50 V | 0.50 V | 12.5:1 |
| 3.00 V | 0.60 V | 14.0:1 |
| 3.30 V | 0.66 V | 14.7:1 |
| 3.50 V | 0.70 V | 15.5:1 |
| 4.00 V | 0.80 V | 18.5:1 |

**CHART 18–1**

A comparison showing what a factory scan tool and a generic OBD-II scan tool might display at various air-fuel ratios.

**STEP 3** Measure the heater circuit for proper resistance or current flow.

**STEP 4** Measure the reference voltage relative to ground. This can vary but is generally 2.4 to 2.6 volts.

**STEP 5** Using jumper wires, connect an ammeter and measure the current in the pump cell control wire.

**RICH EXHAUST (LAMBDA LESS THAN 1.00)** When the exhaust is rich, the Nernst cell voltage will move higher than 0.45 volt. The PCM will pump oxygen from the exhaust into the diffusion gap by applying a negative voltage to the pump cell.

**LEAN EXHAUST (LAMBDA HIGHER THAN 1.00)** When the exhaust is lean, the Nernst cell voltage will move lower than 0.45 volt. The PCM will pump oxygen out of the diffusion gap by applying a positive voltage to the pump cell.

The pump cell is used to pump oxygen into the diffusion gap when the exhaust is rich. The pump cell applies a negative voltage to do this:

- Positive current = lean exhaust
- Negative current = rich exhaust
- ● **SEE FIGURE 18–9.**

## SINGLE-CELL WIDE-BAND OXYGEN SENSORS

**CONSTRUCTION** A typical **single-cell** wide-band oxygen sensor looks similar to a conventional four-wire zirconia oxygen sensor. The typical single-cell wide-band oxygen sensor, usually called an **air-fuel ratio sensor,** has the following construction features:

- It can be made using the cup or planar design.
- Oxygen ($O_2$) is pumped into the diffusion layer similar to the operation of a dual-cell wide-band oxygen sensor.
- ● **SEE FIGURE 18–10.**

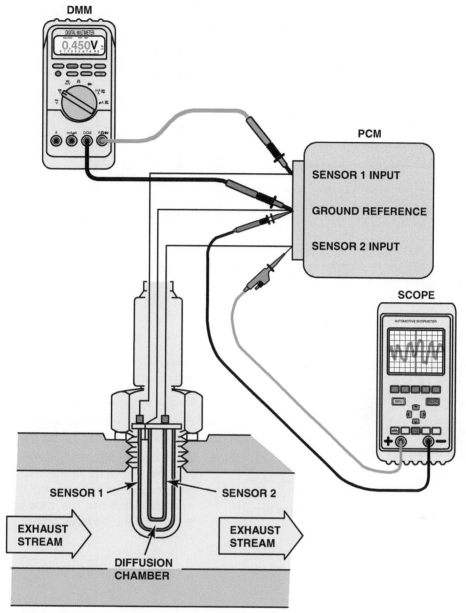

**FIGURE 18–9** Testing a dual-cell wide-band oxygen sensor can be done using a voltmeter or a scope. The meter reading is attached to the Nernst cell and should read stoichiometric (450 mV) at all times. The scope is showing activity to the pump cell with commands from the PCM to keep the Nernst cell at 14.7:1 air-fuel ratio.

- Current flow reverses positive and negative.
- It consists of two cell wires and two heater wires (power and ground).
- The heater usually requires 6 amperes and the ground side is pulse-width modulated.

## TESTING WITH A MILLIAMMETER
The PCM controls the single-cell wide-band oxygen sensor by maintaining a voltage difference of 300 mV (0.3 V) between the two sensor leads. The PCM keeps the voltage difference constant under all operating conditions by increasing or decreasing current between the element of the cell:

- Zero (0 mA) represents lambda or stoichiometric air-fuel ratio of 14.7:1
- +10 mA indicates a lean condition
- −10 mA indicates a rich condition

## TESTING USING A SCAN TOOL
A scan tool will display a voltage reading but can vary depending on the type and maker of scan tool. ● **SEE FIGURE 18–11.**

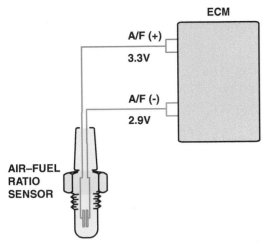

**FIGURE 18–10** A single-cell wide-band oxygen sensor has four wires with two for the heater and two for the sensor itself. The voltage applied to the sensor is 0.4 volt (3.3 − 2.9 = 0.4) across the two leads of the sensor.

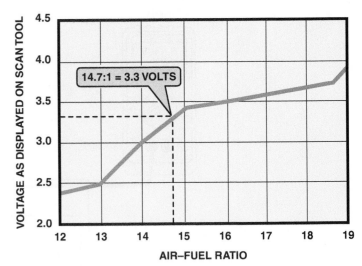

**FIGURE 18–11** The scan tool can display various voltages but will often show 3.3 volts because the PCM is controlling the sensor by applying a low current to the sensor to achieve balance.

# WIDE-BAND OXYGEN SENSOR PATTERN FAILURES

Wide-band oxygen sensors have a long life but can fail. Most of the failures will cause a diagnostic trouble code (DTC) to set, usually causing the malfunction indicator (check engine) lamp to light.

However, one type of failure may not set a DTC when the following occurs:

1. Voltage from the heater circuit bleeds into the Nernst cell.

2. This voltage will cause the engine to operate extremely lean and may or may not set a diagnostic trouble code.

3. When testing indicates an extremely lean condition, unplug the connector to the oxygen sensor. If the engine starts to operate correctly with the sensor unplugged, this is confirmation that the wide-band oxygen sensor has failed and requires replacement.

# SUMMARY

1. Wide-band oxygen sensors are known by many different terms, including the following:
   - Broadband oxygen sensor
   - Wide-range oxygen sensor
   - Air-fuel ratio (AFR) sensor
   - Wide-range air-fuel (WRAF) sensor
   - Lean air-fuel (LAF) sensor
   - Air-fuel (AF) sensor

2. Wide-band oxygen sensors are manufactured using a cup or planar design and are dual-cell or single-cell design.

3. A wide-band oxygen sensor is capable of furnishing the PCM with exhaust air-fuel ratios as rich as 10:1 and as lean as 23:1.

4. The use of a wide-band oxygen sensor allows the engine to achieve more stringent exhaust emission standards.

5. A conventional zirconia oxygen sensor can be made in a cup shape or planar design and is sometimes called a narrow band or two-step sensor.

6. The heater used on a conventional zirconia oxygen sensor uses up to 2 amperes and heats the sensor to about 600°F (315°C). A broadband sensor heater has to heat the sensor to 1,200°F to 1,400°F (650°C to 760°C) and requires up to 8 to 10 amperes.

7. A typical dual-cell wide-band oxygen sensor uses the PCM to apply a current to the pump cell to keep the Nernst cell at 14.7:1:
   - When the exhaust is rich, the PCM applies a negative current to the pump cell.
   - When the exhaust is lean, the PCM applies a positive current to the pump cell.

8. Wide-band oxygen sensors can also be made using a single-cell design.

9. Wide-band oxygen sensors can be best tested using a scan tool, but dual-cell sensors can be checked with a voltmeter or scope. Single-cell sensors can be checked using a milliammeter.

## REVIEW QUESTIONS

1. What type of construction is used to make wide-band oxygen sensors?

2. Why are wide-band oxygen sensors used instead of conventional zirconia sensors?

3. How is the heater different for a wide-band oxygen sensor compared with a conventional zirconia oxygen sensor?

4. How does a wide-range oxygen sensor work?

5. How can a wide-band oxygen sensor be tested?

## CHAPTER QUIZ

1. A wide-band oxygen sensor was first used on a Honda in what model year?
   a. 1992
   b. 1996
   c. 2000
   d. 2006

2. A wide-band oxygen sensor is capable of detecting the air-fuel mixture in the exhaust from _____ (rich) to _____ (lean).
   a. 12:1 to 15:1
   b. 13:1 to 16.7:1
   c. 10:1 to 23:1
   d. 8:1 to 18:1

3. A conventional zirconia oxygen sensor can be made with what designs?
   a. Cup and thimble
   b. Cup and planar
   c. Finger and thimble
   d. Dual cell and single cell

4. A wide-band oxygen sensor can be made using what design?
   a. Cup and thimble
   b. Cup and planar
   c. Finger and thimble
   d. Dual cell and single cell

5. A wide-band oxygen sensor heater could draw how much current (amperes)?
   a. 0.8 to 2 A
   b. 2 to 4 A
   c. 6 to 8 A
   d. 8 to 10 A

6. A wide-band oxygen sensor needs to be heated to what operating temperature?
   a. 600°F (315°C)
   b. 800°F (427°C)
   c. 1,400°F (760°C)
   d. 2,000°F (1,093°C)

7. The two internal chambers of a dual-cell wide-band oxygen sensor include _____.
   a. Single and dual
   b. Nernst and pump
   c. Air reference and diffusion
   d. Inside and outside

8. When the exhaust is rich, the PCM applies a _____ current into the pump cell.
   a. Positive
   b. Negative

9. When the exhaust is lean, the PCM applies a _____ current into the pump cell.
   a. Positive
   b. Negative

10. A dual-cell wide-band oxygen sensor can be tested using a _____.
    a. Scan tool
    b. Voltmeter
    c. Scope
    d. All of the above

# chapter 19

# FUEL PUMPS, LINES, AND FILTERS

**OBJECTIVES:** After studying Chapter 19, the reader should be able to: • Prepare for ASE Engine Performance (A8) certification test content area "C" (Fuel, Air Induction, and Exhaust Systems Diagnosis and Repair). • Describe how fuel pumps work. • Describe how to check an electric fuel pump for proper pressure and volume delivery. • Discuss fuel tanks, lines and filters. • Explain how to check a fuel-pressure regulator.

**KEY TERMS:** Accumulator 247 • Baffle 238 • Check valve 240 • Delivery system 238 • Filter basket 249 • Gerotor 244 • Hydrokinetic pump 244 • Inertia switch 240 • Onboard refueling vapor recovery (ORVR) 239 • Peripheral pump 244 • Residual or rest pressure 243 • Roller cell 243 • Rotary vane pump 243 • Side-channel pump 244 • Turbine pump 244 • Vacuum lock 240 • Vapor lock 240 • Volatile organic compound (VOC) 243

## FUEL DELIVERY SYSTEM

Creating and maintaining a correct air-fuel mixture requires a properly functioning fuel and air **delivery system**. Fuel delivery (and return) systems use many if not all of the following components to make certain that fuel is available under the right conditions to the fuel-injection system:

- Fuel storage tank, filler neck, and gas cap
- Fuel tank pressure sensor
- Fuel pump
- Fuel filter(s)
- Fuel delivery lines and fuel rail
- Fuel-pressure regulator
- Fuel return line (if equipped with a return-type fuel delivery system)

## FUEL TANKS

A vehicle fuel tank is made of corrosion-resistant steel or polyethylene plastic. Some models, such as sport utility vehicles (SUVs) and light trucks, may have an auxiliary fuel tank.

Tank design and capacity are a compromise between available space, filler location, fuel expansion room, and fuel movement. Some later-model tanks deliberately limit tank capacity by extending the filler tube neck into the tank low enough to prevent complete filling or by providing for expansion room.
● **SEE FIGURE 19–1.** A vertical **baffle** in fuel tanks limits fuel sloshing as the vehicle moves.

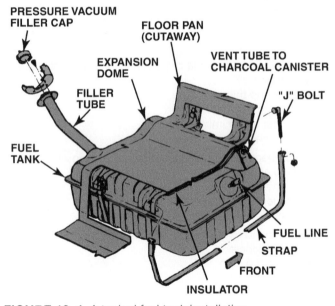

**FIGURE 19–1** A typical fuel tank installation.

Regardless of size and shape, all fuel tanks incorporate most if not all of the following features:

- Inlet or filler tube through which fuel enters the tank
- Filler cap with pressure holding and relief features
- An outlet to the fuel line leading to the fuel pump or fuel injector
- Fuel pump mounted within the tank
- Tank vent system
- Fuel pickup tube and fuel level sending unit

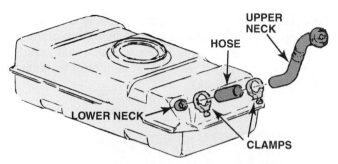

**FIGURE 19-2** A three-piece filler tube assembly. The main three parts include the upper neck, hose and lower neck.

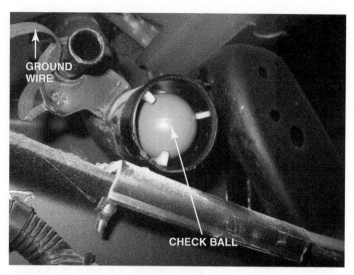

**FIGURE 19-3** A view of a typical filler tube with the fuel tank removed. Notice the ground strap used to help prevent the buildup of static electricity as the fuel flows into the plastic tank. The check ball looks exactly like a ping-pong ball.

**FIGURE 19-4** Vehicles equipped with onboard refueling vapor recovery usually have a reduced-size fill tube.

**TANK LOCATION AND MOUNTING** Most vehicles use a horizontally suspended fuel tank, usually mounted below the rear of the floor pan, just ahead of or behind the rear axle. Fuel tanks are located there so that frame rails and body components protect the tank in the event of a crash. To prevent squeaks, some models have insulated strips cemented on the top or sides of the tank wherever it contacts the underbody.

Fuel inlet location depends on the tank design and filler tube placement. It is located behind a filler cap and is often a hinged door in the outer side of either rear fender panel.

Generally, a pair of metal retaining straps holds a fuel tank in place. Underbody brackets or support panels hold the strap ends using bolts. The free ends are drawn underneath the tank to hold it in place, then bolted to other support brackets or to a frame member on the opposite side of the tank.

**FILLER TUBES** Fuel enters the tank through a large tube extending from the tank to an opening on the outside of the vehicle. ● **SEE FIGURE 19-2.**

Effective in 1993, federal regulations require manufacturers to install a device to prevent fuel from being siphoned through the filler neck. Federal authorities recognized methanol as a poison, and methanol used in gasoline is a definite health hazard. Additionally, gasoline is a suspected carcinogen (cancer-causing agent). To prevent siphoning, manufacturers welded a filler-neck check-ball tube in fuel tanks. To drain check-ball-equipped fuel tanks, a technician must disconnect the check-ball tube at the tank and attach a siphon directly to the tank. ● **SEE FIGURE 19-3.**

**Onboard refueling vapor recovery (ORVR)** systems have been developed to reduce evaporative emissions during refueling. ● **SEE FIGURE 19-4.** These systems add components to the filler neck and the tank. One ORVR system utilizes a tapered filler neck with a smaller diameter tube and a check valve. When fuel flows down the neck, it opens the normally closed check valve. The vapor passage to the charcoal canister is opened. The decreased size neck and the opened air passage allow fuel and vapor to flow rapidly into the tank and the canister respectively. When the fuel has reached a predetermined level, the check valve closes, and the fuel tank pressure increases. This forces the nozzle to shut off, thereby preventing the tank from being overfilled.

**PRESSURE-VACUUM FILLER CAP** Fuel and vapors are sealed in the tank by the safety filler cap. The safety cap must release excess pressure or excess vacuum. Either condition could cause fuel tank damage, fuel spills, and vapor escape. Typically, the cap will release if the pressure is over 1.5 to 2 PSI (10 to 14 kPa) or if the vacuum is 0.15 to 0.3 PSI (1 to 2 kPa).

**FUEL PICKUP TUBE** The fuel pickup tube is usually a part of the fuel sender assembly or the electric fuel pump assembly. Since dirt and sediment eventually gather on the bottom of a fuel tank, the fuel pickup tube is fitted with a filter sock or strainer to prevent contamination from entering the fuel lines. The woven plastic strainer also acts as a water separator by preventing water from being drawn up with the fuel. The filter sock usually is designed to filter out particles that are larger than 70 to 100 microns, or 30 microns if a gerotor-type fuel pump is used. One micron is 0.000039 in. ● **SEE FIGURE 19-5.**

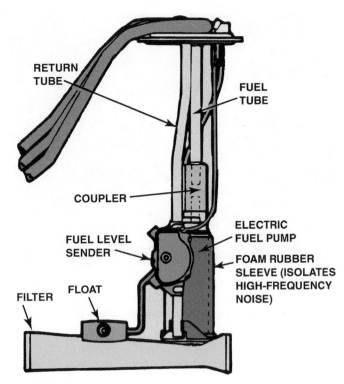

**FIGURE 19–5** The fuel pickup tube is part of the fuel sender and pump assembly.

Labels in figure:
RETURN TUBE
FUEL TUBE
COUPLER
FUEL LEVEL SENDER
ELECTRIC FUEL PUMP
FOAM RUBBER SLEEVE (ISOLATES HIGH-FREQUENCY NOISE)
FILTER
FLOAT

**NOTE: The human eye cannot see anything smaller than about 40 microns.**

The filter is made from woven Saran resin (copolymer of vinylidene chloride and vinyl chloride). The filter blocks any water that may be in the fuel tank, unless it is completely submerged in water. In that case, it will allow water through the filter. This filter should be replaced whenever the fuel pump is replaced.

**TANK VENTING REQUIREMENTS** Fuel tanks must be vented to prevent a **vacuum lock** as fuel is drawn from the tank. As fuel is used and its level drops in the tank, the space above the fuel increases. As the air in the tank expands to fill this greater space, its pressure drops. Without a vent, the air pressure inside the tank would drop below atmospheric pressure, developing a vacuum which prevents the flow of fuel. Under extreme pressure variance, the tank could collapse. Venting the tank allows outside air to enter as the fuel level drops, preventing a vacuum from developing.

An EVAP system vents gasoline vapors from the fuel tank directly to a charcoal-filled vapor storage canister and uses an unvented filler cap. Many filler caps contain valves that open to relieve pressure or vacuum above specified safety levels. Systems that use completely sealed caps have separate pressure and vacuum relief valves for venting.

Because fuel tanks are not vented directly to the atmosphere, the tank must allow for fuel expansion, contraction, and overflow that can result from changes in temperature or overfilling. One way is to use a dome in the top of the tank. Many General Motors vehicles use a design that includes a vertical slosh baffle that reserves up to 12% of the total tank capacity for fuel expansion.

## ROLLOVER LEAKAGE PROTECTION

All vehicles have one or more devices to prevent fuel leaks in case of vehicle rollover or a collision in which fuel may spill.

Variations of the basic one-way **check valve** may be installed in any number of places between the fuel tank and the engine. The valve may be installed in the fuel return line, vapor vent line, or fuel tank filler cap.

In addition to the rollover protection devices, some vehicles use devices to ensure that the fuel pump shuts off when an accident occurs. On some air vane sensors, a microswitch is built into the sensor to switch on the fuel pump as soon as intake airflow causes the vane to lift from its rest position. ● **SEE FIGURE 19–6.**

Ford vehicles use an **inertia switch.** ● **SEE FIGURE 19–7.** The inertia switch is installed in the rear of the vehicle between the electric fuel pump and its power supply. With any sudden impact, such as a jolt from another vehicle in a parking lot, the inertia switch opens and shuts off power to the fuel pump. The switch must be reset manually by pushing a button to restore current to the pump.

## FUEL LINES

Fuel and vapor lines made of steel, nylon tubing, or fuel-resistant rubber hoses connect the parts of the fuel system. Fuel lines supply fuel to the throttle body or fuel rail. They also return excess fuel and vapors to the tank. Depending on their function, fuel and vapor lines may be either rigid or flexible.

Fuel lines must remain as cool as possible. If any part of the line is located near too much heat, the gasoline passing through it vaporizes, and **vapor lock** occurs. When this happens, the fuel pump supplies only vapor that passes into the injectors. Without liquid gasoline, the engine stalls, and a hot restart problem develops.

The fuel delivery system supplies 10 to 15 PSI (69 to 103 kPa) or up to 35 PSI (241 kPa) to many throttle-body injection units and up to 60 PSI (414 kPa) for multiport fuel-injection systems. Fuel-injection systems retain residual or rest pressure in the lines for a half hour or longer when the engine is turned off to prevent hot engine restart problems. Higher-pressure systems such as these require special fuel lines.

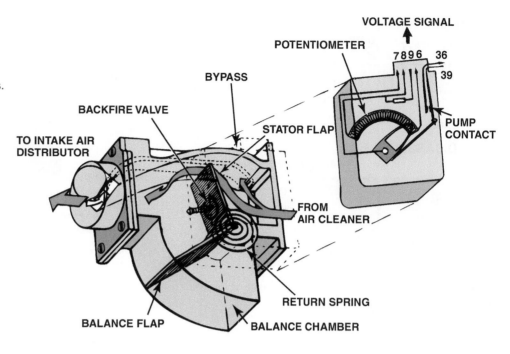

**FIGURE 19–6** On some vehicles equipped with an airflow sensor, a switch is used to energize the fuel pump. In the event of a collision, the switch opens, and the fuel flow stops.

VOLTAGE SIGNAL

POTENTIOMETER

7896  36

39

BYPASS

BACKFIRE VALVE

STATOR FLAP

PUMP CONTACT

TO INTAKE AIR DISTRIBUTOR

FROM AIR CLEANER

RETURN SPRING

BALANCE FLAP

BALANCE CHAMBER

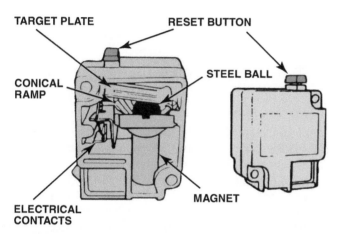

TARGET PLATE    RESET BUTTON

CONICAL RAMP

STEEL BALL

ELECTRICAL CONTACTS

MAGNET

**FIGURE 19–7** Ford uses an inertia switch to turn off the electric fuel pump in an accident.

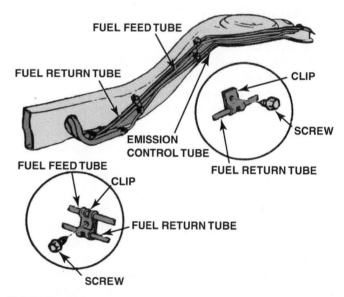

FUEL FEED TUBE

FUEL RETURN TUBE

CLIP

SCREW

EMISSION CONTROL TUBE

FUEL RETURN TUBE

FUEL FEED TUBE

CLIP

FUEL RETURN TUBE

SCREW

**FIGURE 19–8** Fuel lines are routed along the frame or body and secured with clips.

## RIGID LINES

All fuel lines fastened to the body, frame, or engine are made from nylon reinforced plastic or seamless steel tubing. Steel springs may be wound around the tubing at certain points to protect against impact damage.

Only steel tubing, or that recommended by the manufacturer, should be used when replacing rigid fuel lines. *Never substitute copper or aluminum tubing for steel tubing.* These materials do not withstand normal vehicle vibration and could combine with the fuel to cause a chemical reaction.

## FLEXIBLE LINES

Most fuel systems use synthetic rubber hose sections where flexibility is needed. Short hose sections often connect steel fuel lines to other system components. The fuel delivery hose inside diameter (ID), is usually 3/16" or 3/8" (8 or 10 millimeters) and the return line ID is normally 1/4" (6 millimeters).

Fuel-injection systems require special-composition reinforced hoses specifically made for these higher-pressure systems. Similarly, vapor vent lines must be made of materials that resist fuel vapors. Replacement vent hoses are usually marked with the designation "EVAP" to indicate their intended use.

## FUEL LINE MOUNTING

Fuel supply lines from the tank to a throttle body or fuel rail are routed to follow the frame along the underbody of the vehicle. Vapor and return lines may be routed with the fuel supply line. All rigid lines are fastened to the frame rail or underbody with screws and clamps or with clips.
● **SEE FIGURE 19–8.**

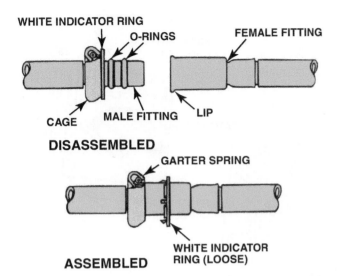

FIGURE 19-9 Some Ford metal line connections use spring locks and O-rings.

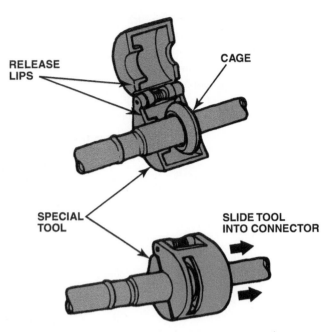

FIGURE 19-10 Ford spring-lock connectors require a special tool for disassembly.

**FUEL-INJECTION LINES AND CLAMPS** Hoses used for fuel-injection systems are made of materials with high resistance to oxidation and deterioration. Replacement hoses for injection systems should always be equivalent to original equipment manufacturer (OEM) hoses.

Screw-type clamps are essential on injected engines and should have rolled edges to prevent hose damage.

**CAUTION:** *Do not use spring-type clamps on fuel-injected engines—they cannot withstand the fuel pressures involved.*

**FUEL-INJECTION FITTINGS AND NYLON LINES** Because of their operating pressures, fuel-injection systems often use special kinds of fittings to ensure leakproof connections. Some high-pressure fittings on GM vehicles with port fuel-injection systems use O-ring seals instead of the traditional flare connections. When disconnecting such a fitting, inspect the O-ring for damage and replace it if necessary. *Always* tighten O-ring fittings to the specified torque value to prevent damage.

Other manufacturers also use O-ring seals on fuel line connections. In all cases, the O-rings are made of special materials that withstand contact with gasoline and oxygenated fuel blends. Some manufacturers specify that the O-rings be replaced every time the fuel system connection is opened. When replacing one of these O-rings, a new part specifically designed for fuel system service must be used.

Ford also uses spring-lock connectors to join male and female ends of steel tubing. ● **SEE FIGURE 19-9.** The coupling is held together by a garter spring inside a circular cage. The flared end of the female fitting slips behind the spring to lock the coupling together.

General Motors has used nylon fuel lines with quick-connect fittings at the fuel tank and fuel filter since the early 1990s. Like the GM threaded couplings used with steel lines,

**? FREQUENTLY ASKED QUESTION**

**Just How Much Fuel Is Recirculated?**

Approximately 80% of the available fuel pump volume is released to the fuel tank through the fuel pressure regulator at idle speed. As an example, a passenger vehicle cruising down the road at 60 miles per hour gets 30 miles per gallon. With a typical return-style fuel system pumping about 30 gallons per hour from the tank, it would therefore burn 2 gallons per hour and return about 28 gallons per hour to the tank!

nylon line couplings use internal O-ring seals. Unlocking the metal connectors requires a special quick-connector separator tool; plastic connectors can be released without the tool. ● **SEE FIGURES 19-10 AND 19-11.**

**FUEL LINE LAYOUT** Fuel pressures have tended to become higher to prevent vapor lock, and a major portion of the fuel routed to the fuel-injection system returns to the tank by way of a fuel return line or return-type systems. This allows better control, within limits, of heat absorbed by the gasoline as it is routed through the engine compartment. Throttle-body and multiport injection systems have typically used a pressure regulator to control fuel pressure in the throttle body or fuel rail and also allow excess fuel not used by the injectors to return to the tank. However, the warmer fuel in the tank may create problems, such as an excessive rise in fuel vapor pressures in the tank.

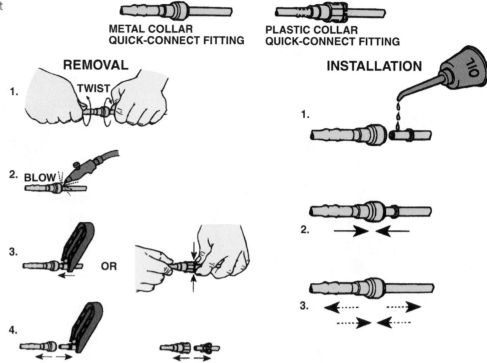

**FIGURE 19–11** Typical quick-connect steps.

METAL COLLAR
QUICK-CONNECT FITTING

PLASTIC COLLAR
QUICK-CONNECT FITTING

REMOVAL

INSTALLATION

With late-model vehicles, there has been some concern about too much heat being sent back to the fuel tank, causing rising in-tank temperatures and increases in fuel vaporization and **volatile organic compound (VOC)** (hydrocarbon) emissions. To combat this problem, manufacturers have placed the pressure regulator back by the tank instead of under the hood on mechanical returnless systems. In this way, returned fuel is not subjected to the heat generated by the engine and the underhood environment. To prevent vapor lock in these systems, pressures have been raised in the fuel rail, and injectors tend to have smaller openings to maintain control of the fuel spray under pressure.

Not only must the fuel be filtered and supplied under adequate pressure, but there must also be a consistent *volume* of fuel to assure smooth engine performance even under the heaviest of loads.

## ELECTRIC FUEL PUMPS

The electric fuel pump is a pusher unit. When the pump is mounted in the tank, the entire fuel supply line to the engine can be pressurized. Because the fuel, when pressurized, has a higher boiling point, it is unlikely that vapor will form to interfere with fuel flow.

Most vehicles use the impeller or turbine pumps. ● **SEE FIGURE 19–12.** All electrical pumps are driven by a small electric motor, but the turbine pump turns at higher speeds and is quieter than the others.

**POSITIVE DISPLACEMENT PUMP** A positive displacement pump is a design that forces everything that enters the pump to leave the pump.

In the **roller cell** or vane pump, the impeller draws fuel into the pump and then pushes it out through the fuel line to the injection system. All designs of pumps use a variable-sized chamber to draw in fuel. When the maximum volume has been reached, the supply port closes, and the discharge opens. Fuel is then forced out the discharge as this volume decreases. The chambers are formed by rollers or gears in a rotor plate. Because this type of pump uses no valves to move the fuel, the fuel flows steadily through the entire pump housing, including the electrical portion which keeps the pump cool. Usually, only when a vehicle runs out of fuel is there a risk of pump damage.

Most electric fuel pumps are equipped with a fuel outlet check valve that closes to maintain fuel pressure when the pump shuts off. **Residual** or **rest pressure** prevents vapor lock and hot-start problems on these systems.

● **FIGURE 19–13** shows the pumping action of a **rotary vane pump.** The pump consists of a central impeller disk,

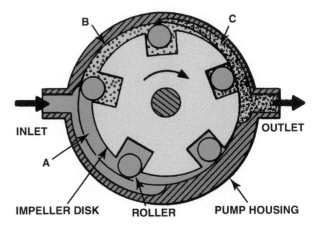

**FIGURE 19–13** The pumping action of an impeller or rotary vane pump.

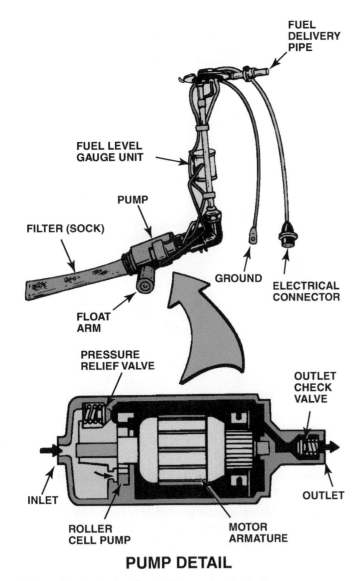

## PUMP DETAIL

**FIGURE 19–12** A roller cell-type electric fuel pump.

several rollers or vanes that ride in notches in the impeller, and a pump housing that is offset from the impeller centerline. The impeller is mounted on the end of the motor armature and spins whenever the motor is running. The rollers are free to slide in and out within the notches in the impeller to maintain sealing contact. Unpressurized fuel enters the pump, fills the spaces between the rollers, and is trapped between the impeller, the housing, and two rollers. An internal gear pump, called a **gerotor**, is another type of positive displacement pump that is often used in engine oil pumps. It uses the meshing of internal and external gear teeth to pressurize the fuel. ● **SEE FIGURE 19–14** for an example of a gerotor-type fuel pump that uses an impeller as the first stage and is used to move the fuel gerotor section where it is pressurized.

## HYDROKINETIC FLOW PUMP DESIGN The word *hydro*
means liquid, and the term *kinetic* refers to motion, so the term **hydrokinetic pump** means that this design of pump rapidly

moves the fuel to create pressure. This design of pump is a nonpositive displacement pump design.

A **turbine pump** is the most common because it tends to be less noisy. Also known as **peripheral** and **side-channel pumps,** these units use an impeller that accelerates the fuel particles before actually discharging them into a tract where they generate pressure via pulse exchange. Actual pump volume is controlled by using a different number of impeller blades, and in some cases a higher number of impellers, or different shapes along the side discharge channels. These units are fitted more toward lower operating pressures of less than 60 PSI. ● **SEE FIGURE 19–15** for an example of a two-stage turbine pump. The turbine impeller has a staggered blade design to minimize pump harmonic noise and to separate vapor from the liquid fuel. The end cap assembly contains a pressure relief valve and a radio-frequency interference (RFI) suppression module. The check valve is usually located in the upper fuel pipe connector assembly.

After fuel passes through the strainer, it is drawn into the lower housing inlet port by the impellers. It is pressurized and delivered to the convoluted fuel tube for transfer through a check valve into the fuel feed pipe. A typical electric fuel pump used on a fuel-injection system delivers about 40 to 50 gallons per hour or 0.6 to 0.8 gallon per minute at a pressure of 70 to 90 PSI.

## MODULAR FUEL SENDER ASSEMBLY The modular
fuel sender consists of a fuel level sensor, a turbine pump, and a jet pump. The reservoir housing is attached to the cover containing fuel pipes and the electrical connector. Fuel is transferred from the pump to the fuel pipe through a convoluted (flexible) fuel pipe. The convoluted fuel pipe eliminates the need for rubber hoses, nylon pipes, and clamps. The reservoir dampens fuel slosh to maintain a constant fuel level available to the roller vane pump; it also reduces noise.

Some of the flow, however, is returned to the jet pump for recirculation. Excess fuel is returned to the reservoir through one of the three hollow support pipes. The hot fuel quickly

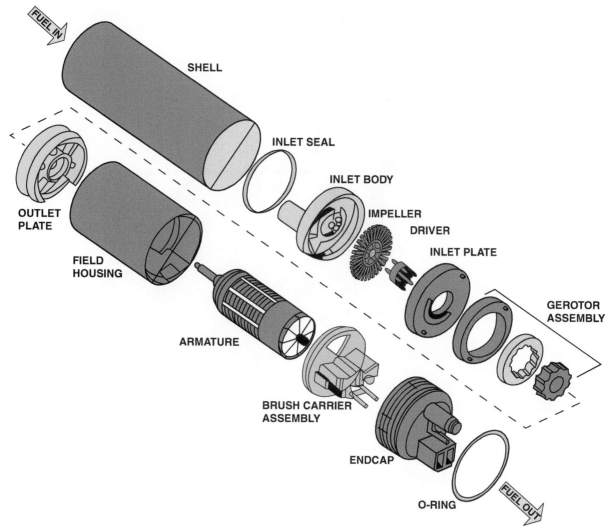

**FIGURE 19–14** An exploded view of a gerotor electric fuel pump.

mixes with the cooler fuel in the reservoir; this minimizes the possibility of vapor lock. In these modules, the reservoir is filled by the jet pump. Some of the fuel from the pump is sent through the jet pump to lift fuel from the tank into the reservoir.

## ELECTRIC PUMP CONTROL CIRCUITS
Fuel pump circuits are controlled by the fuel pump relay. Fuel pump relays are activated initially by turning the ignition key to on, which allows the pump to pressurize the fuel system. As a safety precaution, the relay deenergizes after a few seconds until the key is moved to the crank position. Once an ignition coil signal, or "tach" signal, is received by the engine control computer, indicating the engine is rotating, the relay remains energized even with the key released to the run position.

**CHRYSLER.** On Chrysler vehicles, the PCM must receive an engine speed (RPM) signal during cranking before it can energize a circuit driver inside the power module to activate an

 **FREQUENTLY ASKED QUESTION**

### Why Are Many Fuel Pump Modules Spring Loaded?

Fuel modules that contain the fuel pickup sock, fuel pump, and fuel level sensor are often spring loaded when fitted to a plastic fuel tank. The plastic material shrinks when cold and expands when hot, so having the fuel module spring loaded ensures that the fuel pickup sock will always be the same distance from the bottom of the tank. ● **SEE FIGURE 19–16**.

automatic shutdown (ASD) relay to power the fuel pump, ignition coil, and injectors. As a safety precaution, if the RPM signal to the logic module is interrupted, the logic module signals the power module to deactivate the ASD, turning off the pump, coil,

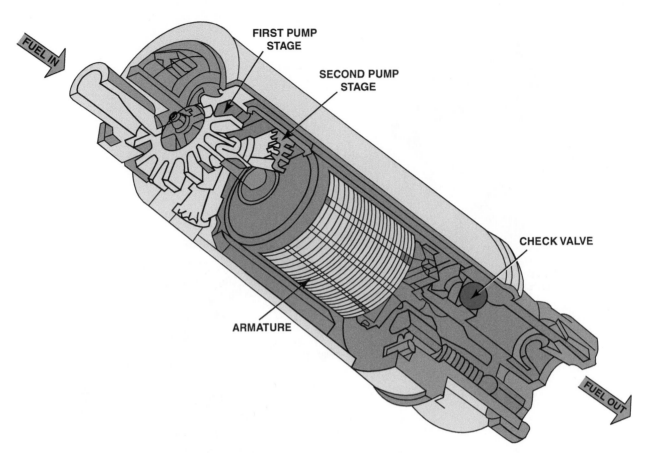

FIGURE 19–15 A cutaway view of a typical two-stage turbine electric fuel pump.

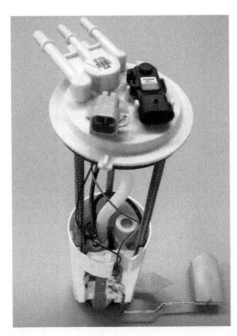

FIGURE 19–16 A typical fuel pump module assembly, which includes the pickup strainer and fuel pump, as well as the fuel-pressure sensor and fuel level sensing unit.

and injectors. In some vehicles, the oil pressure switch circuit may be used as a safety circuit to activate the pump in the ignition switch run position.

**GENERAL MOTORS.** General Motors systems energize the pump with the ignition switch to initially pressurize the fuel lines but then deactivate the pump if an RPM signal is not received within one or two seconds. The pump is reactivated as soon as engine cranking is detected. The oil pressure sending unit serves as a backup to the fuel pump relay on some vehicles. In case of pump relay failure, the oil pressure switch will operate the fuel pump once oil pressure reaches about 4 PSI (28 kPa).

**FORD.** Most Ford vehicles with fuel injection have an inertia switch between the fuel pump relay and fuel pump. When the ignition switch is turned to the on position, the electronic engine control (EEC) power relay energizes, providing current to the fuel pump relay and a timing circuit in the EEC module. If the RPM signal is not received by the PCM within about one second, the timing circuit opens the ground circuit to deenergize the fuel pump relay and shut down the pump. This circuit is designed to prepressurize the system. Once the key is turned to the start position, power to the pump is sent through the relay and inertia switch.

The inertia switch opens under a specified impact, such as a collision. When the switch opens, current to the pump shuts off

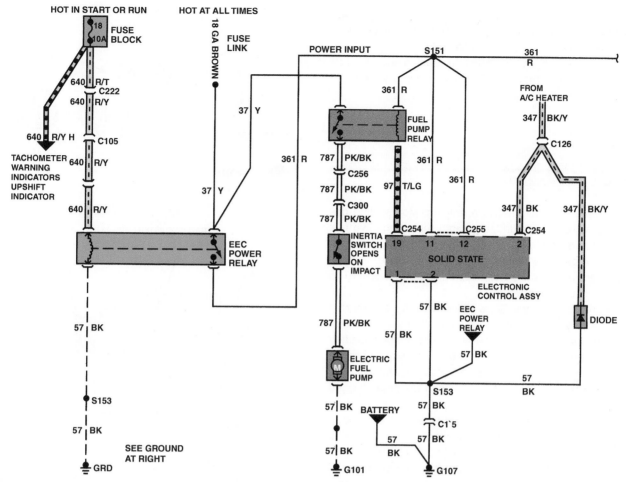

**FIGURE 19–17** A schematic showing that an inertia switch is connected in series between the fuel pump relay and the fuel pump.

because the fuel pump relay will not energize. The switch must be reset manually by opening the trunk and depressing the reset button before current flow to the pump can be restored. ● **SEE FIGURE 19–17** for a schematic of a typical fuel system that uses an inertia switch in the power feed circuit to the electric fuel pump.

**PUMP PULSATION DAMPENING** Some manufacturers use an **accumulator** in the system to reduce pressure pulses and noise. Others use a pulsator located at the outlet of the fuel pump to absorb pressure pulsations that are created by the pump. These pulsators are usually used on roller vane pumps and are a source of many internal fuel leaks. ● **SEE FIGURE 19–18.**

**NOTE: Some experts suggest that the pulsator be removed and replaced with a standard section of fuel line to prevent the loss of fuel pressure that results when the connections on the pulsator loosen and leak fuel back into the tank.**

**VARIABLE SPEED PUMPS** Another way to help reduce noise, current draw, and pump wear is to reduce the speed of the pump when less than maximum output is required. Pump

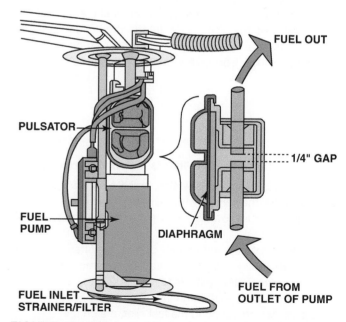

**FIGURE 19–18** A typical fuel pulsator used mostly with roller vane-type pumps to help even out the pulsation in pressure that can cause noise.

speed and pressure can be regulated by controlling the voltage supplied to the pump with a resistor switched into the circuit or by letting the engine-control computer pulse-width modulate (PWM) the voltage supply to the pump, through a separate fuel pump driver electronic module. With slower pump speed and pressure, less noise is produced.

# FUEL FILTERS

Despite the care generally taken in refining, storing, and delivering gasoline, some impurities get into the automotive fuel system. Fuel filters remove dirt, rust, water, and other contamination from the gasoline before it can reach the fuel injectors. Most fuel filters are designed to filter particles that are 10 to 20 microns or larger in size.

The useful life of many filters is limited, but vehicles that use a returnless-type fuel-injection system often use filters that are part of the fuel pump assembly and do have any specified replacement interval. This means that they should last the life of the vehicle. If fuel filters are not replaced according to the manufacturer's recommendations, they can become clogged and restrict fuel flow.

In addition to using several different types of fuel filters, a single fuel system may contain two or more filters. The inline filter is located in the line between the fuel pump and the throttle body or fuel rail. ● **SEE FIGURE 19–19.** This filter protects the system from contamination but does not protect the fuel pump. The inline filter usually is a metal or plastic container with a pleated paper element sealed inside.

Fuel filters may be mounted on a bracket on the fender panel, a shock tower, or another convenient place in the engine compartment. They may also be installed under the vehicle near the fuel tank. Fuel filters should be replaced according to the vehicle manufacturer's recommendations, which range from every 30,000 miles (48,000 km) to

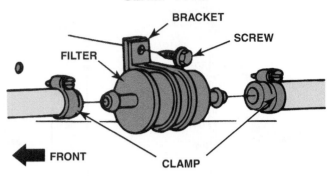

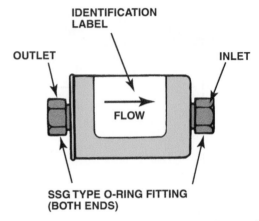

**FIGURE 19–19** Inline fuel filters are usually attached to the fuel line with screw clamps or threaded connections. The fuel filter must be installed in the proper direction or a restricted fuel flow can result.

100,000 miles (160,000 km) or longer. Fuel filters that are part of the fuel pump module assemblies usually do not have any specified service interval.

# FUEL PUMP TESTING

Fuel pump testing includes many different tests and procedures. Even though a fuel pump can pass one test, it does not mean that there is not a fuel pump problem. For example, if the pump motor is rotating slower than normal, it may be able to produce the specified pressure but not enough volume to meet the needs of the engine while operating under a heavy load.

**TESTING FUEL PUMP PRESSURE** Fuel pump–regulated pressure has become more important than ever with a more exact fuel control. Although an increase in fuel pressure does increase fuel volume to the engine, this is *not* the preferred method to add additional fuel as some units will not open correctly at the increased fuel pressure. On the other side of the discussion, many newer engines will not start when fuel pressure is just a few

 **TECH TIP**

**Be Sure That the Fuel Filter Is Installed Correctly**

The fuel filter has flow direction, and if it is installed backwards, the vehicle will most likely have a restricted exhaust (low power at higher engine speeds and loads).

All injectors, throttle body or port, are fitted with one or more filter screens or strainers to remove any particles (generally 10 microns, or 0.00039 in.) that might have passed through the other filters. These screens, which surround the fuel inlet, are on the side of throttle-body injectors and are inserted in the top of port injectors. ● **SEE FIGURE 19–20.**

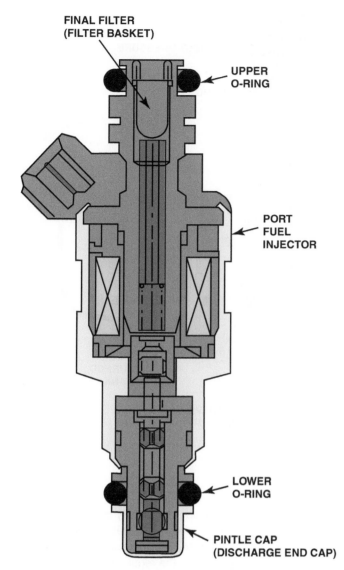

FIGURE 19–20 The final filter, also called a **filter basket**, is the last filter in the fuel system.

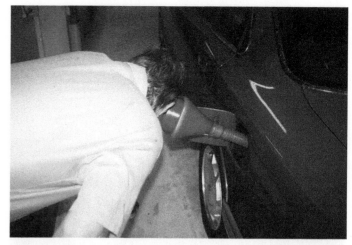

(a)

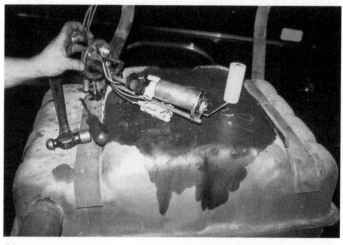

(b)

FIGURE 19–21 (a) A funnel helps in hearing if the electric fuel pump inside the gas tank is working. (b) If the pump is not running, check the wiring and current flow before going through the process of dropping the fuel tank to remove the pump.

PSI low. Correct fuel pressure is very important for proper engine operation. Most fuel-injection systems operate at either a low pressure of about 10 PSI or a high pressure of between 35 and 45 PSI.

| Normal Operating Pressure | (PSI) | Maximum Pump Pressure (PSI) |
|---|---|---|
| Low-pressure TBI units | 9–13 | 18–20 |
| High-pressure TBI units | 25–35 | 50–70 |
| Port fuel-injection systems | 35–45 | 70–90 |
| Central port fuel injection (GM) | 55–64 | 90–110 |

  TECH TIP

**The Ear Test**

No, this is not a test of your hearing but rather using your ear to check that the electric fuel pump is operating. The electric fuel pump inside the fuel tank is often difficult to hear running, especially in a noisy shop environment. A commonly used trick to better hear the pump is to use a funnel in the fuel filter neck. ● SEE FIGURE 19–21.

In both types of systems, maximum fuel pump pressure is about double the normal operating pressure to ensure that a continuous flow of cool fuel is being supplied to the injector(s) to help prevent vapor from forming in the fuel system. Although

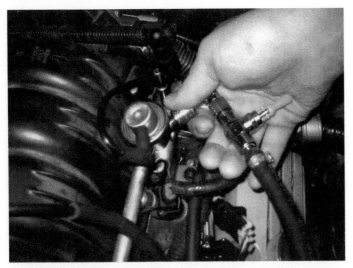

**FIGURE 19–22** The Schrader valve on this General Motors 3800 V-6 is located next to the fuel-pressure regulator.

 **TECH TIP**

### The Rubber Mallet Trick

Often a no-start condition is due to an inoperative electric fuel pump. A common trick is to tap on the bottom of the fuel tank with a rubber mallet in an attempt to jar the pump motor enough to work. Instead of pushing a vehicle into the shop, simply tap on the fuel tank and attempt to start the engine. This is not a repair but rather a confirmation that the fuel pump does indeed require replacement.

vapor or foaming in a fuel system can greatly affect engine operation, the cooling and lubricating flow of the fuel must be maintained to ensure the durability of injector nozzles.

To measure fuel pump pressure, locate the Schrader valve and attach a fuel-pressure gauge. ● **SEE FIGURE 19–22.**

**NOTE: Some vehicles, such as those with General Motors TBI fuel-injection systems, require a specific fuel-pressure gauge that connects to the fuel system. Always follow the manufacturer's recommendations and procedures.**

**REST PRESSURE TEST** If the fuel pressure is acceptable, then check the system for leakdown. Observe the pressure gauge after five minutes. ● **SEE FIGURE 19–23.** The pressure should be the same as the initial reading. If not, then the pressure regulator, fuel pump check valve, or the injectors are leaking.

**DYNAMIC PRESSURE TEST** To test the pressure dynamically, start the engine. If the pressure is vacuum referenced, then the pressure should change when the throttle is cycled. If

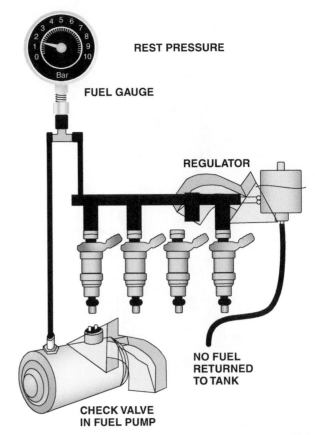

**FIGURE 19–23** The fuel system should hold pressure if the system is leak free.

it does not, then check the vacuum supply circuit. Remove the vacuum line from the regulator and inspect for any presence of fuel. ● **SEE FIGURE 19–24.** There should never be any fuel present on the vacuum side of the regulator diaphragm. When the engine speed is increased, the pressure reading should remain within the specifications.

Some engines do not use a vacuum-referenced regulator. The running pressure remains constant, which is typical for a mechanical returnless-type fuel system. On these systems, the pressure is higher than on return-type systems to help reduce the formation of fuel vapors in the system.

 **TECH TIP**

### The Fuel-Pressure Stethoscope Test

When the fuel pump is energized and the engine is not running, fuel should be heard flowing back to the fuel tank at the outlet of the fuel pressure regulator. ● **SEE FIGURE 19–25.** If fuel is heard flowing through the return line, the fuel pump pressure is higher than the regulator pressure. If no sound of fuel is heard, either the fuel pump or the fuel-pressure regulator is at fault.

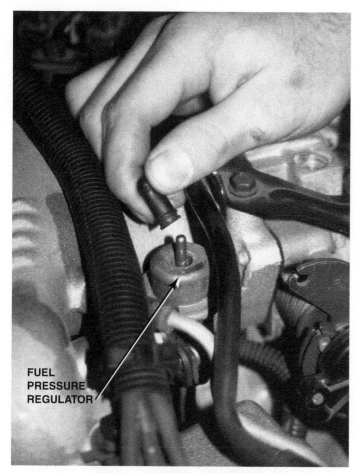

**FIGURE 19–24** If the vacuum hose is removed from the fuel-pressure regulator when the engine is running, the fuel pressure should increase. If it does not increase, then the fuel pump is not capable of supplying adequate pressure or the fuel-pressure regulator is defective. If gasoline is visible in the vacuum hose, the regulator is leaking and should be replaced.

**TESTING FUEL PUMP VOLUME** Fuel pressure alone is not enough for proper engine operation. ● **SEE FIGURE 19–26.** Sufficient fuel capacity (flow) should be at least 2 pints (1 liter) every 30 seconds or 1 pint in 15 seconds. Fuel flow specifications are usually expressed in gallons per minute. A typical specification would be 0.5 gallon per minute or more. Volume testing is shown in ● **SEE FIGURE 19–27.**

All fuel must be filtered to prevent dirt and impurities from damaging the fuel system components and/or engine. The first filter is inside the gas tank and is usually not replaceable separately but is attached to the fuel pump (if the pump is electric) and/or fuel gauge sending unit. The replaceable fuel filter is usually located between the fuel tank and the fuel rail or inlet to the fuel-injection system. Most vehicle manufacturers state in service information when to replace the fuel filter. Most newer vehicles that use returnless-type fuel-injection systems do not have replaceable filters as they are built into the fuel pump module assembly. (Check the

**FIGURE 19–25** Fuel should be heard returning to the fuel tank at the fuel return line if the fuel pump and fuel-pressure regulator are functioning correctly.

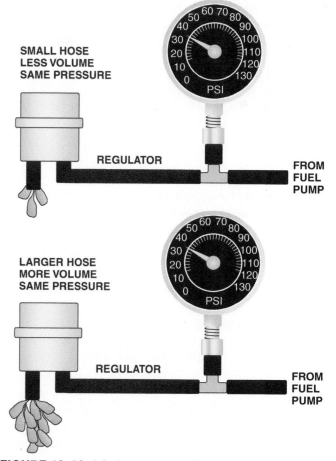

**FIGURE 19–26** A fuel-pressure reading does not confirm that there is enough fuel volume for the engine to operate correctly.

**FIGURE 19-27** A fuel system tester connected in series in the fuel system so all of the fuel used flows through the meter, which displays the rate flow and the fuel pressure.

FUEL PUMP

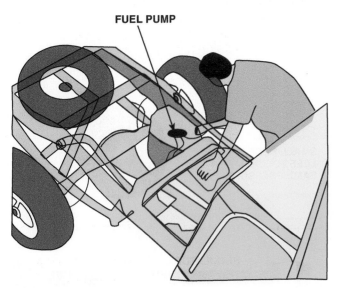

**FIGURE 19-28** Removing the bed from a pickup truck makes gaining access to the fuel pump a lot easier.

vehicle manufacturer's recommendations for exact time and mileage intervals.)

If the fuel filter becomes partially clogged, the following are likely to occur:

1. There will be low power at higher engine speeds. The vehicle usually will not go faster than a certain speed (engine acts as if it has a built-in speed governor).
2. The engine will cut out or miss on acceleration, especially when climbing hills or during heavy-load acceleration.

A weak or defective fuel pump can also be the cause of the symptoms just listed. If an electric fuel pump for a fuel-injected engine becomes weak, additional problems include the following:

1. The engine may be hard to start.
2. There may be a rough idle and stalling.

TECH TIP

**Quick and Easy Fuel Volume Test**

Testing for pump volume involves using a specialized tester or a fuel-pressure gauge equipped with a hose to allow the fuel to be drawn from the system into a container with volume markings to allow for a volume measurement. This test can be hazardous because of flammable gasoline vapors. An alternative test involves connecting a fuel-pressure gauge to the system with the following steps:

**STEP 1**  Start the engine and observe the fuel-pressure gauge. The reading should be within factory specifications (typically between 35 PSI and 45 PSI).

**STEP 2**  Remove the hose from the fuel-pressure regulator. The pressure should increase if the system uses a demand-type regulator.

**STEP 3**  Rapidly accelerate the engine while watching the fuel-pressure gauge. If the fuel volume is okay, the fuel pressure should not drop more than 2 PSI. If the fuel pressure drops more than 2 PSI, replace the fuel filter and retest.

**STEP 4**  After replacing the fuel filter, accelerate the engine and observe the pressure gauge. If the pressure drops more than 2 PSI, replace the fuel pump.

NOTE: The fuel pump could still be delivering less than the specified volume of fuel, but as long as the volume needed by the engine is met, the pressure will not drop. If, however, the vehicle is pulling a heavy load, the demand for fuel volume may exceed the capacity of the pump.

TECH TIP

**Remove the Bed to Save Time?**

The electric fuel pump is easier to replace on many General Motors pickup trucks if the bed is removed. Access to the top of the fuel tank, where the access hole is located, for the removal of the fuel tank sender unit and pump is restricted by the bottom of the pickup truck bed. Rather than drop the tank, it is often much easier to use an engine hoist or a couple of other technicians to lift the bed from the frame after removing only a few fasteners. ● **SEE FIGURE 19-28.**

CAUTION: Be sure to clean around the fuel pump opening so that dirt or debris does not enter the tank when the fuel pump is removed.

3. There may be erratic shifting of the automatic transmission as a result of engine missing due to lack of fuel pump pressure and/or volume.

CAUTION: Be certain to consult the vehicle manufacturer's recommended service and testing procedures before attempting to test or replace any component of a high-pressure electronic fuel-injection system.

## FUEL PUMP CURRENT DRAW TEST

Another test that can and should be performed on a fuel pump is to measure the current draw in amperes. This test is most often performed by connecting a digital multimeter set to read DC amperes and test the current draw. ● SEE FIGURE 19–29 for the hookup for vehicles equipped with a fuel pump relay. Compare the reading to factory specifications. See the chart for an example of typical fuel pump current draw readings.

NOTE: Testing the current draw of an electric fuel pump may not indicate whether the pump is good. A pump that is not rotating may draw normal current.

Using a mini clamp on ammeter is a quick and easy way to measure fuel pump current. Clamp the inductive probe around a wire to the fuel pump or add a fused jumper wire to replace the fuel pump fuse. Start the engine and read the meter display.

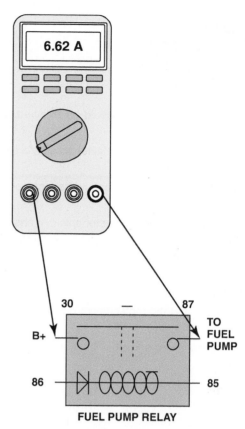

FIGURE 19–29 Hookup for testing fuel pump current draw on any vehicle equipped with a fuel pump relay.

**Fuel Pump Current Draw Table**

| Amperage Reading | Expected Value | Amperage Too High | Amperage Too Low |
|---|---|---|---|
| Throttle-body fuel-injection engines | 2 to 5 amps | • Check the fuel filter. <br>• Check for restrictions in other fuel line areas. <br>• Replace the fuel pump. | • Check for a high-resistance connection. <br>• Check for a high-resistance ground fault. <br>• Replace the fuel pump. |
| Port fuel-injection engines | 4 to 8 amps | • Check the fuel filter. <br>• Check for restrictions in other fuel line areas. <br>• Replace the fuel pump. | • Check for a high-resistance connection. <br>• Check for a high-resistance ground fault. <br>• Replace the fuel pump. |
| Turbo engines | 6 to 10 amps | • Replace the fuel pump. <br>• Check the fuel filter. <br>• Check for restrictions in other fuel line areas. | • Replace the fuel pump. <br>• Check for a high-resistance connection. <br>• Check for a high-resistance ground fault. |
| GM CPI truck engines | 8 to 12 amps | • Replace the fuel pump. <br>• Check the fuel filter. <br>• Check for restrictions in other fuel line areas. <br>• Replace the fuel pump. | • Replace the fuel pump. <br>• Check for a high-resistance connection. <br>• Check for a high-resistance ground fault. <br>• Replace the fuel pump. |

# FUEL PUMP REPLACEMENT

The following recommendations should be followed whenever replacing an electric fuel pump.

- Clean around the fuel pump retainer area before removing the fuel pump assembly.
- The fuel pump strainer (sock) should be replaced with the new pump.
- If the original pump had a defector shield, it should always be used to prevent fuel return bubbles from blocking the inlet to the pump.
- Always check the interior of the fuel tank for evidence of contamination or dirt.
- Double-check that the replacement pump is correct for the application.
- Check that the wiring and electrical connectors are clean and tight.

| Fuel Supply-Related Symptom Guide | |
|---|---|
| **Problem** | **Possible Causes** |
| **Pressure too high after engine start-up.** | 1. Defective fuel-pressure regulator |
| | 2. Restricted fuel return line |
| | 3. Excessive system voltage |
| | 4. Wrong fuel pump |
| **Pressure too low after engine start-up.** | 1. Stuck-open pressure regulator |
| | 2. Low voltage |
| | 3. Poor ground |
| | 4. Plugged fuel filter |
| | 5. Faulty inline fuel pump |
| | 6. Faulty in-tank fuel pump |
| | 7. Partially clogged filter sock |
| | 8. Faulty hose coupling |
| | 9. Leaking fuel line |
| | 10. Wrong fuel pump |
| | 11. Leaking pulsator |
| | 12. Restricted accumulator |
| | 13. Faulty pump check valves |
| | 14. Faulty pump installation |
| **Pressure drops off with key on/engine off. With key off, the pressure does not hold.** | 1. Leaky pulsator |
| | 2. Leaking fuel pump coupling hose |
| | 3. Faulty fuel pump (check valves) |
| | 4. Faulty pressure regulator |
| | 5. Leaking fuel injector |
| | 6. Faulty installation |
| | 7. Lines leaking |

# SUMMARY

1. The fuel delivery system includes the following items:
   - Fuel tank
   - Fuel pump
   - Fuel filter(s)
   - Fuel lines
2. A fuel tank is either constructed of steel with a tin plating for corrosion resistance or polyethylene plastic.
3. Fuel tank filler tubes contain an antisiphoning device.
4. Accident and rollover protection devices include check valves and inertia switches.
5. Most fuel lines are made of nylon plastic.
6. Electric fuel pump types include: roller cell, gerotor, and turbine.
7. Fuel filters remove particles that are 10 to 20 microns or larger in size and should be replaced regularly.
8. Fuel pumps can be tested by checking the following:
   - Pressure
   - Volume
   - Specified current draw

# REVIEW QUESTIONS

1. What are the two materials used to construct fuel tanks?
2. What are the three most commonly used pump designs?
3. What is the proper way to disconnect and connect plastic fuel line connections?
4. Where are the fuel filters located in the fuel system?
5. What accident and rollover devices are installed in a fuel delivery system?
6. What three methods can be used to test a fuel pump?

1. The first fuel filter in the sock inside the fuel tank normally filters particles larger than _____.
   a. 0.001 to 0.003 in.
   b. 0.01 to 0.03 in.
   c. 10 to 20 microns
   d. 70 to 100 microns

2. If it is tripped, which type of safety device will keep the electric fuel pump from operating?
   a. Rollover valve
   b. Inertia switch
   c. Antisiphoning valve
   d. Check valve

3. Fuel lines are constructed from _____.
   a. Seamless steel tubing
   b. Nylon plastic
   c. Copper and/or aluminum tubing
   d. Both a and b

4. What prevents the fuel pump inside the fuel tank from catching the gasoline on fire?
   a. Electricity is not used to power the pump.
   b. No air is around the motor brushes.
   c. Gasoline is hard to ignite in a closed space.
   d. All of the above

5. A good fuel pump should be able to supply how much fuel per minute?
   a. 1/4 pint
   b. 1/2 pint
   c. 1 pint
   d. 0.5 to 0.8 gallon

6. Technician A says that fuel pump modules are spring loaded so that they can be compressed to fit into the opening. Technician B says that they are spring loaded to allow for expansion and contraction of plastic fuel tanks. Which technician is correct?
   a. Technician A only
   b. Technician B only
   c. Both Technicians A and B
   d. Neither Technician A nor B

7. Most fuel filters are designed to remove particles larger than _____.
   a. 10 microns
   b. 20 microns
   c. 70 microns
   d. 100 microns

8. The amperage draw of an electric fuel pump is higher than specified. All of the following are possible causes *except* _____.
   a. Corroded electrical connections at the pump motor
   b. Clogged fuel filter
   c. Restriction in the fuel line
   d. Defective fuel pump

9. A fuel pump is being replaced for the third time. Technician A says that the gasoline could be contaminated. Technician B says that wiring to the pump could be corroded. Which technician is correct?
   a. Technician A only
   b. Technician B only
   c. Both Technicians A and B
   d. Neither Technician A nor B

10. A fuel filter has been accidentally installed backwards. What is the most likely result?
    a. Nothing will be noticed
    b. Reduced fuel economy
    c. Lower power at higher engine speeds and loads
    d. Fuel system pulsation noises may be heard

# chapter 20

# FUEL-INJECTION COMPONENTS AND OPERATION

**OBJECTIVES:** After studying Chapter 20, the reader should be able to: • Prepare for ASE Engine Performance (A8) certification test content area "C" (Fuel, Air Induction, and Exhaust Systems Diagnosis and Repair). • Describe how a port fuel-injection system works. • Describe the fuel injection modes of operation. • Discuss the purpose and function of the fuel-pressure regulator. • Discuss central port injection (CPI) systems. • Explain how a stepper motor works. • List the types of fuel-injection systems.

**KEY TERMS:** Demand delivery system (DDS) 263 • Electronic air control (EAC) 267 • Electronic returnless fuel system (ERFS) 262 • Flare 267 • Fuel rail 264 • Gang fired 259 • Idle speed control (ISC) motor 268 • Mechanical returnless fuel system (MRFS) 263 • Nonchecking 262 • Port fuel injection 256 • Pressure control valve (PCV) 263 • Pressure vent valve (PVV) 263 • Sequential fuel injection (SFI) 259 • Throttle-body injection (TBI) 256

## ELECTRONIC FUEL-INJECTION OPERATION

Electronic fuel-injection systems use the Powertrain control module (PCM) to control the operation of fuel injectors and other functions based on information sent to the PCM from the various sensors. Most electronic fuel-injection systems share the following:

1. Electric fuel pump (usually located inside the fuel tank)
2. Fuel-pump relay (usually controlled by the computer)
3. Fuel-pressure regulator (mechanically operated spring-loaded rubber diaphragm maintains proper fuel pressure)
4. Fuel-injector nozzle or nozzles

● **SEE FIGURE 20–1.** Most electronic fuel-injection systems use the computer to control the following aspects of their operation:

1. **Pulsing the fuel injectors on and off.** The longer the injectors are held open, the greater the amount of fuel injected into the cylinder.
2. **Operating the fuel-pump relay circuit.** The computer usually controls the operation of the electric fuel pump located inside (or near) the fuel tank. The computer uses signals from the ignition switch and RPM signals from the ignition module or system to energize the fuel-pump relay circuit.

**NOTE: This is a safety feature because if the engine stalls and the tachometer (engine speed) signal is lost, the computer will shut off (deenergize) the fuel-pump relay and stop the fuel pump.**

Computer-controlled fuel-injection systems are normally reliable systems if the proper service procedures are followed. Fuel-injection systems use the gasoline flowing through the injectors to lubricate and cool the injector electrical windings and pintle valves.

**NOTE: The fuel does not actually make contact with the electrical windings because the injectors have O-rings at the top and bottom of the winding spool to keep fuel out.**

There are two types of electronic fuel-injection systems:

- **Throttle-body-injection (TBI)** type. A TBI system delivers fuel from a nozzle(s) into the air above the throttle plate. ● **SEE FIGURE 20–2.**
- **Port fuel-injection** type. A port fuel-injection design uses a nozzle for each cylinder, and the fuel is squirted into the intake manifold about 2 to 3 inches (70 to 100 mm) from the intake valve. ● **SEE FIGURE 20–3.**

## SPEED-DENSITY FUEL-INJECTION SYSTEMS

Fuel-injection computer systems require a method for measuring the amount of air the engine is breathing in, in order to match the correct fuel delivery. There are two basic methods used:

1. Speed density
2. Mass airflow

The speed-density method does not require an air quantity sensor but rather calculates the amount of fuel required by the

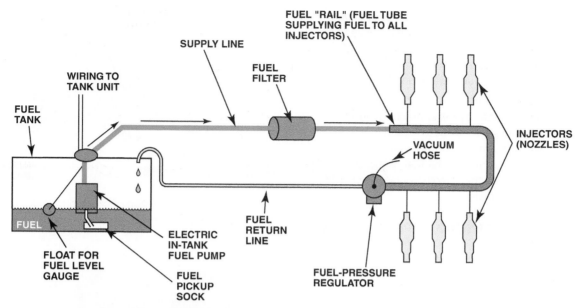

FIGURE 20–1 Typical port fuel-injection system, indicating the location of various components. Notice that the fuel-pressure regulator is located on the fuel return side of the system. The computer does not control fuel pressure but does control the operation of the electric fuel pump (on most systems) and the pulsing on and off of the injectors.

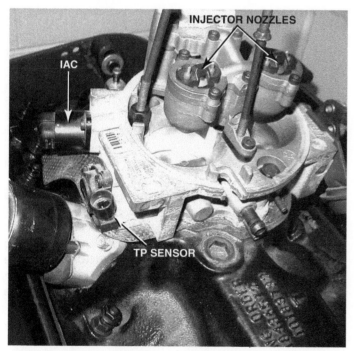

FIGURE 20–2 A dual-nozzle TBI unit on a Chevrolet 4.3-L V-6 engine. The fuel is squirted above the throttle plate, where the fuel mixes with air before entering the intake manifold.

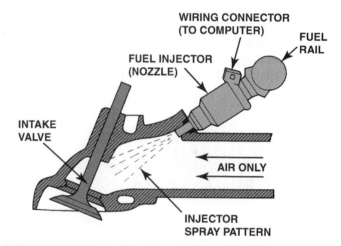

FIGURE 20–3 A typical port fuel-injection system squirts fuel into the low pressure (vacuum) of the intake manifold, about 2 to 3 inches (70 to 100 mm) from the intake valve.

**TECH TIP**

**Two Must-Dos**

For long service life of the fuel system, always do the following:

1. Avoid operating the vehicle on a near-empty tank of fuel. The water or alcohol that may be in the tank becomes more concentrated when the fuel level is low. Dirt that settles near the bottom of the fuel tank can be drawn through the fuel system and cause damage to the pump and injector nozzles.
2. Replace the fuel filter at regular service intervals.

engine. The computer uses information from sensors such as the MAP and TP to calculate the needed amount of fuel:

- **MAP sensor.** The value of the intake (inlet) manifold pressure (vacuum) is a direct indication of engine load.
- **TP sensor.** The position of the throttle plate and its rate of change are used as part of the equation to calculate the proper amount of fuel to inject.

- **Temperature sensors.** Both engine coolant temperature (ECT) and intake air temperature (IAT) are used to calculate the density of the air and the need of the engine for fuel. A cold engine (low-coolant temperature) requires a richer air-fuel mixture than a warm engine.

On speed-density systems, the computer calculates the amount of air in each cylinder by using manifold pressure and engine rpm. The amount of air in each cylinder is the major factor in determining the amount of fuel needed. Other sensors provide information to modify the fuel requirements. The formula used to determine the injector pulse width (PW) in milliseconds (ms) is the following:

**Injector pulse width = MAP/BARO $\times$ RPM/maximum rpm**

The formula is modified by values from other sensors, including the following:

- Throttle position (TP)
- Engine coolant temperature (ECT)
- Intake air temperature (IAT)
- Oxygen sensor (O2S) voltage
- Adaptive memory

A fuel injector delivers atomized fuel into the airstream, where it is instantly vaporized. All throttle-body (TB) fuel-injection systems and many multipoint (port) injection systems use the speed-density method of fuel calculation.

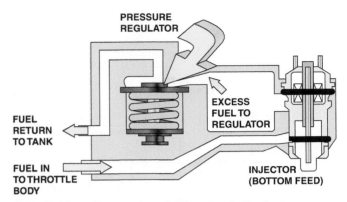

**FIGURE 20–4** The tension of the spring in the fuel-pressure regulator determines the operating pressure on a throttle-body fuel-injection unit.

# MASS AIRFLOW FUEL-INJECTION SYSTEMS

The formula used by fuel-injection systems that use a mass airflow (MAF) sensor to calculate the injection base pulse width is the following:

**Injector pulse width = airflow/rpm**

The formula is modified by other sensor values, such as the following:

- Throttle position
- Engine coolant temperature
- Barometric pressure
- Adaptive memory

NOTE: **Many 4-cylinder engines do not use a MAF sensor because, due to the time interval between intake events, some reverse airflow can occur in the intake manifold. The MAF sensor would "read" this flow of air as being additional air entering the engine, giving the PCM incorrect airflow information. Therefore, most 4-cylinder engines use the speed-density method of fuel control.**

# THROTTLE-BODY INJECTION

The computer controls injector pulses in one of two ways:

- Synchronized
- Nonsynchronized

If the system uses a synchronized mode, the injector pulses once for each distributor reference pulse. In some vehicles, when dual injectors are used in a synchronized system, the injectors pulse alternately. In a nonsynchronized system, the injectors are pulsed once during a given period (which varies according to calibration) completely independent of distributor reference pulses.

The injector always opens the same distance, and the fuel pressure is maintained at a controlled value by the pressure regulator. The regulators used on throttle-body injection systems are not connected to a vacuum like many port fuel-injection systems. The strength of the spring inside the regulator determines at what pressure the valve is unseated, sending the fuel back to the tank and lowering the pressure. ● **SEE FIGURE 20–4.** The amount of fuel delivered by the injector depends on the amount of time (on-time) that the nozzle is open. This is the injector pulse width—the on-time in milliseconds that the nozzle is open.

The PCM commands a variety of pulse widths to supply the amount of fuel that an engine needs at any specific moment:

- A long pulse width delivers more fuel.
- A short pulse width delivers less fuel.

# PORT FUEL INJECTION

The advantages of port fuel-injection design also are related to characteristics of intake manifolds:

- Fuel distribution is equal to all cylinders because each cylinder has its own injector. ● **SEE FIGURE 20–5.**

### How Do the Sensors Affect the Pulse Width?

The base pulse width of a fuel-injection system is primarily determined by the value of the MAF or MAP sensor and engine speed (RPM). However, the PCM relies on the input from many other sensors to modify the base pulse width as needed:

- **TP Sensor.** This sensor causes the PCM to command up to 500% (five times) the base pulse width if the accelerator pedal is depressed rapidly to the floor. It can also reduce the pulse width by about 70% if the throttle is rapidly closed.
- **ECT.** The value of this sensor determines the temperature of the engine coolant, helps determine the base pulse width, and can account for up to 60% of the determining factors.
- **BARO.** The BARO sensor compensates for altitude and adds up to about 10% under high-pressure conditions and subtracts as much as 50% from the base pulse width at high altitudes.
- **IAT.** The intake air temperature is used to modify the base pulse width based on the temperature of the air entering the engine. It is usually capable of adding as much as 20% if very cold air is entering the engine or reducing the pulse width by up to 20% if very hot air is entering the engine.
- **O2S.** This is one of the main modifiers to the base pulse width and can add or subtract up to about 20% to 25% or more, depending on the oxygen sensor activity.

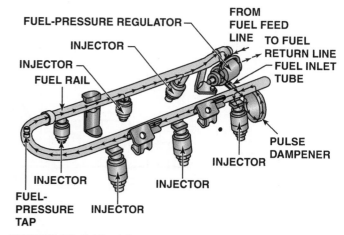

**FIGURE 20–5** The injectors receive fuel and are supported by the fuel rail.

- The fuel is injected almost directly into the combustion chamber, so there is no chance for it to condense on the walls of a cold intake manifold.
- Because the manifold does not have to carry fuel to properly position a TBI unit, it can be shaped and sized to tune the intake airflow to achieve specific engine performance characteristics.

An EFI injector is simply a specialized solenoid. ● **SEE FIGURE 20–6.** It has an armature winding to create a magnetic field, and a needle (pintle), a disc, or a ball valve. A spring holds the needle, disc, or ball closed against the valve seat, and when energized, the armature winding pulls open the valve when it receives a current pulse from the powertrain control module (PCM). When the solenoid is energized, it unseats the valve to inject fuel.

Electronic fuel-injection systems use a solenoid-operated injector to spray atomized fuel in timed pulses into the manifold or near the intake valve. ● **SEE FIGURE 20–7.** Injectors may be sequenced and fired in one of several ways, but their pulse width is determined and controlled by the engine computer.

Port systems have an injector for each cylinder, but they do not all fire the injectors in the same way. Domestic systems use one of three ways to trigger the injectors:

- Grouped double-fire
- Simultaneous double-fire
- Sequential

**GROUPED DOUBLE-FIRE** This system divides the injectors into two equalized groups. The groups fire alternately; each group fires once each crankshaft revolution, or twice per four-stroke cycle. The fuel injected remains near the intake valve and enters the engine when the valve opens. This method of pulsing injectors in groups is sometimes called **gang fired.**

**SIMULTANEOUS DOUBLE-FIRE** This design fires all of the injectors at the same time once every engine revolution: two pulses per four-stroke cycle. Many port fuel-injection systems on 4-cylinder engines use this pattern of injector firing. It is easier for engineers to program this system and it can make relatively quick adjustments in the air-fuel ratio, but it still requires the intake charge to wait in the manifold for varying lengths of time.

**SEQUENTIAL** Sequential firing of the injectors according to engine firing order is the most accurate and desirable method of regulating port fuel injection. However, it is also the most complex and expensive to design and manufacture. In this system, the injectors are timed and pulsed individually, much like the spark plugs are sequentially operated in firing order of the engine. This system is often called **sequential fuel injection,** or **SFI.** Each cylinder receives one charge every two crankshaft revolutions, just before the intake valve opens. This means that the mixture is never static in the intake manifold, and mixture adjustments can be made almost instantaneously between the firing of one injector and the next. A camshaft position sensor (CMP) signal or a special distributor reference pulse informs the PCM when the number 1 cylinder is on its compression stroke. If the sensor fails or the reference pulse is interrupted, some injection systems shut down, while others revert to pulsing the injectors simultaneously.

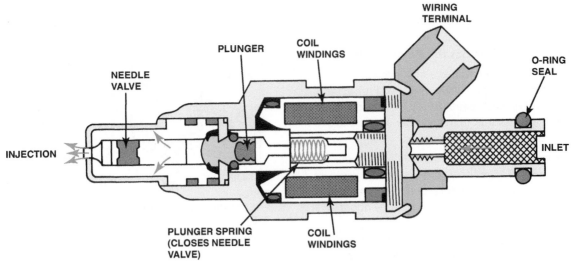

FIGURE 20–6 Cross section of a typical port fuel-injection nozzle assembly. These injectors are serviced as an assembly only; no part replacement or service is possible except for replacement of external O-ring seals.

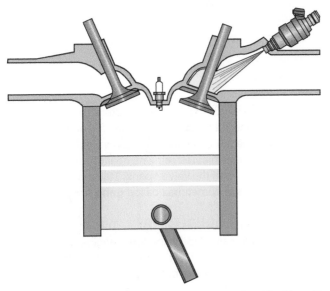

FIGURE 20–7 Port fuel injectors spray atomized fuel into the intake manifold about 3 inches (75 mm) from the intake valve.

FIGURE 20–8 A port fuel-injected engine that is equipped with long, tuned intake manifold runners.

 **FREQUENTLY ASKED QUESTION**

### How Can It Be Determined if the Injection System Is Sequential?

Look at the color of the wires at the injectors. If a sequentially fired injector is used, then one wire color (the pulse wire) will be a different color for each injector. The other wire is usually the same color because all injectors receive voltage from some source. If a group- or batch-fired injection system is being used, then the wire colors will be the same for the injectors that are group fired. For example, a V-6 group-fired engine will have three injectors with a pink and blue wire (power and pulse), and the other three will have pink and green wires.

The major advantage of using port injection instead of the simpler throttle-body injection is that the intake manifolds on port fuel-injected engines only contain air, not a mixture of air and fuel. This allows the engine design engineer the opportunity to design long, "tuned" intake-manifold runners that help the engine produce increased torque at low engine speeds. ● **SEE FIGURE 20–8.**

NOTE: **Some port fuel-injection systems used on engines with four or more valves per cylinder may use two injectors per cylinder. One injector is used all the time, and the second injector is operated by the computer when high engine speed and high-load conditions are detected by the computer. Typically, the second injector injects fuel into the high-speed intake ports of the manifold. This system permits good low-speed power and throttle responses as well as superior high-speed power.**

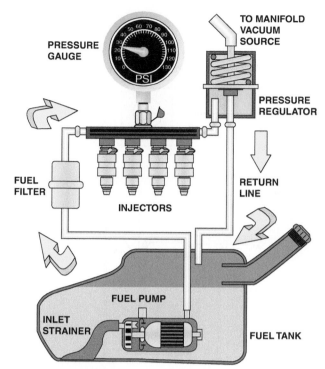

FIGURE 20–9 A typical port fuel-injected system showing a vacuum-controlled fuel-pressure regulator.

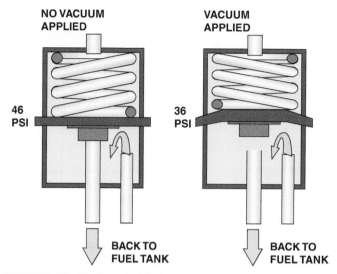

FIGURE 20–10 A typical fuel-pressure regulator that has a spring that exerts 46 pounds of force against the fuel. If 20 inches of vacuum are applied above the spring, the vacuum reduces the force exerted by the spring on the fuel, allowing the fuel to return to the tank at a lower pressure.

FIGURE 20–11 A lack of fuel flow could be due to a restricted fuel-pressure regulator. Notice the fine screen filter. If this filter were to become clogged, higher-than-normal fuel pressure would occur.

## FUEL-PRESSURE REGULATOR

The pressure regulator and fuel pump work together to maintain the required pressure drop at the injector tips. The fuel-pressure regulator typically consists of a spring-loaded, diaphragm-operated valve in a metal housing.

Fuel-pressure regulators on fuel-return-type fuel-injection systems are installed on the return (downstream) side of the injectors at the end of the fuel rail or are built into or mounted upon the throttle-body housing. Downstream regulation minimizes fuel-pressure pulsations caused by pressure drop across the injectors as the nozzles open. It also ensures positive fuel pressure at the injectors at all times and holds residual pressure in the lines when the engine is off. On mechanical returnless systems, the regulator is located back at the tank with the fuel filter.

In order for excess fuel (about 80% to 90% of the fuel delivered) to return to the tank, fuel pressure must overcome spring pressure on the spring-loaded diaphragm to uncover the return line to the tank. This happens when system pressure exceeds operating requirements. With TBI, the regulator is close to the injector tip, so the regulator senses essentially the same air pressure as the injector.

The pressure regulator used in a port fuel-injection system has an intake manifold vacuum line connection on the regulator vacuum chamber. This allows fuel pressure to be modulated by a combination of spring pressure and manifold vacuum acting on the diaphragm. ● SEE FIGURES 20–9 AND 20–10.

### TECH TIP

**Don't Forget the Regulator**
Some fuel-pressure regulators contain a 10-micron filter. If this filter becomes clogged, a lack of fuel flow would result. ● SEE FIGURE 20–11.

In both TBI and port fuel-injection systems, the regulator shuts off the return line when the fuel pump is not running. This maintains pressure at the injectors for easy restarting after hot soak as well as reducing vapor lock.

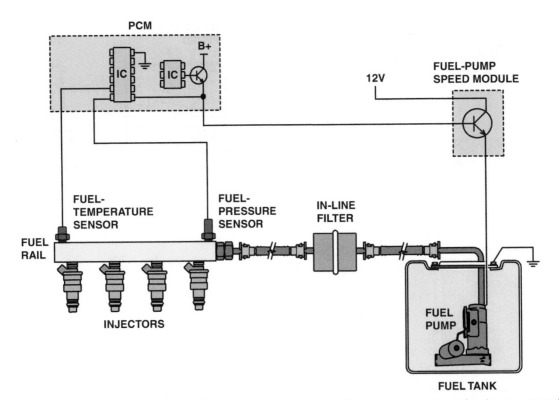

**FIGURE 20–12** The fuel-pressure sensor and fuel-temperature sensor are often constructed together in one assembly to help give the PCM the needed data to control the fuel-pump speed.

**NOTE: Some General Motors throttle-body units do not hold pressure and are called noncheking.**

Port fuel-injection systems generally operate with pressures at the injector of about 30 to 55 PSI (207 to 379 kPa), while TBI systems work with injector pressures of about 10 to 20 PSI (69 to 138 kPa). The difference in system pressures results from the difference in how the systems operate. Since injectors in a TBI system inject the fuel into the airflow at the manifold inlet (above the throttle), there is more time for atomization in the manifold before the air-fuel charge reaches the intake valve. This allows TBI injectors to work at lower pressures than injectors used in a port system.

| Engine Operating Condition | Intake Manifold Vacuum | Fuel Pressure |
| --- | --- | --- |
| Idle or cruise | High | Lower |
| Heavy load | Low | Higher |

The computer can best calculate injector pulse width based on all sensors if the pressure drop across the injector is the same under all operating conditions. A vacuum-controlled fuel-pressure regulator allows the equal pressure drop by reducing the force exerted by the regulator spring at high vacuum (low-load condition) yet allowing the full force of the regulator spring to be exerted when the vacuum is low (high-engine-load condition).

## VACUUM-BIASED FUEL-PRESSURE REGULATOR

The primary reason why many port fuel-injected systems use a vacuum-controlled fuel-pressure regulator is to ensure that there is a constant pressure drop across the injectors. In a throttle-body fuel-injection system, the injector squirts into the atmospheric pressure regardless of the load on the engine. In a port fuel-injected engine, however, the pressure inside the intake manifold changes as the load on the engine increases.

## ELECTRONIC RETURNLESS FUEL SYSTEM

This system is unique because it does not use a mechanical valve to regulate rail pressure. Fuel pressure at the rail is sensed by a pressure transducer, which sends a low-level signal to a controller. The controller contains logic to calculate a signal to the pump power driver. The power driver contains a high-current transistor that controls the pump speed using pulse width modulation (PWM). This system is called the **electronic returnless fuel system (ERFS).** ● SEE FIGURE 20–12. This

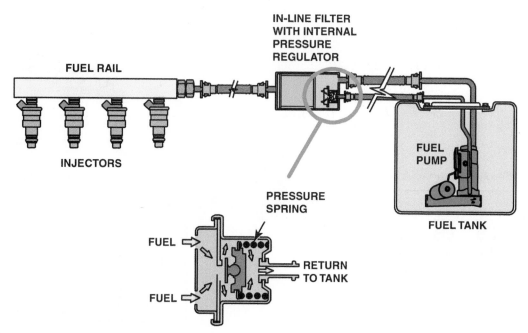

**FIGURE 20–13** A mechanical returnless fuel system. The bypass regulator in the fuel filter controls fuel line pressure.

transducer can be differentially referenced to manifold pressure for closed-loop feedback, correcting and maintaining the output of the pump to a desired rail setting. This system is capable of continuously varying rail pressure as a result of engine vacuum, engine fuel demand, and fuel temperature (as sensed by an external temperature transducer, if necessary). A **pressure vent valve (PVV)** is employed at the tank to relieve overpressure due to thermal expansion of fuel. In addition, a supply-side bleed, by means of an in-tank reservoir using a supply-side jet pump, is necessary for proper pump operation.

## MECHANICAL RETURNLESS FUEL SYSTEM

The first production returnless systems employed the **mechanical returnless fuel system (MRFS)** approach. This system has a bypass regulator to control rail pressure that is located in close proximity to the fuel tank. Fuel is sent by the in-tank pump to a chassis-mounted inline filter with excess fuel returning to the tank through a short return line. ● **SEE FIGURE 20–13.** The inline filter may be mounted directly to the tank, thereby eliminating the shortened return line. Supply pressure is regulated on the downstream side of the inline filter to accommodate changing restrictions throughout the filter's service life. This system is limited to constant rail pressure (*CRP) system calibrations, whereas with ERFS, the pressure transducer can be referenced to atmospheric pressure for CRP systems or differentially referenced to intake manifold pressure for constant differential injector pressure (**CIP) systems.

**NOTE: *CRP is referenced to atmospheric pressure, has lower operating pressure, and is desirable for calibrations using speed/air density sensing. **CIP is referenced to manifold pressure, varies rail pressure, and is desirable in engines that use mass airflow sensing.**

## DEMAND DELIVERY SYSTEM

Given the experience with both ERFS and MRFS, a need was recognized to develop new returnless technologies that could combine the speed control and constant injector pressure attributes of ERFS together with the cost savings, simplicity, and reliability of MRFS. This new technology also needed to address pulsation dampening/hammering and fuel transient response. Therefore, the **demand delivery system (DDS)** technology was developed. A different form of demand pressure regulator has been applied to the fuel rail. It mounts at the head or port entry and regulates the pressure downstream at the injectors by admitting the precise quantity of fuel into the rail as consumed by the engine. Having demand regulation at the rail improves pressure response to flow transients and provides rail pulsation dampening. A fuel pump and a low-cost, high-performance bypass regulator are used within the appropriate fuel sender. ● **SEE FIGURE 20–14.** They supply a pressure somewhat higher than the required rail set pressure to accommodate dynamic line and filter pressure losses. Electronic pump speed control is accomplished using a smart regulator as an integral flow sensor. A **pressure control valve (PCV)** may also be used and can readily reconfigure an existing design fuel sender into a returnless sender.

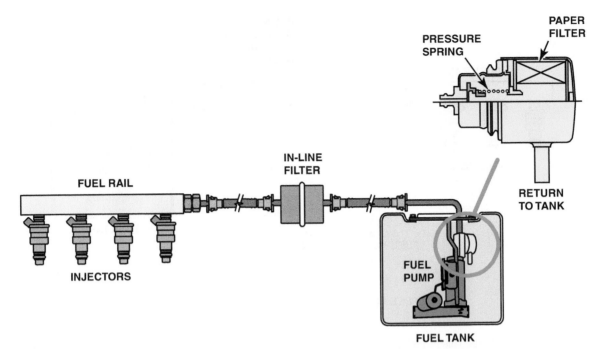

FIGURE 20–14 A demand delivery system uses a fuel pressure regulator attached to the fuel pump assembly.

**Why Are Some Fuel Rails Rectangular Shaped?**

A port fuel-injection system uses a pipe or tubes to deliver fuel from the fuel line to the intended fuel injectors. This pipe or tube is called the **fuel rail**. Some vehicle manufacturers construct the fuel rail in a rectangular cross section. ● SEE FIGURE 20–15. The sides of the fuel rail are able to move in and out slightly, thereby acting as a fuel pulsator evening out the pressure pulses created by the opening and closing of the injectors to reduce underhood noise. A round cross-section fuel rail is not able to deform, and as a result, some manufacturers have had to use a separate dampener.

FIGURE 20–15 A rectangular-shaped fuel rail is used to help dampen fuel system pulsations and noise caused by the injectors opening and closing.

# FUEL INJECTORS

EFI systems use a 12 volt solenoid-operated injectors. ● SEE FIGURE 20–16. This electromagnetic device contains an armature and a spring-loaded needle valve or ball valve assembly. When the computer energizes the solenoid, voltage is applied to the solenoid coil until the current reaches a specified level. This permits a quick pull-in of the armature during turn-on. The armature is pulled off of its seat against spring force, allowing fuel to flow through the inlet filter screen to the spray nozzle, where it is sprayed in a pattern that varies with application. ● SEE FIGURE 20–17. The injector opens the same amount each time it is energized, so the amount of fuel injected depends on the length of time the injector remains open. By angling the director hole plates, the injector sprays fuel more directly at the intake valves, which further atomizes and vaporizes the fuel before it enters the combustion chamber. PFI injectors typically are a top-feed design in which fuel enters the top of the injector and passes through its entire length to keep it cool before being injected.

Ford introduced two basic designs of deposit-resistant injectors on some engines. The design, manufactured by Bosch, uses a four-hole director/metering plate similar to that used by the Rochester Multec injectors. The design manufactured by Nippondenso uses an internal upstream orifice in the adjusting tube. It also has a redesigned pintle/seat containing a wider tip opening that tolerates deposit buildup without affecting injector performance.

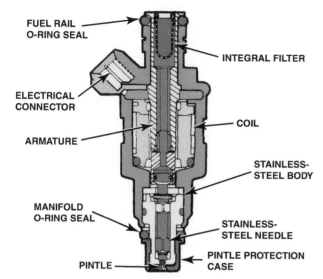

FIGURE 20–16 A multiport fuel injector. Notice that the fuel flows straight through and does not come in contact with the coil windings.

FUEL RAIL O-RING SEAL
INTEGRAL FILTER
ELECTRICAL CONNECTOR
COIL
ARMATURE
STAINLESS-STEEL BODY
MANIFOLD O-RING SEAL
STAINLESS-STEEL NEEDLE
PINTLE PROTECTION CASE
PINTLE

FIGURE 20–17 Each of the eight injectors shown are producing a correct spray pattern for the applications. While all throttle-body injectors spray a conical pattern, most port fuel injections do not.

## CENTRAL PORT INJECTION

A cross between port fuel injection and throttle-body injection, CPI was introduced in the early 1990s by General Motors. The CPI assembly consists of a single fuel injector, a pressure regulator, and six poppet nozzle assemblies with nozzle tubes. ● SEE FIGURE 20–18. The central sequential fuel injection (CSFI) system has six injectors in place of just one used on the CPI unit.

When the injector is energized, its armature lifts off of the six fuel tube seats, and pressurized fuel flows through the nozzle tubes to each poppet nozzle. The increased pressure causes each poppet nozzle ball to also lift from its seat, allowing fuel to flow from the nozzle. This hybrid injection system combines the single injector of a TBI system with the equalized fuel

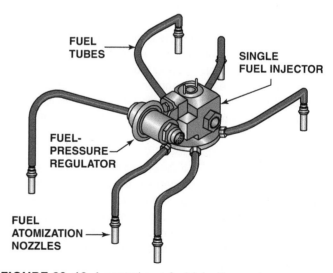

FUEL TUBES
SINGLE FUEL INJECTOR
FUEL-PRESSURE REGULATOR
FUEL ATOMIZATION NOZZLES

FIGURE 20–18 A central port fuel-injection system.

distribution of a PFI system. It eliminates the individual fuel rail while allowing more efficient manifold tuning than is otherwise possible with a TBI system. Newer versions use six individual solenoids to fire one for each cylinder. ● SEE FIGURE 20–19.

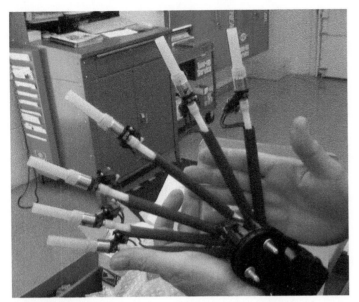

**FIGURE 20–19** A factory replacement unit for a CSFI unit that has individual injectors at the ends that go into the intake manifold instead of poppet valves.

# FUEL-INJECTION MODES OF OPERATION

All fuel-injection systems are designed to supply the correct amount of fuel under a wide range of engine operating conditions. These modes of operation include the following:

| | |
|---|---|
| Starting (cranking) | Acceleration enrichment |
| Clear flood | Deceleration enleanment |
| Idle (run) | Fuel shutoff |

**STARTING MODE** When the ignition is turned to the start position, the engine cranks, and the PCM energizes the fuel pump relay. The PCM also pulses the injectors on, basing the pulse width on engine speed and engine coolant temperature. The colder the engine is, the greater the pulse width. Cranking mode air-fuel ratio varies from about 1.5:1 at −40°F (−40°C) to 14.7:1 at 200°F (93°C).

**CLEAR FLOOD MODE** If the engine becomes flooded with too much fuel, the driver can depress the accelerator pedal to greater than 80% to enter the clear flood mode. When the PCM detects that the engine speed is low (usually below 600 RPM) and the throttle-position (TP) sensor voltage is high (WOT), the injector pulse width is greatly reduced or even shut off entirely, depending on the vehicle.

**OPEN-LOOP MODE** Open-loop operation occurs during warm-up before the oxygen sensor can supply accurate information to the PCM. The PCM determines injector pulse width based on values from the MAF, MAP, TP, ECT, and IAT sensors.

**?** FREQUENTLY ASKED QUESTION

**What Is Battery Voltage Correction?**

Battery voltage correction is a program built into the PCM that causes the injector pulse width to increase if there is a drop in electrical system voltage. Lower battery voltage would cause the fuel injectors to open slower than normal and the fuel pump to run slower. Both of these conditions can cause the engine to run leaner than normal if the battery voltage is low. Because a lean air-fuel mixture can cause the engine to overheat, the PCM compensates for the lower voltage by adding a percentage to the injector pulse width. This richer condition will help prevent serious engine damage. The idle speed is also increased to turn the alternator faster if low battery voltage is detected.

**CLOSED-LOOP MODE** Closed-loop operation is used to modify the base injector pulse width as determined by feedback from the oxygen sensor to achieve proper fuel control.

**ACCELERATION ENRICHMENT MODE** During acceleration, the throttle-position (TP) voltage increases, indicating that a richer air-fuel mixture is required. The PCM then supplies a longer injector pulse width and may even supply extra pulses to supply the needed fuel for acceleration.

**DECELERATION ENLEANMENT MODE** When the engine decelerates, a leaner air-fuel mixture is required to help reduce emissions and to prevent deceleration backfire. If the deceleration is rapid, the injector may be shut off entirely for a short time and then pulsed on enough to keep the engine running.

**FUEL SHUTOFF MODE** Besides shutting off fuel entirely during periods of rapid deceleration, PCM also shuts off the injector when the ignition is turned off to prevent the engine from continuing to run.

# IDLE CONTROL

Port fuel-injection systems generally use an auxiliary air bypass to control idle speed. ● **SEE FIGURE 20–20.** This air bypass or regulator provides needed additional airflow and thus more fuel. The engine needs more power when cold to maintain its normal idle speed to overcome the increased friction from cold lubricating oil. It does this by opening an intake air passage to let more air into the engine just as depressing the accelerator pedal would open the throttle valve, allowing more air into the engine. The system is calibrated to maintain engine idle speed at a specified value regardless of engine temperature.

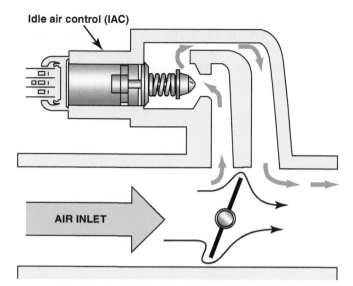

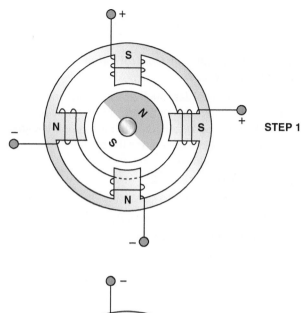

**FIGURE 20-20** The small arrows indicate the air bypassing the throttle plate in the closed throttle position. This air is called minimum air. The air flowing through the IAC (blue arrows) is the airflow that determines the idle speed.

Most PFI systems use an idle air control (IAC) motor to regulate idle bypass air. The IAC is computer controlled and is either a solenoid-operated valve or a stepper motor that regulates the airflow around the throttle. The idle air control valve is also called an **electronic air control (EAC)** valve.

When the engine stops, most IAC units will retract outward to get ready for the next engine start. When the engine starts, the engine speed is high to provide for proper operation when the engine is cold. Then, as the engine gets warmer, the computer reduces engine idle speed gradually by reducing the number of counts or steps commanded by the IAC.

When the engine is warm and restarted, the idle speed should momentarily increase, then decrease to normal idle speed. This increase and then decrease in engine speed is often called an engine **flare.** If the engine speed does not flare, then the IAC may not be working (it may be stuck in one position).

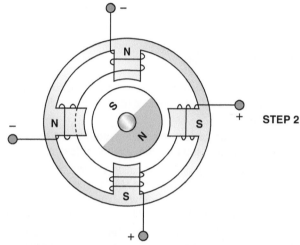

**FIGURE 20-21** Most stepper motors use four wires, which are pulsed by the computer to rotate the armature in steps.

## STEPPER MOTOR OPERATION

A digital output is used to control stepper motors. Stepper motors are direct-current motors that move in fixed steps or increments from deenergized (no voltage) to fully energized (full voltage). A stepper motor often has as many as 120 steps of motion.

A common use for stepper motors is as an idle air control (IAC) valve, which controls engine idle speeds and prevents stalls due to changes in engine load. When used as an IAC, the stepper motor is usually a reversible DC motor that moves in increments, or steps. The motor moves a shaft back and forth to operate a conical valve. When the conical valve is moved back,

more air bypasses the throttle plates and enters the engine, increasing idle speed. As the conical valve moves inward, the idle speed decreases.

When using a stepper motor that is controlled by the PCM, it is very easy for the PCM to keep track of the position of the stepper motor. By counting the number of steps that have been sent to the stepper motor, the PCM can determine the relative position of the stepper motor. While the PCM does not actually receive a feedback signal from the stepper motor, it does know how many steps forward or backward the motor should have moved.

A typical stepper motor uses a permanent magnet and two electromagnets. Each of the two electromagnetic windings is controlled by the computer. The computer pulses the windings and changes the polarity of the windings to cause the armature of the stepper motor to rotate 90 degrees at a time. Each 90-degree pulse is recorded by the computer as a "count" or "step," thus the name given to this type of motor. ● **SEE FIGURE 20-21.**

### Why Does the Idle Air Control Valve Use Milliamperes?

Some Chrysler vehicles, such as the Dodge minivan, use linear solenoid idle air control (LSIAC) valves. The PCM uses regulated current flow through the solenoid to control idle speed and the scan tool display is in milliamperes (mA):

| | |
|---|---|
| Closed position | = 180 to 200 mA |
| Idle | = 300 to 450 mA |
| Light cruise | = 500 to 700 mA |
| Fully open | = 900 to 950 mA |

Idle airflow in a TBI system travels through a passage around the throttle and is controlled by a stepper motor. In some applications, an externally mounted permanent magnet motor called the **idle speed control (ISC) motor** mechanically advances the throttle linkage to advance the throttle opening.

## SUMMARY

1. A fuel-injection system includes the electric fuel pump and fuel pump relay, fuel-pressure regulator, and fuel injectors (nozzles).

2. The two types of fuel-injection systems are the throttle-body design and the port fuel-injection design.

3. The two methods of fuel-injection control are the speed-density system, which uses the MAP to measure the load on the engine, and the mass airflow, which uses the MAF sensor to directly measure the amount of air entering the engine.

4. The amount of fuel supplied by fuel injectors is determined by how long they are kept open. This opening time is called the pulse width and is measured in milliseconds.

5. The fuel-pressure regulator is usually located on the fuel return on return-type fuel-injection systems.

6. TBI-type fuel-injection systems do not use a vacuum-controlled fuel-pressure regulator, whereas many port fuel-injection systems use a vacuum-controlled regulator to monitor equal pressure drop across the injectors.

7. Other fuel designs include the electronic returnless, the mechanical returnless, and the demand delivery systems.

## REVIEW QUESTIONS

1. What are the two basic types of fuel-injection systems?

2. What is the purpose of the vacuum-controlled (biased) fuel-pressure regulator?

3. How many sensors are used to determine the base pulse width on a speed-density system?

4. How many sensors are used to determine the base pulse width on a mass airflow system?

5. What are the three types of returnless fuel-injection systems?

## CHAPTER QUIZ

1. Technician A says that the fuel-pump relay is usually controlled by the PCM. Technician B says that a TBI injector squirts fuel above the throttle plate. Which technician is correct?
   a. Technician A only
   b. Technician B only
   c. Both Technicians A and B
   d. Neither Technician A nor B

2. Why are some fuel rails rectangular in shape?
   a. Increases fuel pressure
   b. Helps keep air out of the injectors
   c. Reduces noise
   d. Increases the speed of the fuel through the fuel rail

3. Which fuel-injection system uses the MAP sensor as the primary sensor to determine the base pulse width?
   a. Speed density
   b. Mass airflow
   c. Demand delivery
   d. Mechanical returnless

4. Why is a vacuum line attached to a fuel-pressure regulator on many port fuel-injected engines?
   a. To draw fuel back into the intake manifold through the vacuum hose
   b. To create an equal pressure drop across the injectors
   c. To raise the fuel pressure at idle
   d. To lower the fuel pressure under heavy engine load conditions to help improve fuel economy

5. Which sensor has the greatest influence on injector pulse width besides the MAF sensor?
   a. IAT          c. ECT
   b. BARO         d. TP

6. Technician A says that the port fuel-injection injectors operate using 5 volts from the computer. Technician B says that sequential fuel injectors all use a different wire color on the injectors. Which technician is correct?
   a. Technician A only
   b. Technician B only
   c. Both Technicians A and B
   d. Neither Technician A nor B

7. Which type of port fuel-injection system uses a fuel-temperature and/or fuel-pressure sensor?
   a. All port fuel-injected engines
   b. TBI units only
   c. Electronic returnless systems
   d. Demand delivery systems

8. Dampeners are used on some fuel rails to _____.
   a. Increase the fuel pressure in the rail
   b. Reduce (decrease) the fuel pressure in the rail
   c. Reduce noise
   d. Trap dirt and keep it away from the injectors

9. Where is the fuel-pressure regulator located on a vacuum-biased port fuel-injection system?
   a. In the tank
   b. At the inlet of the fuel rail
   c. At the outlet of the fuel rail
   d. Near or on the fuel filter

10. What type of device is used in a typical idle air control?
    a. DC motor
    b. Stepper motor
    c. Pulsator-type actuator
    d. Solenoid

# chapter 21

# GASOLINE DIRECT-INJECTION SYSTEMS

**OBJECTIVES:** **After studying Chapter 21, the reader should be able to:** • Prepare for the ASE Engine Performance (A8) certification test content area "C" (Fuel, Air Induction, and Exhaust Systems Diagnosis). • Describe the differences between port fuel-injection and gasoline direct-injection systems. • List the various modes of operation of a gasoline direct-injection system. • Explain how a gasoline direct-injection system works. • Perform a visual inspection of the gasoline direct-injection system and identify the parts.

**KEY TERMS:** Gasoline direct injection (GDI) 270 • Homogeneous mode 272 • Spark ignition direct injection (SIDI) 270 • Stratified mode 272

## DIRECT FUEL INJECTION

Several vehicle manufacturers such as Audi, Mitsubishi, Mercedes, BMW, Toyota/Lexus, Mazda, Ford, and General Motors are using **gasoline direct-injection (GDI)** systems, which General Motors refers to as a **spark ignition direct injection (SIDI)** system. A direct-injection system sprays high-pressure fuel, up to 2,900 PSI, into the combustion chamber as the piston approaches the top of the compression stroke. With the combination of high-pressure swirl injectors and modified combustion chamber, almost instantaneous vaporization of the fuel occurs. This, combined with a higher compression ratio, allows a direct-injected engine to operate using a leaner-than-normal air-fuel ratio, which results in improved fuel economy with higher power output and reduced exhaust emissions.
● **SEE FIGURE 21–1.**

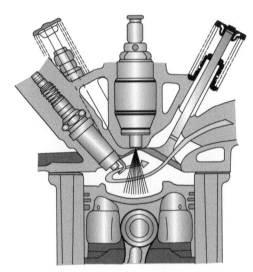

**FIGURE 21–1** A gasoline direct-injection (GDI) system injects fuel under high pressure directly into the combustion chamber.

**ADVANTAGES OF GDI** The use of direct injection compared with port fuel injection has many advantages, including the following:

- Improved fuel economy due to reduced pumping losses and heat loss
- Allows a higher compression ratio for higher engine efficiency
- Allows the use of lower-octane gasoline
- The volumetric efficiency is higher
- Less need for extra fuel for acceleration
- Improved cold starting and throttle response
- Allows the use of higher percentage of EGR to reduce exhaust emissions

- Up to 25% improvement in fuel economy
- 12% to 15% reduction in exhaust emissions

**DISADVANTAGES OF GDI**

- Higher cost due to high-pressure pump and injectors
- More components compared with port fuel injection
- Because of the high compression, a $NO_x$ storage catalyst is sometimes required to meet emission standards, especially in Europe. (● **SEE FIGURE 21–2**)
- Uses up to six operating modes, depending on engine load and speed, which requires more calculations to be performed by the powertrain control module (PCM).

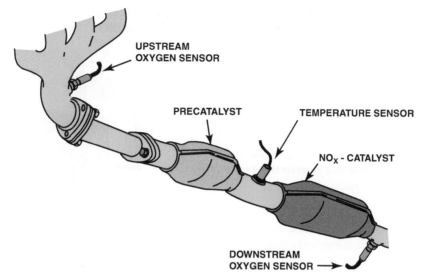

**FIGURE 21–2** An engine equipped with a gasoline direct injection (GDI) sometimes requires a NO$_x$ catalyst to meet exhaust emission standards.

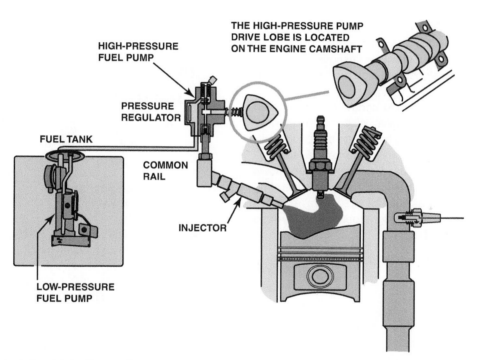

**FIGURE 21–3** A typical direct-injection system uses two pumps—one low-pressure electric pump in the fuel tank and a high-pressure pump driven by the camshaft. The high pressure fuel system operates at a pressure as low as 500 PSI during light-load conditions and as high as 2,900 PSI under heavy loads.

## DIRECT-INJECTION FUEL DELIVERY SYSTEM

**LOW-PRESSURE SUPPLY PUMP** The fuel pump in the fuel tank supplies fuel to the high-pressure fuel pump at a pressure of approximately 60 PSI. The fuel filter is located in the fuel tank and is part of the fuel-pump assembly. It is not usually serviceable as a separate component. The powertrain control module (PCM) controls the output of the high-pressure pump, which has a range between 500 PSI (3,440 kPa) and 2,900 PSI (15,200 kPa) during engine operation. ● **SEE FIGURE 21–3.**

**HIGH-PRESSURE PUMP** In a General Motors system, the engine control module (ECM) controls the output of the high-pressure pump, which has a range between 500 PSI

(3,440 kPa) and 2,900 PSI (15,200 kPa) during engine operation. The high-pressure fuel pump connects to the pump in the fuel tank through the low-pressure fuel line. The pump consists of a single-barrel piston pump, which is driven by the engine camshaft. The pump plunger rides on a three-lobed cam on the camshaft. The high-pressure pump is cooled and lubricated by the fuel itself. ● **SEE FIGURE 21–4.**

**FUEL RAIL**   The fuel rail stores fuel from the high pressure pump for use by each injector. All injectors receive the same pressure as what is present in the fuel rail.

**FUEL-PRESSURE REGULATOR**   An electric pressure-control valve is installed between the pump inlet and outlet valves. The fuel rail pressure sensor connects to the PCM with three wires:

- 5-volt reference
- Ground
- Signal

The sensor signal provides an analog signal to the PCM that varies in voltage as fuel rail pressure changes. Low pressure results in a low-voltage signal, and high pressure results in a high-voltage signal.

The PCM uses internal drivers to control the power feed and ground for the pressure control valve. When both PCM drivers are deactivated, the inlet valve is held open by spring pressure. This causes the high-pressure fuel pump to default to low-pressure mode. The fuel from the high-pressure fuel pump flows through a line to the fuel rail and injectors. The actual operating pressure can vary from as low as 500 PSI (6,200 kPa) at idle to over 2,000 PSI (13,800 kPa) during high-speed or heavy-load conditions. ● **SEE FIGURE 21–5.**

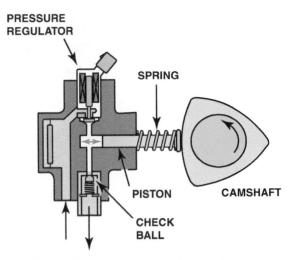

**FIGURE 21–4** A typical camshaft-driven high-pressure pump used to increase fuel pressure to 2,000 PSI or higher.

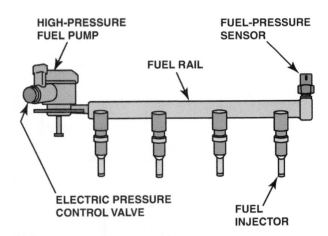

**FIGURE 21–5** A gasoline direct-injection (GDI) fuel rail and pump assembly with the electric pressure control valve.

## GDI FUEL INJECTORS

Each high-pressure fuel injector assembly is an electrically magnetic injector mounted in the cylinder head. In the GDI system, the PCM controls each fuel injector with 50 to 90 volts (usually 60 to 70 volts), depending on the system, which is created by a boost capacitor in the PCM. During the high-voltage boost phase, the capacitor is discharged through an injector, allowing for initial injector opening. The injector is then held open with 12 volts. The high-pressure fuel injector has a small slit or six precision-machined holes that generate the desired spray pattern. The injector also has an extended tip to allow for cooling from a water jacket in the cylinder head.

● **SEE CHART 21–1** for an overview of the differences between a port fuel-injection system and a GDI system.

## MODES OF OPERATION

The two basic modes of operation include the following:

1. **Stratified mode.** In this mode of operation, the air-fuel mixture is richer around the spark plug than it is in the rest of the cylinder.

2. **Homogeneous mode.** In this mode of operation, the air-fuel mixture is the same throughout the cylinder.

There are variations of these modes that can be used to fine-tune the air-fuel mixture inside the cylinder. For example, Bosch, a supplier to many vehicle manufacturers, uses six modes of operation, including the following:

- **Homogeneous mode.** In this mode, the injector is pulsed one time to create an even air-fuel mixture in the cylinder. The injection occurs during the intake stroke. This mode is used during high-speed and/or high-torque conditions.

## PORT FUEL-INJECTION SYSTEM COMPARED WITH GDI SYSTEM

| | PORT FUEL INJECTION | GDI |
|---|---|---|
| Fuel pressure | 35 to 60 PSI | Lift pump—50 to 60 PSI High-pressure pump—500 to 2,900 PSI |
| Injection pulse width at idle | 1.5 to 3.5 ms | About 0.4 ms (400 μs) |
| | 12 to 16 ohms | 1 to 3 ohms |
| Injector voltage | 6 V for low-resistance injectors, 12 V for most injectors | 50 to 90 V |
| Number of injections per event | One | 1 to 3 |
| Engine compression ratio | 8:1 to 11:1 | 11:1 to 13:1 |

**CHART 21-1**

A comparison chart showing the major differences between a port fuel-injection system and a gasoline direct-injection (GDI) system.

- **Homogeneous lean mode.** Similar to the homogeneous mode except that the overall air-fuel mixture is slightly lean for better fuel economy. The injection occurs during the intake stroke. This mode is used under steady, light-load conditions.

- **Stratified mode.** In this mode of operation, the injection occurs just before the spark occurs, resulting in lean combustion and reducing fuel consumption.

- **Homogeneous stratified mode.** In this mode, there are two injections of fuel:

  - The first injection is during the intake stroke.

  - The second injection is during the compression stroke. As a result of these double injections, the rich air-fuel mixture around the spark plug is ignited first. Then the rich mixture ignites the leaner mixture. The advantages of this mode include lower exhaust emissions than the stratified mode and less fuel consumption than the homogeneous lean mode.

- **Homogeneous knock protection mode.** The purpose of this mode is to reduce the possibility of spark knock from occurring under heavy loads at low engine speeds. There are two injections of fuel:

  - The first injection occurs on the intake stroke.

  - The second injection occurs during the compression stroke with the overall mixture being stoichiometric.

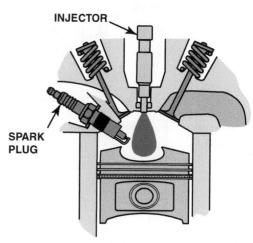

**SPRAY-GUIDED COMBUSTION**

**FIGURE 21–6** In this design, the fuel injector is at the top of the cylinder and sprays fuel into the cavity of the piston.

As a result of this mode, the PCM does not need to retard ignition timing as much to operate knock free.

- **Stratified catalyst heating mode.** In this mode, there are two injections:

  - The first injection is on the compression stroke just before combustion.

  - The second injection occurs after combustion occurs to heat the exhaust. This mode is used to quickly warm the catalytic converter and to burn the sulfur from the $NO_x$ catalyst.

## PISTON TOP DESIGNS

GDI systems use a variety of shapes of piston and injector locations depending on make and model of engine. Three of the most commonly used designs include the following:

- **Spray-guided combustion.** In this design, the injector is placed in the center of the combustion chamber and injects fuel into the dished-out portion of the piston. The shape of the piston helps guide and direct the mist of fuel in the combustion chamber. ● **SEE FIGURE 21–6.**

- **Swirl combustion.** This design uses the shape of the piston and the position of the injector at the side of the combustion chamber to create turbulence and swirl of the air-fuel mixture. ● **SEE FIGURE 21–7.**

- **Tumble combustion.** Depending on when the fuel is injected into the combustion chamber, this helps determine how the air-fuel mixture is moved or tumbled. ● **SEE FIGURE 21–8.**

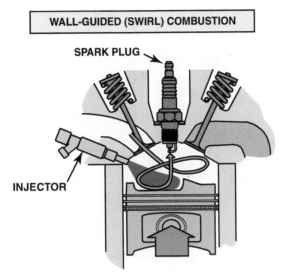

**WALL-GUIDED (SWIRL) COMBUSTION**

SPARK PLUG

INJECTOR

**FIGURE 21–7** The side injector combines with the shape of the piston to create a swirl as the piston moves up on the compression stroke.

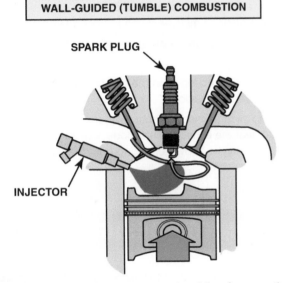

**WALL-GUIDED (TUMBLE) COMBUSTION**

SPARK PLUG

INJECTOR

**FIGURE 21–8** The piston creates a tumbling force as the piston moves upward.

## LEXUS PORT- AND DIRECT-INJECTION SYSTEMS

**OVERVIEW** Many Lexus vehicles use GDI, and in some engines, they also use a conventional port fuel-injection system. The Lexus D-4S system combines direct-injection injectors located in the combustion chamber with port fuel injectors in the intake manifold near the intake valve. The two injection systems work together to supply the fuel needed by the

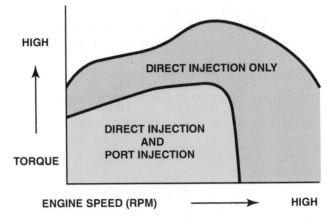

**FIGURE 21–9** Notice that there are conditions when both the port fuel injector located in the intake manifold and the gasoline direct injector located in the cylinder operate to provide the proper air-fuel mixture.

engine. ● **SEE FIGURE 21–9** for how the two systems are used throughout the various stages of engine operation.

**COLD-START WARM-UP** To help reduce exhaust emissions after a cold start, the fuel system uses a stratified change mode. This results in a richer air-fuel mixture near the spark plug and allows for the spark to be retarded to increase the temperature of the exhaust. As a result of the increased exhaust temperature, the catalytic converter rapidly reaches operating temperature, which reduces exhaust emissions.

## ENGINE START SYSTEM

An engine equipped with GDI could use the system to start the engine. This is most useful during idle stop mode when the engine is stopped while the vehicle is at a traffic light to save fuel. The steps used in the Mitsubishi start-stop system, called the *smart idle stop system (SISS)*, allow the engine to be started without a starter motor and include the following steps:

**STEP 1** The engine is stopped. The normal stopping position of an engine when it stops is 70 degrees before top dead center, plus or minus 20 degrees. This is because the engine stops with one cylinder on the compression stroke, and the PCM can determine the cylinder position, using the crankshaft and camshaft position sensors.

**STEP 2** When a command is made to start the engine by the PCM, fuel is injected into the cylinder that is on the compression stroke and ignited by the spark plug.

**STEP 3** The piston on the compression stroke is forced downward, forcing the crankshaft to rotate counterclockwise or in the opposite direction to normal operation.

**STEP 4** The rotation of the crankshaft then forces the companion cylinder toward the top of the cylinder.

**STEP 5** Fuel is injected, and the spark plug is fired, forcing the piston down, causing the crankshaft to rotate in the normal (clockwise) direction. Normal combustion events continue, allowing the engine to keep running.

## GDI SERVICE

**NOISE ISSUES**  GDI systems operate at high pressure, and the injectors can often be heard with the engine running and the hood open. This noise can be a customer concern because the clicking sound is similar to noisy valves. If a noise issue is the customer concern, check the following:

- Check a similar vehicle to determine if the sound is louder or more noticeable than normal.
- Check that nothing under the hood is touching the fuel rail. If another line or hose is in contact with the fuel rail, the sound of the injectors clicking can be transmitted throughout the engine, making the sound more noticeable.
- Check for any technical service bulletins (TSBs) that may include new clips or sound insulators to help reduce the noise.

**CARBON ISSUES**  Carbon is often an issue in engines equipped with GDI systems. Carbon can affect engine operation by accumulating in two places:

- **On the injector itself.** Because the injector tip is in the combustion chamber, fuel residue can accumulate on the injector, reducing its ability to provide the proper spray pattern and amount of fuel. Some injector designs are more likely to be affected by carbon than others. For example, if the injector uses small holes, these tend to become clogged more often than an injector that uses a single slit opening, where the fuel being sprayed out tends to blast away any carbon. ● **SEE FIGURE 21–10.**

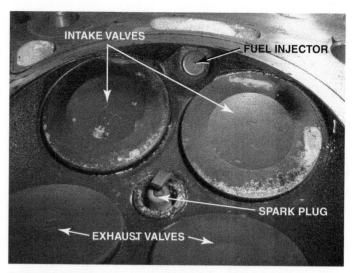

**FIGURE 21–10** There may become a driveability issue because the gasoline direct-injection (GDI) injector is exposed to combustion carbon and fuel residue.

- **The backside of the intake valve.** This is a common place for fuel residue and carbon to accumulate on engines equipped with GDI. The accumulation of carbon on the intake valve can become so severe that the engine will start and idle but lack power to accelerate the vehicle. The carbon deposits restrict the airflow into the cylinder enough to decrease engine power.

**NOTE: Lexus engines that use both port and GDI injectors do not show intake valve deposits. It is thought that the fuel being sprayed onto the intake valve from the port injector helps keep the intake valve clean.**

**CARBON CLEANING.**  Most experts recommend the use of Techron®, a fuel system dispersant, to help keep carbon from accumulating. The use of a dispersant every six months or every 6,000 miles has proven to help prevent injector and intake valve deposits.

If the lack of power is discovered and there are no stored diagnostic trouble codes, a conventional carbon cleaning procedure will likely restore power if the intake valves are coated.

## SUMMARY

1. A GDI system uses a fuel injector that delivers a short squirt of fuel directly into the combustion chamber rather than in the intake manifold, near the intake valve on a port fuel injection system.

2. The advantages of using GDI instead of port fuel injection include the following:
   - Improved fuel economy
   - Reduced exhaust emissions
   - Greater engine power

3. Some of the disadvantages of GDI systems compared with a port fuel-injection system include the following:
   - Higher cost
   - The need for $NO_x$ storage catalyst in some applications
   - More components

4. The operating pressure can vary from as low as 500 PSI during some low-demand conditions to as high as 2,900 PSI.

5. The fuel injectors are open for a very short period of time and are pulsed using a 50- to 90-V pulse from a capacitor circuit.

6. GDI systems can operate in many modes, which are separated into the two basic modes:
   - Stratified mode
   - Homogeneous mode
7. GDI can be used to start an engine without the use of a starter motor for idle-stop functions.

8. GDI does create a louder clicking noise from the fuel injectors than port fuel-injection injectors.
9. Carbon deposits on the injector and the backside of the intake valve are a common problem with engines equipped with GDI systems.

## REVIEW QUESTIONS

1. What are two advantages of GDI compared with port fuel injection?
2. What are two disadvantages of GDI compared with port fuel injection?
3. How is the fuel delivery system different from a port fuel-injection system?
4. What are the basic modes of operation of a GDI system?

## CHAPTER QUIZ

1. Where is the fuel injected in an engine equipped with GDI?
   a. Into the intake manifold near the intake valve
   b. Directly into the combustion chamber
   c. Above the intake port
   d. In the exhaust port
2. The fuel pump inside the fuel tank on a vehicle equipped with GDI produces about what fuel pressure?
   a. 5 to 10 PSI
   b. 10 to 20 PSI
   c. 20 to 40 PSI
   d. 50 to 60 PSI
3. The high-pressure fuel pumps used in GDI systems are powered by _____.
   a. Electricity (DC motor)
   b. Electricity (AC motor)
   c. The camshaft
   d. The crankshaft
4. The high-pressure fuel pump pressure is regulated by using _____.
   a. An electric pressure-control valve
   b. A vacuum-biased regulator
   c. A mechanical regulator at the inlet to the fuel rail
   d. A non-vacuum-biased regulator
5. The fuel injectors operate under a fuel pressure of about _____.
   a. 35 to 45 PSI
   b. 90 to 150 PSI
   c. 500 to 2,900 PSI
   d. 2,000 to 5,000 PSI

6. The fuel injectors used on a GDI system are pulsed on using what voltage?
   a. 12 to 14 V
   b. 50 to 90 V
   c. 100 to 110 V
   d. 200 to 220 V
7. Which mode of operation results in a richer air-fuel mixture near the spark plug?
   a. Stoichiometric
   b. Homogeneous
   c. Stratified
   d. Knock protection
8. Some engines that use a GDI system also have port injection.
   a. True
   b. False
9. A GDI system can be used to start an engine without the need for a starter.
   a. True
   b. False
10. A lack of power from an engine equipped with GDI could be due to _____.
    a. Noisy injectors
    b. Carbon on the injectors
    c. Carbon on the intake valves
    d. Both b and c

# chapter 22
# ELECTRONIC THROTTLE CONTROL SYSTEM

**OBJECTIVES:** **After studying Chapter 22, the reader should be able to:** • Prepare for ASE Engine Performance (A8) test content area "E" (Computerized Engine Controls Diagnosis and Repair). • Describe the purpose and function of an electronic throttle control (ETC) system. • Explain how an electronic throttle control system works. • List the parts of a typical electronic throttle control system. • Describe how to diagnose faults in an electronic throttle control system.

**KEY TERMS:** Accelerator pedal position (APP) sensor 277 • Coast-down stall 283 • Default position 279 • Drive-by-wire 277 • Electronic throttle control (ETC) 277 • Fail-safe position 279 • Neutral position 279 • Servomotor 279 • Throttle position (TP) sensor 277

## ELECTRONIC THROTTLE CONTROL (ETC) SYSTEM

**ADVANTAGES OF ETC** The absence of any mechanical linkage between the throttle pedal and the throttle body requires the use of an electric actuator motor. The electronic throttle system has the following advantages over the conventional cable:

- Eliminates the mechanical throttle cable, thereby reducing the number of moving parts.

- Eliminates the need for cruise control actuators and controllers.

- Helps reduce engine power for traction control (TC) and electronic stability control (ESC) systems.

- Used to delay rapid applications of torque to the transmission/transaxle to help improve driveability and to smooth shifts.

- Helps reduce pumping losses by using the electronic throttle to open at highway speeds with greater fuel economy. The ETC opens the throttle to maintain engine and vehicle speed as the powertrain control module (PCM) leans the air-fuel ratio, retards ignition timing, and introduces additional exhaust gas recirculation (EGR) to reducing pumping losses.

- Used to provide smooth engine operation, especially during rapid acceleration.

- Eliminates the need for an idle air control valve.

The electronic throttle can be called **drive-by-wire,** but most vehicle manufacturers use the term **electronic throttle control (ETC)** to describe the system that opens the throttle valve electrically.

**PARTS INVOLVED** The typical ETC system includes the following components:

1. **Accelerator pedal position (APP)** sensor, also called accelerator pedal sensor (APS)

2. Electronic throttle actuator (servomotor), which is part of the electronic throttle body

3. **Throttle position (TP) sensor**

4. Electronic control unit, which is usually the powertrain control module (PCM)
   ● **SEE FIGURE 22–1.**

## NORMAL OPERATION OF THE ETC SYSTEM

Driving a vehicle equipped with an ETC system is about the same as driving a vehicle with a conventional mechanical throttle cable and throttle valve. However, the driver may notice some differences that are to be considered normal. These normal conditions include the following:

- The engine may not increase above idle speed when depressing the accelerator pedal when the gear selector is in Park.

- If the engine speed does increase when the accelerator is depressed with the transmission in Park or Neutral, the engine speed will likely be limited to less than 2,000 RPM.

- While accelerating rapidly, there is often a slight delay before the engine responds. ● **SEE FIGURE 22–2.**

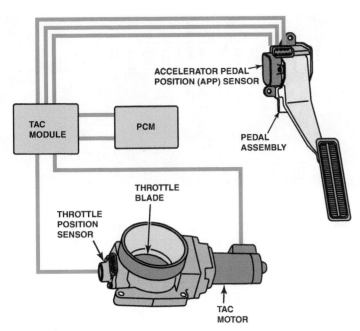

**FIGURE 22–1** The throttle pedal is connected to the accelerator pedal position (APP) sensor. The electronic throttle body includes a throttle position (TP) sensor to provide throttle angle feedback to the vehicle computer. Some systems use a throttle actuator control (TAC) module to operate the throttle blade (plate).

- While at cruise speed, the accelerator pedal may or may not cause the engine speed to increase if the accelerator pedal is moved slightly.

## ACCELERATOR PEDAL POSITION SENSOR

**CABLE-OPERATED SYSTEM** Honda Accords until 2008 model year used a cable attached to the accelerator pedal to operate the APP sensor located under the hood. A similar arrangement was used in Dodge RAM trucks in 2003. In both of these applications, the throttle cable was simply moving the APP sensor and not moving the throttle plate. The throttle plate is controlled by the PCM and moved by the ETC motor.

**TWO SENSORS** The accelerator pedal position sensor uses two and sometimes three separate sensors, which act together to give accurate accelerator pedal position information to the controller but also are used to check that the sensor is working properly. They function just like a throttle position (TP) sensor, and two are needed for proper system function. One APP sensor output signal increases as the pedal is depressed, and the other signal decreases. The controller compares the signals with a lookup table to determine the pedal position. Using two or three signals improves redundancy should one sensor fail and allows the PCM to quickly detect a malfunction. When three sensors

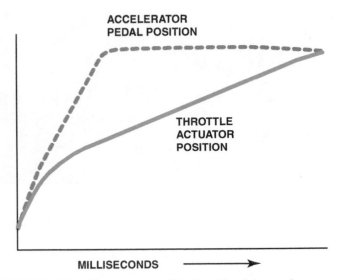

**FIGURE 22–2** The opening of the throttle plate can be delayed as long as 30 milliseconds (0.03 sec.) to allow time for the amount of fuel needed to catch up to the opening of the throttle plate.

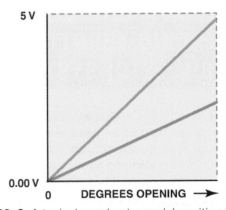

**FIGURE 22–3** A typical accelerator pedal position (APP) sensor, showing two different output voltage signals that are used by the PCM to determine accelerator pedal position. Two (or three in some applications) are used as a double check because this is a safety-related sensor.

are used, the third signal can either decrease or increase with pedal position, but its voltage range will still be different from the other two. ● **SEE FIGURE 22–3.**

## THROTTLE BODY ASSEMBLY

The throttle body assembly contains the following components:
- Throttle plate
- Electric actuator DC motor
- Dual TP sensors
- Gears used to multiply the torque of the DC motor
- Springs used to hold the throttle plate in the default location

**FREQUENTLY ASKED QUESTION**

### What Is the "Spring Test"?

The spring test is a self-test performed by the PCM whenever the engine is started. The PCM operates the throttle to check if it can react to the command and return to the default (home) position. This self-test is used by the PCM to determine that the spring and motor are working correctly and may be noticed by some vehicle owners by the following factors:

- A slight delay in the operation of the starter motor. The PCM performs this test when the ignition switch is turned to the "on" position. While it takes just a short time to perform the test, it can be sensed by the driver that there could be a fault in the ignition switch or starter motor circuits.
- A slight "clicking" sound may also be heard coming from under the hood when the ignition is turned on. This is normal and is related to the self-test on the throttle as it opens and closes.

**THROTTLE PLATE AND SPRING**   The throttle plate is held slightly open by a concentric clock spring. The spring applies a force that will close the throttle plate if power is lost to the actuator motor. The spring is also used to open the throttle plate slightly from the fully closed position.

**ELECTRONIC THROTTLE BODY MOTOR**   The actuator is a DC electric motor and is often called a **servomotor.** The throttle plate is held in a **default position** by a spring inside the throttle body assembly. This partially open position, also called the **neutral position** or the **fail-safe position,** is about 16% to 20% open. This default position varies depending on the vehicle and usually results in an engine speed of 1,200 to 1,500 RPM:

- The throttle plate is driven closed to achieve speeds lower than the default position, such as idle speed.
- The throttle plate is driven open to achieve speeds higher than the default position, such as during acceleration. ● **SEE FIGURE 22–4.**

The throttle plate motor is driven by a bidirectional pulse-width-modulated (PWM) signal from the PCM or ETC module using an H-bridge circuit. ● **SEE FIGURE 22–5a, b.**

The H-bridge circuit is controlled by the powertrain control module (PCM) by the following:

- Reversing the polarity of power and ground brushes to the DC motor
- Pulse-width modulating the current through the motor

The PCM monitors the position of the throttle from the two TP sensors. The PCM then commands the throttle plate to the desired position. ● **SEE FIGURE 22–6.**

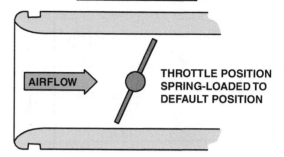

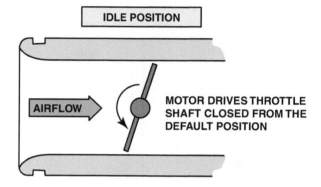

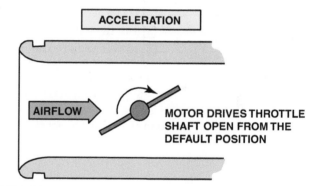

**FIGURE 22–4**   The default position for the throttle plate is in slightly open position. The servomotor then is used to close it for idle and open it during acceleration.

**FREQUENTLY ASKED QUESTION**

### Why Not Use a Stepper Motor for ETC?

A stepper motor is a type of motor that has multiple windings and is pulsed by a computer to rotate a certain number of degrees when pulsed. The disadvantage is that a stepper motor is too slow to react compared with a conventional DC electric motor and is the reason a stepper motor is not used in ETC systems.

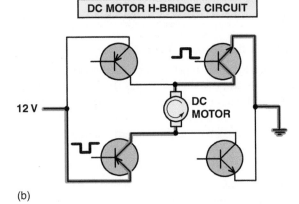

(a)                                (b)

**FIGURE 22–5** (a) An H-bridge circuit is used to control the direction of the DC electric motor of the electronic throttle control (ETC) unit. (b) To reverse the direction of operation, the polarity of the current through the motor is reversed.

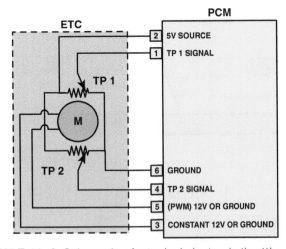

**FIGURE 22–6** Schematic of a typical electronic throttle control (ETC) system. Note that terminal #5 is always pulse-width modulated and that terminal #3 is always constant, but both power and ground are switched to change the direction of the motor.

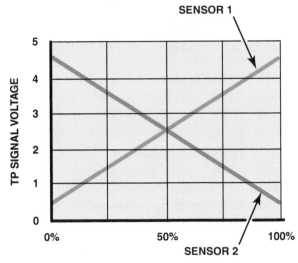

**FIGURE 22–7** The two TP sensors used on the throttle body of an electronic throttle body assembly produce opposite voltage signals as the throttle is opened. The total voltage of both combined at any throttle plate position is 5 volts.

# TP SENSOR

Two TP sensors are used in the throttle body assembly to provide TP signals to the PCM. Two sensors are used as a fail-safe measure and for diagnosis. There are two types of TP sensors used in ETC systems: potentiometers and Hall effect.

**THREE-WIRE POTENTIOMETER SENSORS** These sensors use a 5-volt reference from the PCM and produce an analog (variable) voltage signal that is proportional to the throttle plate position. The two sensors produce opposite signals as the throttle plate opens:

- One sensor starts at low voltage (about 0.5 V) and increases as the throttle plate is opened.
- The second sensor starts at a higher voltage (about 4.5 V) and produces a lower voltage as the throttle plate is opened. ● **SEE FIGURE 22–7.**

**How Do You Calibrate a New APP Sensor?**

Whenever an accelerator pedal position (APP) sensor is replaced, it should be calibrated before it will work correctly. Always check service information for the exact procedure to follow after APP sensor replacement. Here is a typical example of the procedure:

**STEP 1**   Make sure the accelerator pedal is fully released.

**STEP 2**   Turn the ignition switch on (engine off) and wait at least 2 seconds.

**STEP 3**   Turn the ignition switch off and wait at least 10 seconds.

**STEP 4**   Turn the ignition switch on (engine on) and wait at least 2 seconds.

**STEP 5**   Turn the ignition switch off and wait at least 10 seconds.

(a)

(b)

**FIGURE 22-8** (a) A "reduced power" warning light indicates a fault with the electronic throttle control (ETC) system on some General Motors vehicles. (b) A symbol showing an engine with an arrow pointing down is used on some General Motors vehicles to indicate a fault with the ETC system.

**HALL-EFFECT TP SENSORS** Some vehicle manufacturers, Honda, for example, use a noncontact Hall-effect TP sensor. Because there is not physical contact, this type of sensor is less likely to fail due to wear.

## DIAGNOSIS OF ETC SYSTEMS

**FAULT MODE** ETC systems can have faults like any other automatic system. Because of the redundant sensors in accelerator pedal position (APP) sensors and TP sensor, many faults result in a "*limp home*" situation instead of a total failure. The limp home mode is also called the "*fail-safe mode*" and indicates the following actions performed by the PCM:

- Engine speed is limited to the default speed (about 1,200 to 1,600 RPM).
- There is slow or no response when the accelerator pedal is depressed.
- The cruise control system is disabled.
- A diagnostic trouble code (DTC) is set.
- An ETC warning lamp on the dash will light. The warning lamp may be labeled differently, depending on the vehicle manufacturer. Examples include the following:
  - General Motors vehicle—Reduced power lamp (● **SEE FIGURE 22-8**)
  - Ford—Wrench symbol (amber or green) (● **SEE FIGURE 22-9**)

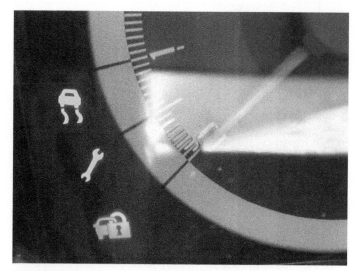

**FIGURE 22-9** A wrench symbol warning lamp on a Ford vehicle. The symbol can also be green.

  - Chrysler—Red lightning bolt symbol (● **SEE FIGURE 22-10**)
- The engine will run and can be driven slowly. This limp-in mode operation allows the vehicle to be driven off of the road and to a safe location.

The ETC may enter the limp-in mode if any of the following has occurred:

- Low battery voltage has been detected
- PCM failure
- One TP and the MAP sensor have failed
- Both TP sensors have failed
- The ETC actuator motor has failed
- The ETC throttle spring has failed

**FIGURE 22–10** A symbol used on a Chrysler vehicle indicating a fault with the electronic throttle control (ETC).

**FIGURE 22–11** The throttle plate stayed where it was moved by the technician, which indicates that there is a problem with the electronic throttle body control assembly.

 **REAL WORLD FIX**

**The High-Idle Toyota**

The owner of a Toyota Camry complained that the engine would idle at over 1,200 RPM compared with a normal 600 to 700 RPM. The vehicle would also not accelerate. Using a scan tool, a check for DTCs showed one code: P2101—"TAC motor circuit low."

Checking service information led to the inspection of the ETC throttle body assembly. With the ignition key out of the ignition and the inlet air duct off the throttle body, the technician used a screwdriver to gently push to see if the throttle plate worked:

**Normal operation**—The throttle plate should move and then spring back quickly to the default position.

**Abnormal operation**—If the throttle plate stays where it is moved or does not return to the default position, there is a fault with the throttle body assembly. ● **SEE FIGURE 22–11.**

**Solution:** The technician replaced the throttle body assembly with an updated version, and proper engine operation was restored. The technician disassembled the old throttle body and found it was corroded inside because of moisture entering the unit through the vent hose. ● **SEE FIGURE 22–12.**

**VACUUM LEAKS** The ETC system is able to compensate for many vacuum leaks. A vacuum leak at the intake manifold for example will allow air into the engine that is not measured by the mass airflow sensor. The ETC system will simply move the throttle as needed to achieve the proper idle speed to compensate for the leak.

**DIAGNOSTIC PROCEDURE** If a fault occurs in the ETC system, check service information for the specified procedure to follow for the vehicle being checked. Most vehicle service information includes the following steps:

**STEP 1** Verify the customer concern.

**STEP 2** Use a factory scan tool or an aftermarket scan tool with original equipment capability and check for DTCs.

**STEP 3** If there are stored DTCs, follow service information instructions for diagnosing the system.

**STEP 4** If there are no stored DTCs, check scan tool data for possible fault areas in the system.

**SCAN TOOL DATA** Scan data related to the ETC system can be confusing. Typical data and the meaning include the following:

- **APP indicated angle.** The scan tool will display a percentage ranging from 0% to 100%. When the throttle is released, the indicated angle should be 0%. When the throttle is depressed to wide open, the reading should indicate 100%.

- **TP desired angle.** The scan tool will display a percentage ranging from 0% to 100%. This represents the desired throttle angle as commanded by the driver of the vehicle.

- **TP indicated angle.** The TP indicated angle is the angle of the measured throttle opening, and it should agree with the TP desired angle.

- **TP sensors 1 and 2.** The scan tool will display "agree" or "disagree." If the PCM or throttle actuator control (TAC) module receives a voltage signal from one of the TP sensors that is not in the proper relationship to the other TP sensor, the scan tool will display "disagree."

**FIGURE 22–12** A corroded electronic throttle control (ETC) assembly shown with the cover removed.

**FIGURE 22–13** Notice the small motor gear on the left drives a larger plastic gear (black), which then drives the small gear in mesh with the section of a gear attached to the throttle plate. This results in a huge torque increase from the small motor and helps explain why it could be dangerous to insert a finger into the throttle body assembly.

## ETC THROTTLE FOLLOWER TEST

On some vehicles, such as many Chrysler vehicles, the operation of the ETC can be tested using a factory or factory-level scan tool. To perform this test, use the "throttle follower test" procedure as shown on the scan tool. An assistant is needed to check that the throttle plate is moving as the accelerator pedal is depressed. This test cannot be done normally because the PCM does not normally allow the throttle plate to be moved unless the engine is running.

## SERVICING ELECTRONIC THROTTLE SYSTEMS

**ETC-RELATED PERFORMANCE ISSUES**    The only service that an ETC system may require is a cleaning of the throttle body. Throttle body cleaning is a routine service procedure on port fuel-injected engines and is still needed when the throttle is being opened by an electric motor rather than a throttle cable tied to a mechanical accelerator pedal. The throttle body may need cleaning if one or more of the following symptoms are present:

- Lower-than-normal idle speed
- Rough idle
- Engine stalls when coming to a stop (called a **coast-down stall**)

If any of the above conditions exists, a throttle body cleaning will often correct these faults.

CAUTION: Some vehicle manufacturers add a nonstick coating to the throttle assembly and warn that cleaning could remove this protective coating. Always follow the vehicle manufacturer's recommended procedures.

**THROTTLE BODY CLEANING PROCEDURE**    Before attempting to clean a throttle body on an engine equipped with an ETC system, be sure that the ignition key is out of the vehicle and the ready light is off if working on a Toyota/Lexus hybrid electric vehicle to avoid the possibility of personal injury.

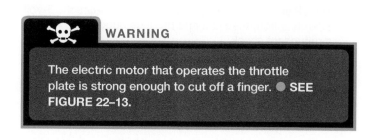

**WARNING**

The electric motor that operates the throttle plate is strong enough to cut off a finger. ● **SEE FIGURE 22–13.**

To clean the throttle, perform the following steps:

**STEP 1**    With the ignition off and the key removed from the ignition, remove the air inlet hose from the throttle body.

**STEP 2**    Spray throttle body cleaner onto a shop cloth.

**STEP 3**    Open the throttle body and use the shop cloth to remove the varnish and carbon deposits from the throttle body housing and throttle plate.

CAUTION: Do not spray cleaner into the throttle body assembly. The liquid cleaner could flow into and damage the throttle position (TP) sensors.

**STEP 4**    Reinstall the inlet hose being sure that there are no air leaks between the hose and the throttle body assembly.

**STEP 5**    Start the engine and allow the PCM to learn the correct idle. If the idle is not correct, check service information for the specified procedures to follow to perform a throttle relearn.

**THROTTLE BODY RELEARN PROCEDURE** When installing a new throttle body or PCM or sometimes after cleaning the throttle body, the throttle position has to be learned by the PCM. After the following conditions have been met, a typical throttle body relearn procedure for a General Motors vehicle includes the following:

- Accelerator pedal released
- Battery voltage higher than 8 volts
- Vehicle speed must be zero
- Engine coolant temperature (ECT) higher than 40°F (5°C) and lower than 212°F (100°C)

- Intake air temperature (IAT) higher than 40°F (5°C)
- No throttle DTCs set

If all of the above conditions are met, perform the following steps:

**STEP 1** Turn the ignition on (engine off) for 30 seconds.

**STEP 2** Turn the ignition off and wait 30 seconds.

Start the engine and the idle learn procedure should cause the engine to idle at the correct speed.

## SUMMARY

1. Using an electronic throttle control (ETC) system on an engine has many advantages over a conventional method that uses a mechanical cable between the accelerator pedal and the throttle valve.

2. The major components of an ETC system include the following:
   - Accelerator pedal position (APP) sensor
   - ETC actuator motor and spring
   - Throttle position (TP) sensor
   - Electronic control unit

3. The TP sensor is actually two sensors that share the 5-volt reference from the PCM and produce opposite signals as a redundant check.

4. Limp-in mode is commanded if there is a major fault in the system, which can allow the vehicle to be driven enough to be pulled off the road to safety.

5. The diagnostic procedure for the ETC system includes verifying the customer concern, using a scan tool to check for DTCs, and checking the value of the TP and APP sensors.

6. Servicing the ETC system includes cleaning the throttle body and throttle plate.

## REVIEW QUESTIONS

1. What parts can be deleted if an engine uses an electronic throttle control (ETC) system instead of a conventional accelerator pedal and cable to operate the throttle valve?

2. How can the use of an ETC system improve fuel economy?

3. How is the operation of the throttle different on a system that uses an ETC system compared with a conventional mechanical system?

4. What component parts are included in an ETC system?

5. What is the default or limp-in position of the throttle plate?

6. What dash warning light indicates a fault with the ETC system?

## CHAPTER QUIZ

1. The use of an electronic throttle control (ETC) system allows the elimination of all except _____.
   a. Accelerator pedal
   b. Mechanical throttle cable (most systems)
   c. Cruise control actuator
   d. Idle air control

2. The throttle plate is spring loaded to hold the throttle slightly open how far?
   a. 3% to 5%
   b. 8% to 10%
   c. 16% to 20%
   d. 22% to 28%

3. The throttle plate actuator motor is what type of electric motor?
   a. Stepper motor
   b. DC motor
   c. AC motor
   d. Brushless motor

4. The actuator motor is controlled by the PCM through what type of circuit?
   a. Series
   b. Parallel
   c. H-bridge
   d. Series-parallel

5. When does the PCM perform a self-test of the ETC system?
   a. During cruise speed when the throttle is steady
   b. During deceleration
   c. During acceleration
   d. When the ignition switch is first rotated to the on position before the engine starts

6. The throttle position sensor used in the throttle body assembly of an ETC system is what type?
   a. Single potentiometer
   b. Two potentiometers that read in the opposite direction
   c. Hall-effect sensor
   d. Either b or c

7. A green wrench symbol is displayed on the dash. What does this mean?
   a. A fault in the ETC in a Ford has been detected.
   b. A fault in the ETC in a Honda has been detected.
   c. A fault in the ETC in a Chrysler has been detected.
   d. A fault in the ETC in a General Motors vehicle has been detected.

8. A technician is checking the operation of the ETC system by depressing the accelerator pedal with the ignition in the on (run) position (engine off). What is the most likely result if the system is functioning correctly?
   a. The throttle goes to wide open when the accelerator pedal is depressed all the way.
   b. There is no throttle movement.
   c. The throttle will open partially but not all of the way.
   d. The throttle will perform a self-test by closing and then opening to the default position.

9. With the ignition off and the key out of the ignition, what should happen if a technician uses a screwdriver and pushes gently on the throttle plate in an attempt to open the valve?
   a. Nothing. The throttle should be kept from moving by the motor, which is not energized with the key off.
   b. The throttle should move and stay where it is moved and not go back unless moved back.
   c. The throttle should move and then spring back to the home position when released.
   d. The throttle should move closed but not open further than the default position.

10. The throttle body may be cleaned (if recommended by the vehicle manufacturer) if what conditions are occurring?
    a. Coast-down stall
    b. Rough idle
    c. Lower-than-normal idle speed
    d. Any of the above

**OBJECTIVES:** **After studying Chapter 23, the reader should be able to:** • Prepare for ASE Engine Performance (A8) certification test content area "C" (Fuel, Air Induction, and Exhaust Systems Diagnosis and Repair). • Explain how to test the fuel injection system using a scan tool. • Explain how to check a fuel-pressure regulator. • Describe how to test fuel injectors. • Explain how to diagnose electronic fuel-injection problems. • Describe how to service the fuel-injection system.

**KEY TERMS:** Graphing multimeter (GMM) 287 • Idle air control counts 288 • Idle air control (IAC) 295 • Noid light 289 • Peak-and-hold injector 294 • Pressure transducer 287 • Saturation 294

## PORT FUEL-INJECTION PRESSURE REGULATOR DIAGNOSIS

Most port fuel-injected engines use a vacuum hose connected to the fuel-pressure regulator. At idle, the pressure inside the intake manifold is low (high vacuum). Manifold vacuum is applied above the diaphragm inside the fuel-pressure regulator. This reduces the pressure exerted on the diaphragm and results in a lower, about 10 PSI (69 kPa), fuel pressure applied to the injectors. To test a vacuum-controlled fuel-pressure regulator, follow these steps:

1. Connect a fuel-pressure gauge to monitor the fuel pressure.

2. Locate the fuel-pressure regulator and disconnect the vacuum hose from the regulator.

   **NOTE: If gasoline drips out of the vacuum hose when removed from the fuel-pressure regulator, the regulator is defective and will require replacement.**

3. With the engine running at idle speed, reconnect the vacuum hose to the fuel-pressure regulator while watching the fuel-pressure gauge. The fuel pressure should drop (about 10 PSI, or 69 kPa) when the hose is reattached to the regulator.

4. Using a hand-operated vacuum pump, apply vacuum (20 in. Hg) to the regulator. The regulator should hold

**FIGURE 23–1** If the vacuum hose is removed from the fuel-pressure regulator when the engine is running, the fuel pressure should increase. If it does not increase, then the fuel pump is not capable of supplying adequate pressure or the fuel-pressure regulator is defective. If gasoline is visible in the vacuum hose, the regulator is leaking and should be replaced.

vacuum. If the vacuum drops, replace the fuel-pressure regulator. ● **SEE FIGURE 23–1.**

**NOTE: Some vehicles do not use a vacuum-regulated fuel-pressure regulator. Many of these vehicles use a regulator located inside the fuel tank that supplies a constant fuel pressure to the fuel injectors.**

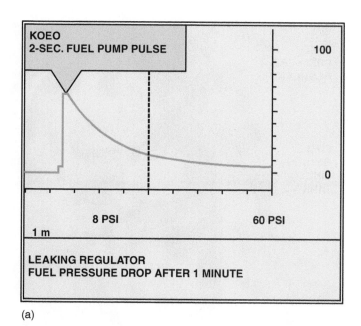

(a)

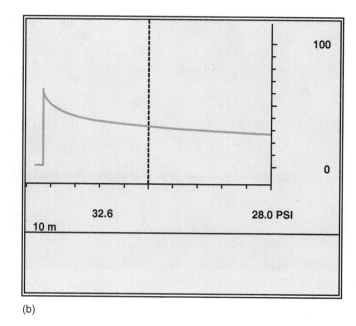

(b)

**FIGURE 23–2** (a) A fuel-pressure graph after key on, engine off (KOEO) on a TBI system. (b) Pressure drop after 10 minutes on a normal port fuel-injection system.

 **TECH TIP**

**Pressure Transducer Fuel-Pressure Test**

Using a **pressure transducer** and a **graphing multimeter (GMM)** or digital storage oscilloscope (DSO) allows the service technician to view the fuel pressure over time. ● **SEE FIGURE 23–2(a).** Note that the fuel pressure dropped from 15 PSI to 6 PSI on a TBI-equipped vehicle after just one minute. A normal pressure holding capability is shown in ● **FIGURE 23–2(b)** when the pressure dropped only about 10% after 10 minutes on a port fuel-injection system.

**FIGURE 23–3** A clogged PCV system caused the engine oil fumes to be drawn into the air cleaner assembly. This is what the technician discovered during a visual inspection.

# DIAGNOSING ELECTRONIC FUEL-INJECTION PROBLEMS USING VISUAL INSPECTION

All fuel-injection systems require the proper amount of clean fuel delivered to the system at the proper pressure and the correct amount of filtered air. The following items should be carefully inspected before proceeding to more detailed tests:

- Check the air filter and replace as needed.
- Check the air induction system for obstructions.
- Check the conditions of all vacuum hoses. Replace any hose that is split, soft (mushy), or brittle.

- Check the positive crankcase ventilation (PCV) valve for proper operation or replacement as needed. ● **SEE FIGURE 23–3.**

  NOTE: The use of an incorrect PCV valve can cause a rough idle or stalling.

- Check all fuel-injection electrical connections for corrosion or damage.
- Check for gasoline at the vacuum port of the fuel-pressure regulator if the vehicle is so equipped. Gasoline in the vacuum hose at the fuel-pressure regulator indicates that the regulator is defective and requires replacement.

FIGURE 23–4 All fuel injectors should make the same sound with the engine running at idle speed. A lack of sound indicates a possible electrically open injector or a break in the wiring. A defective computer could also be the cause of a lack of clicking (pulsing) of the injectors.

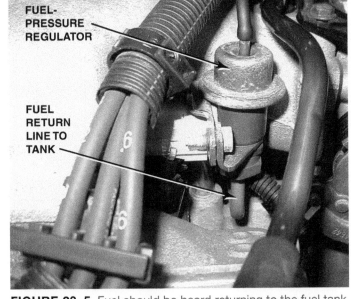

FIGURE 23–5 Fuel should be heard returning to the fuel tank at the fuel return line if the fuel-pump and fuel-pressure regulator are functioning correctly.

TECH TIP

**Stethoscope Fuel-Injection Test**

A commonly used test for injector operation is to listen to the injector using a stethoscope with the engine operating at idle speed. ● SEE FIGURE 23–4. All injectors should produce the same clicking sound. If any injector makes a clunking or rattling sound, it should be tested further or replaced. With the engine still running, place the end of the stethoscope probe to the return line from the fuel-pressure regulator. ● SEE FIGURE 23–5. Fuel should be heard flowing back to the fuel tank if the fuel-pump pressure is higher than the fuel-regulator pressure. If no sound of fuel is heard, then either the fuel pump or the fuel-pressure regulator is at fault.

## SCAN TOOL VACUUM LEAK DIAGNOSIS

If a vacuum (air) leak occurs on an engine equipped with a speed-density type of fuel injection, the extra air would cause the following to occur:

- The idle speed increases because of the extra air just as if the throttle pedal were depressed.
- The MAP sensor reacts to the increased air from the vacuum leak as an additional load on the engine.

TECH TIP

**Quick and Easy Leaking Injector Test**

Leaking injectors may be found by disabling the ignition, unhooking all injectors, and checking exhaust for hydrocarbons (HC) using a gas analyzer while cranking the engine (maximum HC = 300 PPM).

- The computer increases the injector pulse width slightly longer because of the signal from the MAP sensor.
- The air-fuel mixture remains unchanged.
- The idle air control (IAC) counts will decrease, thereby attempting to reduce the engine speed to the target idle speed stored in the computer memory. ● SEE FIGURE 23–6.

Therefore, one of the best indicators of a vacuum leak on a speed-density fuel-injection system is to look at the IAC counts or percentage. Normal **IAC counts** or percentage is usually 15 to 25. A reading of less than 5 indicates a vacuum leak.

If a vacuum leak occurs on an engine equipped with a mass airflow type of fuel-injection system, the extra air causes the following to occur:

- The engine will operate leaner than normal because the extra air has not been measured by the MAF sensor.
- The idle speed will likely be lower because of the leaner-than-normal air-fuel mixture.
- The IAC counts or percentage will often increase in an attempt to return the engine speed to the target speed stored in the computer.

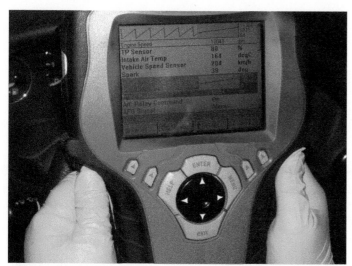

**FIGURE 23–6** Using a scan tool to check for idle air control (IAC) counts or percentage as part of a diagnostic routine.

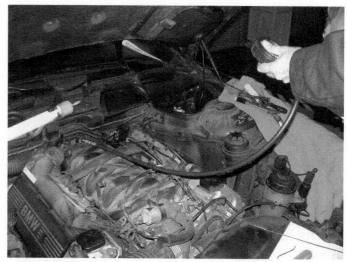

**FIGURE 23–7** Checking the fuel pressure using a fuel-pressure gauge connected to the Schrader valve.

---

## PORT FUEL-INJECTION SYSTEM DIAGNOSIS

To determine if a port fuel-injection system—including the fuel pump, injectors, and fuel-pressure regulator—is operating correctly, take the following steps:

1. Attach a fuel-pressure gauge to the Schrader valve on the fuel rail. ● **SEE FIGURE 23–7.**

2. Turn the ignition key on or start the engine to build up the fuel-pump pressure (to about 35 to 45 PSI).

3. Wait 20 minutes and observe the fuel pressure retained in the fuel rail and note the PSI reading. The fuel pressure should not drop more than 20 PSI (140 kPa) in 20 minutes. If the drop is less than 20 PSI in 20 minutes, everything is

okay; if the drop is *greater,* then there is a possible problem with the following:

- The check valve in the fuel pump
- Leaking injectors, lines, or fittings
- A defective (leaking) fuel-pressure regulator

To determine which unit is defective, perform the following:

- Reenergize the electric fuel pump.

- Clamp the fuel *supply* line and wait 10 minutes (see Caution box). If the pressure drop does not occur, replace the fuel pump. If the pressure drop still occurs, continue with the next step.

- Repeat the pressure buildup of the electric pump and clamp the fuel return line. If the pressure drop time is now okay, replace the fuel-pressure regulator.

- If the pressure drop still occurs, one or more of the injectors is leaking. Remove the injectors with the fuel rail and hold over paper. Replace those injectors that drip one or more drops after 10 minutes with pressurized fuel.

**CAUTION: Do not clamp plastic fuel lines. Connect shut-off valves to the fuel system to shut off supply and return lines. ● SEE FIGURE 23–8.**

## TESTING FOR AN INJECTOR PULSE

One of the first checks that should be performed when diagnosing a no-start condition is whether the fuel injectors are being pulsed by the computer. Checking for proper pulsing of the injector is also important in diagnosing a weak or dead cylinder.

A **noid light** is designed to electrically replace the injector in the circuit and to flash if the injector circuit is working correctly. ● **SEE FIGURE 23–9.** To use a noid light, disconnect the

**FIGURE 23–8** Shutoff valves must be used on vehicles equipped with plastic fuel lines to isolate the cause of a pressure drop in the fuel system.

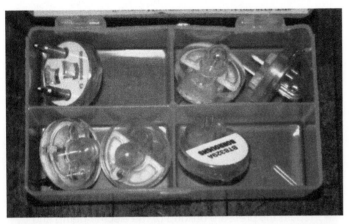

(a)

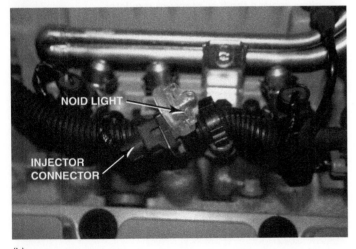

(b)

**FIGURE 23–9** (a) Noid lights are usually purchased as an assortment so that one is available for any type or size of injector wiring connector. (b) The connector is unplugged from the injector, and a noid light is plugged into the injector connector. The noid light should flash when the engine is being cranked if the power circuit and the pulsing to ground by the computer are functioning okay.

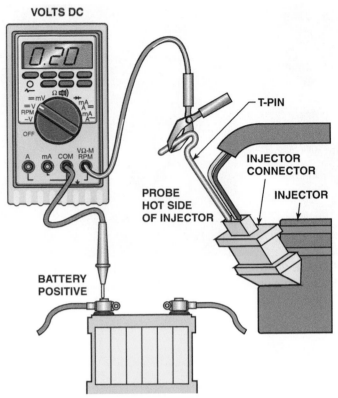

**VOLTS DC**

**FIGURE 23–10** Use a DMM set to read DC volts to check the voltage drop of the positive circuit to the fuel injector. A reading of 0.5 volt or less is generally considered to be acceptable.

electrical connector at the fuel injector and plug the noid light into the injector harness connections. Crank or start the engine. The noid light should flash regularly.

**NOTE: The term *noid* is simply an abbreviation of the word *solenoid*. Injectors use a movable iron core and are therefore solenoids. Therefore, a noid light is a replacement for the solenoid (injector).**

Possible noid light problems and causes include the following:

1. **The light is off and does not flash.** The problem is an open circuit in either the power side or the ground side (or both) of the injector circuit.

2. **The noid light flashes dimly.** A dim noid light indicates excessive resistance or low voltage available to the injector. Both the power and the ground side must be checked.

3. **The noid light is on and does not flash.** If the noid light is on, then both a power and a ground are present. Because the light does not flash (blink) when the engine is being cranked or started, a short-to-ground fault exists either in the computer itself or in the wiring between the injector and the computer.

**CAUTION: A noid lamp must be used with caution. The computer may show a good noid light operation and have low supply voltage. ● SEE FIGURE 23–10.**

# CHECKING FUEL-INJECTOR RESISTANCE

Each port fuel injector must deliver an equal amount of fuel, or the engine will idle roughly or perform poorly.

The electrical balance test involves measuring the injector coil-winding resistance. For best engine operation, all injectors should have the same electrical resistance. To measure the resistance, carefully release the locking feature of the connector and remove the connector from the injector.

| Injector Resistance Table | | |
| --- | --- | --- |
| Manufacturer | Injector Application | Resistance Values |
| **General Motors** | | |
| | Quad 4 | 1.95–2.15 Ω |
| | CPI Vortec 4.3L | 1.48–1.52 Ω |
| | MFI Bosch Style Injector (1985–1989) 2.8L | 15.95–16.35 Ω |
| | MFI Black Multec Injector 2.8L, 3.1L, 3.3L, 3.4L | 11.8–12.6 Ω |
| | MFI 3800 | 14.3–14.7 Ω |
| | MFI 3.8L, 5.0L, 5.7L | 15.8–16.6 Ω |
| | MFI 5.7 LT5-ZR1 | 11.8–12.6 Ω |
| | TBI 220 Series 2.8L, 3.1L, 4.3L, 5.0L, 5.7L, 7.4L | 1.16–1.36 Ω |
| | TBI 295 Series 4.3L, 6.0L, 7.0L | 1.42–1.62 Ω |
| | TBI 700 Series 2.0L, 2.2L, 2.5L | 1.42–1.62 Ω |
| **Chrysler Brand** | | |
| | MFI Early Years through 1992 (majority of) | 2.4 Ω |
| | MFI Later Years after 1992 (majority of) | 14.5 Ω |
| | TBI Low-Pressure Systems (majority of) | 1.3 Ω |
| | TBI High-Pressure Systems (majority of) | 0.7 Ω |
| **Ford** | | |
| | MFI (majority of) | 15.0–18.0 Ω |
| | TBI Low-Pressure 1.9L (1987–1990) | 1.0–2.0 Ω |
| | TBI Low-Pressure 2.3L (1985–1987) | 1.0–2.0 Ω |
| | TBI Low-Pressure 2.5L (1986–1990) | 1.0–2.0 Ω |
| | TBI High-Pressure 3.8L (1984–1987) | 1.5–2.5 Ω |
| | TBI High-Pressure 5.0L (1981–1985) | 1.5–3.5 Ω |

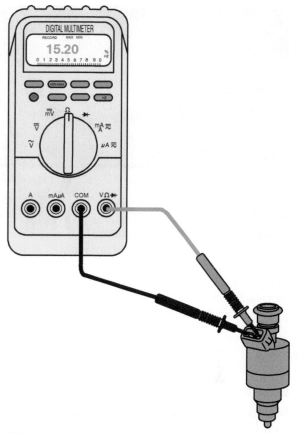

**FIGURE 23–11** Connections and settings necessary to measure fuel-injector resistance.

**NOTE: Some engines require specific procedures to gain access to the injectors. Always follow the manufacturer's recommended procedures.**

With an ohmmeter, measure the resistance across the injector terminals. Be sure to use the low-ohms feature of the digital ohmmeter to read in tenths (0.1) of an ohm. ● **SEE FIGURES 23–11 AND 23–12.** Check service information for the resistance specification of the injectors. Measure the resistance of all of the injectors. Replace any injector that does not fall within the resistance range of the specification. The resistance of the injectors should be measured twice—once when the engine (and injectors) are cold and once after the engine has reached normal operating temperature. If any injector measures close to specification, make certain that the terminals of the injector are electrically sound and perform other tests to confirm an injector problem before replacement.

# MEASURING RESISTANCE OF GROUPED INJECTORS

Many vehicles are equipped with a port fuel-injection system that "fires" two or more injectors at a time. For example, a V-6 may group all three injectors on one bank to pulse on at the

**FIGURE 23–12** To measure fuel-injector resistance, a technician constructed a short wiring harness with a double banana plug that fits into the V and COM terminals of the meter and an injector connector at the other end. This setup makes checking resistance of fuel injectors quick and easy.

 **TECH TIP**

**Equal Resistance Test**

All fuel injectors should measure the specified resistance. However, the specification often indicates that the temperature of the injectors be at room temperature and of course will vary according to the temperature. Rather than waiting for all of the injectors to achieve room temperature, measure the resistance and check that they are all within 0.4 ohm of each other. To determine the difference, record the resistance of each injector and then subtract the lowest resistance reading from the highest resistance reading to get the difference. If more than 0.4 ohm, then further testing will be needed to verify defective injector(s).

same time. Then the other three injectors will be pulsed on. This sequence alternates. To measure the resistance of these injectors, it is often easiest to measure each group of three that is wired in parallel. The resistance of three injectors wired in parallel is one-third of the resistance of each individual injector. An example follows:

**Injector resistance = 12 ohms (Ω)**

**Three injectors in parallel = 4 ohms (Ω)**

A V-6 has two groups of three injectors. Therefore, both groups should measure the same resistance. If both groups measure 4 ohms, then it is likely that all six injectors are okay. However, if one group measures only 2.9 ohms and the other group measures 4 ohms, then it is likely that one or more fuel injectors are defective (shorted). This means that the technician now has reasonable cause to remove the intake manifold to get access to each injector for further testing. ● **SEE FIGURE 23–13.**

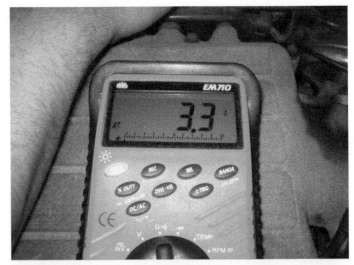

(a)

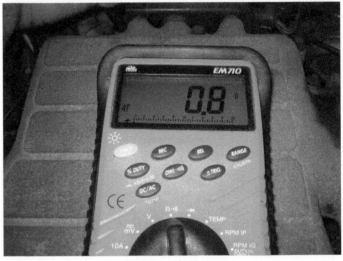

(b)

**FIGURE 23–13** (a) The meter is connected to read one group of three 12-ohm injectors. The result should be 4 ohms, and this reading is a little low, indicating that at least one injector is shorted (low resistance). (b) This meter is connected to the other group of three injectors and indicates that most, if not all three, injectors are shorted. The technician replaced all six injectors, and the engine ran great.

# MEASURING RESISTANCE OF INDIVIDUAL INJECTORS

While there are many ways to check injectors, the first test is to measure the resistance of the coil inside and compare it to factory specifications. ● **SEE FIGURE 23–14.** If the injectors are not accessible, check service information for the location of the electrical connector for the injectors. Unplug the connector and measure the resistance of each injector at the injector side of the connector. Use service information to determine the wire colors for the power side and the pulse side of each injector.

FIGURE 23–14 If an injector has the specified resistance, this does not mean that it is okay. This injector had the specified resistance, yet it did not deliver the correct amount of fuel because it was clogged.

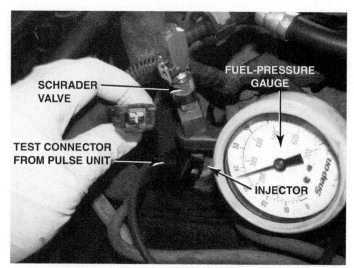

FIGURE 23–15 Connect a fuel-pressure gauge to the fuel rail at the Schrader valve.

## PRESSURE-DROP BALANCE TEST

The pressure balance test involves using an electrical timing device to pulse the fuel injectors on for a given amount of time, usually 500 ms, or 0.5 second, and observing the drop in pressure that accompanies the pulse. If the *fuel flow* through each injector is equal, the drop in pressure in the system will be equal. Most manufacturers recommend that the pressures be within about 1.5 PSI (10 kPa) of each other for satisfactory engine performance. This test method not only tests the electrical functioning of the injector (for definite time and current pulse) but also tests for mechanical defects that could affect fuel flow amounts.

The purpose of running this injector balance test is to determine which injector is restricted, inoperative, or delivering fuel differently than the other injectors. Replacing a complete set of injectors can be expensive. The basic tools needed are the folowing:

- Accurate pressure gauge with pressure relief
- Injector pulser with time control
- Necessary injector connection adapters
- Safe receptacle for catching and disposing of any fuel released

STEP 1    Attach the pressure gauge to the fuel delivery rail on the supply side. Make sure the connections are safe and leakproof.

STEP 2    Attach the injector pulser to the first injector to be tested.

STEP 3    Turn the ignition key to the on position to prime the fuel rail. Note the static fuel-pressure reading. ● SEE FIGURE 23–15.

STEP 4    Activate the pulser for the timed firing pulses.

STEP 5    Note and record the new static rail pressure after the injector has been pulsed.

STEP 6    Reenergize the fuel pump and repeat this procedure for all of the engine injectors.

STEP 7    Compare the two pressure readings and compute the pressure drop for each injector. Compare the pressure drops of the injectors to each other. Any variation in pressure drops will indicate an uneven fuel delivery rate between the injectors.

An example follows:

| Injector | 1 | 2 | 3 | 4 | 5 | 6 |
|---|---|---|---|---|---|---|
| Initial pressure | 40 | 40 | 40 | 40 | 40 | 40 |
| Second pressure | 30 | 30 | 35 | 30 | 20 | 30 |
| Pressure drop | 10 | 10 | 5 | 10 | 20 | 10 |
| Possible problem | OK | OK | Restriction | OK | Leak | OK |

## INJECTOR VOLTAGE-DROP TESTS

Another test of injectors involves pulsing the injector and measuring the voltage drop across the windings as current is flowing. A typical voltage-drop tester is shown in ● FIGURE 23–16. The tester, which is recommended for use by General Motors Corporation, pulses the injector while a digital multimeter is connected to the unit, which will display the voltage drop as the current flows through the winding.

CAUTION: Do not test an injector using a pulse-type tester more than one time without starting the engine to help avoid a hydrostatic lock caused by the flow of fuel into the cylinder during the pulse test.

**FIGURE 23–16** An injector tester being used to check the voltage drop through the injector while the tester is sending current through the injectors. This test is used to check the coil inside the injector. This same tester can be used to check for equal pressure drop of each injector by pulsing the injector on for 500 ms.

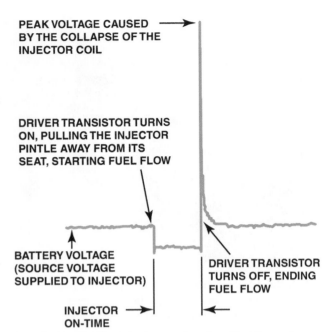

PEAK VOLTAGE CAUSED BY THE COLLAPSE OF THE INJECTOR COIL

DRIVER TRANSISTOR TURNS ON, PULLING THE INJECTOR PINTLE AWAY FROM ITS SEAT, STARTING FUEL FLOW

BATTERY VOLTAGE (SOURCE VOLTAGE SUPPLIED TO INJECTOR)

DRIVER TRANSISTOR TURNS OFF, ENDING FUEL FLOW

INJECTOR ON-TIME

**FIGURE 23–18** The injector on-time is called the pulse width. *(Courtesy of Fluke Corporation)*

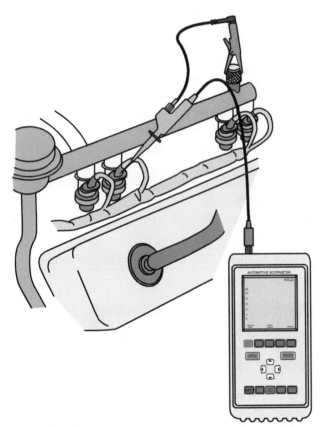

**FIGURE 23–17** A digital storage oscilloscope can be easily connected to an injector by carefully back probing the electrical connector.

Record the highest voltage drop observed on the meter display during the test. Repeat the voltage-drop test for all of the injectors. The voltage drop across each injector should be within 0.1 volt of each other. If an injector has a higher-than-normal voltage drop, the injector windings have higher-than-normal resistance.

## SCOPE-TESTING FUEL INJECTORS

A scope (analog or digital storage) can be connected into each injector circuit. There are three types of injector drive circuits, and each type of circuit has its own characteristic pattern. ● **SEE FIGURE 23–17** for an example of how to connect a scope to read a fuel-injector waveform.

**SATURATED SWITCH TYPE** In a saturated switch-type injector-driven circuit, voltage (usually a full 12 volts) is applied to the injector. The ground for the injector is provided by the vehicle computer. When the ground connection is completed, current flows through the injector windings. Because of the resistance and inductive reactance of the coil itself, it requires a fraction of a second (about 3 ms, or 0.003 second) for the coil to reach **saturation,** or maximum current flow. Most saturated switch-type fuel injectors have 12 to 16 ohms of resistance. This resistance, as well as the computer switching circuit, control and limit the current flow through the injector. A voltage spike occurs when the computer shuts off (opens the injector ground-side circuit) the injectors. ● **SEE FIGURE 23–18.**

**PEAK-AND-HOLD TYPE** A **peak-and-hold** type is typically used for TBI and some port low-resistance injectors. Full battery voltage is applied to the injector, and the ground side is controlled through the computer. The computer provides a high initial current flow (about 4 amperes) to flow through the injector windings to open the injector core. Then the computer reduces the current to a lower level (about 1 ampere). The hold current

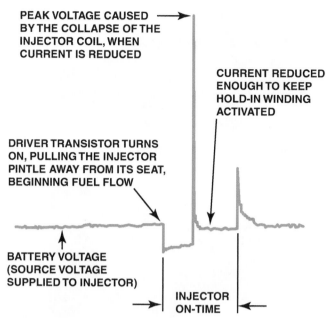

PEAK VOLTAGE CAUSED BY THE COLLAPSE OF THE INJECTOR COIL, WHEN CURRENT IS REDUCED

CURRENT REDUCED ENOUGH TO KEEP HOLD-IN WINDING ACTIVATED

DRIVER TRANSISTOR TURNS ON, PULLING THE INJECTOR PINTLE AWAY FROM ITS SEAT, BEGINNING FUEL FLOW

BATTERY VOLTAGE (SOURCE VOLTAGE SUPPLIED TO INJECTOR)

INJECTOR ON-TIME

**FIGURE 23–19** A typical peak-and-hold fuel-injector waveform. Most fuel injectors that measure less than 6 ohms will usually display a similar waveform.

**FIGURE 23–20** A set of six reconditioned injectors. The sixth injector is barely visible at the far right.

is enough to keep the injector open yet conserves energy and reduces the heat buildup that would occur if the full current flow remains on as long as the injector is commanded on. Typical peak-and-hold-type injector resistance ranges from 2 to 4 ohms.

The scope pattern of a typical peak-and-hold-type injector shows the initial closing of the ground circuit, then a voltage spike as the current flow is reduced. Another voltage spike occurs when the lower level current is turned off (opened) by the computer. ● **SEE FIGURE 23–19.**

**PULSE-WIDTH MODULATED TYPE** A pulse-width modulated type of injector drive circuit uses lower-resistance coil injectors. Battery voltage is available at the positive terminal of the injector and the computer provides a variable-duration connection to ground on the negative side of the injector.

**?** FREQUENTLY ASKED QUESTION

**If Three of Six Injectors Are Defective, Should I Also Replace the Other Three?**

This is a good question. Many service technicians "recommend" that the three good injectors also be replaced along with the other three that tested as being defective. The reasons given by these technicians include the following:

- All six injectors have been operating under the same fuel, engine, and weather conditions.
- The labor required to replace all six is just about the same as replacing only the three defective injectors.
- Replacing all six at the same time helps ensure that all of the injectors are flowing the same amount of fuel so that the engine is operating most efficiently.

With these ideas in mind, the customer should be informed and offered the choice. Complete sets of injectors such as those in ● **FIGURE 23–20** can be purchased at a reasonable cost.

The computer can vary the time intervals that the injector is grounded for very precise fuel control.

Each time the injector circuit is turned off (ground circuit opened), a small voltage spike occurs. It is normal to see multiple voltage spikes on a scope connected to a pulse-width modulated type of fuel injector.

## IDLE AIR SPEED CONTROL DIAGNOSIS

On an engine equipped with fuel injection (TBI or port injection), the idle speed is controlled by increasing or decreasing the amount of air bypassing the throttle plate. Again, an electronic stepper motor or pulse-width modulated solenoid is used to maintain the correct idle speed. This control is often called the **idle air control (IAC)**. ● **SEE FIGURES 23–21 THROUGH 23–23.**

When the engine stops, most IAC units will retract outward to get ready for the next engine start. When the engine starts, the engine speed is high to provide for proper operation when the engine is cold. Then, as the engine gets warmer, the computer reduces engine idle speed gradually by reducing the number of counts or steps commanded by the IAC.

When the engine is warm and restarted, the idle speed should momentarily increase, then decrease to normal idle speed. This increase and then decrease in engine speed is often called an engine flare. If the engine speed does not flare, then the IAC may not be working (it may be stuck in one position).

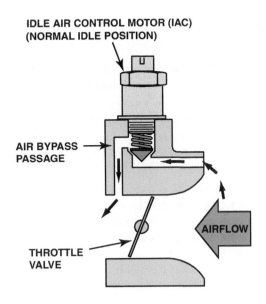

IDLE AIR CONTROL MOTOR (IAC)
(NORMAL IDLE POSITION)

AIR BYPASS
PASSAGE

AIRFLOW

THROTTLE
VALVE

(FULLY EXTENDED POSITION)

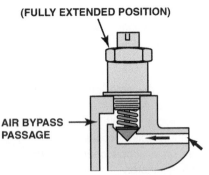

AIR BYPASS
PASSAGE

**FIGURE 23–21** An idle air control (IAC) controls idle speed by controlling the amount of air that passes around the throttle plate. More airflow results in a higher idle speed.

**FIGURE 23–22** A typical idle air control (IAC).

**FIGURE 23–23** Some idle air control (IAC) units are purchased with the housing as shown. Carbon buildup in these passages can cause a rough or unstable idling or stalling.

🚗 **REAL WORLD FIX**

**There Is No Substitute for a Thorough Visual Inspection**

An intermittent "check engine" light and a random-misfire diagnostic trouble code (DTC) P0300 was being diagnosed. A scan tool did not provide any help because all systems seemed to be functioning normally. Finally, the technician removed the engine cover and discovered a mouse nest. ● **SEE FIGURE 23–24.**

## FUEL-INJECTION SERVICE

After many years of fuel-injection service, some service technicians still misunderstand the process of proper fuel-system handling. Much has been said over the years with regard to when and how to perform injector cleaning. Some manufacturers have suggested methods of cleaning, while others have issued bulletins to prohibit any cleaning at all.

All engines using fuel injection do require some type of fuel-system maintenance. Normal wear and tear with today's underhood temperatures and changes in gasoline quality contribute to the buildup of olefin wax, dirt, water, and many other additives. Unique to each engine is an air-control design that also may contribute different levels of carbon deposits, such as oil control.

Fuel-injection system service should include the following operations:

1. **Check fuel-pump operating pressure and volume.** The missing link here is volume. Most working technicians assume that if the pressure is correct, the volume is also okay. Hook up a fuel-pressure tester to the fuel rail inlet to quickly test the fuel pressure with the engine running. At the same time, test the volume of the pump by sending fuel into the holding tank. (One ounce per second is the usual specification.) ● **SEE FIGURE 23–25.** A two-line system tester is the recommended procedure to use and is attached to the fuel inlet and the return on the fuel rail. The vehicle onboard system is looped and returns fuel to the tank.

2. **Test the fuel-pressure regulator for operation and leakage.** At this time, the fuel-pressure regulator would be tested for operational pressure and proper regulation, including leakage. (This works well, as the operator has total control of rail pressure with a unit control valve.) Below are some points to ponder:

   ■ Good pressure does not mean proper volume. For example, a clogged filter may test okay on pressure, but the restriction may not allow proper volume under load. ● **SEE FIGURE 23–26.**

(a)

(b)

**FIGURE 23–24** (a) Nothing looks unusual when the hood is first opened. (b) When the cover is removed from the top of the engine, a mouse or some other animal nest is visible. The animal had already eaten through a couple of injector wires. At least the cause of the intermittent misfire was discovered.

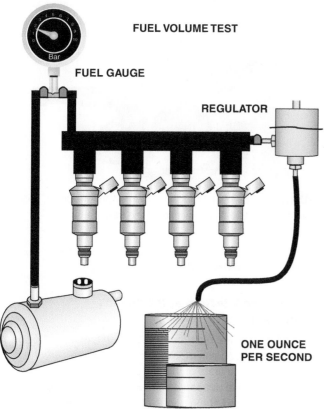

**FIGURE 23–25** Checking fuel-pump volume using a hose from the outlet of the fuel-pressure regulator into a calibrated container.

- It is a good idea to use the vehicle's own gasoline to service the system versus a can of shop gasoline that has been sitting around for some time.
- Pressure regulators do fail, and a lot more do not properly shut off fuel, causing higher-than-normal pump wear and shorter service life.

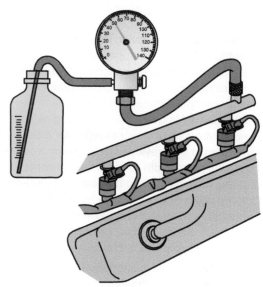

**FIGURE 23–26** Testing fuel-pump volume using a fuel-pressure gauge with a bleed hose inserted into a suitable container. The engine is running during this test.

3. **Flush the entire fuel rail and upper fuel-injector screens, including the fuel-pressure regulator.** Raise the input pressure to a point above regulator setting to allow a constant flow of fuel through the inlet pressure side of the system, through the fuel rail, and out the open fuel-pressure regulator. In most cases the applied pressure is 75 to 90 PSI (517 to 620 kPa) but will be maintained by the presence of a regulator. At this point, cleaning chemical is added to the fuel at a 5:1 mixture and allowed to flow through the system for 15 to 30 minutes. ● **SEE FIGURE 23–27.** Results are best on a hot engine with the fuel supply looped and the engine not running. Below are some points to ponder:
   - This flush is the fix most vehicles need first. The difference is that the deposits are removed to a remote tank

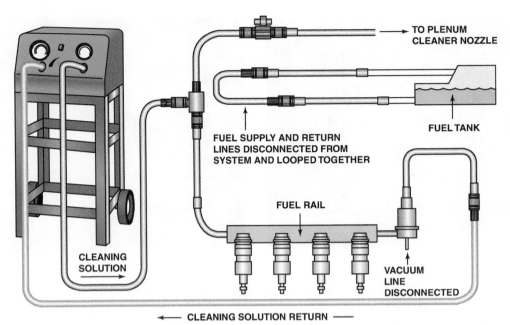

**FIGURE 23–27** A typical two-line cleaning machine hookup, showing an extension hose that can be used to squirt a cleaning solution into the throttle body while the engine is running on the cleaning solution and gasoline mixture.

and filter versus attempting to soften the deposits and blow them through the upper screens.

- Most injectors use a 10-micron final filter screen. A 25% restriction in the upper screen would increase the injector on-time approximately 25%.
- **Clean the fuel injectors.** Start the engine and adjust the output pressure closer to regulator pressure or lower than in the previous steps. Lower pressure will cause the pulse width to open up somewhat longer and allow the injectors to be cleaned. Slow speed (idle) position will take a longer time frame, and operating temperature will be reached. Clean injectors are the objective, but the chemical should also decarbon the engine valves, pistons, and oxygen sensor.

4. **Decarbon the engine assembly.** On most vehicles, the injector spray will help the decarboning process. On others, you may need to enhance the operation with external addition of a mixture through the PCV hose, throttle plates, or IACs.

5. **Clean the throttle plate and IAC passages.** Doing this service alone on most late-model engines will show a manifold vacuum increase of up to 2 in. Hg. Stop the engine and clean the areas as needed, then use a handheld fuel injector connected in parallel with the pressure hose, along with a pulser to allow cleaning of the throttle plates with the same chemical as injectors are running on. ● **SEE FIGURE 23–28.** This works well, as air is drawn into IAC passages on a running engine and will clean the passages without IAC removal.

6. **Relearn the onboard computer.** Some vehicles may have been running in such a poor state of operation that the onboard computer may need to be relearned. Consult service information for the suggested relearn procedures for each particular vehicle.

**FIGURE 23–28** To thoroughly clean a throttle body, it is sometimes best to remove it from the vehicle.

🔧 **TECH TIP**

**Check the Injectors at the "Bends and the Ends"**

Injectors that are most likely to become restricted because of clogging of the filter basket screen are the injectors at the ends of the rail, especially on returnless systems where dirt can accumulate. Also, the injectors that are located at the bends of the fuel rail are subject to possible clogging because of the dirt being deposited where the fuel makes a turn in the rail.

This service usually takes approximately one hour for the vehicle to run out of fuel and the entire service to be performed. The good thing is that the technician may do other services while this is being performed. Some technicians may install a set of plugs or change the fuel filter while the engine is flushing. This service should restore the fuel system to original operations.

**Be Sure to Clean the Fuel Rail**

Whenever you service the fuel injectors or if you suspect that there may be a fuel-injector problem, remove the entire fuel rail assembly and check the passages for contamination. Always thoroughly clean the rail when replacing fuel injectors.

All of the previously listed steps may be performed using a *two-line* fuel-injector service unit, such as Carbon Clean, Auto Care, Injector Test, DeCarbon, or Motor-Vac.

| Fuel-Injection Symptom Chart | |
|---|---|
| **Symptom** | **Possible Causes** |
| **Hard cold starts** | • Low fuel pressure |
| | • Leaking fuel injectors |
| | • Contaminated fuel |
| | • Low-volatility fuel |
| | • Dirty throttle plate |
| **Garage stalls** | • Low fuel pressure |
| | • Insufficient fuel volume |
| | • Restricted fuel injector |
| | • Contaminated fuel |
| | • Low-volatility fuel |
| **Poor cold performance** | • Low fuel pressure |
| | • Insufficient fuel volume |
| | • Contaminated fuel |
| | • Low-volatility fuel |
| **Tip-in hesitation** (hesitation just as the accelerator pedal is depressed) | • Low fuel pressure |
| | • Insufficient fuel volume |
| | • Intake valve deposits |
| | • Contaminated fuel |
| | • Low-volatility fuel |

# FUEL-SYSTEM SCAN TOOL DIAGNOSTICS

Diagnosing a faulty fuel system can be a difficult task. However, it can be made easier by utilizing the information available via the serial data stream. By observing the long-term fuel trim and the short-term fuel trim, we can determine how the fuel system is performing. Short-term fuel trim and long-term fuel trim can help us to zero in on specific areas of trouble. Readings should be taken at idle and at 3,000 RPM. Use the following chart as a guide:

| Condition | Long-Term Fuel Trim at Idle | Long-Term Fuel Trim at 3,000 RPM |
|---|---|---|
| **System normal** | 0% ± 10% | 0% ± 10% |
| **Vacuum leak** | HIGH | OK |
| **Fuel flow problem** | OK | HIGH |
| **Low fuel pressure** | HIGH | HIGH |
| **High fuel pressure** | *OK or LOW | *OK or LOW |

*High fuel pressure will affect trim at idle, at 3,000 RPM, or both.

**1** The tools needed to diagnose a circuit containing a relay include a digital multimeter (DMM), a fused jumper wire, and an assortment of wiring terminals.

**2** Start the diagnosis by locating the relay center. It is under the hood on this General Motors vehicle, so access is easy. Not all vehicles are this easy.

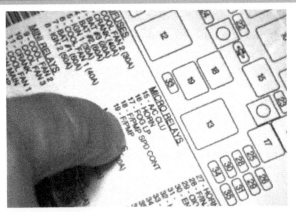

**3** The chart under the cover for the relay center indicates the location of the relay that controls the electric fuel pump.

**4** Locate the fuel-pump relay and remove by using a puller if necessary. Try to avoid rocking or twisting the relay to prevent causing damage to the relay terminals or the relay itself.

**5** Terminals 85 and 86 represent the coil inside the relay. Terminal 30 is the power terminal, 87a is the normally closed contact, and 87 is the normally open contact.

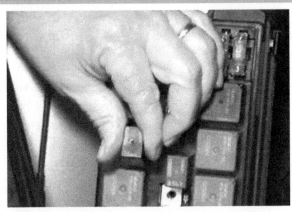

**6** The terminals are also labeled on most relays.

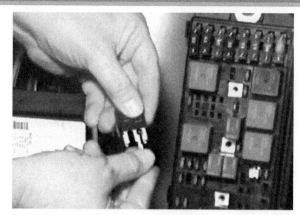

**7** To help make good electrical contact with the terminals without doing any harm, select the proper-size terminal from the terminal assortment.

**8** Insert the terminals into the relay socket in 30 and 87.

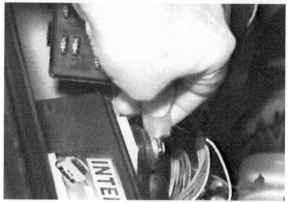

**9** To check for voltage at terminal 30, use a test light or a voltmeter. Start by connecting the alligator clip of the test light to the positive (+) terminal of the battery.

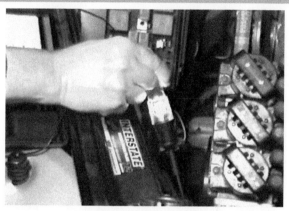

**10** Touch the test light to the negative (−) terminal of the battery or a good engine ground to check the test light.

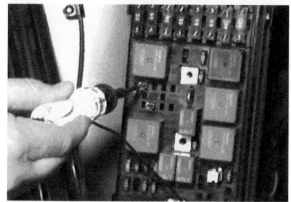

**11** Use the test light to check for voltage at terminal 30 of the relay. The ignition may have to be in the on (run) position.

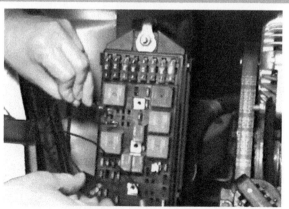

**12** To check to see if the electric fuel pump can be operated from the relay contacts, use a fused jumper wire and touch the relay contacts that correspond to terminals 30 and 87 of the relay.

CONTINUED ▶

# FUEL-PUMP RELAY CIRCUIT DIAGNOSIS (CONTINUED)

**13** Connect the leads of the meter to contacts 30 and 87 of the relay socket. The reading of 4.7 amperes is okay because the specification is 4 to 8 amperes.

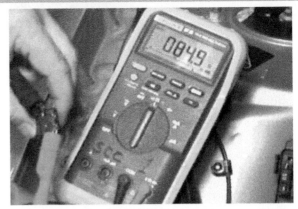

**14** Set the meter to read ohms (Ω) and measure the resistance of the relay coil. The usual reading for most relays is between 60 and 100 ohms.

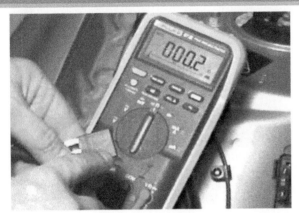

**15** Measure between terminal 30 and 87a. Terminal 87a is the normally closed contact, and there should be little, if any, resistance between these two terminals, as shown.

**16** To test the normally open contacts, connect one meter lead to terminal 30 and the other lead to terminal 87. The ohmmeter should show an open circuit by displaying OL.

**17** Connect a fused jumper wire to supply 12 volts to terminal 86 and a ground to terminal 85 of the relay. If the relay clicks, then the relay coil is able to move the armature (movable arm) of the relay.

**18** After testing, be sure to reinstall the relay and the relay cover.

**1** Start the fuel-injector cleaning process by bringing the vehicle's engine up to operating temperature. Shut off the engine, remove the cap from the fuel rail test port, and install the appropriate adapter.

**2** The vehicle's fuel pump is disabled by removing its relay or fuse. In some cases, it may be necessary to disconnect the fuel pump at the tank if the relay or fuse powers more than just the pump.

**3** Turn the outlet valve of the canister to the OFF or CLOSED position.

**4** Remove the fuel-injector cleaning canister's top and regulator assembly. Note that there is an O-ring seal located here that must be in place for the canister's top to seal properly.

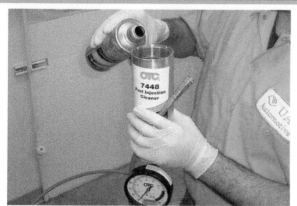

**5** Pour the injection system cleaning fluid into the open canister. Rubber gloves are highly recommended for this step as the fluid is toxic.

**6** Replace the canister's top (making sure it is tight) and connect its hose to the fuel rail adapter. Be sure that the hose is routed away from exhaust manifolds and other hazards.

CONTINUED ▶

# FUEL-INJECTOR CLEANING (CONTINUED)

**7** Hang the canister from the vehicle's hood and adjust the air pressure regulator to full OPEN position (CCW).

**8** Connect shop air to the canister and adjust the air pressure regulator to the desired setting. Canister pressure can be read directly from the gauge.

**9** Canister pressure should be adjusted to 5 PSI below system fuel pressure. An alternative for return-type systems is to block the fuel return line to the tank.

**10** Open the outlet valve on the canister.

**11** Start the vehicle's engine and let run at 1,000 to 1,500 RPM. The engine is now running on fuel-injector cleaning fluid provided by the canister.

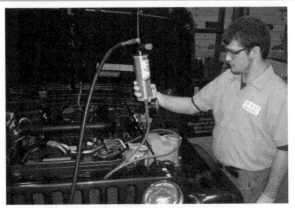

**12** Continue the process until the canister is empty and the engine stalls. Remove the cleaning equipment, enable the vehicle's fuel pump, and run the engine to check for leaks.

1. A typical throttle-body fuel injector uses a computer-controlled injector solenoid to spray fuel into the throttle-body unit above the throttle plates.

2. A typical port fuel-injection system uses an individual fuel injector for each cylinder and squirts fuel directly into the intake manifold about 3 inches (80 mm) from the intake valve.

3. A typical fuel-injection system fuel pressure should not drop more than 20 PSI in 20 minutes.

4. A noid light can be used to check for the presence of an injector pulse.

5. Injectors can be tested for resistance and should be within 0.3 to 0.4 ohm of each other.

6. Different designs of injectors have a different scope waveform depending on how the computer pulses the injector on and off.

7. An idle air control unit controls idle speed and can be tested for proper operation using a scan tool or scope.

## REVIEW QUESTIONS

1. List the ways fuel injectors can be tested.
2. List the steps necessary to test a fuel-pressure regulator.
3. Describe why it may be necessary to clean the throttle plate of a port fuel-injected engine.

## CHAPTER QUIZ

1. Most port fuel-injected engines operate on how much fuel pressure?
   a. 3 to 5 PSI (21 to 35 kPa)
   b. 9 to 13 PSI (62 to 90 kPa)
   c. 35 to 45 PSI (240 to 310 kPa)
   d. 55 to 65 PSI (380 to 450 kPa)

2. Fuel injectors can be tested using _____.
   a. An ohmmeter
   b. A stethoscope
   c. A scope
   d. All of the above

3. Throttle-body fuel-injection systems use what type of injector driver?
   a. Peak and hold
   b. Saturated switch
   c. Pulse-width modulated
   d. Pulsed

4. Port fuel-injection systems generally use what type of injector driver?
   a. Peak and hold
   b. Saturated switch
   c. Pulse-width modulated
   d. Pulsed

5. The vacuum hose from the fuel-pressure regulator was removed from the regulator and gasoline dripped out of the hose. Technician A says that is normal and that everything is okay. Technician B says that one or more of the injectors may be defective, causing the fuel to get into the hose. Which technician is correct?
   a. Technician A only
   b. Technician B only
   c. Both Technicians A and B
   d. Neither Technician A nor B

6. The fuel pressure drops rapidly when the engine is turned off. Technician A says that one or more injectors could be leaking. Technician B says that a defective check valve in the fuel pump could be the cause. Which technician is correct?
   a. Technician A only
   b. Technician B only
   c. Both Technicians A and B
   d. Neither Technician A nor B

7. In a typical port fuel-injection system, which injectors are most subject to becoming restricted?
   a. Any of them equally
   b. The injectors at the end of the rail on a returnless system
   c. The injectors at the bends in the rail
   d. Either b or c

8. What component pulses the fuel injector on most vehicles?
   a. Electronic control unit (computer)
   b. Ignition module
   c. Crankshaft sensor
   d. Both b and c

9. Fuel-injection service is being discussed. Technician A says that the throttle plate(s) should be cleaned. Technician B says that the fuel rail should be cleaned. Which technician is correct?
   a. Technician A only
   b. Technician B only
   c. Both Technicians A and B
   d. Neither Technician A nor B

10. If the throttle plate needs to be cleaned, what symptoms will be present regarding the operation of the engine?
    a. Stalls
    b. Rough idle
    c. Hesitation on acceleration
    d. All of the above

# chapter 24

# VEHICLE EMISSION STANDARDS AND TESTING

**OBJECTIVES:** **After studying Chapter 24, the reader should be able to:** • Prepare for ASE Engine Performance (A8) certification test content area "D" (Emissions Control Systems Diagnosis and Repair) and ASE L1 certification test content area "F" (I/M Failure Diagnosis). • Discuss emission standards. • Identify the reasons why excessive amounts of HC, CO, and $NO_x$ exhaust emissions are created. • Describe how to baseline a vehicle after an exhaust emission failure. • List acceptable levels of HC, CO, $CO_2$, and $O_2$ with and without a catalytic converter. • List four possible causes for high readings for HC, CO, and $NO_x$.

**KEY TERMS:** Acceleration simulation mode (ASM) 309 • ASM 25/25 test 309 • ASM 50/15 test 309 • Clean Air Act Amendments (CAAA) 306 • Federal Test Procedure (FTP) 308 • I/M 240 test 310 • Lean indicator 313 • Non-methane hydrocarbon (NMHC) 311 • Ozone 313 • Rich indicator 312 • Sealed Housing for Evaporative Determination (SHED) test 308 • Smog 313 • State Implementation Plan (SIP) 308

## EMISSION STANDARDS IN THE UNITED STATES

In the United States, emissions standards are managed by the Environmental Protection Agency (EPA) as well as some U.S. state governments. Some of the strictest standards in the world are formulated in California by the California Air Resources Board (CARB).

**TIER 1 AND TIER 2** Federal emission standards are set by the **Clean Air Amendments (CAAA)** of 1990 grouped by tier. All vehicles sold in the United States must meet Tier 1 standards that went into effect in 1994 and are the least stringent. Additional Tier 2 standards have been optional since 2001 and was fully phased in by 2009. The current Tier 1 standards are different between automobiles and light trucks (SUVs, pickup trucks, and minivans), but Tier 2 standards will be the same for both types of vehicles.

There are several ratings that can be given to vehicles, and a certain percentage of a manufacturer's vehicles must meet different levels in order for the company to sell its products in affected regions. Beyond Tier 1, and in order by stringency, are the following levels:

- **TLEV Transitional Low-Emission Vehicle.** More stringent for HC than Tier 1.
- **LEV** (also known as **LEV I**): **Low-Emission Vehicle,** an intermediate California standard about twice as stringent as Tier 1 for HC and $NO_x$.

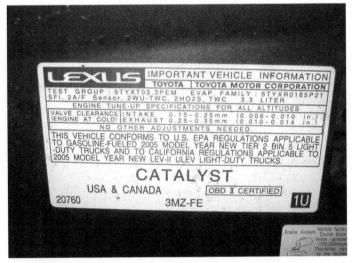

**FIGURE 24–1** The underhood decal showing that this Lexus RX-330 meets both national (Tier 2; BIN 5) and California LEV-II (ULEV) regulation standards.

- **ULEV** (also known as **ULEV I**): **Ultra-Low-Emission Vehicle.** A stronger California standard emphasizing very low HC emissions.
- **ULEV II: Ultra-Low-Emission Vehicle.** A cleaner-than-average vehicle certified under the Phase II LEV standard. Hydrocarbon and carbon monoxide emissions levels are nearly 50% lower than those of a LEV II-certified vehicle. ● SEE FIGURE 24–1.
- **SULEV: Super-Ultra-Low-Emission Vehicle.** A California standard even tighter than ULEV, including much

lower HC and NO$_x$ emissions; roughly equivalent to Tier 2 Bin 2 vehicles.

- **ZEV: Zero-Emission Vehicle.** A California standard prohibiting any tailpipe emissions. The ZEV category is largely restricted to electric vehicles and hydrogen-fueled vehicles. In these cases, any emissions that are created are produced at another site, such as a power plant or hydrogen reforming center, unless such sites run on renewable energy.

  **NOTE: A battery-powered electric vehicle charged from the power grid will still be up to 10 times cleaner than even the cleanest gasoline vehicles over their respective lifetimes.**

- **PZEV: Partial Zero-Emission Vehicle.** Compliant with the SULEV standard; additionally has near-zero evaporative emissions and a 15 year/150,000 mile warranty on its emission control equipment.

  Tier 2 standards are even more stringent. Tier 2 variations are appended with "II," such as LEV II or SULEV II. Other categories have also been created:

  - **ILEV: Inherently Low-Emission Vehicle-** a vehicle certified to meet the transitional low-emission vehicle standards established by the California Air Resources Board (CARB).

  - **AT-PZEV: Advanced Technology Partial Zero-Emission Vehicle.** If a vehicle meets the PZEV standards and is using high-technology features, such as an electric motor or high-pressure gaseous fuel tanks for compressed natural gas, it qualifies as an AT-PZEV. Hybrid electric vehicles such as the Toyota Prius can qualify, as can internal combustion engine vehicles that run on natural gas (CNG), such as the Honda Civic GX. These vehicles are classified as "partial" ZEV because they receive partial credit for the number of ZEV vehicles that automakers would otherwise be required to sell in California.

  - **NLEV: National Low-Emission Vehicle.** All vehicles nationwide must meet this standard, which started in 2001.

**FEDERAL EPA BIN NUMBER** The higher the tier number, the newer the regulation; the lower the bin number, the cleaner the vehicle. The Toyota Prius is a very clean Bin 3, while the Hummer H2 is a dirty Bin 11. ● **SEE CHARTS 24-1 THROUGH 24-3.**

**SMOG EMISSION INFORMATION** New vehicles are equipped with a sticker that shows the relative level of smog-causing emissions created by the vehicle compared to others on the market. Smog-causing emissions include unburned hydrocarbons (HC) and oxides of nitrogen (NO$_x$). ● **SEE FIGURE 24-2.**

**CALIFORNIA STANDARDS** The pre-2004 California Air Resources Board (CARB) standards as a whole were known as LEV I. Within that, there were four possible ratings: Tier 1, TLEV, LEV, and ULEV. The newest CARB rating system (since January 1, 2004) is known as LEV II. Within that rating system there are three primary ratings: LEV, ULEV, and SULEV. States other than California are given the option to use the federal EPA standards, or they can adopt California's standards.

| CERTIFICATION LEVEL | NMOG (G/MI) | CO (G/MI) | NO$_x$ (G/MI) |
|---|---|---|---|
| Bin 1 | 0.0 | 0.0 | 0.0 |
| Bin 2 | 0.010 | 2.1 | 0.02 |
| Bin 3 | 0.055 | 2.1 | 0.03 |
| Bin 4 | 0.070 | 2.1 | 0.04 |
| Bin 5 | 0.090 | 4.2 | 0.07 |
| Bin 6 | 0.090 | 4.2 | 0.10 |
| Bin 7 | 0.090 | 4.2 | 0.15 |
| Bin 8a | 0.125 | 4.2 | 0.20 |
| Bin 8b | 0.156 | 4.2 | 0.20 |
| Bin 9a | 0.090 | 4.2 | 0.30 |
| Bin 9b | 0.130 | 4.2 | 0.30 |
| Bin 9c | 0.180 | 4.2 | 0.30 |
| Bin 10a | 0.156 | 4.2 | 0.60 |
| Bin 10b | 0.230 | 6.4 | 0.60 |
| Bin 10c | 0.230 | 6.4 | 0.60 |
| Bin 11 | 0.230 | 7.3 | 0.90 |

**CHART 24-1**

EPA Tier 2—120,000-Mile Tailpipe Emission Limits. After January 2007, the highest allowable bin is 8. NMOG stands for non-methane organic gases which is a measure of all gases except those often created naturally by animals.
*Source:* Data compiled from the Environmental Protection Agency (EPA).

NOTE: The bin number is determined by the type and weight of the vehicle.

| U.S. EPA VEHICLE INFORMATION PROGRAM (THE HIGHER THE SCORE, THE LOWER THE EMISSIONS) | |
|---|---|
| **SELECTED EMISSIONS STANDARDS** | **SCORE** |
| Bin 1 and ZEV | 10 |
| PZEV | 9.5 |
| Bin 2 | 9 |
| Bin 3 | 8 |
| Bin 4 | 7 |
| Bin 5 and LEV II cars | 6 |
| Bin 6 | 5 |
| Bin 7 | 4 |
| Bin 8 | 3 |
| Bin 9a and LEV I cars | 2 |
| Bin 9b | 2 |
| Bin 10a | 1 |
| Bin 10b and Tier 1 cars | 1 |
| Bin 11 | 0 |

**CHART 24-2**

Air Pollution Score
*Source:* Courtesy of the Environmental Protection Agency (EPA).

| MINIMUM FUEL ECONOMY (MPG) COMBINED CITY-HIGHWAY LABEL VALUE | | | | | |
|---|---|---|---|---|---|
| SCORE | GASOLINE | DIESEL | E-85 | LPG | CNG* |
| 10 | 44 | 50 | 31 | 28 | 33 |
| 9 | 36 | 41 | 26 | 23 | 27 |
| 8 | 30 | 35 | 22 | 20 | 23 |
| 7 | 26 | 30 | 19 | 17 | 20 |
| 6 | 23 | 27 | 17 | 15 | 18 |
| 5 | 21 | 24 | 15 | 14 | 16 |
| 4 | 19 | 22 | 14 | 12 | 14 |
| 3 | 17 | 20 | 12 | 11 | 13 |
| 2 | 16 | 18 | — | — | 12 |
| 1 | 15 | 17 | 11 | 10 | 11 |
| 0 | 14 | 16 | 10 | 9 | 10 |

**CHART 24–3**

Greenhouse Gas Score
*Source:* Courtesy of the Environmental Protection Agency (EPA).
*CNG assumes a gallon equivalent of 121.5 cubic feet.

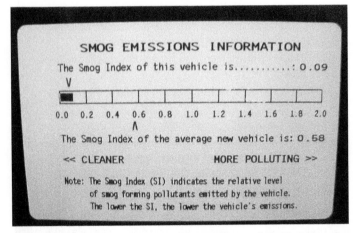

**FIGURE 24–2** This label on a Toyota Camry hybrid shows the relative smog-producing emissions, but this does not include carbon dioxide ($CO_2$), which may increase global warming.

## EUROPEAN STANDARDS

Europe has its own set of standards that vehicles must meet, which includes the following tiers:

- Euro I (1992–1995)
- Euro II (1995–1999)
- Euro III (1999–2005)
- Euro IV (2005–2008)
- Euro V (2008+)

Vehicle emission standards and technological advancements have successfully reduced pollution from cars and trucks

by about 90% since the 1970s. Unfortunately, there currently are more vehicles on the road, and they are being driven more miles each year, partially offsetting the environmental benefits of individual vehicle emissions reductions.

## EXHAUST ANALYSIS TESTING

The Clean Air Act Amendments require enhanced Inspection and Maintenance (I/M) programs in areas of the country that have the worst air quality and the Northeast Ozone Transport region. The states must submit to the EPA a **State Implementation Plan (SIP)** for their programs. Each enhanced I/M program is required to include as a minimum the following items:

- Computerized emission analyzers
- Visual inspection of emission control items
- Minimum waiver limit (to be increased based on the inflation index)
- Remote on-road testing of one-half of 1% of the vehicle population
- Registration denial for vehicles not passing an I/M test
- Denial of waiver for vehicles that are under warranty or that have been tampered with
- Annual inspections
- OBD-II systems check for 1996 and newer vehicles

**FEDERAL TEST PROCEDURE (FTP)** The **Federal Test Procedure (FTP)** is the test used to certify all new vehicles before they can be sold. Once a vehicle meets these standards, it is certified by the EPA for sale in the United States. The FTP test procedure is a loaded-mode test lasting for a total duration of 505 seconds and is designed to simulate an urban driving trip. A cold start-up representing a morning start and a hot start after a soak period is part of the test. In addition to this drive cycle, a vehicle must undergo evaporative testing. Evaporative emissions are determined using the **Sealed Housing for Evaporative Determination (SHED)** test, which measures the evaporative emissions from the vehicle after a heat-up period representing a vehicle sitting in the sun. In addition, the vehicle is driven and then tested during the hot soak period.

**NOTE: A SHED is constructed entirely of stainless steel. The walls, floors, and ceiling, plus the door, are all constructed of stainless steel because it does not absorb hydrocarbons, which could offset test results.**

The FTP is a much more stringent test of vehicle emissions than is any test type that uses equipment that measures percentages of exhaust gases. The federal emission standards for each model year vehicle are the same for that model regardless of what size engine the vehicle is equipped with. This is why larger V-8 engines often are equipped with more emission control devices than smaller 4- and 6-cylinder engines.

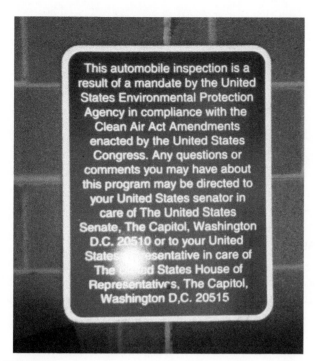

FIGURE 24–3 Photo of a sign taken at an emissions test facility.

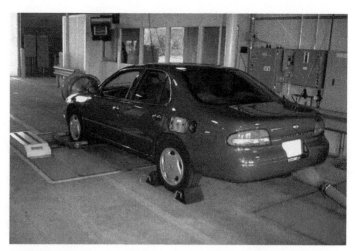

FIGURE 24–4 A vehicle being tested during an enhanced emission test.

**I/M TEST PROGRAMS** There are a variety of I/M testing programs that have been implemented by the various states. These programs may be centralized testing programs or decentralized testing programs. Each state is free to develop a testing program suitable to their needs as long as they can demonstrate to the EPA that their plan will achieve the attainment levels set by the EPA. This approach has led to a variety of different testing programs. ● **SEE FIGURE 24–3.**

**VISUAL TAMPERING CHECKS** Visual tampering checks may be part of an I/M testing program and usually include checking for the following items:

- Catalytic converter
- Fuel tank inlet restrictor
- Exhaust gas recirculation (EGR)
- Evaporative emission system
- Air-injection reaction system (AIR)
- Positive crankcase ventilation (PCV)

If any of these systems are missing, not connected, or tampered with, the vehicle will fail the emissions test and will have to be repaired/replaced by the vehicle owner before the vehicle can pass the emission test. Any cost associated with repairing or replacing these components may not be used toward the waiver amount required for the vehicle to receive a waiver.

**ONE-SPEED AND TWO-SPEED IDLE TEST** The one-speed and two-speed idle test measures the exhaust emissions from the tailpipe of the vehicle at idle and/or at 2,500 RPM. This uses stand-alone exhaust gas sampling equipment that measures the emissions in percentages. Each state chooses the standards that the vehicle has to meet in order to pass the test. The advantage to using this type of testing is that the equipment is relatively cheap and allows states to have decentralized testing programs because many facilities can afford the necessary equipment required to perform this test.

**LOADED-MODE TEST** The loaded-mode test uses a dynamometer that places a "single weight" load on the vehicle. The load applied to the vehicle varies with the speed of the vehicle. Typically, a 4-cylinder vehicle speed would be 24 mph, a 6-cylinder vehicle speed would be 30 mph, and an 8-cylinder vehicle speed would be 34 mph. Conventional stand-alone sampling equipment is used to measure HC and CO emissions. This type of test is classified as a Basic I/M test by the EPA. ● **SEE FIGURE 24–4.**

**ACCELERATION SIMULATION MODE (ASM)** The **ASM-type** of test uses a dynamometer that applies a heavy load on the vehicle at a steady-state speed. The load applied to the vehicle is based on the acceleration rate on the second simulated hill of the FTP. This acceleration rate is 3.3 mph/sec/sec (read as 3.3 mph per second per second, which is the unit of acceleration). There are different ASM tests used by different states.

The **ASM 50/15** test places a load of 50% on the vehicle at a steady 15 mph. This load represents 50% of the horsepower required to simulate the FTP acceleration rate of 3.3 mph/sec. This type of test produces relatively high levels of $NO_x$ emissions; therefore, it is useful in detecting vehicles that are emitting excessive $NO_x$.

The **ASM 25/25** test places a 25% load on the vehicle while it is driven at a steady 25 mph. This represents 25% of the load required to simulate the FTP acceleration rate of 3.3 mph/sec. Because this applies a smaller load on the vehicle at a higher speed, it will produce a higher level of HC and CO emissions than the ASM 50/15. $NO_x$ emissions will tend to be lower with this type of test.

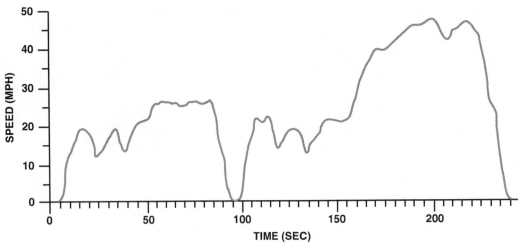

**FIGURE 24–5** Trace showing the Inspection/Maintenance 240 test. The test duplicates an urban test loop around Los Angeles, California. The first "hump" in the curve represents the vehicle being accelerated to about 20 mph, then driving up a small hill to about 30 mph and coming to a stop at 94 seconds. Then, the vehicle accelerates while climbing a hill and speeding up to about 50 mph during this second phase of the test.

**I/M 240 TEST** The **I/M 240** test is the EPA's enhanced test. It is actually a portion of the 505-second FTP test used by the manufacturers to certify their new vehicles. The "240" stands for 240 seconds of drive time on a dynamometer. This is a loaded-mode transient test that uses constant volume sampling equipment to measure the exhaust emissions in mass just as is done during the FTP. The I/M 240 test simulates the first two hills of the FTP drive cycle. ● **FIGURE 24–5** shows the I/M 240 drive trace.

**OBD-II TESTING** In 1999, the EPA requested that states adopt OBD-II systems testing for 1996 and newer vehicles. The OBD-II system is designed to illuminate the MIL and store trouble codes any time a malfunction exists that would cause the vehicle emissions to exceed 1 1/2 times the FTP limits. If the OBD-II system is working correctly, the system should be able to detect a vehicle failure that would cause emissions to increase to an unacceptable level. The EPA has determined that the OBD-II system should detect emission failures of a vehicle even before that vehicle would fail an emissions test of the type that most states are employing. Furthermore, the EPA has determined that, as the population of OBD-II-equipped vehicles increases and the population of older non-OBD-II-equipped vehicles decreases, tailpipe testing will no longer be necessary.

The OBD-II testing program consists of a computer that can scan the vehicle OBD-II system using the DLC connector. The technician first performs a visual check of the vehicle MIL light to determine if it is working correctly. Next, the computer is connected to the vehicle's DLC connector. The computer will scan the vehicle OBD-II system and determine if there are any codes stored that are commanding the MIL light on. In addition, it will scan the status of the readiness monitors and determine if they have all run and passed. If the readiness monitors have all run and passed, it indicates that the OBD-II system has tested all the components of the emission control system. An OBD-II vehicle would fail this OBD-II test if the following occur:

- The MIL light does not come on with the key on, engine off.
- The MIL is commanded on.
- A number (varies by state) of the readiness monitors have not been run.

If none of these conditions are present, the vehicle will pass the emissions test.

**REMOTE SENSING** The EPA requires that, in high-enhanced areas, states perform on-the-road testing of vehicle emissions. The state must sample 0.5% of the vehicle population base in high-enhanced areas. This may be accomplished by using a remote sensing device. This type of sensing may be done through equipment that projects an infrared light through the exhaust stream of a passing vehicle. The reflected beam can then be analyzed to determine the pollutant levels coming from the vehicle. If a vehicle fails this type of test, the vehicle owner will receive notification in the mail that he or she must take the vehicle to a test facility to have the emissions tested.

**RANDOM ROADSIDE TESTING** Some states may implement random roadside testing that would usually involve visual checks of the emission control devices to detect tampering. Obviously, this method is not very popular, as it can lead to traffic tie-ups and delays on the part of commuters.

Exhaust analysis is an excellent tool to use for the diagnosis of engine performance concerns. In areas of the country that require exhaust testing to be able to get license plates, exhaust analysis must be able to do the following:

- Establish a baseline for failure diagnosis and service
- Identify areas of engine performance that are and are not functioning correctly
- Determine that the service and repair of the vehicle have been accomplished and are complete

FIGURE 24–6 A partial stream sampling exhaust probe being used to measure exhaust gases in parts per million (ppm) or percent (%).

**? FREQUENTLY ASKED QUESTION**

**What Does NMHC Mean?**

NMHC means **nonmethane hydrocarbon,** and it is the standard by which exhaust emission testing for hydrocarbons is evaluated. Methane is natural gas and can come from animals, animal waste, and other natural sources. By not measuring methane gas, all background sources are eliminated, giving better results as to the true amount of unburned hydrocarbons that are present in the exhaust stream.

# EXHAUST ANALYSIS AND COMBUSTION EFFICIENCY

A popular method of engine analysis, as well as emission testing, involves the use of five-gas exhaust analysis equipment. ● **SEE FIGURE 24–6.** The five gases analyzed and their significance are discussed next.

**HYDROCARBONS** Hydrocarbons (HC) are unburned gasoline and are measured in parts per million (ppm). A correctly operating engine should burn (oxidize) almost all the gasoline; therefore, very little unburned gasoline should be present in the exhaust. Acceptable levels of HC are 50 ppm or less. High levels of HC could be due to excessive oil consumption caused by weak piston rings or worn valve guides. The most common cause of excessive HC emissions is a fault in the ignition system. Items that should be checked include the following:

- Spark plugs
- Spark plug wires
- Distributor cap and rotor (if the vehicle is so equipped)
- Ignition timing (if possible)
- Ignition coil

**CARBON MONOXIDE** Carbon monoxide (CO) is unstable and will easily combine with any oxygen to form stable carbon dioxide ($CO_2$). The fact that CO combines with oxygen is the reason that CO is a poisonous gas (in the lungs, it combines with oxygen to form $CO_2$ and deprives the brain of oxygen). CO levels of a properly operating engine should be less than 0.5%. High levels of CO can be caused by clogged or restricted crankcase ventilation devices such as the PCV valve, hose(s), and tubes. Other items that might cause excessive CO include the following:

- Clogged air filter
- Incorrect idle speed
- Too-high fuel-pump pressure
- Any other items that can cause a rich condition

**CARBON DIOXIDE** Carbon dioxide ($CO_2$) is the result of oxygen in the engine combining with the carbon of the gasoline. An acceptable level of $CO_2$ is between 12% and 15%. A high reading indicates an efficiently operating engine. If the $CO_2$ level is low, the mixture may be either too rich or too lean.

**OXYGEN** The next gas is oxygen ($O_2$). There is about 21% oxygen in the atmosphere, and most of this oxygen should be "used up" during the combustion process to oxidize all the hydrogen and carbon (hydrocarbons) in the gasoline. Levels of $O_2$ should be very low (about 0.5%). High levels of $O_2$, especially at idle, could be due to an exhaust system leak.

**NOTE: Adding 10% alcohol to gasoline provides additional oxygen to the fuel and will result in lower levels of CO and higher levels of $O_2$ in the exhaust.**

**OXIDES OF NITROGEN** An oxide of nitrogen (NO) is a colorless, tasteless, and odorless gas when it leaves the engine, but as soon as it reaches the atmosphere and mixes with more oxygen, nitrogen oxides ($NO_2$) are formed. $NO_2$ is reddish-brown and has an acid and pungent smell. NO and $NO_2$ are grouped together and referred to as $NO_x$, where x represents any number of oxygen atoms. $NO_x$, the symbol used to represent all oxides of nitrogen, is the fifth gas commonly tested using a five-gas analyzer. The exhaust gas recirculation (EGR) system is the major controlling device limiting the formation of $NO_x$.

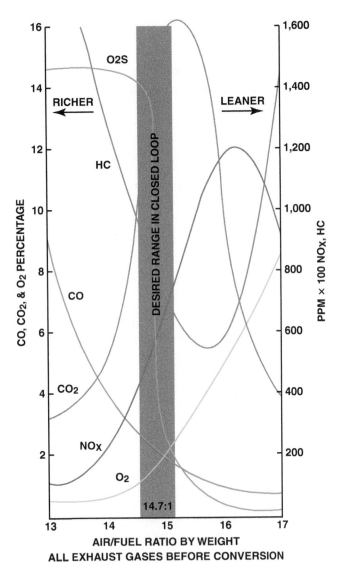

FIGURE 24–7 Exhaust emissions are very complex. When the air-fuel mixture becomes richer, some exhaust emissions are reduced, while others increase.

Acceptable exhaust emissions include the following:

| | Without Catalytic Converter | With Catalytic Converter |
|---|---|---|
| **HC** | 300 ppm or less | 30 to 50 ppm or less |
| **CO** | 3% or less | 0.3% to 0.5% or less |
| **O₂** | 0% to 2% | 0% to 2% |
| **CO₂** | 12% to 15% or higher | 12% to 15% or higher |
| **NOₓ** | Less than 100 ppm at idle and less than 1,000 ppm at WOT | Less than 100 ppm at idle and less than 1,000 ppm at WOT |

● **SEE FIGURE 24–7.**

## HC TOO HIGH

High hydrocarbon exhaust emissions are usually caused by an engine misfire. What burns the fuel in an engine? The ignition system ignites a spark at the spark plug to ignite the proper mixture inside the combustion chamber. If a spark plug does not ignite the mixture, the resulting unburned fuel is pushed out of the cylinder on the exhaust stroke by the piston through the exhaust valves and into the exhaust system. Therefore, if any of the following ignition components or adjustments are not correct, excessive HC emission is likely:

1. Defective or worn spark plugs
2. Defective or loose spark plug wires
3. Defective distributor cap and/or rotor
4. Incorrect ignition timing (either too far advanced or too far retarded)
5. A lean air-fuel mixture can also cause a misfire. This condition is referred to as a lean misfire. A lean air-fuel mixture can be caused by low fuel-pump pressure, a clogged fuel filter, or a restricted fuel injector.

**NOTE: To make discussion easier in future reference to these items, this list of ignition components and checks can be referred to simply as "spark stuff."**

## CO TOO HIGH

Excessive carbon monoxide is an indication of too rich an air-fuel mixture. CO is the **rich indicator.** The higher the CO reading, the richer the air-fuel mixture. High concentrations of CO indicate that not enough oxygen was available for the amount of fuel. Common causes of high CO include the following:

- Too-high fuel-pump pressure
- Defective fuel-pressure regulator
- Clogged air filter or PCV valve

### ? FREQUENTLY ASKED QUESTION

**How Can My Worn-Out, Old, High-Mileage Vehicle Pass an Exhaust Emission Test?**

Age and mileage of a vehicle are generally not factors when it comes to passing an exhaust emission test. Regular maintenance is the most important factor for passing an enhanced inspection and maintenance (I/M) exhaust analysis test. Failure of the vehicle owner to replace broken accessory drive belts, leaking air pump tubes, defective spark plug wires, or a cracked exhaust manifold can lead to failure of other components such as the catalytic converter. Tests have shown that if the vehicle is properly cared for, even an engine that has 300,000 miles (483,000 km) can pass an exhaust emission test.

### CO Equals O₂

If the exhaust is rich, CO emissions will be higher than normal. If the exhaust is lean, $O_2$ emissions will be higher than normal. Therefore, if the CO reading is the same as the $O_2$ reading, then the engine is operating correctly. For example, if both CO and $O_2$ are 0.5% and the engine develops a vacuum leak, the $O_2$ will rise. If a fuel-pressure regulator were to malfunction, the resulting richer air-fuel mixture would increase CO emissions. Therefore, if both the rich indicator (CO) and the lean indicator ($O_2$) are equal, the engine is operating correctly.

**NOTE: One technician remembers "CO" as meaning "clogged oxygen" and always looks for restricted airflow into the engine whenever high CO levels are detected.**

- Defective injectors

# MEASURING OXYGEN AND CARBON DIOXIDE

Two gas exhaust analyzers (HC and CO) work well, but both HC and CO are consumed (converted) inside the catalytic converter. The amount of leftover oxygen coming out of the tailpipe is an indication of leanness. The higher the $O_2$ level, the leaner the exhaust. Oxygen therefore is the **lean indicator.** Acceptable levels of $O_2$ are 0% to 2%.

NOTE: A hole in the exhaust system can draw outside air (oxygen) into the exhaust system. Therefore, to be assured of an accurate reading, carefully check the exhaust system for leaks. Using a smoke machine is an easy method to locate leaks in the exhaust system.

Carbon dioxide ($CO_2$) is a measure of efficiency. The higher the level of $CO_2$ in the exhaust stream, the more efficiently the engine is operating. Levels of 12% to 15% are considered to be acceptable. Because $CO_2$ levels peak at an air-fuel mixture of 14.7:1, a lower level of $CO_2$ indicates either a too-rich or a too-lean condition. The $CO_2$ measurement by itself does not indicate which condition is present. An example follows:

$CO_2$ = 8% (This means that efficiency is low and that the air-fuel mixture is not correct.)

Look at $O_2$ and CO levels.
A high $O_2$ indicates lean and a high CO indicates rich.

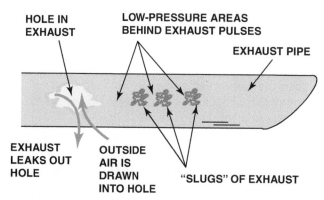

**FIGURE 24–8** A hole in the exhaust system can cause outside air (containing oxygen) to be drawn into the exhaust system. This extra oxygen can be confusing to a service technician because the extra $O_2$ in the exhaust stream could be misinterpreted as a too-lean air-fuel mixture.

TECH TIP

### How to Find a Leak in the Exhaust System

A hole in the exhaust system can dilute the exhaust gases with additional oxygen ($O_2$). ● **SEE FIGURE 24–8.**

This additional $O_2$ in the exhaust can lead the service technician to believe that the air-fuel mixture is too lean. To help identify an exhaust leak, perform an exhaust analysis at idle and at 2,500 RPM (fast idle) and compare with the following:

- If the $O_2$ is high at idle and at 2,500 RPM, the mixture is lean at both idle and at 2,500 RPM.
- If the $O_2$ is low at idle and high at 2,500 RPM, this usually means that the vehicle is equipped with a working AIR pump.
- If the $O_2$ is high at idle, but okay at 2,500 RPM, a hole in the exhaust or a small vacuum leak that is "covered up" at higher speed is indicated.

# PHOTOCHEMICAL SMOG FORMATION

Oxides of nitrogen are formed by high temperature—over 2,500°F (1,370°C)—and/or pressures inside the combustion chamber. Oxides of nitrogen contribute to the formation of photochemical **smog** when sunlight reacts chemically with $NO_x$ and unburned hydrocarbons (HC). Smog is a term derived by combining the words *smoke* and *fog*. Ground-level ozone is a constituent of smog. **Ozone** is an enriched oxygen molecule with three atoms of oxygen ($O_3$) instead of the normal two atoms of oxygen ($O_2$).

Ozone in the upper atmosphere is beneficial because it blocks out harmful ultraviolet rays that contribute to skin cancer. However, at ground level, this ozone (smog) is an irritant to the respiratory system.

**Your Nose Knows**

Using the nose, a technician can often identify a major problem without having to connect the vehicle to an exhaust analyzer. An example follows:

- The strong smell of exhaust is due to excessive unburned hydrocarbon (HC) emissions. Look for an ignition system fault that could prevent the proper burning of the fuel. A vacuum leak could also cause a lean misfire and cause excessive HC exhaust emissions.
- If your eyes start to burn or water, suspect excessive oxides of nitrogen ($NO_x$) emissions. The oxides of nitrogen combine with the moisture in the eyes to form a mild solution of nitric acid. The acid formation causes the eyes to burn and water. Excessive $NO_x$ exhaust emissions can be caused by the following:
  - A vacuum leak causing higher-than-normal combustion chamber temperature
  - Overadvanced ignition timing causing higher-than-normal combustion chamber temperature
  - Lack of proper amount of exhaust gas recirculation (EGR) (This is usually noticed above idle on most vehicles.)
- Dizzy feeling or headache. This is commonly caused by excessive carbon monoxide (CO) exhaust emissions. Get into fresh air as soon as possible. A probable cause of high levels of CO is an excessively rich air-fuel mixture.

# TESTING FOR OXIDES OF NITROGEN

Because the formation of $NO_x$ occurs mostly under load, the most efficient method to test for $NO_x$ is to use a portable exhaust analyzer that can be carried in the vehicle while the vehicle is being driven under a variety of conditions.

**SPECIFICATIONS FOR $NO_x$**    From experience, a maximum reading of 1,000 parts per million (ppm) of $NO_x$ under loaded driving conditions will generally mean that the vehicle will pass an enhanced I/M roller test. A reading of over 100 ppm at idle should be considered excessive.

**Check for Dog Food?**

A commonly experienced problem in many parts of the country involves squirrels or other animals placing dog food into the air intake ducts of vehicles. Dog food is often found packed tight in the ducts against the air filter. An air intake restriction reduces engine power and vehicle performance.

 REAL WORLD FIX

**The Case of the Retarded Exhaust Camshaft**

A Toyota equipped with a double overhead camshaft (DOHC) inline 6-cylinder engine failed the state-mandated enhanced exhaust emission test for $NO_x$. The engine ran perfectly without spark knocking (ping), which is usually a major reason for excessive $NO_x$ emissions. The technician checked the following:

- The ignition timing, which was found to be set to specifications (if too far advanced, can cause excessive $NO_x$)
- The cylinders, which were decarbonized using top engine cleaner
- The EGR valve, which was inspected and the EGR passages cleaned

After all the items were completed, the vehicle was returned to the inspection station, where the vehicle again failed for excessive $NO_x$ emissions (better but still over the maximum allowable limit).

After additional hours of troubleshooting, the technician decided to go back to basics and start over again. A check of the vehicle history with the owner indicated that the only previous work performed on the engine was a replacement timing belt over a year before. The technician discovered that the exhaust cam timing was retarded two teeth, resulting in late closing of the exhaust valve. The proper exhaust valve timing resulted in a slight amount of exhaust being retained in the cylinder. This extra exhaust was added to the amount supplied by the EGR valve and helped reduce $NO_x$ emissions. After repositioning the timing belt, the vehicle passed the emissions test well within the limits.

| Exhaust Gas Summary Chart | |
|---|---|
| **Gas** | **Cause and Correction** |
| **High HC** | Engine misfire or incomplete burning of fuel caused by the following:<br>1. Ignition system fault<br>2. Lean misfire<br>3. Too low an engine temperature (thermostat) |
| **High CO** | condition caused by the following:<br>1. Leaking fuel injectors or fuel-pressure regulator<br>2. Clogged air filter or PCV system<br>3. Excessive fuel pressure |
| **High HC and CO** | Excessively rich condition caused by the following:<br>1. All items included under high CO<br>2. Fouled spark plugs causing a misfire to occur<br>3. Possible nonoperating catalytic converter |
| **High NO$_x$** | Excessive combustion chamber temperature caused by the following:<br>1. Nonoperating EGR valve<br>2. Clogged EGR passages<br>3. Engine operating temperature too high because of cooling system restriction, worn water pump impeller, or other faults in the cooling system<br>4. Lean air-fuel mixture<br>5. High compression caused by excessive carbon buildup in the cylinders |

 **REAL WORLD FIX**

### O2S Shows Rich, but Pulse Width Is Low

A service technician was attempting to solve a driveability problem. The computer did not indicate any diagnostic trouble codes (DTCs). A check of the oxygen sensor voltage indicated a higher-than-normal reading almost all the time. The pulse width to the port injectors was lower than normal. The lower-than-normal pulse width indicates that the computer is attempting to reduce fuel flow into the engine by decreasing the amount of on-time for all the injectors.

What could cause a rich mixture if the injectors were being commanded to deliver a lean mixture? Finally, the technician shut off the engine and took a careful look at the entire fuel-injection system. Although the vacuum hose was removed from the fuel-pressure regulator, fuel was found dripping from the vacuum hose. The problem was a defective fuel-pressure regulator that allowed an uncontrolled amount of fuel to be drawn by the intake manifold vacuum into the cylinders. While the computer tried to reduce fuel by reducing the pulse width signal to the injectors, the extra fuel being drawn directly from the fuel rail caused the engine to operate with too rich an air-fuel mixture.

## SUMMARY

1. Excessive hydrocarbon (HC) exhaust emissions are created by a lack of proper combustion, such as a fault in the ignition system, too lean an air-fuel mixture, or too-cold engine operation.

2. Excessive carbon monoxide (CO) exhaust emissions are usually created by a rich air-fuel mixture.

3. Excessive oxides of nitrogen (NO$_x$) exhaust emissions are usually created by excessive heat or pressure in the combustion chamber or a lack of the proper amount of exhaust gas recirculation (EGR).

4. Carbon dioxide (CO$_2$) levels indicate efficiency. The higher the CO$_2$, the more efficient the engine operation.

5. Oxygen (O$_2$) indicates leanness. The higher the O$_2$, the leaner the air-fuel mixture.

6. A vehicle should be driven about 20 miles, especially during cold weather, to allow the engine to be fully warm before an enhanced emissions test.

## REVIEW QUESTIONS

1. List the five exhaust gases and their maximum allowable readings for a fuel-injected vehicle equipped with a catalytic converter.

2. List two causes of a rich exhaust.

3. List two causes of a lean exhaust.

4. List those items that should be checked if a vehicle fails an exhaust test for excessive NO$_x$ emissions.

1. Technician A says that high HC emission levels are often caused by a fault in the ignition system. Technician B says that high $CO_2$ emissions are usually caused by a richer-than-normal air-fuel mixture. Which technician is correct?
   a. Technician A only
   b. Technician B only
   c. Both Technicians A and B
   d. Neither Technician A nor B

2. HC and CO are high, and $CO_2$ and $O_2$ are low. This could be caused by a _____.
   a. Rich mixture
   b. Lean mixture
   c. Defective ignition component
   d. Clogged EGR passage

3. Which gas is generally considered to be the rich indicator? (The higher the level of this gas, the richer the air-fuel mixture.)
   a. HC
   b. CO
   c. $CO_2$
   d. $O_2$

4. Which gas is generally considered to be the lean indicator? (The higher the level of this gas, the leaner the air-fuel mixture.)
   a. HC
   b. CO
   c. $CO_2$
   d. $O_2$

5. Which exhaust gas indicates efficiency? (The higher the level of this gas, the more efficient the engine operates.)
   a. HC
   b. CO
   c. $CO_2$
   d. $O_2$

6. All of the gases are measured in percentages except _____.
   a. HC
   b. CO
   c. $CO_2$
   d. $O_2$

7. After the following exhaust emissions were measured, how was the engine operating?

   HC = 766 ppm   $CO_2$ = 8.2%   CO = 4.6%   $O_2$ = 0.1%
   a. Too rich
   b. Too lean

8. Technician A says that carbon inside the engine can cause excessive $NO_x$ to form. Technician B says that excessive $NO_x$ could be caused by a cooling system fault causing the engine to operate too hot. Which technician is correct?
   a. Technician A only
   b. Technician B only
   c. Both Technicians A and B
   d. Neither Technician A nor B

9. A clogged EGR passage could cause excessive _____ exhaust emissions.
   a. HC
   b. CO
   c. $NO_x$
   d. $CO_2$

10. An ignition fault could cause excessive _____ exhaust emissions.
    a. HC
    b. CO
    c. $NO_x$
    d. $CO_2$

# chapter
# 25

# EVAPORATIVE EMISSION CONTROL SYSTEMS

**OBJECTIVES:** **After studying Chapter 25, the reader should be able to:** • Prepare for the ASE Engine Performance (A8) certification test content area "D" (Emission Control Systems). • Describe the purpose and function of the evaporative emission control system. • Discuss how the evaporative emission control system is tested under OBD-II regulations. • Explain methods for diagnosing and testing faults in the evaporative emission control system.

**KEY TERMS:** Adsorption 318 • Evaporative control (EVAP) system 317 • Fuel tank pressure (FTP) 323 • Leak detection pump (LDP) 321 • Onboard refueling vapor recovery (ORVR) 321 • Purge valve 321 • Vent valve 321 • Volatile organic compounds (VOC) 317

## EVAPORATIVE EMISSION CONTROL SYSTEM

**PURPOSE AND FUNCTION** The purpose of the evaporative emission control system is to trap and hold gasoline vapors, also called **volatile organic compounds (VOCs)**. The **evaporative control (EVAP) system** includes the charcoal canister, hoses, and valves. These vapors are routed into a charcoal canister, then into the intake airflow, where they are burned in the engine instead of being released into the atmosphere.

**COMMON COMPONENTS** The fuel tank filler caps used on vehicles with modern EVAP systems are a special design. Most EVAP fuel tank filler caps have a built-in pressure-vacuum relief valve. When pressure or vacuum exceeds a calibrated value, the valve opens. Once the pressure or vacuum has been relieved, the valve closes. If a sealed cap is used on an EVAP system that requires a pressure-vacuum relief design, a vacuum may develop in the fuel system, or the fuel tank may be damaged by fuel expansion or contraction. ● **SEE FIGURE 25–1.**

**EVAP SYSTEM OPERATION** The canister is located under the hood or underneath the vehicle and is filled with activated charcoal granules that can hold up to one-third of their own weight in fuel vapors. ● **SEE FIGURE 25–2.**

**NOTE: Some vehicles with large or dual fuel tanks may have dual canisters.**

**? FREQUENTLY ASKED QUESTION**

**When Filling My Fuel Tank, Why Should I Stop When the Pump Clicks Off?**

Every fuel tank has an upper volume chamber that allows for expansion of the fuel when hot. The volume of the chamber is between 10% and 20% of the volume of the tank. For example, if a fuel tank had a capacity of 20 gallons, the expansion chamber volume would be from 2 to 4 gallons. A hose is attached at the top of the chamber and vented to the charcoal canister. If extra fuel is forced into this expansion volume, liquid gasoline can be drawn into the charcoal canister. This liquid fuel can saturate the canister and create an overly rich air-fuel mixture when the canister purge valve is opened during normal vehicle operation. This extra-rich air-fuel mixture can cause the vehicle to fail an exhaust emissions test, reduce fuel economy, and possibly damage the catalytic converter. To avoid problems, simply add fuel to the next dime's worth after the nozzle clicks off. This will ensure that the tank is full yet not overfilled.

Activated charcoal is an effective vapor trap because of its great surface area. Each gram of activated charcoal has a surface area of 1,100 square meters, or more than 1/4 acre. Typical canisters hold either 300 or 625 grams of charcoal *with a surface area equivalent to 80 or 165 football fields.* By a process

**FIGURE 25-1** A capless system from a Ford Flex does not use a replaceable cap; instead, it is spring-loaded closed.

**FIGURE 25-2** A charcoal canister can be located under the hood or underneath the vehicle.

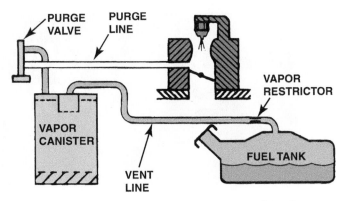

**FIGURE 25-3** The EVAP system includes all of the lines, hoses, and valves, plus the charcoal canister.

electric vacuum solenoid and one or more purge valves. Under normal conditions, most engine control systems permit purging only during closed-loop operation at cruising speeds. During other engine operation conditions, such as open-loop mode, idle, deceleration, or wide-open throttle, the PCM prevents canister purging.

**EVAPORATIVE PRESSURES** Pressures can build inside the fuel system and are usually measured in units of inches of water, abbreviated "in. $H_2O$" (28 in. $H_2O$ equals 1 pound per square inch, or 1 PSI). Pressure buildup can be caused by the following:

- Fuel evaporation rates (volatility)
- Gas tank size (fuel surface area and volume)
- Fuel level (liquid versus vapor)
- Fuel slosh (driving conditions)
- Temperature (ambient, in-tank, close to the tank)
- Returned fuel from the rail

Some scan tools display other units of measure for the EVAP system that makes understanding the system difficult. ● **SEE CHART 25-1** for pressure conversions between pounds per square inch (PSI), inches of mercury (in. Hg), and inches of water (in. $H_2O$).

called **adsorption,** the fuel vapor molecules adhere to the carbon surface. This attaching force is not strong, so the system purges the vapor molecules quite simply by sending a fresh airflow through the charcoal:

- **Vapor purging.** During engine operation, stored vapors are drawn from the canister into the engine through a hose connected to the throttle body or the air cleaner. This "purging" process mixes unburned gasoline (hydrocarbons, abbreviated HCs) vapors from the canister with the existing air-fuel charge. ● **SEE FIGURES 25-3 AND 25-4.**
- **Computer-controlled purge.** The PCM controls when the canister purges on most engines. This is done by an

# NONENHANCED EVAPORATIVE CONTROL SYSTEMS

Prior to 1996, evaporative systems were referred to as nonenhanced evaporative control (EVAP) systems. This term refers to evaporative systems that had limited diagnostic capabilities. While they are often PCM controlled, their diagnostic capability is usually limited to their ability to detect

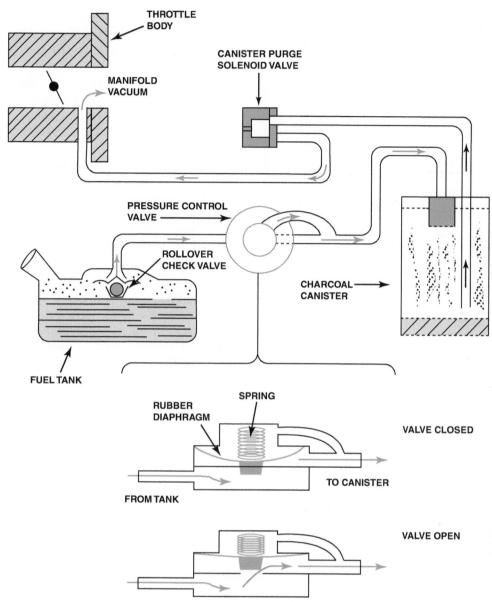

**FIGURE 25–4** A typical EVAP system. Note that when the computer turns on the canister purge solenoid valve, manifold vacuum draws any stored vapors from the canister into the engine. Manifold vacuum also is applied to the pressure control valve. When this valve opens, fumes from the fuel tank are drawn into the charcoal canister and eventually into the engine. When the solenoid valve is turned off (or the engine stops and there is no manifold vacuum), the pressure control valve is spring-loaded shut to keep vapors inside the fuel tank from escaping to the atmosphere.

if purge has occurred. Many of these older systems have a diagnostic switch that could sense if purge is occurring and set a code if no purge is detected. This system does not check for leaks. On some vehicles, the PCM also has the capability of monitoring the integrity of the purge solenoid and circuit. These systems' limitations are their ability to check the integrity of the evaporative system on the vehicle. They could not detect leaks or missing or loose gas caps that could lead to excessive evaporative emissions from the vehicle. Nonenhanced evaporative systems use either a canister purge solenoid or a vapor management valve to control purge vapor.

## ENHANCED EVAPORATIVE CONTROL SYSTEM

**BACKGROUND** Beginning in 1996 with OBD-II vehicles, manufacturers were required to install systems that are able to detect both purge flow and evaporative system leakage:

- The systems on models produced between 1996 and 2000 must be able to detect a leak as small as 0.040 inches in diameter.

| PSI | INCHES HG | INCHES $H_2O$ |
|---|---|---|
| 14.7 | 29.93 | 407.19 |
| 1.0 | 2.036 | 27.7 |
| 0.9 | 1.8 | 24.93 |
| 0.8 | 1.63 | 22.16 |
| 0.7 | 1.43 | 19.39 |
| 0.6 | 1.22 | 16.62 |
| 0.5 | 1.018 | 13.85 |
| 0.4 | 0.814 | 11.08 |
| 0.3 | 0.611 | 8.31 |
| 0.2 | 0.407 | 5.54 |
| 0.1 | 0.204 | 2.77 |
| 0.09 | 0.183 | 2.49 |
| 0.08 | 0.163 | 2.22 |
| 0.07 | 0.143 | 1.94 |
| 0.06 | 0.122 | 1.66 |
| 0.05 | 0.102 | 1.385 |

**CHART 25–1**

Pressure conversions.

NOTE: 1 PSI = 28 in. $H_2O$
0.25 PSI = 7 in. $H_2O$

- Beginning in the model year 2000, the enhanced systems started a phase-in of 0.020-inch diameter leak detection.
- All vehicles built after 1995 have enhanced evaporative systems with the ability to detect purge flow and system leakage. If either of these two functions fails, the system is required to set a diagnostic trouble code (DTC) and turn on the malfunction indicator lamp (MIL) to warn the driver of the failure. ● **SEE FIGURE 25–5.**

**VENT VALVE** The canister **vent valve** is a *normally open* valve and is closed only when commanded by the PCM during testing of the system. The vent valve is closed only during testing by the PCM as part of the mandated OBD-II standards. The vent solenoid is located under the vehicle in most cases and is exposed to the environment, making this valve subject to rust and corrosion.

**PURGE VALVE** The canister **purge valve,** also called the *canister purge (CANP) solenoid,* is normally closed and is pulsed open by the PCM during purging. The purge valve is connected to intake manifold vacuum using a rubber hose to draw gasoline vapors from the charcoal canister into the engine when the purge valve is commanded open. Most purge valves are pulsed on and off to better control the amount of fumes being drawn into the intake manifold.

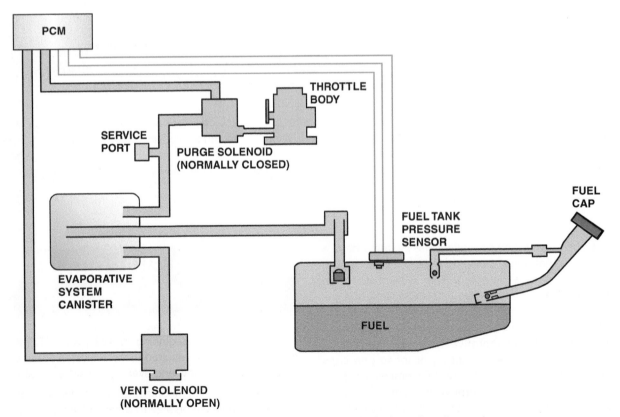

**FIGURE 25–5** An enhanced EVAP system is able to perform system and leak detection diagnosis.

**Problems after Refueling? Check the Purge Valve**

The purge valve is normally closed and open only when the PCM is commanding the system to purge. If the purge solenoid were to become stuck in the open position, gasoline fumes would be allowed to flow directly from the gas tank to the intake manifold. When refueling, this would result in a lot of fumes being forced into the intake manifold and as a result cause a hard-to-start condition after refueling. This would also result in a rich exhaust and likely black exhaust when first starting the engine after refueling. While the purge solenoid is usually located under the hood of most vehicles and is less subject to rust and corrosion as with the vent valve, it can still fail.

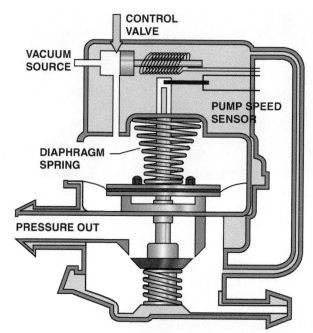

**FIGURE 25–6** A leak detection pump (LDP) used on some Chrysler and other vehicles to pressurize (slightly) the fuel system to check for leaks.

# LEAK DETECTION PUMP SYSTEM

**PURPOSE AND FUNCTION** Many vehicles use a vacuum operated **leak detection pump (LDP)** as part of the evaporative control system diagnosis equipment. ● **SEE FIGURE 25–6.**

**OPERATION** The system works to test for leaks as follows:

- The purge solenoid is normally closed.
- The vent valve in the LDP is normally open. Filtered fresh air is drawn through the LDP to the canister.
- The LDP uses a spring attached to a diaphragm to apply pressure (7.5 in. $H_2O$) to the fuel tank.
- The PCM monitors the LDP switch that is triggered if the pressure drops in the fuel tank.
- The time between LDP solenoid off and LDP switch close is called the pump period. This time period is inversely proportional to the size of the leak. The shorter the pump period, the larger the leak. The longer the pump period, the smaller the leak.

  EVAP large leak (greater than 0.080 in.): less than 0.9 second

  EVAP medium leak (0.040 to 0.080 in.): 0.9 to 1.2 seconds

  EVAP small leak (0.020 to 0.040 in.): 1.2 to 6 seconds

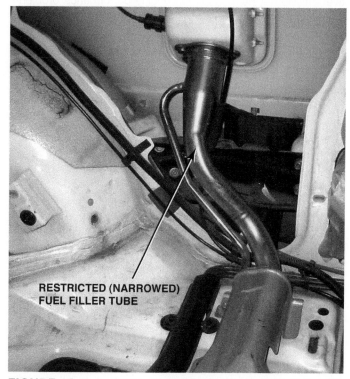

**FIGURE 25–7** A restricted fuel fill pipe shown on vehicle with the interior removed.

# ONBOARD REFUELING VAPOR RECOVERY

**PURPOSE AND FUNCTION** The **onboard refueling vapor recovery (ORVR)** system was first introduced on some 1998 vehicles. Previously de`signed EVAP systems allowed fuel vapor to escape to the atmosphere during refueling.

**OPERATION** The primary feature of most ORVR systems is the restricted tank filler tube, which is about 1 inch (25 mm) in diameter. This reduced size filler tube creates an aspiration effect, which tends to draw outside air into the filler tube. During refueling, the fuel tank is vented to the charcoal canister, which captures the gas fumes, and with air flowing into the filler tube, no vapors can escape to the atmosphere. ● **SEE FIGURE 25–7.**

**FIGURE 25–8** Some vehicles will display a message if an evaporative control system leak is detected that could be the result of a loose gas cap.

## DIAGNOSING THE EVAP SYSTEM

**SYMPTOMS** Before vehicle emissions testing began in many parts of the country, little service work was done on the evaporative emission system. Common engine performance problems that can be caused by a fault in this system include the following:

- **Poor fuel economy.** A leak in a vacuum-valve diaphragm can result in engine vacuum drawing in a constant flow of gasoline vapors from the fuel tank. This usually results in a drop in fuel economy of 2 to 4 miles per gallon (mpg). Use a hand-operated vacuum pump to check that the vacuum diaphragm can hold vacuum.

- **Poor performance.** A vacuum leak in the system can cause the engine to run rough. Age, heat, and time all contribute to the deterioration of rubber hoses.

**STATE EVAP TESTS** Enhanced exhaust emissions (I/M-240) testing tests the evaporative emission system. A leak in the system is tested by pressurizing the entire fuel system to a level below 1 PSI (about 14 in. $H_2O$). The system is typically pressurized with nitrogen, a nonflammable gas that makes up 78% of our atmosphere. The pressure in the system is then shut off and the pressure monitored. If the pressure drops below a set standard, then the vehicle fails the test. This test determines if there is a leak in the system.

**HINT: To help pass the evaporative section of an enhanced emissions test, arrive at the test site with less than a half tank of fuel. This means that the rest of the volume of the fuel tank is filled with air. It takes longer for the pressure to drop from a small leak when the volume of the air is greater compared to when the tank is full and the volume of air remaining in the tank is small.**

**LOCATING LEAKS IN THE SYSTEM** Leaks in the evaporative emission control system will cause the malfunction check gas cap indication lamp to light on some vehicles. ● **SEE FIGURE 25–8.**

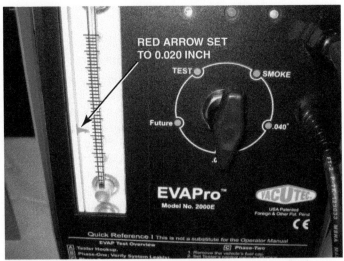

**FIGURE 25–9** To test for a leak, this tester was set to the 0.020-inch hole and turned on. The ball rose in the scale on the left, and the red arrow was moved to that location. If when testing the system for leaks the ball rises higher than the arrow, then the leak is larger than 0.02 inch. If the ball does not rise to the level of the arrow, the leak is smaller than 0.020 inch.

**FIGURE 25–10** This unit is applying smoke to the fuel tank through an adapter, and the leak was easily found to be the gas cap seal.

A leak will also cause a gas smell, which would be most noticeable if the vehicle were parked in an enclosed garage. The first step is to determine if there is a leak in the system by setting the EVAP tester to rate the system for either a 0.040-inch-or a 0.020-inch-hole-size leak. ● **SEE FIGURE 25–9.**

After it has been determined that a leak exists and it is larger than specified, one of two methods can be used to check for leaks in the evaporative system:

- **Smoke machine testing.** The most efficient method of leak detection is to introduce smoke under low pressure from a machine specifically designed for this purpose. ● **SEE FIGURE 25–10.**

**FIGURE 25–11** An emission tester that uses nitrogen to pressurize the fuel system.

- **Nitrogen gas pressurization.** This method uses nitrogen gas under a very low pressure (lower than 1 PSI) in the fuel system. The service technician then listens for the escaping air, using amplified headphones. ● SEE FIGURE 25–11.

## EVAPORATIVE SYSTEM MONITOR

**OBD-II REQUIREMENTS** OBD-II computer programs not only detect faults but also *periodically test various systems* and alert the driver before emissions-related components are harmed by system faults:

- Serious faults cause a blinking malfunction indicator lamp (MIL) or even an engine shutdown.
- Less serious faults may simply store a code but not illuminate the MIL.

The OBD-II requirements did not affect fuel system design. However, one new component, a fuel evaporative canister purge line pressure sensor, was added for monitoring purge line pressure during tests. The OBD-II requirements state that vehicle fuel systems are to be routinely tested *while under way* by the PCM.

All OBD-II vehicles perform a canister purge system pressure test, as commanded by the PCM. While the vehicle is being driven, the vapor line between the canister and the purge valve is monitored for pressure changes:

- When the canister purge solenoid is open, the line should be under a vacuum since vapors must be drawn from the canister into the intake system. However, when the purge solenoid is closed, there should be no vacuum in the line. The pressure sensor detects if a vacuum is present, and the information is compared to the command given to the solenoid.

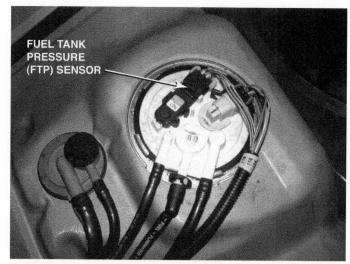

**FIGURE 25–12** The fuel tank pressure sensor (black unit with three wires) looks like a MAP sensor and is usually located on top of the fuel pump module (white unit).

- If, during the canister purge cycle, no vacuum exists in the canister purge line, a code is set indicating a possible fault, which could be caused by an inoperative or clogged solenoid or a blocked or leaking canister purge fuel line. Likewise, if vacuum exists when no command for purge is given, a stuck solenoid is evident, and a code is set. The EVAP system monitor tests for purge volume and leaks.

A typical EVAP monitor first closes off the system to atmospheric pressure and opens the purge valve during cruise operation. A **fuel tank pressure (FTP)** sensor then monitors the rate with which vacuum increases in the system. The monitor uses this information to determine the purge volume flow rate. To test for leaks, the EVAP monitor closes the purge valve, creating a completely closed system. The fuel tank pressure sensor then monitors the leak-down rate. If the rate exceeds PCM-stored values, a leak greater than or equal to the OBD-II standard of 0.04 inch (1 mm) or 0.02 inch (0.5 mm) exists. After two consecutive failed trips testing either purge volume or the presence of a leak, the PCM lights the MIL and sets a DTC.

The fuel tank pressure sensor is similar to a MAP sensor, and instead of monitoring intake manifold absolute pressure, it is used to monitor fuel tank pressure. ● SEE FIGURE 25–12.

**ENGINE-OFF NATURAL VACUUM** System integrity (leakage) can also be checked after the engine is shut off. The premise is that a warm evaporative system will cool down after the engine is shut off and the vehicle is stable. A slight vacuum will be created in the gas tank during this cool-down period. If a specific level of vacuum is reached and maintained, the system is said to have integrity (no leakage). Actually, the vacuum is created after a period of time because the vapor pressure tends to increase after the engine is shut off and gradually decreases over time. The PCM monitors the pressure rise and decrease over time and triggers a diagnostic trouble code (DTC) if the pressure indicates a leak in the system. ● SEE FIGURE 25–13.

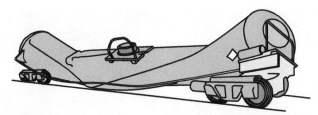

FIGURE 25–13 A tank car was cleaned using steam, and then both the bottom drain and the top vent were closed. The next day, the tank had collapsed because of the air pressure difference when the inside cooled. The higher outside air pressure caused the tank to collapse.

 TECH TIP

**Always Tighten the Cap Correctly**

Many diagnostic trouble codes (DTCs) are set because the gas cap has not been properly installed. To be sure that a screw-type gas cap is properly sealed, tighten it until you hear three clicks. The clicking is a ratchet device, and the clicking does not harm the cap. Therefore, if a P0440 or similar DTC is set, check the cap. ● **SEE FIGURE 25–14.**

# TYPICAL EVAP MONITOR

The PCM will run the EVAP monitor when the following enable criteria are met:

- Barometric pressure (BARO) greater than 70 kPa (20.7 in. Hg or 10.2 PSI)
- Intake air temperature (IAT) between 39°F and 86°F (4°C to 30°C) at engine start-up
- Engine coolant temperature (ECT) between 39°F and 86°F (4°C to 30°C) at engine start-up
- ECT and IAT within 3°F of each other at engine start-up
- Fuel level within 15% to 85%
- Throttle position (TP) sensor between 9% and 35%

A typical EVAP monitor first closes off the system to atmospheric pressure and opens the purge valve during cruise operation. A fuel tank pressure (FTP) sensor then monitors the rate with which vacuum increases in the system. ● **SEE FIGURE 25–15.**

The monitor uses this information to determine the purge volume flow rate. To test for leaks, the EVAP monitor closes the purge valve, creating a completely closed system. The fuel tank pressure sensor then monitors the leak-down rate. If the rate exceeds PCM-stored values, a leak greater than or equal to the OBD-II standard of 0.04 inch (1 mm) or 0.02 inch (0.5 mm) exists.

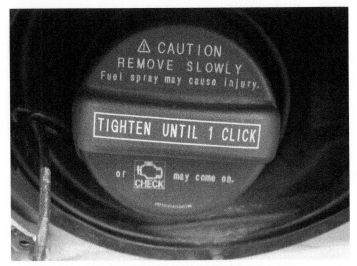

FIGURE 25–14 This Toyota cap warns that the check engine light will come on if not tightened until one click.

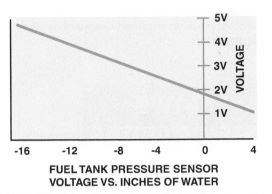

DIFFERENTIAL PRESSURE INCHES (H2O)

FUEL TANK PRESSURE SENSOR
VOLTAGE VS. INCHES OF WATER

FIGURE 25–15 To easily check the fuel tank pressure sensor, remove the cap, and the sensor should read about 1.7 volts.

**RUNNING THE EVAP MONITOR** Four tests are performed during a typical EVAP monitor. A DTC is assigned to each test:

1. **Weak vacuum test (P0440—large leak).** This test identifies gross leaks. During the monitor, the vent solenoid is closed, and the purge solenoid is duty cycled. The fuel tank pressure (FTP) should indicate a vacuum of approximately 6 to 10 in. $H_2O$.

2. **No flow during purging (P0441—no flow during purging).** This test uses the fuel tank pressure (FTP) sensor to determine that there was no change in fuel tank pressure during purging. This fault could be due to a defective purge valve or a gross leak caused by faults such as a defective or missing gas cap.

3. **Small leak test (P0442—small leak).** After the large leak test passes, the PCM checks for a small leak by keeping the vent solenoid closed and closing the purge solenoid. The system is now sealed. The PCM measures the change in FTP voltage over time.

FIGURE 25–16 The fuel level must be above 15% and below 85% before the EVAP monitor will run on most vehicles.

 **TECH TIP**

**Keep the Fuel Tank Properly Filled**

Most evaporative system monitors will not run unless the fuel level is between 15% and 85%. In other words, if a driver always runs with close to an empty tank or always tries to keep the tank full, the EVAP monitor may not run. ● **SEE FIGURE 25–16.**

## EVAP SYSTEM-RELATED DIAGNOSTIC TROUBLE CODES

| Diagnostic Trouble Code | Description | Possible Causes |
|---|---|---|
| P0440 | Evaporative system fault | • Loose gas cap<br>• Defective EVAP vent<br>• Cracked charcoal canister<br>• EVAP vent or purge vapor line problems |
| P0442 | Small leak detected | • Loose gas cap<br>• Defective EVAP vent or purge solenoid<br>• EVAP vent or purge line problems |
| P0446 | EVAP canister vent blocked | • EVAP vent or purge solenoid electrical problems<br>• Restricted EVAP canister vent line |

4. **Excess vacuum test (P0446).** This test checks for vent path restrictions. With the vent solenoid open and purge commanded, the PCM should not see excessive vacuum in the EVAP system. Typical EVAP system vacuum with the vent solenoid open is about 5 to 6 in. $H_2O$.

## SUMMARY

1. The purpose of the evaporative emission control (EVAP) system is to reduce the release of volatile organic compounds (VOCs) into the atmosphere.

2. A carbon (charcoal) canister is used to trap and hold gasoline vapors until they can be purged and run into the engine to be burned.

3. Pressures inside the EVAP system are low and are measured in inches of water (1 PSI = 28 in. $H_2O$).

4. A typical EVAP system uses a canister purge valve, which is normally closed, and a canister vent valve, which is normally open.

5. OBD-II regulation requires that the evaporative emission control system be checked for leakage and proper purge flow rates.

6. External leaks can best be located by pressurizing the fuel system with low-pressure smoke.

## REVIEW QUESTIONS

1. What components are used in a typical evaporative emission control system?

2. How does the computer control the purging of the vapor canister?

3. What is the difference between an enhanced and a nonenhanced evaporative control system?

4. Why is the vent valve subject to rust and corrosion?

5. What are the parameters (enable criteria) that must be met for the evaporative system monitor to run?

## CHAPTER QUIZ

1. What is the substance used in a vapor canister to absorb volatile organic compounds?
   a. Desiccant
   b. Organic absorber
   c. Pleated paper
   d. Carbon

2. Which valve(s) is (are) normally closed?
   a. Canister purge valve
   b. Canister vent valve
   c. Both canister purge and canister vent valves
   d. Neither canister purge nor canister vent valve

3. All of the following can increase the pressure in the evaporative emission control system except _____.
   a. Fuel temperature
   b. Returned fuel from the fuel-injection system
   c. Inlet fuel to the fuel pump
   d. Volatility of the fuel

4. Evaporative emission control systems operate on low pressure measured in inches of water (in. $H_2O$). One PSI is equal to how many inches of water?
   a. 1
   b. 10
   c. 18
   d. 28

5. Inadequate purge flow rate will trigger which DTC?
   a. P0440
   b. P0446
   c. P0300
   d. P0440 or P0446

6. Two technicians are discussing a state emission test. Technician A says that a vent valve that is not able to close can cause the system to fail the on-board test. Technician B says that a leaking gas cap can cause a failure of the EVAP test. Which technician is correct?
   a. Technician A only
   b. Technician B only
   c. Both Technicians A and B
   d. Neither Technician A nor B

7. Which EVAP valve is subject to rust and corrosion more than all of the others?
   a. Purge valve
   b. Vacuum control valve
   c. Vent valve
   d. Roll over check valve

8. Before an evaporative emission monitor will run, the fuel level must be where?
   a. At least 75% full
   b. Over 25%
   c. Between 15% and 85%
   d. The level of the fuel in the tank is not needed to run the monitor test

9. Technician A says that low-pressure smoke installed in the fuel system can be used to check for leaks. Technician B says that nitrogen under low pressure can be installed in the fuel system to check for leaks. Which technician is correct?
   a. Technician A only
   b. Technician B only
   c. Both Technicians A and B
   d. Neither Technician A nor B

10. A small leak is detected by the evaporative emission control system monitor that could be caused by a loose gas cap. Which DTC will likely be set?
    a. P0440
    b. P0442
    c. P0446
    d. P0440, P0441, or P0442

**OBJECTIVES:** After studying Chapter 26, the reader should be able to: • Prepare for the ASE Engine Performance (A8) certification test content area "D" (Emission Control Systems). • Describe the purpose and function of the exhaust gas recirculation system. • Discuss how the exhaust gas recirculation system is tested under OBD-II regulations. • Explain methods for diagnosing and testing for faults in the exhaust gas recirculation system.

**KEY TERMS:** Delta pressure feedback EGR (DPFE) sensor 331 • Detonation 328 • Digital EGR valve 330 • EGR valve position (EVP) sensor 329 • Electronic vacuum regulator valve (EVRV) 332 • Exhaust gas recirculation (EGR) 327 • Inert 327 • Linear EGR valve 330 • Nitrogen oxides (NOₓ) 327 • Pressure feedback EGR (PFE) sensor 329

## EXHAUST GAS RECIRCULATION SYSTEMS

**INTRODUCTION** **Exhaust gas recirculation (EGR)** is an emission control system that lowers the amount of **nitrogen oxides (NOₓ)** formed during combustion. In the presence of sunlight, $NO_x$ reacts with hydrocarbons in the atmosphere to form ozone ($O_3$) or photochemical smog, an air pollutant.

**NOₓ FORMATION** Nitrogen ($N_2$) and oxygen ($O_2$) molecules are separated into individual atoms of nitrogen and oxygen during the combustion process. These molecules then bond to form $NO_x$ ($NO$, $NO_2$). When combustion flame front temperatures exceed 2,500°F (1,370°C), $NO_x$ is formed inside the cylinder, which is then discharged into the atmosphere from the tailpipe. ● **SEE FIGURE 26–1.**

**CONTROLLING NOₓ** To handle the $NO_x$ generated above 2,500°F (1,370°C), the most efficient method to meet $NO_x$ emissions without significantly affecting engine performance, fuel economy, and other exhaust emissions is to use exhaust gas recirculation (EGR). The EGR system routes small quantities, usually between 6% and 10%, of exhaust gas into the intake manifold.

Here, the exhaust gas mixes with and takes the place of some intake charge. This leaves less room for the intake charge to enter the combustion chamber. The recirculated exhaust gas is **inert** (chemically inactive) and does not enter into the combustion process. The result is a lower peak combustion temperature. When the combustion temperature is lowered, the production of oxides of nitrogen is reduced.

**FIGURE 26–1** Nitrogen oxides (NOₓ) create a red-brown haze that often hangs over major cities.

The EGR system has some means of interconnecting the exhaust and intake manifolds. ● **SEE FIGURE 26–2.**

The EGR valve controls the flow of exhaust gases through the interconnecting passages:

■ On V-type engines, the intake manifold crossover is used as a source of exhaust gas for the EGR system. A cast passage connects the exhaust crossover to the EGR valve. The exhaust gas is sent from the EGR valve to openings in the manifold.

■ On inline-type engines, an external tube is generally used to carry exhaust gas to the EGR valve. This tube is often designed to be long so that the exhaust gas is cooled before it enters the EGR valve.

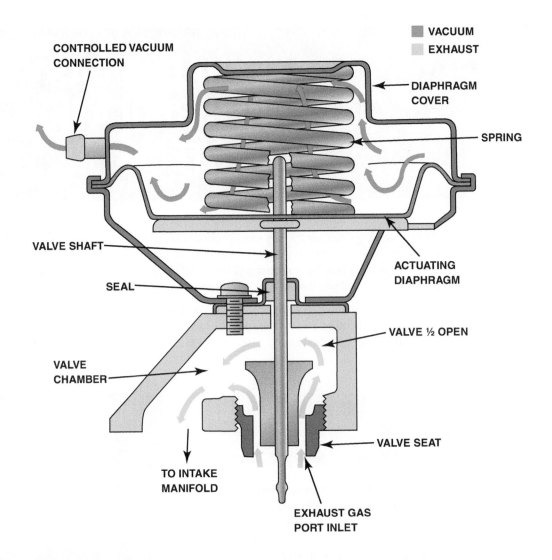

**FIGURE 26–2** When the EGR valve opens, the exhaust gases flow through the valve and into passages in the intake manifold.

VACUUM
EXHAUST

CONTROLLED VACUUM CONNECTION

DIAPHRAGM COVER

SPRING

VALVE SHAFT

ACTUATING DIAPHRAGM

SEAL

VALVE ½ OPEN

VALVE CHAMBER

VALVE SEAT

TO INTAKE MANIFOLD

EXHAUST GAS PORT INLET

**EGR SYSTEM OPERATION** Since small amounts of exhaust are all that is needed to lower peak combustion temperatures, the orifice through which the exhaust passes is small.

EGR is usually not required during the following conditions because the combustion temperatures are low:

- During idle speed
- When the engine is cold
- At wide-open throttle (WOT) (Not allowing EGR allows the engine to provide extra power when demanded. While the $NO_x$ formation is high during these times, the overall effect of not using EGR during WOT conditions is minor.)

The level of $NO_x$ emission changes according to engine speed, temperature, and load. Many systems use a cooler to reduce the temperature of the exhaust gases before they enter the intake manifold. The cooler the exhaust gases, the more effective they are at reducing the formation of $NO_x$.

**EGR BENEFITS** In addition to lowering $NO_x$ levels, the EGR system also helps control detonation. **Detonation,** also called spark knock or ping, occurs when high pressure and heat cause the air-fuel mixture to ignite. This uncontrolled combustion can severely damage the engine.

Using the EGR system allows for greater ignition timing advance and for the advance to occur sooner without detonation problems, which increases power and efficiency.

**POSITIVE AND NEGATIVE BACK PRESSURE EGR VALVES** Some vacuum-operated EGR valves used on older engines are designed with a small valve inside that bleeds off any applied vacuum and prevents the valve from opening:

- **Positive back pressure EGR valves.** These EGR valves require a positive back pressure in the exhaust system. At low engine speeds and light engine loads, the EGR system is not needed, and the back pressure in it is also low. Without enough back pressure, the EGR valve does not open even though vacuum may be present at the EGR valve. ● **SEE FIGURE 26–3.**
- **Negative back pressure EGR valves.** On each exhaust stroke, the engine emits an exhaust "pulse." Each pulse represents a positive pressure. Behind each pulse is a small area of low pressure. Some EGR valves react to this low-pressure area by closing a small internal valve, which allows the EGR valve to be opened by vacuum.

## POSITIVE BACK PRESSURE EGR VALVE OPERATION

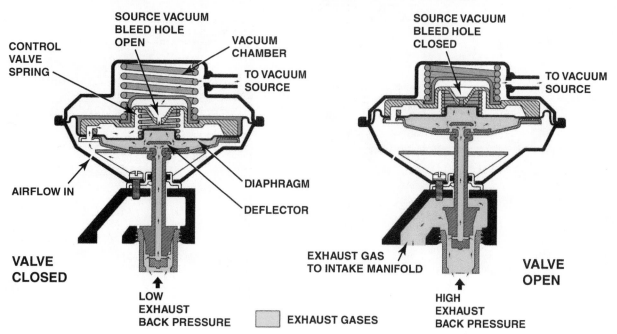

**FIGURE 26–3** Back pressure in the exhaust system is used to close the control valve, allowing engine vacuum to open the EGR valve.

The following conditions must occur before a back pressure-type vacuum-controlled EGR will operate:

1. Vacuum must be applied to the EGR valve itself. The vacuum source can be ported vacuum (above the throttle plate) or manifold vacuum (below the throttle plate) and by the computer through a solenoid valve.

2. Exhaust back pressure must be present to close an internal valve inside the EGR to allow the vacuum to move the diaphragm.

**NOTE: Installing a high-performance exhaust system could prevent a back pressure vacuum-operated EGR valve from opening. If this is occurs, excessive combustion chamber pressure may lead to severe spark knock, piston damage, or a blown head gasket.**

**COMPUTER-CONTROLLED EGR SYSTEMS** Most vehicles today use the Powertrain Control Module (PCM) to operate the EGR system. Many PCM-controlled EGR systems have one or more solenoids controlling the EGR vacuum. The PCM controls a solenoid to shut off vacuum to the EGR valve at cold engine temperatures, idle speed, and WOT operation. If two solenoids are used, one acts as an off/on control of supply vacuum, while the second solenoid vents vacuum when EGR flow is not desired or needs to be reduced. The second solenoid is used to control a vacuum air bleed, allowing atmospheric pressure in to modulate EGR flow according to vehicle operating conditions. ● **SEE FIGURE 26–4.**

**EGR VALVE POSITION SENSORS** Most PCM vacuum-operated EGR systems use a sensor to indicate EGR operation.

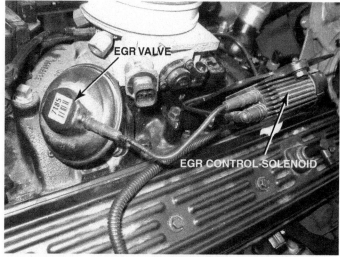

**FIGURE 26–4** Typical vacuum-operated EGR valve. The operation of the valve is controlled by the PCM by pulsing the EGR control solenoid on and off.

Onboard diagnostics generation II (OBD-II) EGR system monitors require an EGR sensor to verify that the valve opened. A linear potentiometer on the top of the EGR valve stem indicates valve position to the PCM. This is called an **EGR valve position (EVP) sensor.** Some later-model Ford EGR systems, however, use a feedback signal provided by an EGR exhaust back pressure sensor that converts the exhaust back pressure to a voltage signal. This sensor is called a **pressure feedback EGR (PFE) sensor.**

On some EGR systems, the top of the valve contains a vacuum regulator and EGR pintle-position sensor in one assembly

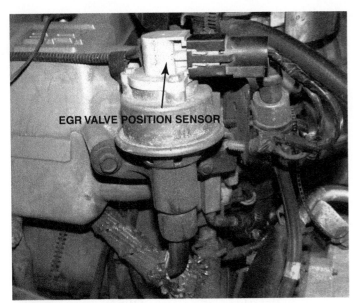

FIGURE 26–5 An EGR valve position sensor on top of an EGR valve.

FIGURE 26–6 Digital EGR valve as used on some older General Motors engines.

TECH TIP

**Find the Root Cause**

Excessive back pressure, such as that caused by a partially clogged exhaust system, could cause the plastic sensors on the EGR valve to melt. Always check for a restricted exhaust whenever replacing a failed EGR valve sensor.

sealed inside a nonremovable plastic cover. The pintle-position sensor provides a voltage output to the PCM, which increases as the duty cycle increases, allowing the PCM to monitor valve operation. ● **SEE FIGURE 26–5.**

**DIGITAL EGR VALVES** General Motors used a **digital EGR valve** design on some engines. Unlike vacuum-operated EGR valves, the digital EGR valve consists of three solenoids controlled by the powertrain control module (PCM). Each solenoid controls a different size orifice in the base—small, medium, and large. The PCM controls the ground circuit of each of the solenoids individually. It can produce any of seven different flow rates, using the solenoids to open the three valves in different combinations. The digital EGR valve offers precise control and using a swivel pintle design helps prevent carbon deposit problems. ● **SEE FIGURE 26–6.**

**LINEAR EGR** Most General Motors and many other vehicles use a **linear EGR valve** that contains a pulse-width modulated solenoid to precisely regulate exhaust gas flow and a feedback potentiometer that signals the PCM regarding the actual position of the valve. ● **SEE FIGURES 26–7 AND 26–8.**

FIGURE 26–7 A General Motors linear EGR valve.

## OBD-II EGR MONITORING STRATEGIES

**PURPOSE AND FUNCTION** In 1996, the U.S. EPA began requiring OBD-II systems in all passenger cars and most light-duty trucks. These systems include emission system monitors that alert the driver and the technician if an emission system is malfunctioning. The OBD-II system performs this test by opening and closing the EGR valve. The PCM monitors either the oxygen or MAP sensor for a change in signal voltage. If the EGR system fails, a diagnostic trouble code (DTC) is set. If the system fails two consecutive times, the malfunction indicator lamp (MIL) is lit.

## MONITORING STRATEGIES EGR monitoring strategies include the following:

- Some vehicle manufacturers, such as Chrysler, monitor the difference in the exhaust oxygen sensor's voltage activity as the EGR valve opens and closes. Oxygen in the exhaust decreases when the EGR valve is open and increases when the EGR valve is closed because exhaust gas is inert (contains very little oxygen) and actually displaces oxygen. The PCM sets a DTC if the sensor signal does not change.

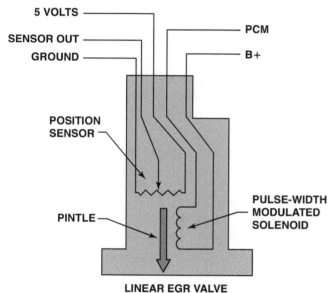

FIGURE 26–8 The EGR valve pintle is pulse-width modulated and a three-wire potentiometer provides pintle-position information back to the PCM.

- Most Fords use an EGR monitor test sensor called a **delta pressure feedback EGR (DPFE) sensor.** This sensor measures the pressure differential between two sides of a metered orifice positioned just below the EGR valve's exhaust side. Pressure between the orifice and the EGR valve decreases when the EGR opens because it becomes exposed to the lower pressure in the intake. The DPFE sensor recognizes this pressure drop, compares it to the relatively higher pressure on the exhaust side of the orifice, and signals the value of the pressure difference to the PCM. ● SEE FIGURE 26–9.

- Many vehicle manufacturers use the manifold absolute pressure (MAP) sensor as the EGR monitor on some applications. After meeting the enable criteria (operating condition requirements), the EGR monitor is run. The PCM monitors the MAP sensor while it commands the EGR valve to open. The MAP sensor signal should change in response to the sudden change in manifold pressure or the fuel trim changes created by a change in the oxygen sensor voltage. If the signal value falls outside the acceptable value in the lookup table, a DTC sets. If the EGR fails on two consecutive trips, the PCM lights the MIL. ● SEE FIGURE 26–10.

# DIAGNOSING A DEFECTIVE EGR SYSTEM

## SYMPTOMS If the EGR valve is not opening or the flow of the exhaust gas is restricted, then the following symptoms are likely:

- Detonation (spark knock or ping) during acceleration or during cruise (steady-speed driving)

- Excessive oxides of nitrogen ($NO_x$) exhaust emissions

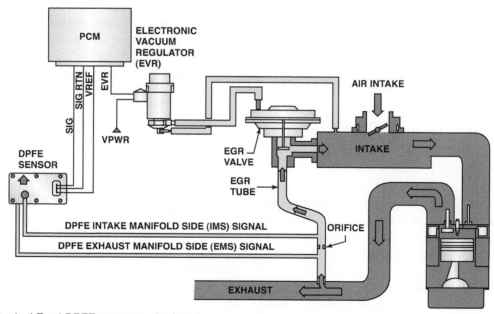

FIGURE 26–9 A typical Ford DPFE sensor and related components.

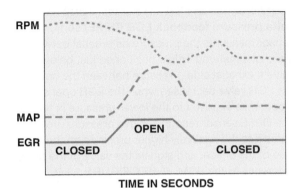

**FIGURE 26–10** An OBD-II active test. The PCM opens the EGR valve and then monitors the MAP sensor and/or engine speed (RPM) to verify that it meets acceptable values.

## TECH TIP

**Watch Out for Carbon Balls!**

EGR valves can get stuck partially open by a chunk of carbon, and the valve or solenoid will test as defective. When the valve (or solenoid) is removed, small chunks or balls of carbon often fall into the exhaust manifold passage. When the replacement valve is installed, the carbon balls can be drawn into the new valve again, causing the engine to idle roughly or stall.

To help prevent this problem, start the engine with the EGR valve or solenoid removed. Any balls or chunks of carbon will be blown out of the passage by the exhaust. Stop the engine and install the replacement EGR valve or solenoid.

If the EGR valve is stuck open or partially open, then the following symptoms are likely:

- Rough idle or frequent stalling
- Poor performance/low power, especially at low engine speed

## EGR TESTING PROCEDURES

The first step in almost any diagnosis is to perform a thorough visual inspection. To check for proper operation of a vacuum-operated EGR valve, follow these steps:

**STEP 1** **Check the vacuum diaphragm of the EGR valve to see if it can hold vacuum.** Because many EGR valves require exhaust back pressure to function correctly, the engine should be running at a fast idle during this test.

**STEP 2** **Apply vacuum from a hand-operated vacuum pump and check for proper operation.** The valve itself should move when vacuum is applied, and the

## REAL WORLD FIX

**The Blazer Story**

The owner of a Chevrolet Blazer equipped with a 4.3-L, V-6 engine complained that the engine would stumble and hesitate at times. Everything seemed to be functioning correctly, except that the service technician discovered a weak vacuum going to the EGR valve at idle. This vehicle was equipped with an EGR valve-control solenoid, called an **electronic vacuum regulator valve (EVRV)** by General Motors Corporation. The PCM pulses the solenoid to control the vacuum that regulates the operation of the EGR valve. The technician checked the service manual for details on the workings of the system. The technician discovered that vacuum should be present at the EGR valve only when the gear selector indicates a drive gear (drive, low, reverse). Because the technician discovered the vacuum at the solenoid to be leaking, the solenoid was obviously defective and required replacement. After replacement of the solenoid (EVRV), the hesitation problem was solved.

NOTE: The technician also discovered in the service manual that blower-type exhaust hoses should not be connected to the tailpipe on any vehicle while performing an inspection of the EGR system. The vacuum created by the system could cause false EGR valve operation to occur.

engine operation should be affected. The EGR valve should be able to hold the vacuum that was applied. If the vacuum drops off, then the valve is likely to be defective.

**STEP 3** **Monitor engine vacuum drop.** Connect a vacuum gauge to an intake manifold vacuum source and monitor the engine vacuum at idle (should be 17 to 21 in. Hg at sea level). Raise the speed of the engine to 2,500 RPM and note the vacuum reading (should be 17 to 21 in. Hg or higher).

Activate the EGR valve using a scan tool or vacuum pump, if vacuum controlled, and observe the vacuum gauge. The results are as follows:

- The vacuum should drop 6 to 8 in. Hg.
- If the vacuum drops less than 6 to 8 in. Hg, the valve or the EGR passages are clogged.
- If the EGR valve is able to hold vacuum but the engine is not affected when the valve is opened, then the exhaust passage(s) must be checked for restriction.

See the Tech Tip "The Snake Trick." If the EGR valve will not hold vacuum, the valve itself is likely to be defective and require replacement.

## TECH TIP

### The Snake Trick

The EGR passages on many intake manifolds become clogged with carbon, which reduces the flow of exhaust and the amount of exhaust gases in the cylinders. This reduction can cause spark knock (detonation) and increased emissions of oxides of nitrogen ($NO_x$) (especially important in areas with enhanced exhaust emissions testing).

To quickly and easily remove carbon from exhaust passages, cut an approximately 1-foot (30-cm) length from stranded wire, such as garage door guide wire or an old speedometer cable. Flare the end and place the end of the wire into the passage. Set your drill on reverse and turn it on, and the wire will pull its way through the passage, cleaning the carbon as it goes, just like a snake in a drainpipe. Some vehicles, such as Hondas, require that plugs be drilled out to gain access to the EGR passages.
● **SEE FIGURE 26–11.**

**FIGURE 26–11** Removing the EGR passage plugs from the intake manifold on a Honda.

# EGR-RELATED OBD-II DIAGNOSTIC TROUBLE CODES

| Diagnostic Trouble Code | Description | Possible Causes |
|---|---|---|
| P0400 | Exhaust gas recirculation flow problems | • EGR valve<br>• EGR valve hose or electrical connection<br>• Defective PCM |
| P0401 | Exhaust gas recirculation flow insufficient | • EGR valve<br>• Clogged EGR ports or passages |
| P0402 | Exhaust gas recirculation flow excessive | • Stuck-open EGR valve<br>• Vacuum hose(s) misrouted<br>• Electrical wiring shorted |

## SUMMARY

1. Oxides of nitrogen ($NO_x$) are formed inside the combustion chamber because of heat exceeding 2,500°F (1,370°C).

2. Recirculating 6% to 10% inert exhaust gases back into the intake system reduces peak temperature inside the combustion chamber and reduces $NO_x$ exhaust emissions.

3. EGR is usually not needed during cold engine operation, at idle speeds or during wide-open throttle conditions.

4. Vacuum-operated EGR valves are usually exhaust back pressure controlled to help match EGR flow into the intake with the load on the engine.

5. Many EGR systems use a feedback potentiometer to signal the PCM about the position of the EGR valve pintle.

6. Some EGR valves are solenoids or pulse-width modulated pintles.

7. OBD-II requires that the flow rate be tested, which can be achieved by opening the EGR valve and observing the reaction of the MAP sensor.

1. What causes the formation of oxides of nitrogen?
2. How does the use of exhaust gas reduce $NO_x$ exhaust emission?
3. How does the DPFE sensor work?
4. How does the PCM determine that the exhaust flow through the EGR system meets OBD-II regulations?

## CHAPTER QUIZ

1. What causes the nitrogen and the oxygen in the air to combine and form $NO_x$?
   a. Sunlight
   b. Any spark will cause this to occur
   c. Heat above 2,500°F (1,370°C)
   d. Chemical reaction in the catalytic converter

2. Exhaust gas recirculation (EGR) is generally not needed under all the following conditions *except* _____.
   a. Idle speed
   b. Cold engine
   c. Cruise speed
   d. Wide-open throttle (WOT)

3. Technician A says that a low-restriction exhaust system could prevent a back pressure-type vacuum-controlled EGR valve from opening correctly. Technician B says restricted exhaust can cause the EGR valve position sensor to fail. Which technician is correct?
   a. Technician A only
   b. Technician B only
   c. Both Technicians A and B
   d. Neither Technician A nor B

4. EGR is used to control which exhaust emission?
   a. Unburned hydrocarbons (HC)
   b. Oxides of nitrogen ($NO_x$)
   c. Carbon monoxide (CO)
   d. Both $NO_x$ and CO

5. A typical EGR pintle-position sensor is what type of sensor?
   a. Rheostat
   b. Piezoelectric
   c. Wheatstone bridge
   d. Potentiometer

6. OBD-II regulations require that the EGR system be tested. Technician A says that the PCM can monitor the commanded position of the EGR valve to determine if it is functioning correctly. Technician B says that the PCM can open the EGR valve and monitor for a change in the MAP sensor or oxygen sensor reading to detect if the system is functioning correctly. Which technician is correct?
   a. Technician A only
   b. Technician B only
   c. Both Technicians A and B
   d. Neither Technician A nor B

7. Two technicians are discussing clogged EGR passages. Technician A says clogged EGR passages can cause excessive $NO_x$ exhaust emission. Technician B says that clogged EGR passages can cause the engine to ping (spark knock or detonation). Which technician is correct?
   a. Technician A only
   b. Technician B only
   c. Both Technicians A and B
   d. Neither Technician A nor B

8. An EGR valve that is partially stuck open would *most likely* cause what condition?
   a. Rough idle/stalling
   b. Excessive $NO_x$ exhaust emissions
   c. Ping (spark knock or detonation)
   d. Missing at highway speed

9. When testing an EGR system for proper operation using a vacuum gauge, how much should the vacuum drop when the EGR is commanded on by a scan tool?
   a. 1 to 2 in. Hg
   b. 3 to 5 in. Hg
   c. 6 to 8 in. Hg
   d. 8 to 10 in. Hg

10. A P0401 DTC (exhaust gas recirculation flow insufficient) is being discussed. Technician A says that a defective EGR valve could be the cause. Technician B says that clogged EGR passages could be the cause. Which technician is correct?
    a. Technician A only
    b. Technician B only
    c. Both Technicians A and B
    d. Neither Technician A nor B

# chapter 27

# POSITIVE CRANKCASE VENTILATION AND SECONDARY AIR-INJECTION SYSTEMS

**OBJECTIVES:** **After studying Chapter 27, the reader should be able to:** • Prepare for the ASE Engine Performance (A8) certification test content area "D" (Emission Control Systems). • Describe the purpose and function of the positive crankcase ventilation (PCV) and seconday air-injection (SAI) systems. • Discuss how the PCV and SAI systems are tested under OBD-II regulations. • Explain methods for diagnosing and testing faults in the PCV and secondary air injection (SAI) systems.

**KEY TERMS:** Air-injection reaction (AIR) 339 • Blowby 335 • Check valve 339 • Positive crankcase ventilation (PCV) 335 • Secondary air injection (SAI) 339 • Smog pump 339 • Thermactor pump 339

## CRANKCASE VENTILATION

**PURPOSE AND FUNCTION** The problem of crankcase ventilation has existed since the beginning of the automobile because no piston ring, new or old, can provide a perfect seal between the piston and the cylinder wall. When an engine is running, the pressure of combustion forces the piston downward. This same pressure also forces gases and unburned fuel from the combustion chamber, past the piston rings, and into the crankcase. This process of gases leaking past the rings is called **blowby,** and the gases form crankcase vapors.

These combustion by-products, particularly unburned hydrocarbons (HC) caused by blowby, must be ventilated from the crankcase. However, the crankcase cannot be vented directly to the atmosphere because the hydrocarbon vapors add to air pollution. **Positive crankcase ventilation (PCV)** systems were developed to ventilate the crankcase and recirculate the vapors to the engine's induction system so they can be burned in the cylinders. PCV systems help reduce HC and CO emissions.

All systems use the following:

1. PCV valve or calibrated orifice, or orifice and separator
2. PCV inlet air filter plus all connecting hoses

   ● **SEE FIGURE 27–1.**

An oil/vapor or oil/water separator is used in some systems instead of a valve or orifice, particularly with turbocharged and fuel-injected engines. The oil/vapor separator lets oil condense and drain back into the crankcase. The oil/water separator accumulates moisture and prevents it from freezing during cold engine starts.

**FIGURE 27–1** A PCV valve in a cutaway valve cover, showing the baffles that prevent liquid oil from being drawn into the intake manifold.

The air for the PCV system is drawn after the air cleaner filter, which acts as a PCV filter.

**NOTE: Some older designs drew from the dirty side of the air cleaner, where a separate crankcase ventilation filter was used.**

**PCV VALVES** The PCV valve in most systems is a one-way valve containing a spring-operated plunger that controls valve flow rate. ● **SEE FIGURE 27–2.**

Flow rate is established for each engine, and a valve for a different engine should not be substituted. The flow rate is

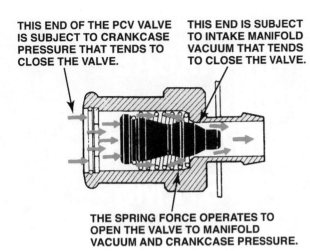

THIS END OF THE PCV VALVE IS SUBJECT TO CRANKCASE PRESSURE THAT TENDS TO CLOSE THE VALVE.

THIS END IS SUBJECT TO INTAKE MANIFOLD VACUUM THAT TENDS TO CLOSE THE VALVE.

THE SPRING FORCE OPERATES TO OPEN THE VALVE TO MANIFOLD VACUUM AND CRANKCASE PRESSURE.

**FIGURE 27–2** Spring force, crankcase pressure, and intake manifold vacuum work together to regulate the flow rate through the PCV valve.

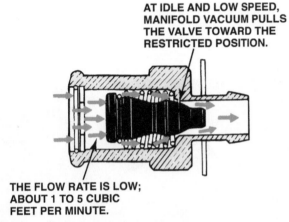

AT IDLE AND LOW SPEED, MANIFOLD VACUUM PULLS THE VALVE TOWARD THE RESTRICTED POSITION.

THE FLOW RATE IS LOW; ABOUT 1 TO 5 CUBIC FEET PER MINUTE.

**FIGURE 27–3** Air flows through the PCV valve during idle, cruising, and light-load conditions.

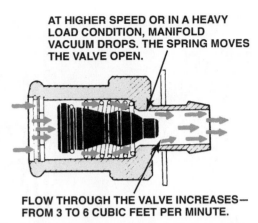

AT HIGHER SPEED OR IN A HEAVY LOAD CONDITION, MANIFOLD VACUUM DROPS. THE SPRING MOVES THE VALVE OPEN.

FLOW THROUGH THE VALVE INCREASES— FROM 3 TO 6 CUBIC FEET PER MINUTE.

**FIGURE 27–4** Air flows through the PCV valve during acceleration and when the engine is under a heavy load.

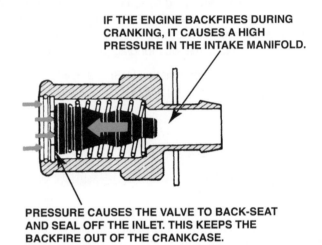

IF THE ENGINE BACKFIRES DURING CRANKING, IT CAUSES A HIGH PRESSURE IN THE INTAKE MANIFOLD.

PRESSURE CAUSES THE VALVE TO BACK-SEAT AND SEAL OFF THE INLET. THIS KEEPS THE BACKFIRE OUT OF THE CRANKCASE.

**FIGURE 27–5** PCV valve operation in the event of a backfire.

determined by the size of the plunger and the holes inside the valve. PCV valves usually are located in the valve cover or intake manifold.

The PCV valve regulates airflow through the crankcase under all driving conditions and speeds. When manifold vacuum is high (at idle, cruising, and light-load operation), the PCV valve restricts the airflow to maintain a balanced air-fuel ratio. ● **SEE FIGURE 27–3.**

It also prevents high intake manifold vacuum from pulling oil out of the crankcase and into the intake manifold. Under high speed or heavy loads, the valve opens and allows maximum airflow. ● **SEE FIGURE 27–4.**

If the engine backfires, the valve will close instantly to prevent a crankcase explosion. ● **SEE FIGURE 27–5.**

**ORIFICE-CONTROLLED SYSTEMS** The closed PCV system used on some 4-cylinder engines contains a calibrated orifice instead of a PCV valve. The orifice may be located in the valve cover or intake manifold or in a hose connected between the valve cover, air cleaner, and intake manifold.

While most orifice flow control systems work the same as a PCV valve system, they may not use fresh air scavenging of the crankcase. Crankcase vapors are drawn into the intake manifold in calibrated amounts depending on manifold pressure and the orifice size. If vapor availability is low, as during idle, air is drawn in with the vapors. During off-idle operation, excess vapors are sent to the air cleaner.

At idle, PCV flow is controlled by a 0.05-inch (1.3-mm) orifice. As the engine moves off idle, ported vacuum pulls a spring-loaded valve off of its seat, allowing PCV flow to pass through a 0.09-inch (2.3-mm) orifice.

**SEPARATOR SYSTEMS** Turbocharged and many fuel-injected engines use an oil/vapor or oil/water separator and a calibrated orifice instead of a PCV valve. In the most common applications, the air intake throttle body acts as the source for crankcase ventilation vacuum, and a calibrated orifice acts as the metering device.

## PCV SYSTEM DIAGNOSIS

**SYMPTOMS** If the PCV valve or orifice is not clogged, intake air flows freely and the PCV system functions properly. Engine design includes the air and vapor flow as a calibrated part of

**The Whistling Engine**

An older vehicle was being diagnosed for a whistling sound whenever the engine was running, especially at idle. It was finally discovered that the breather in the valve cover was plugged and caused high vacuum in the crankcase. The engine was sucking air from what was likely the rear main seal lip, making the "whistle" noise. After replacing the breather and PCV, the noise stopped.

 TECH TIP

**Check for Oil Leaks with the Engine Off**

The owner of an older vehicle equipped with a V-6 engine complained to his technician that he smelled burning oil, but only *after* shutting off the engine. The technician found that the rocker cover gaskets were leaking. But why did the owner only notice the smell of hot oil when the engine was shut off? Because of the positive crankcase ventilation (PCV) system, engine vacuum tends to draw oil away from gasket surfaces. When the engine stops, however, engine vacuum disappears, and the oil remaining in the upper regions of the engine will tend to flow down and out through any opening. Therefore, a good technician should check an engine for oil leaks not only with the engine running but also shortly after shutdown.

**The Oil-Burning Chevrolet Astro Van**

An automotive instructor was driving a Chevrolet Astro van to Fairbanks, Alaska, in January. It was cold, around −32°F (−36°C). As he pulled into Fairbanks and stopped at a traffic light, he smelled burning oil. He thought it was the vehicle ahead of him because it was an older model and in poor condition. However, when he stopped at the hotel he still smelled burning oil. He looked under the van and discovered a large pool of oil. After checking the oil and finding very little left, he called a local shop and was told to bring it in. The technician looked over the situation and said, "You need to put some cardboard across the grill to stop the PCV valve from freezing up." Apparently the PCV valve froze, which then caused the normal blowby gases to force several quarts out the dipstick tube. After installing the cardboard, the instructor had no further problems.

**CAUTION: Do not cover the radiator when driving unless under severe cold conditions and carefully watch the coolant temperature to avoid overheating the engine.**

and in the valley area of most V-type engines. Several methods can be used to test a PCV system.

**RATTLE TEST** The rattle test is performed by simply removing the PCV valve and giving it a shake:

- If the PCV valve does *not* rattle, it is definitely defective and must be replaced.
- If the PCV valve *does* rattle, it does not necessarily mean that the PCV valve is good. All PCV valves contain springs that can become weaker with age and with heating and cooling cycles. Replace any PCV valve with the *exact* replacement according to the vehicle manufacturer's recommended intervals.

**THE 3 × 5 CARD TEST** Remove the oil-fill cap (where oil is added to the engine) and start the engine.

**NOTE: Use care on some overhead camshaft engines. With the engine running, oil may be sprayed from the open oil-fill opening.**

Hold a 3 × 5 card over the opening (a dollar bill or any other piece of paper can be used for this test):

- If the PCV system, including the valve and hoses, is functioning correctly, the card should be held down on the oil-fill opening by the slight vacuum inside the crankcase.
- If the card will not stay, carefully inspect the PCV valve, hose(s), and manifold vacuum port for carbon buildup (restriction). Clean or replace as necessary.

the air-fuel mixture. In fact, some engines receive as much as 30% of the idle air through the PCV system. For this reason, a flow problem in the PCV system results in driveability problems.

A blocked or plugged PCV system may cause the following to occur:

- Rough or unstable idle
- Excessive oil consumption
- Oil in the air filter housing
- Oil leaks due to excessive crankcase pressure

Before attempting expensive engine repairs, check the condition of the PCV system.

**PCV SYSTEM PERFORMANCE CHECK** A properly operating positive crankcase ventilation system should be able to draw vapors from the crankcase and into the intake manifold. If the pipes, hoses, and PCV valve itself are not restricted, vacuum is applied to the crankcase. A slight vacuum is created in the crankcase (usually less than 1 in. Hg if measured at the dipstick) and is also applied to other areas of the engine. Oil drainback holes provide a path for oil to drain back into the oil pan. These holes also allow crankcase vacuum to be applied under the rocker covers

FIGURE 27–6 Using a gauge that measures vacuum in units of inches of water to test the vacuum at the dipstick tube, being sure that the PCV system is capable of drawing a vacuum on the crankcase (28 in. $H_2O$ = 1 PSI, or about 2 in. Hg of vacuum).

**NOTE: On some 4-cylinder engines, the 3 × 5 card may vibrate on the oil-fill opening when the engine is running at idle speed. This is normal because of the time intervals between intake strokes on a 4-cylinder engine.**

**SNAP-BACK TEST** The proper operation of the PCV valve can be checked by placing a finger over the inlet hole in the valve when the engine is running and removing the finger rapidly. Repeat several times. The valve should "snap back." If the valve does not snap back, replace the valve.

**CRANKCASE VACUUM TEST** Sometimes the PCV system can be checked by testing for a weak vacuum at the oil dipstick tube using an inches-of-water manometer or gauge as follows:

**STEP 1** Remove the oil-fill cap or vent PCV opening and cover the opening.

**STEP 2** Remove the oil dipstick (oil level indicator).

**STEP 3** Connect a water manometer or gauge to the dipstick tube.

**STEP 4** Start the engine and observe the gauge at idle and at 2,500 RPM. ● **SEE FIGURE 27–6.**

The gauge should show some vacuum, especially at 2,500 RPM. If not, carefully inspect the PCV system for blockages or other faults.

**PCV MONITOR** Starting with 2004 and newer vehicles, all vehicle PCMs monitor the PCV system for proper operation as part of the OBD-II system. The PCV monitor will fail if the PCM detects an opening between the crankcase and the PCV valve or between the PCV valve and the intake manifold. ● **SEE FIGURE 27–7.**

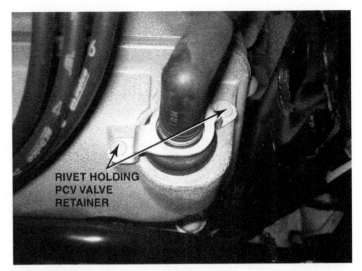

FIGURE 27–7 Most PCV valves used on newer vehicles are secured with fasteners, making it more difficult to disconnect and thereby less likely to increase emissions.

**? FREQUENTLY ASKED QUESTION**

**What Are the Wires for at the PCV Valve?**

Ford uses an electric heater to prevent ice from forming inside the PCV valve and causing blockage.

Water is a by-product of combustion, and resulting moisture can freeze when the outside air temperature is low. General Motors and others clip a heater hose to the PCV hose to provide the heat needed to prevent an ice blockage.

# PCV-RELATED DIAGNOSTIC TROUBLE CODES

| Diagnostic Trouble Code | Description | Possible Causes |
|---|---|---|
| P0101 | MAF or airflow circuit range problem | ● Defective PCV valve or hose/connections or MAF circuit fault |
| P0505 | Idle control system problem | ● Defective PCV valve or hose/connections |

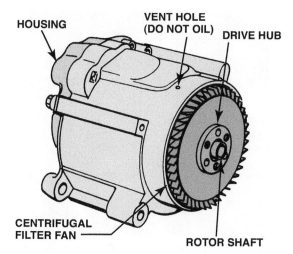

**FIGURE 27–8** A typical belt-driven AIR pump. Air enters through the revolving fins behind the drive pulley. The fins act as an air filter because dirt is heavier than air, and therefore the dirt is deflected off of the fins at the same time air is being drawn into the pump.

# SECONDARY AIR-INJECTION SYSTEM

**PURPOSE AND FUNCTION**   The **secondary air-injection (SAI)** system provides the air necessary for the oxidizing process either at the exhaust manifold or inside the catalytic converter.

**NOTE: This system is commonly called   meaning air-injection reaction. Therefore, an AIR pump does pump air.**

**PARTS AND OPERATION**   The SAI pump, also called an AIR pump, a **smog pump,** or **thermactor pump,** is mounted at the front of the engine and can be driven by a belt from the crankshaft pulley. It pulls fresh air in through an external filter and pumps the air under slight pressure to each exhaust port through connecting hoses or a manifold. The typical SAI system includes the following components:

- A belt-driven pump with inlet air filter (older models) (● **SEE FIGURE 27–8.**)
- An electrically driven air pump (newer models)
- One or more air distribution manifolds and nozzles
- One or more exhaust check valves
- Connecting hoses for air distribution
- Air management valves and solenoids on all newer applications

With the introduction of $NO_x$ reduction converters (also called dual-bed, three-way converters, or TWC), the output of the SAI pump is sent to the center of the converter, where the extra air can help oxidize unburned hydrocarbons (HC)

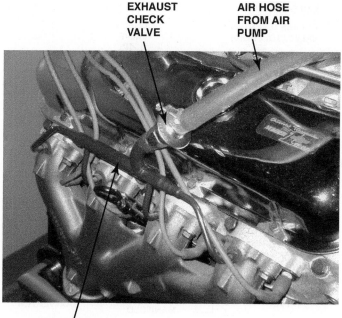

**FIGURE 27–9** The external air manifold and exhaust check valve on a restored muscle car engine.

and carbon monoxide (CO) into water vapor ($H_2O$) and carbon dioxide ($CO_2$).

The computer controls the airflow from the pump by switching on and off various solenoid valves.

**AIR DISTRIBUTION MANIFOLDS AND NOZZLES**   The secondary air-injection system sends air from the pump to a nozzle installed near each exhaust port in the cylinder head. This provides equal air injection for the exhaust from each cylinder and makes it available at a point in the system where exhaust gases are the hottest.

Air is delivered to the exhaust system in one of two ways:

1. An external air manifold, or manifolds, distributes the air through injection tubes with stainless-steel nozzles. The nozzles are threaded into the cylinder heads or exhaust manifolds close to each exhaust valve. This method is used primarily with smaller engines.

2. An internal air manifold distributes the air to the exhaust ports near each exhaust valve through passages cast in the cylinder head or the exhaust manifold. This method is used mainly with larger engines.

**EXHAUST CHECK VALVES**   All air-injection systems use one or more one-way check valves to protect the air pump and other components from reverse exhaust flow. A **check valve** contains a spring-type metallic disc or reed that closes under exhaust back pressure. Check valves are located between the air manifold and the switching valve(s). If exhaust pressure exceeds injection pressure or if the air pump fails, the check valve spring closes the valve to prevent reverse exhaust flow. ● **SEE FIGURE 27–9.**

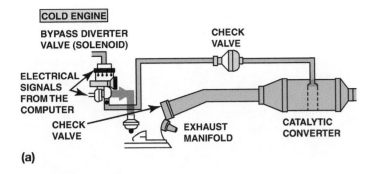

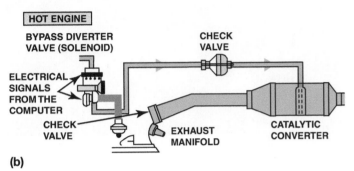

**FIGURE 27–10** (a) When the engine is cold and before the oxygen sensor is hot enough to achieve closed loop, the air-flow from the air pump is directed to the exhaust manifold(s) through the one-way check valves, which keep the exhaust gases from entering the switching solenoids and the pump itself. (b) When the engine achieves closed loop, the air is directed to the catalytic converter.

**NOTE: These check valves commonly fail, resulting in excessive exhaust emissions (CO, especially). When the check valve fails, hot exhaust can travel up to and destroy the switching valve(s) and air pump itself.**

**BELT-DRIVEN AIR PUMPS** The belt-driven air pump uses a centrifugal filter just behind the drive pulley. As the pump rotates, underhood air is drawn into the pump and slightly compressed. The system uses either vacuum- or solenoid-controlled diverter valves to air directed to the following:

- The exhaust manifold, when the engine is cold to help oxidize carbon monoxide (CO) and unburned hydrocarbons (HC) into carbon dioxide ($CO_2$) and water vapor ($H_2O$)
- The catalytic converter when the engine is warm on some models to help provide the extra oxygen needed for the efficient conversion of CO and HC into $CO_2$ and $H_2O$
- The air cleaner, during deceleration or wide-open throttle (WOT) engine operation ● **SEE FIGURE 27–10.**

**ELECTRIC MOTOR–DRIVEN AIR PUMPS** This style of pump is generally used only during cold engine operation and is computer controlled. The secondary air-injection (SAI) system helps reduce hydrocarbons (HC) and carbon monoxide (CO).

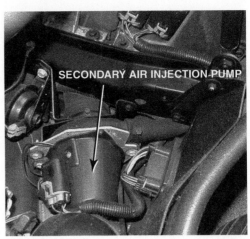

**FIGURE 27–11** A typical electric motor–driven SAI pump. This unit is on a Chevrolet Corvette and only works when the engine is cold.

The air flowing to the exhaust manifold also helps to warm the three-way catalytic converters quickly on engine start-up so conversion of exhaust gases may occur sooner:

- The SAI pump solenoids are controlled by the PCM. The PCM turns on the SAI pump by providing the ground to complete the circuit, which energizes the SAI pump solenoid relay. When air to the exhaust ports is desired, the PCM energizes the relay in order to turn on the solenoid and the SAI pump. ● **SEE FIGURE 27–11.**
- The PCM turns on the SAI pump during start-up any time the engine coolant temperature is above 32°F (0°C). A typical electric SAI pump operates for a maximum of four minutes or until the system enters closed-loop operation.

## SECONDARY AIR-INJECTION SYSTEM DIAGNOSIS

**SYMPTOMS** The air pump system should be inspected if an exhaust emissions test failure occurs. In severe cases, the exhaust will enter the air cleaner assembly, resulting in a horribly running engine because the extra exhaust displaces the oxygen needed for proper combustion. With the engine running, check for normal operation. ● **SEE CHART 27–1.**

**VISUAL INSPECTION** Carefully inspect all parts of the SAI system, including the following:

- Hoses and pipes (Any that have holes and leak air or exhaust require replacement.)
- Check valve(s), when a pump has become inoperative
- Exhaust gases, which could have gotten past the check valve and damaged the pump (Look for signs of overheated areas upstream from the check valves. In severe cases, the exhaust can enter the air cleaner assembly,

| Engine Operation | Normal Operation of a Typical SAI System |
|---|---|
| Cold engine (open-loop operation) | Air is diverted to the exhaust manifold(s) or cylinder head |
| Warm engine (closed-loop operation) | Air is diverted to the catalytic converter |
| Deceleration | Air is diverted to the air cleaner assembly |
| Wide-open throttle | Air is diverted to the air cleaner assembly |

**CHART 27-1**

Typical SAI system operation showing location of airflow from the pump.

destroying the air filter and greatly reducing engine power.)

- Drive belt on an engine-driven pump, for wear and proper tension (If the belt is worn or damaged, check that the AIR pump rotates.)

**FOUR-GAS EXHAUST ANALYSIS** An SAI system can be easily tested using an exhaust gas analyzer and the following steps:

1. Start the engine and allow it to run until normal operating temperature is achieved.

2. Connect the analyzer probe to the tailpipe and observe the exhaust readings for hydrocarbons (HC) and carbon monoxide (CO).

3. Using the appropriate pinch-off pliers, shut off the airflow from the SAI system. Observe the HC and CO readings. If the SAI system is working correctly, the HC and CO levels should increase when the SAI system is shut off.

4. Record the $O_2$ reading with the SAI system still inoperative. Unclamp the pliers and watch the $O_2$ readings. If the system is functioning correctly, the $O_2$ level should increase by 1% to 4%.

## SAI-RELATED DIAGNOSTIC TROUBLE CODE

| Diagnostic Trouble Code | Description | Possible Causes |
|---|---|---|
| P0410 | SAI solenoid circuit fault | • Defective SAI solenoid<br>• Loose or corroded electrical connections<br>• Loose, missing, or defective rubber hose(s) |

## SUMMARY

1. Positive crankcase ventilation (PCV) systems use a valve or a fixed orifice to control the crankcase vapors from the crankcase back into the intake system.

2. A PCV valve regulates the flow of crankcase vapors depending on engine vacuum and seals the crankcase vent in the event of a backfire.

3. As much as 30% of the air needed by the engine at idle speed flows through the PCV system.

4. PCV tests include the rattle test, card test, snap-back test, and crankcase vacuum test.

5. The AIR system forces air at low pressure into the exhaust to reduce CO and HC exhaust emissions.

6. Exhaust check valves are used between the AIR pump and the exhaust manifold to prevent exhaust gases from flowing into and damaging the AIR pump and valves.

## REVIEW QUESTIONS

1. What exhaust emissions do the PCV valve and the SAI system control?

2. How does a PCV valve work?

3. What does the abbreviation PCV mean?

4. What does the abbreviation AIR mean?

1. The PCV system controls which exhaust emission(s)?
   a. HC
   b. CO
   c. $NO_x$
   d. Both HC and CO

2. How much of the air needed by the engine flows through the PCV system when the engine is at idle speed?
   a. 1% to 3%
   b. 5% to 10%
   c. 10% to 20%
   d. Up to 30%

3. Technician A says that if the PCV valve was defective or clogged, the engine could idle rough. Technician B says that the engine may stall. Which technician is correct?
   a. Technician A only
   b. Technician B only
   c. Both Technicians A and B
   d. Neither Technician A nor B

4. Technician A says that if a PCV valve rattles, then it is okay and does not need to be replaced. Technician B says that if a PCV valve does not rattle, it should be replaced. Which technician is correct?
   a. Technician A only
   b. Technician B only
   c. Both Technicians A and B
   d. Neither Technician A nor B

5. Technician A says that the PCV system should create a slight pressure in the crankcase at idle. Technician B says that the PCV system should create a slight vacuum in the crankcase at 2,500 RPM. Which technician is correct?
   a. Technician A only
   b. Technician B only
   c. Both Technicians A and B
   d. Neither Technician A nor B

6. The SAI system is used to reduce which exhaust emission(s)?
   a. HC
   b. CO
   c. $NO_x$
   d. Both HC and CO

7. Two technicians are discussing exhaust check valves used in SAI systems. Technician A says that they are used to prevent the output from the SAI pump from entering the intake manifold. Technician B says the check valves are used to keep the exhaust from entering the AIR pump. Which technician is correct?
   a. Technician A only
   b. Technician B only
   c. Both Technicians A and B
   d. Neither Technician A nor B

8. Where is the output of the AIR pump directed when the engine is cold?
   a. Exhaust manifold
   b. Catalytic converter
   c. Air cleaner assembly
   d. To the atmosphere

9. The switching valves on the AIR pump have failed several times. Technician A says that a defective exhaust check valve could be the cause. Technician B says that a leaking exhaust system at the muffler could be the cause. Which technician is correct?
   a. Technician A only
   b. Technician B only
   c. Both Technicians A and B
   d. Neither Technician A nor B

10. When checking for the proper operation of the AIR system using an exhaust gas analyzer, how much should the oxygen ($O_2$) levels increase when the pump is allowed to function?
    a. 1% to 4%
    b. 5% to 10%
    c. 10% to 20%
    d. Up to 30%

# chapter 28

# CATALYTIC CONVERTERS

**OBJECTIVES:** **After studying Chapter 28, the reader should be able to:** • Prepare for ASE Engine Performance (A8) certification test content area "D" (Emission Control Systems). • Describe the purpose and function of the catalytic converter. • Discuss how the catalytic converter is tested under OBD-II regulations. • Explain the method for diagnosing and testing the catalytic converter.

**KEY TERMS:** Catalysts 343 • Catalytic converter 343 • Cerium 344 • Light-off temperature 344 • Light-off converter (LOC) 345 • Oxygen storage capacity (OSC) 345 • Palladium 344 • Platinum 344 • Preconverter 345 • Pup (mini) converter 345 • Rhodium 344 • Tap test 346 • Three-way converter (TWC) 344 • Washcoat 343

## CATALYTIC CONVERTERS

**PURPOSE AND FUNCTION** A **catalytic converter** is an aftertreatment device used to reduce exhaust emissions outside of the engine. The catalytic converter uses a *catalyst:*

- A **catalyst** is a chemical that helps start a chemical reaction but does not enter into the chemical reaction.
- The catalyst materials on the surface of the material inside the converter help create a chemical reaction.
- The chemical reaction changes harmful exhaust emissions into nonharmful exhaust emissions.
- The *converter* therefore converts harmful exhaust gases into water vapor ($H_2O$) and carbon dioxide ($CO_2$).

This device is installed in the exhaust system between the exhaust manifold and the muffler and usually is positioned beneath the passenger compartment. The location of the converter is important since as much of the exhaust heat as possible must be retained for effective operation. The nearer it is to the engine, the better. ● **SEE FIGURE 28–1.**

**CATALYTIC CONVERTER CONSTRUCTION** Most catalytic converters are constructed of a ceramic material in a honeycomb shape with square openings for the exhaust gases:

- There are approximately 400 openings per square inch (62 per sq. cm), and the wall thickness is about 0.006 inch (1.5 mm).
- The substrate is then coated with a porous aluminum material called the **washcoat,** which makes the surface rough.

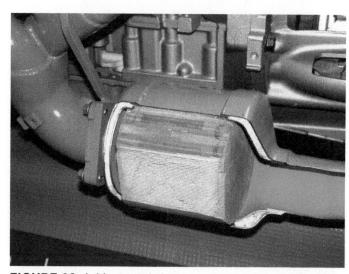

**FIGURE 28–1** Most catalytic converters are located as close to the exhaust manifold as possible, as seen in this display of a Chevrolet Corvette.

- The catalytic materials are then applied on top of the washcoat. The substrate is contained within a round or oval shell made by welding together two stamped pieces of aluminum or stainless steel. ● **SEE FIGURE 28–2.**

The ceramic substrate in monolithic converters is not restrictive; however, the converter can be physically broken if exposed to shock or severe jolts. Monolithic converters can be serviced only as a unit.

An exhaust pipe is connected to the manifold or header to carry gases through a catalytic converter and then to the muffler or silencer. V-type engines can use dual converters or route the exhaust into one catalytic converter by using a Y-exhaust pipe.

**CATALYTIC CONVERTER OPERATION** The converter substrate contains small amounts of **rhodium, palladium,** and **platinum.** These elements act as catalysts. As mentioned, a catalyst is an element that starts a chemical reaction without becoming a part of, or being consumed in, the process. In a **three-way** (catalytic) **converter (TWC)** all three exhaust emissions ($NO_x$, HC, and CO) are converted to carbon dioxide ($CO_2$) and water ($H_2O$). As the exhaust gas passes through the catalyst, oxides of nitrogen ($NO_x$) are chemically reduced (that is, nitrogen and oxygen are separated) in the first section of the catalytic converter. In the second section of the catalytic converter, most of the hydrocarbons and carbon monoxide remaining in the exhaust gas are oxidized to form harmless carbon dioxide ($CO_2$) and water vapor ($H_2O$). ● **SEE FIGURE 28–3.**

Since the early 1990s, many converters also contain **cerium,** an element that can store oxygen. The purpose of the cerium is to provide oxygen to the oxidation bed of the converter when the exhaust is rich and lacks enough oxygen for proper oxidation. When the exhaust is lean, the cerium absorbs the extra oxygen. For the most efficient operation, the converter should have a 14.7:1 air-fuel ratio but can use a mixture that varies slightly:

- A rich exhaust is required for reduction—stripping the oxygen ($O_2$) from the nitrogen in $NO_x$.
- A lean exhaust is required to provide the oxygen necessary to oxidize HC and CO (combining oxygen with HC and CO to form $H_2O$ and $CO_2$).

If the catalytic converter is not functioning correctly, ensure that the air-fuel mixture being supplied to the engine is correct and that the ignition system is free of defects.

**CONVERTER LIGHT-OFF TEMPERATURE** The catalytic converter does not work when cold, so it must be heated to its **light-off temperature** of close to 500°F (260°C) before it starts working at 50% effectiveness. When fully effective, the converter reaches a temperature range of 900°F to 1,600°F (482°C to 871°C). In spite of the intense heat, however, catalytic reactions do not generate a flame associated with a simple burning reaction. Because of the extreme heat (almost as hot as combustion chamber temperatures), a converter remains hot long after the engine is shut off. Most vehicles use a series of heat shields to protect the passenger compartment and other parts of the chassis from excessive heat. Vehicles have been known to start fires because of the hot converter causing tall grass or dry leaves beneath the just-parked vehicle to ignite, especially if the engine is idling. This is most likely to occur if the heat shields have been removed from the converter.

**CONVERTER USAGE** A catalytic converter must be located as close as possible to the exhaust manifold to work effectively. The farther back the converter is positioned in the exhaust system, the more the exhaust gases cool before they

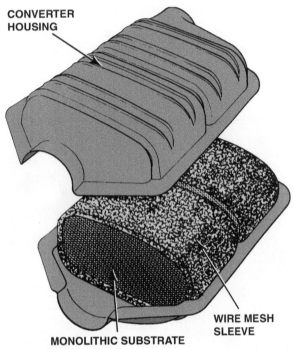

**FIGURE 28–2** A typical catalytic converter with a monolithic substrate.

CONVERTER HOUSING

MONOLITHIC SUBSTRATE

WIRE MESH SLEEVE

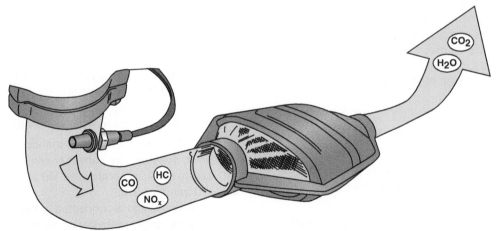

**FIGURE 28–3** The three-way catalytic converter first separates the $NO_x$ into nitrogen and oxygen and then converts the HC and CO into harmless water ($H_2O$) and carbon dioxide ($CO_2$). The nitrogen (N) passes through the converter and exits the tailpipe and enters the atmosphere which is about 78% nitrogen.

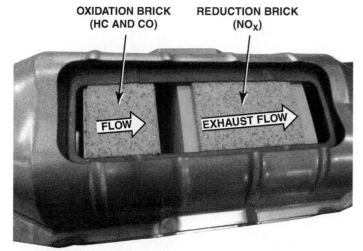

FIGURE 28–4 The small oxidation section of the converter helps build heat for the reduction section to reduce $NO_x$ emissions in the rear brick on most newer vehicles.

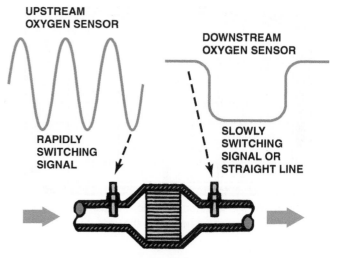

FIGURE 28–5 The OBD-II catalytic converter monitor compares the signals of upstream and downstream oxygen sensors to determine converter efficiency.

reach the converter. Since positioning in the exhaust system affects the oxidation process, vehicle manufacturers that use only an oxidation converter generally locate it underneath the front of the passenger compartment.

Some vehicles have used a small, quick heating oxidation converter called a **preconverter** or a **pup (mini) converter** that connects directly to the exhaust manifold outlet. These have a small catalyst surface area close to the engine that heats up rapidly to start the oxidation process more quickly during cold engine warm-up. For this reason, they were often called **light-off converters (LOCs).** The larger main converter, under the passenger compartment, completes the oxidation reaction started in the LOC.

Most older vehicles used a catalytic converter that had the reduction section first to separate the oxygen from the nitrogen in NOx. The oxygen released during this action help provide extra oxygen to help oxidize the HC and CO into harmless water ($H_2O$) and carbon dioxide ($CO_2$). However, since 2004, emission standards for oxides of nitrogen are stricter, and therefore a larger reduction section is often needed. Therefore, the reduction section is now often after the oxidation section, which is the opposite of the way it was in converters for older models. ● **SEE FIGURE 28–4.**

## OBD-II CATALYTIC CONVERTER PERFORMANCE

The PCM determines if the catalytic converter is ready for testing based on the following conditions, which may vary by vehicle make, model, and year:

- Closed-loop status achieved
- IAT sensor temperature higher than 32°F (0°C)
- ECT sensor temperature higher than 165°F (18°C)
- MAF sensor input from 15 to 32 g/sec
- Engine load less than 65% and steady
- Engine speed less than 4,000 RPM
- All of the above conditions met for at least four minutes

These factors are the enable criteria that must be achieved before the OBD-II catalyst monitor will run.

## OBD-II CATALYTIC CONVERTER PERFORMANCE

With OBD-II-equipped vehicles, catalytic converter performance is monitored by a heated oxygen sensor ($HO_2S$) both before and after the converter. ● **SEE FIGURE 28–5.**

The converters used on these vehicles have **oxygen storage capacity (OSC),** due mostly to the cerium coating in the catalyst rather than the precious metals used. When the three-way converter (TWC) is operating as it should, the post-converter $HO_2S$ is far less active than the preconverter sensor. The converter stores, then releases, the oxygen during normal reduction and oxidation of the exhaust gases, smoothing out the variations in oxygen being released.

Where a cycling sensor voltage output is expected before the converter, because of the converter action, the postconverter $HO_2S$ should read a steady signal with little fluctuation. ● **SEE FIGURE 28–6.**

**NOTE: Because of more demanding exhaust emission standards for oxides of nitrogen ($NO_x$) starting in 2004, the reduction part of the converter is now usually located downstream from the oxidation section. This is opposite of the way an older style converter was constructed. With better fuel injection systems and ignition systems, the amount of CO and HC exhaust emissions is lower than in the past. By using the oxidation section first creates heat to help the reduction section better control oxides of nitrogen emissions. The rear "brick" or reduction section is also larger than the oxidation section.**

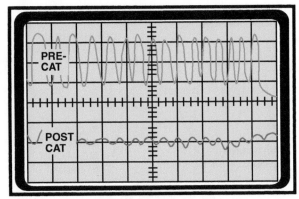

**FIGURE 28–6** The waveform of a downstream O2S sensor from a properly functioning converter shows little, if any, activity.

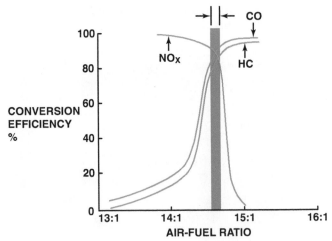

**FIGURE 28–7** The highest catalytic converter efficiency occurs when the air-fuel mixture is about 14.7:1.

**CONVERTER-DAMAGING CONDITIONS** Since converters have no moving parts, they require no periodic service. Under federal law, catalyst effectiveness is warranted for 80,000 miles or eight years.

The three main causes of premature converter failure are the following:

- **Contamination.** Substances that can destroy the converter include exhaust that contains excess engine oil, antifreeze, sulfur (from poor fuel), and various other chemical substances.

- **Excessive temperatures.** Although a converter operates at high temperatures, it can be destroyed by excessive temperatures. This most often occurs either when too much unburned fuel enters the converter, or with excessively lean mixtures. Excessive temperatures may be caused by long idling periods on some vehicles since more heat develops at those times than when driving at normal highway speeds. Severe high temperatures can cause the converter to melt down, leading to the internal parts breaking apart and either clogging the converter or moving downstream to plug the muffler. In either case, the restricted exhaust flow severely reduces engine power.

- **Improper air-fuel mixtures.** Rich mixtures or raw fuel in the exhaust can be caused by engine misfiring or an excessively rich air-fuel mixture resulting from a defective coolant temp sensor or defective fuel injectors. Lean mixtures are commonly caused by intake manifold leaks. When either of these circumstances occurs, the converter can become a catalytic furnace, causing the previously described damage. For most efficient catalytic converter operation, the air-fuel mixture should be near 14.7:1. ● **SEE FIGURE 28–7.**

To avoid excessive catalyst temperatures and the possibility of fuel vapors reaching the converter, observe the following rules:

1. Do not use fuel additives or cleaners that are not converter safe.

2. Do not crank an engine for more than 40 seconds when it is flooded or misfiring.

3. Do not turn off the ignition switch when the vehicle is in motion.

4. Do not disconnect a spark plug wire for more than 30 seconds.

5. Repair engine problems such as dieseling, misfiring, or stumbling as soon as possible.

# DIAGNOSING CATALYTIC CONVERTERS

**TAP TEST** The simple **tap test** involves tapping (not pounding) on the catalytic converter using a rubber mallet. If the substrate inside the converter is broken, the converter will rattle when hit. If the converter rattles, a replacement converter is required. ● **SEE FIGURE 28–8.**

**TESTING BACK PRESSURE WITH A PRESSURE GAUGE** Exhaust system back pressure can be measured directly by installing a pressure gauge in an exhaust opening. This can be accomplished in one of the following ways:

1. To test at the oxygen sensor, remove the inside of an old, discarded oxygen sensor and thread in an adapter to convert it to a vacuum or pressure gauge.

FIGURE 28–8 A catalytic converter that rattles when tapped was removed, and the substrate, or what was left of it, fell out. This converter has to be replaced and the root cause of why it failed found and corrected.

NOTE: An adapter can be easily made by inserting a metal tube or pipe into an old oxygen sensor housing. A short section of brake line works great. The pipe can be brazed to the oxygen sensor housing, or it can be glued with epoxy. An 18-mm compression gauge adapter can also be adapted to fit into the oxygen sensor opening. ● SEE FIGURE 28–9.

2. To test the exhaust back pressure at the exhaust gas recirculation (EGR) valve, remove the EGR valve and fabricate a plate equipped with a fitting for a pressure gauge.

3. To test at the secondary air-injection (SAI) check valve, remove the check valve from the exhaust tubes leading to the exhaust manifold. Use a rubber cone with a tube inside to seal against the exhaust tube. Connect the tube to a pressure gauge.

At idle, the maximum back pressure should be less than 1.5 PSI (10 kPa), and it should be less than 2.5 PSI (15 kPa) at 2,500 RPM. Pressure readings higher than these indicate that the exhaust system is restricted, and further testing will be needed to determine the location of the restriction. ● SEE FIGURE 28–10.

## TESTING FOR BACK PRESSURE USING A VACUUM GAUGE
An exhaust restriction can be tested indirectly by checking the intake manifold vacuum with the engine operating at a fast idle speed (about 2,500 RPM). If the exhaust is restricted, some exhaust can pass, and the effect may not be noticeable when the engine is at idle speed. However, when the engine is operating at a higher speed, the exhaust gases can build up behind the restriction and eventually will not be able to leave the combustion chamber. When some of the exhaust is left behind at the end of the exhaust stroke, the resulting pressure in the combustion chamber reduces engine vacuum. To test for an exhaust restriction using a vacuum gauge, perform the following steps:

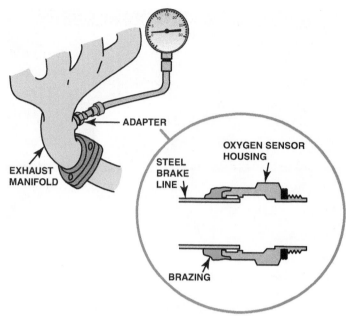

FIGURE 28–9 A back pressure tool can be made by using an oxygen sensor housing and epoxy or braze to hold the tube to the housing.

FIGURE 28–10 This partially melted catalytic converter tested okay at idle but had excessive back pressure at idle speeds.

STEP 1 Attach a vacuum gauge to an intake manifold vacuum source.

STEP 2 Start the engine. Record the engine manifold vacuum reading. The engine vacuum should read 17 to 21 in. Hg when the engine is at idle speed.

STEP 3 Increase the engine speed to 2,500 RPM and hold that speed for 60 seconds while looking at the vacuum gauge.

**Results**

■ If the vacuum reading is equal to or higher than the vacuum reading when the engine was at idle speed, the exhaust system is *not* restricted.

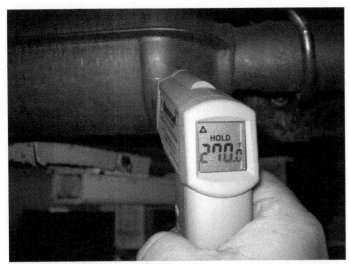

**FIGURE 28-11** The temperature of the outlet should be at least 10% hotter than the temperature of the inlet. If a converter is not working, the inlet temperature will be hotter than the outlet temperature.

- If the vacuum reading is lower than the vacuum reading when the engine was at idle speed, then the exhaust *is* restricted. Further testing will be needed to determine the location of the restriction.

### TESTING A CATALYTIC CONVERTER FOR TEMPERATURE RISE
A properly working catalytic converter should be able to reduce $NO_x$ exhaust emissions into nitrogen (N) and oxygen ($O_2$) and oxidize unburned hydrocarbon (HC) and carbon monoxide (CO) into harmless carbon dioxide ($CO_2$) and water vapor ($H_2O$). During these chemical processes, the catalytic converter should increase in temperature at least 10% if the converter is working properly. To test the converter, operate the engine at 2,500 RPM for at least two minutes to fully warm the converter. Measure the inlet and the outlet temperatures using an infrared pyrometer as shown ● **SEE FIGURE 28-11.**

**NOTE: If the engine is extremely efficient, the converter may not have any excessive unburned hydrocarbons or carbon monoxide to convert! In this case, a spark plug wire could be grounded out using a vacuum hose and a test light to create some unburned hydrocarbon in the exhaust. Do not ground out a cylinder for longer than 10 seconds, or the excessive amount of unburned hydrocarbon could overheat and damage the converter.**

### CATALYTIC CONVERTER EFFICIENCY TESTS
The efficiency of a catalytic converter can be determined using an exhaust gas analyzer:

- **Oxygen level test.** With the engine warm and in closed loop, check the oxygen ($O_2$) and carbon monoxide (CO) levels. A good converter should be able to oxide the extra hydrocarbons caused by the rapid acceleration:
  - If $O_2$ is zero, go to the snap-throttle test.

- If $O_2$ is greater than zero, check the CO level.
- If CO is greater than zero, the converter is *not* functioning correctly.
- **Snap-throttle test.** With the engine warm and in closed loop, snap the throttle to wide-open throttle (WOT) in park or neutral and observe the oxygen reading:
  - The $O_2$ reading should not exceed 1.2%; if it does, the converter is *not* working.
  - If the $O_2$ rises to 1.2%, the converter may have low efficiency.
  - If the $O_2$ remains below 1.2%, then the converter is okay.

## CATALYTIC CONVERTER REPLACEMENT GUIDELINES

Because a catalytic converter is a major exhaust gas emission control device, the U.S. Environmental Protection Agency (EPA) has strict guidelines for its replacement, including the following:

- If a converter is replaced on a vehicle with less than 80,000 miles or eight years, depending on the year of the vehicle, an original equipment catalytic converter *must* be used as a replacement.
- The replacement converter must be of the same design as the original. If the original had an AIR pump fitting, so must the replacement.
- The old converter must be kept for possible inspection by the authorities for 60 days.

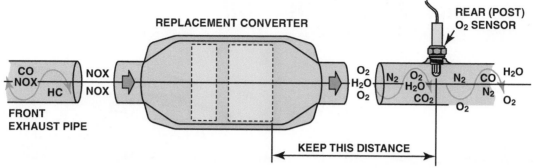

FIGURE 28–12 Whenever replacing a catalytic converter with a universal unit, first measure the distance between the rear brick and the center of the rear oxygen sensor. Be sure that the replacement unit is installed to the same dimension.

**TECH TIP**

**Catalytic Converters Are Murdered**

Catalytic converters start a chemical reaction but do not enter into the chemical reaction. Therefore, catalytic converters neither wear out nor die of old age. If a catalytic converter is found to be defective (nonfunctioning or clogged), look for the *root* cause. Remember this:

"Catalytic converters do not commit suicide—they're murdered."

Items that should be checked when a defective catalytic converter is discovered include all components of the ignition and fuel systems. Excessive unburned fuel can cause the catalytic converter to overheat and fail. The oxygen sensor must be working and fluctuating from 0.5 to 5 Hz (times per second) to provide the necessary air-fuel mixture variations for maximum catalytic converter efficiency.

■ A form must be completed and signed by both the vehicle owner and a representative from the service facility. This form must state the cause of the converter failure and must remain on file for two years.

## CATALYTIC CONVERTER–RELATED DIAGNOSTIC TROUBLE CODE

| Diagnostic Trouble Code | Description | Possible Causes |
|---|---|---|
| P0422 | Catalytic converter efficiency failure | • Engine mechanical fault<br>• Exhaust leaks<br>• Fuel contaminants, such as engine oil, coolant, or sulfur |

# CATALYTIC CONVERTER OPERATION

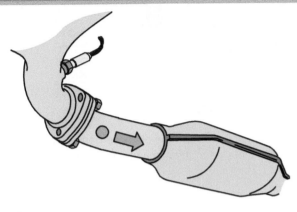

**1** Carbon monoxide leaves the engine through the exhaust valve on the exhaust stroke.

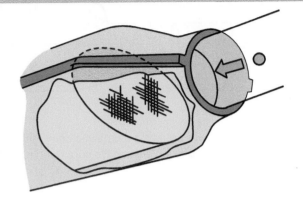

**2** The CO molecule is starting to enter the converter.

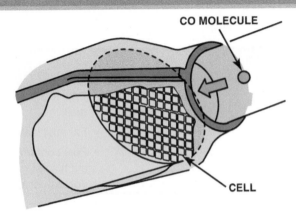

CO MOLECULE

CELL

**3** A CO molecule is ready to enter a cell. The number of cells ranges from 300 to 900 per sq. in. The substrate is cordierite (Mg, AL, Si) or foil-backed metal with a 0.002- to 0.006-inch (0.05- to 0.15-mm)-thick wall.

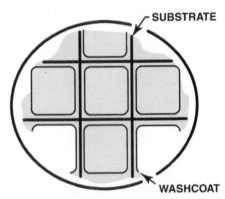

SUBSTRATE

WASHCOAT

**4** The CO molecule enters a cell. The substrate is coated with porous aluminum ($AL_2O_3$) called the washcoat. The catalytic material is sprayed onto the washcoat.

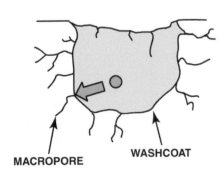

MACROPORE  WASHCOAT

**5** The CO molecule enters a micropore, which has been created in the porous washcoat.

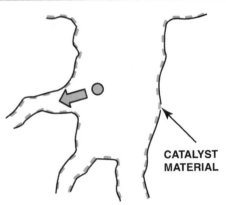

CATALYST MATERIAL

**6** The CO molecule enters a smaller micropore.

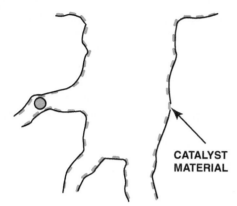

**7** The CO molecule is absorbed onto a catalyst side. Only a few grams of catalyst material are applied to the washcoat.

CATALYST MATERIAL

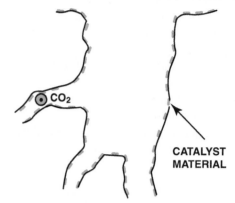

**8** The CO molecule is converted to a $CO_2$ molecule.

CATALYST MATERIAL

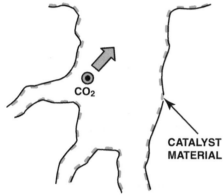

**9** The $CO_2$ molecule is exiting the small micropore.

CATALYST MATERIAL

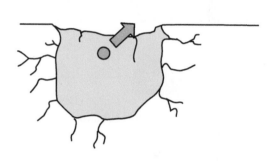

**10** The $CO_2$ molecule is exiting the larger micropore.

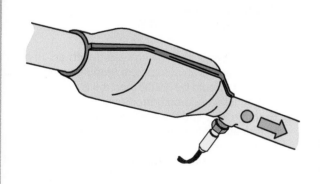

**11** The $CO_2$ molecule is exiting the converter.

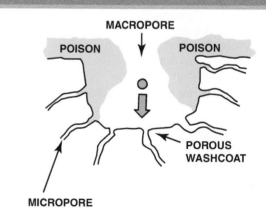

**12** A poisoned converter.

MACROPORE

POISON    POISON

POROUS WASHCOAT

MICROPORE

1. A catalytic converter is an after treatment device that reduces exhaust emissions outside of the engine.
2. The honeycomb shape of the catalytic converter is constructed of a ceramic material about 0.006 inch thick with small square openings.
3. A catalyst is an element that starts a chemical reaction but is not consumed in the process.
4. The catalyst materials used in a catalytic converter include rhodium, palladium, and platinum.
5. A catalytic converter has to be over 500°F (260°C) before it starts to become effective and is therefore mounted as close as possible to the exhaust parts of the engine.
6. The OBD-II system monitor compares the relative activity of a rear oxygen sensor to the precatalytic oxygen sensor to determine catalytic converter efficiency.
7. Catalytic converters can be tested for restriction and for efficiency.

## REVIEW QUESTIONS

1. What are the three most commonly used catalysts in a catalytic converter?
2. How does a catalytic converter reduce $NO_x$ to nitrogen and oxygen?
3. Why must a catalytic converter be mounted close to the exhaust ports of the engine?
4. How does the computer monitor catalytic converter performance?
5. What tests can be performed by a service technician to test the catalytic converter?

## CHAPTER QUIZ

1. What is applied to the ceramic substrate to make the surface porous?
   a. Honeycomb filler
   b. Washcoat
   c. Aluminum
   d. Cerium
2. Two technicians are discussing catalytic converters. Technician A says that the exhaust mixture must fluctuate between rich and lean for the best efficiency. Technician B says that the air-fuel mixture must be leaner than 14.7:1 for best performance from a three-way catalytic converter. Which technician is correct?
   a. Technician A only
   b. Technician B only
   c. Both Technicians A and B
   d. Neither Technician A nor B
3. A catalytic converter has to be at least how hot before it starts to work?
   a. 500°F (260°C)
   b. 1,000°F (540°C)
   c. 1,500°F (815°C)
   d. 2,000°F (1,100°C)
4. What two primary sensors does the PCM use to check the catalytic converter?
   a. Catalytic converter temperature sensor and rear oxygen sensor
   b. Precat and postcat oxygen sensor
   c. Precat oxygen sensor and MAF
   d. MAP and TP
5. A catalytic converter can be harmed by _____.
   a. Excessive engine oil
   b. Antifreeze
   c. Sulfur from poor-quality fuel
   d. Any of the above
6. Two technicians are discussing testing a catalytic converter. Technician A says that a vacuum gauge can be used and observed to see if the vacuum drops with the engine at 2,500 RPM for 60 seconds. Technician B says that a pressure gauge can be used to check for back pressure. Which technician is correct?
   a. Technician A only
   b. Technician B only
   c. Both Technicians A and B
   d. Neither Technician A nor B
7. A catalytic converter is being tested with an infrared pyrometer. Which is an acceptable (good converter) result?
   a. The inlet should be hotter than the outlet by 10%.
   b. The outlet should be hotter than the inlet by 10%.
   c. Both the inlet and the outlet should be the same temperature after the converter reaches operating temperature.
   d. The temperature of a catalytic converter is the best test to perform to locate a restricted (clogged) unit.

8. Which exhaust gas reading indicates a good catalytic converter?
   a. $O_2$ is zero
   b. CO is zero
   c. Both a and b
   d. Neither a nor b

9. A P0422 (catalytic converter efficiency failure) is set. What is a possible cause?
   a. Engine mechanical fault
   b. Exhaust leak
   c. Fuel contamination
   d. Any of the above

10. Technician A says that the catalytic converter is warranted for eight years or 80,000 miles, whichever comes first. Technician B says that after replacing the catalytic converter, the old converter must be kept for possible inspection for 60 days. Which technician is correct?
    a. Technician A only
    b. Technician B only
    c. Both Technicians A and B
    d. Neither Technician A nor B

# IGNITION SYSTEM OPERATION AND DIAGNOSIS

**OBJECTIVES:** **After studying Chapter 29, the reader should be able to:** • Prepare for ASE Engine Performance (A8) certification test content area "B" (Ignition System Diagnosis and Repair). • Explain how ignition coils create 40,000 volts or more. • Discuss crankshaft position sensor and pickup coil operation. • Describe the operation of waste-spark and coil-on-plug (COP) ignition systems. • Describe how to test ignition coils. • Explain how to test spark plug wire. • Describe the test procedure for the diagnosis and repair of electronic ignition systems. • Explain how to inspect and replace spark plugs. • Discuss what to inspect and look for during a visual inspection of the ignition system. • List the steps necessary to check and/or adjust ignition timing on engines equipped with a distributor-type ignition system.

**KEY TERMS:** Coil-on-plug (COP) ignition 355 • Companion cylinders 361 • Detonation 365 • Distributor ignition 355 • Electronic ignition 355 • EMI 355 • Firing order 360 • Hall effect 357 • ICM 356 • Ignition coil 355 • Ignition timing 375 • Ion-sensing ignition 365 • Iridium spark plugs 372 • Knock sensors 365 • Magnetic pulse generator 357 • Pickup coil 357 • Ping 365 • Platinum spark plugs 372 • Primary ignition circuit 356 • Primary winding 355 • Schmitt trigger 358 • • • Spark knock 365 • Spark plugs 372 • Spark tester 367 • Switching 356 • Track 370 • Transistor 357 • Trigger 357 • Turns ratio 355 • Waste-spark system 355

## IGNITION SYSTEM

**PURPOSE AND FUNCTION** The ignition system includes components and wiring necessary to create and distribute a high voltage (up to 40,000 volts or more) and send to the spark plug. A high-voltage arc occurs across the gap of a spark plug at the right time inside the combustion chamber. The spark raises the temperature of the air-fuel mixture and starts the combustion process inside the cylinder.

**BACKGROUND** All ignition systems apply battery voltage (close to 12 volts) to the positive side of the ignition coil(s) and pulse the negative side to ground:

- **Early ignition systems.** Before the mid-1970s, ignition systems used a mechanically opened set of contact points to make and break the electrical connection to ground. A cam lobe, located in and driven by the distributor, opened the points. There was one lobe for each cylinder. The points used a rubbing block that was lubricated by applying a thin layer of grease on the cam lobe at each service interval. Each time the points opened, a high voltage was created in the ignition coil. The high-voltage then traveled to each spark plug through the distributor cap and rotor. The distributor was used twice in the creation of the spark, as follows:

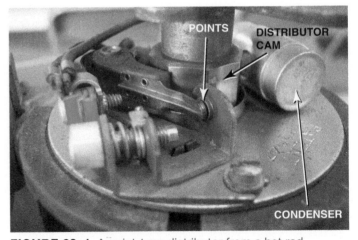

**FIGURE 29–1** A point-type distributor from a hot rod.

1. It was connected to the camshaft which rotated the distributor cam, causing the points to open and close.
2. It used a rotor to send the high-voltage from the coil entering the center of the distributor cap to inserts connected to spark plug wires to each cylinder.

● **SEE FIGURE 29–1.**

- **Electronic ignition.** Since the mid-1970s, ignition systems have used sensors, such as a pickup coil and reluctor (trigger wheel), to trigger or signal an electronic module that switches the primary ground circuit of the ignition coil. **Distributor ignition** is the term specified by the Society of Automotive Engineers (SAE) for an ignition system that uses a distributor. **Electronic ignition** is the term specified by the SAE for an ignition system that does not use a distributor. Electronic ignition system types include the following:

1. **Waste-spark system.** This type of system uses one ignition coil to fire the spark plugs for two cylinders at the same time.

2. **Coil-on-plug (COP) system.** This type of system uses a single ignition coil for each cylinder with the coil placed above or near the spark plug.

## IGNITION COIL CONSTRUCTION

The heart of any ignition system is the **ignition coil.** When the coil negative lead is grounded, the primary (low-voltage) circuit of the coil is complete, and a magnetic field is created around the coil windings. When the circuit is opened, the magnetic field collapses and induces a high voltage in the secondary winding of the ignition coil.

The coil creates a high-voltage spark by electromagnetic induction. Many ignition coils contain two separate but electrically connected windings of copper wire. Other coils are true transformers in which the primary and secondary windings are not electrically connected. ● **SEE FIGURE 29–2.**

The center of an ignition coil contains a core of laminated soft iron (thin strips of soft iron). This core increases the magnetic strength of the coil:

- **Secondary coil winding.** Surrounding the laminated core are approximately 20,000 turns of fine wire (approximately 42 gauge). The winding is called the **secondary winding.**

- **Primary coil winding.** Surrounding the secondary windings are approximately 150 turns of heavy wire (approximately 21 gauge). The winding is called the **primary winding.** The secondary winding has about 100 times the number of turns of the primary winding, referred to as the **turns ratio** (approximately 100:1).

In older coils, these windings are surrounded with a thin metal shield and insulating paper and placed into a metal container filled with transformer oil to help cool the coil windings. Other coil designs use an air-cooled, epoxy-sealed E coil. The *E coil* is so named because the laminated, soft iron core is E shaped, with the coil wire turns wrapped around the center "finger" of the E and the primary winding wrapped inside the secondary winding. ● **SEE FIGURES 29–3 AND 29–4.**

## IGNITION COIL OPERATION

All ignition systems use electromagnetic induction to produce a high-voltage spark from the ignition coil. **Electromagnetic induction (EMI)** means that a current can be created in a conductor (coil winding) by a moving magnetic field. The magnetic field in an ignition coil is produced by current flowing through the primary winding of

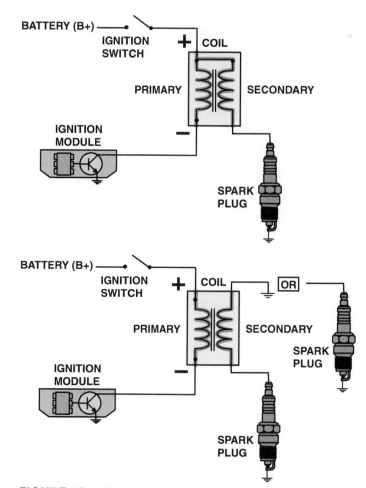

**FIGURE 29–2** Some ignition coils are electrically connected, called married (top figure), whereas others use separate primary and secondary windings, called divorced (lower figure). The polarity (positive or negative) of a coil is determined by the direction in which the coil is wound.

**FIGURE 29–3** The steel lamination used in an E coil helps increase the magnetic field strength, which helps the coil produce higher energy output for a more complete combustion in the cylinders.

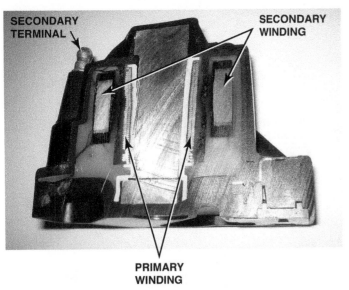

**FIGURE 29–4** The primary windings are inside the secondary windings on this General Motors coil.

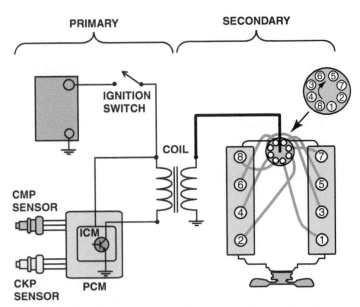

**FIGURE 29–5** The primary ignition system is used to trigger and therefore create the secondary (high-voltage) spark from the ignition coil.

the coil. An ignition coil is able to increase battery voltage to 40,000 volts or more in the following way:

- Battery voltage is applied to the primary winding.
- A ground is provided to the primary winding by the **ignition control module (ICM),** igniter, or PCM.
- Current (approximately 2 to 6 amperes) flows in the primary coil creating a magnetic field in the primary winding.
- When the ground is opened by the ICM, the built-up magnetic field collapses.
- The movement of the collapsing magnetic field induces a voltage of 250 to 400 volts in the primary winding and 20,000 to 40,000 volts or more in the secondary winding with a current of 0.020 to 0.080 ampere.
- The high voltage created in the secondary winding is high enough to jump the air gap at the spark plug.
- The electrical arc at the spark plug ignites the air-fuel mixture in the combustion chamber of the engine.
- For each spark that occurs, the coil must be charged with a magnetic field and then discharged.

> **⚠ WARNING**
>
> The spark from an ignition coil is strong enough to cause physical injury. Always follow the exact service procedure and avoid placing hands near the secondary ignition components when the engine is running.

The ignition components that regulate the current in the coil primary winding by turning it on and off are known collectively as the **primary ignition circuit.** When the primary circuit is carrying current, the secondary circuit is off. When the primary circuit is turned off, the secondary circuit has high voltage. The components necessary to create and distribute the high voltage produced in the secondary windings of the coil are called the **secondary ignition circuit.** ● **SEE FIGURE 29–5.**

These circuits include the following components:

- Primary ignition circuit
  1. Battery
  2. Ignition switch
  3. Primary windings of coil
  4. Pickup coil (crankshaft position sensor)
  5. Ignition control module (igniter)
- Secondary ignition circuit
  1. Secondary windings of coil
  2. Distributor cap and rotor (if the vehicle is so equipped)
  3. Spark plug wires
  4. Spark plugs

## IGNITION SWITCHING AND TRIGGERING

**SWITCHING** For any ignition system to function, the primary current must be turned on to charge the coil and off to allow the coil to discharge, creating a high-voltage spark. This turning on and off of the primary circuit is called **switching.** The unit that does

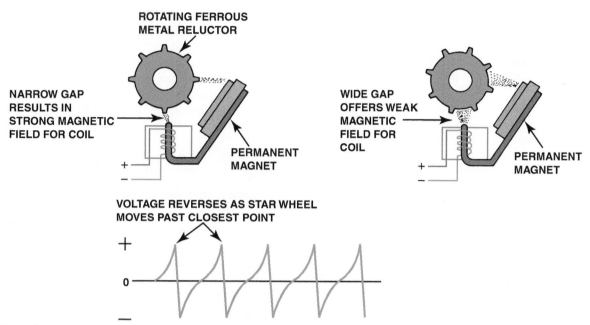

**FIGURE 29–6** Operation of a typical pulse generator (pickup coil). At the bottom is a line drawing of a typical scope pattern of the output voltage of a pickup coil. The module receives this voltage from the pickup coil and opens the ground circuit to the ignition coil when the voltage starts down from its peak (just as the reluctor teeth start moving away from the pickup coil).

the switching is an electronic switch, such as a power transistor. This power transistor can be found in the following locations:

- Ignition control module (ICM) or igniter
- PCM (computer)

**NOTE: On some coil-on-plug (COP) systems, the ICM is part of the ignition coil itself and is serviced as an assembly.**

**TRIGGERING** The device that signals the switching of the coil on and off or just on in most instances is called the **trigger.** A trigger is typically a pickup coil in some distributor-type ignitions and a crankshaft position sensor (CKP) on electronic systems (waste spark and coil on plug). There are three types of devices used for triggering:

1. Magnetic sensor
2. Hall-effect switch
3. Optical sensor

**PRIMARY CIRCUIT OPERATION** To get a spark out of an ignition coil, the primary coil circuit must be turned on and off. The primary circuit current switching is controlled by a **transistor** (electronic switch) inside the ignition module (or igniter) or PCM and is controlled by one of several devices, including the following:

- **Magnetic sensor.** A simple and common ignition electronic switching device is the magnetic pulse generator system. This is a type of magnetic sensor, often called a **magnetic pulse generator** or **pickup coil,** and is installed in the distributor housing. The pulse generator consists of a trigger wheel (reluctor) and a pickup coil. The pickup coil consists of an iron core wrapped with fine wire, in a coil at one end and attached to a permanent magnet at the other end. The center of the coil is called the pole piece. The pickup coil signal

triggers the transistor inside the module and is also used by the PCM for piston position information and engine speed (RPM). The reluctor is shaped so that the magnetic strength changes enough to create a usable varying signal for use by the module to trigger the coil. ● **SEE FIGURE 29–6.**

*Magnetic crankshaft position sensors* use the changing strength of the magnetic field surrounding a coil of wire to signal the module and computer. This signal is used by the electronics in the module and computer to determine piston position and engine speed (RPM). This sensor operates similarly to the distributor magnetic pickup coil. The crankshaft position sensor uses the strength of the magnetic field surrounding a coil of wire to signal the ICM. The rotating crankshaft has notches cut into it that trigger the magnetic position sensor, which change the strength of the magnetic field as the notches pass by the position sensor. ● **SEE FIGURE 29–7.**

- **Hall-effect switch.** This switch also uses a stationary sensor and rotating trigger wheel (shutter). Unlike the magnetic pulse generator, the Hall-effect switch requires a small input voltage to generate an output or signal voltage. **Hall effect** has the ability to generate a voltage signal in semiconductor material (gallium arsenate crystal) by passing current through it in one direction and applying a magnetic field to it at a right angle to its surface. If the input current is held steady and the magnetic field fluctuates, an output voltage is produced that changes in proportion to field strength. Most Hall-effect switches in distributors have the following:

1. Hall element or device
2. Permanent magnet
3. Rotating ring of metal blades (shutters) similar to a trigger wheel (Another method uses a stationary sensor with a rotating magnet.) ● **SEE FIGURE 29–8.**

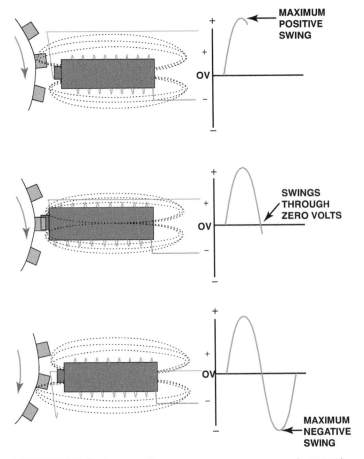

MAXIMUM POSITIVE SWING

0V

SWINGS THROUGH ZERO VOLTS

0V

0V

MAXIMUM NEGATIVE SWING

**FIGURE 29–7** A magnetic sensor uses a permanent magnet surrounded by a coil of wire. The notches of the crankshaft (or camshaft) creates a variable magnetic field strength around the coil and create an analog signal when the engine rotates. When a metallic section is close to the sensor, the magnetic field is stronger because metal is a better conductor of magnetic lines of force than air.

Some blades are designed to hang down, typically found in Bosch and Chrysler systems, while others may be on a separate ring on the distributor shaft, typically found in General Motors and Ford Hall-effect distributors. There are two types of Hall effect sensors used, including the following:

- When the shutter blade enters the gap between the magnet and the Hall element, it creates a magnetic shunt that changes the field strength through the Hall element.

- This analog signal is sent to a **Schmitt trigger** inside the sensor itself, which converts the analog signal into a digital signal. A digital (on or off) voltage signal is created at a varying frequency to the ignition module or onboard computer. ● **SEE FIGURE 29–9.**

- **Optical sensors.** These use light from an LED and a phototransistor to signal the computer. An interrupter disc between the LED and the phototransistor has slits that allow the light from the LED to

trigger the phototransistor on the other side of the disc. Most optical sensors (usually located inside the distributor) use two rows of slits to provide individual cylinder recognition (low resolution) and precise distributor angle recognition (high resolution) signals that are used for cylinder misfire detection. ● **SEE FIGURE 29–10** on page 360.

TECH TIP

**Optical Distributors Do Not Like Light**

Optical distributors use the light emitted from LEDs to trigger phototransistors. Most optical distributors use a shield between the distributor rotor and the optical interrupter ring. Sparks jump the gap from the rotor tip to the distributor cap inserts. This shield blocks the light from the electrical arc from interfering with the detection of the light from the LEDs.

If this shield is not replaced during service, the light signals are reduced, and the engine may not operate correctly. ● **SEE FIGURE 29–11** on page 360.

This can be difficult to detect because nothing looks wrong during a visual inspection. Remember that all optical distributors must be shielded between the rotor and the interrupter ring.

TECH TIP

**The Tachometer Trick**

When diagnosing a no-start or intermediate missing condition, check the operation of the tachometer. If the tachometer does not indicate engine speed (no-start condition) or drops toward zero (engine missing), then the problem is due to a defect in the *primary* ignition circuit. The tachometer gets its signal from the pulsing of the primary winding of the ignition coil. The following components in the primary circuit could cause the tachometer to not work when the engine is cranking:

- Pickup coil
- Crankshaft position sensor
- Ignition module (igniter)
- Coil primary wiring

If the vehicle is not equipped with a tachometer, use a scan tool to look at engine RPM. The results are as follows:

- No or an unstable engine RPM reading means the problem is in the primary ignition circuit.
- A steady engine RPM reading means the problem is in the secondary ignition circuit or is a fuel-related problem.

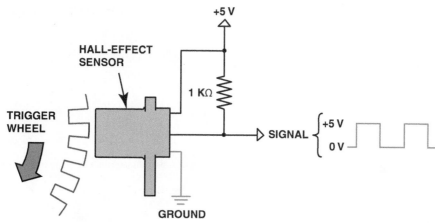

**FIGURE 29–8** A Hall-effect sensor produces a digital on-off voltage signal whether it is used with a blade or a notched wheel.

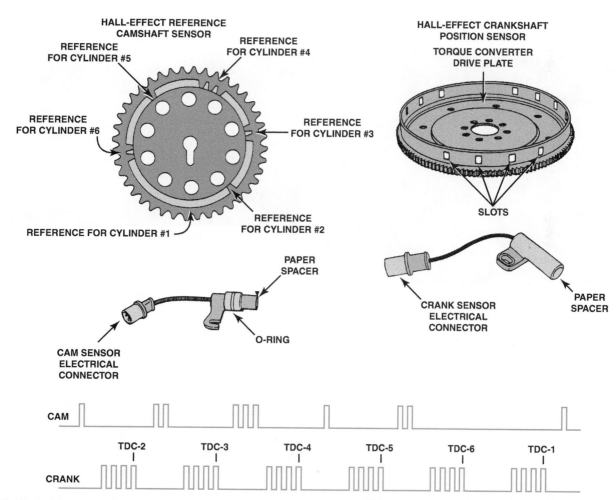

**FIGURE 29–9** Some Hall-effect sensors look like magnetic sensors. This Hall-effect camshaft reference sensor and crankshaft position sensor have an electronic circuit built in that creates a 0- to 5-volt signal as shown at the bottom. These Hall-effect sensors have three wires: a power supply (8 volts) from the computer (controller), a signal (0 to 5 volts), and a signal ground.

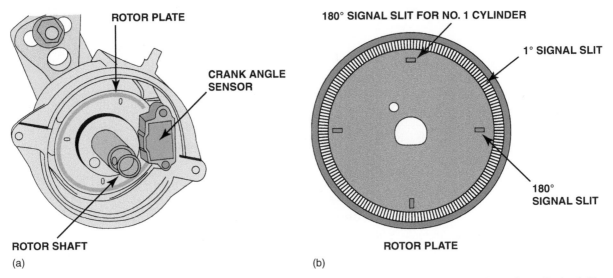

ROTOR PLATE

CRANK ANGLE
SENSOR

ROTOR SHAFT

(a)

180° SIGNAL SLIT FOR NO. 1 CYLINDER

1° SIGNAL SLIT

180°
SIGNAL SLIT

ROTOR PLATE

(b)

**FIGURE 29–10** (a) Typical optical distributor. (b) Cylinder I slit signals the computer the piston position for cylinder I. The 1-degree slits provide accurate engine speed information to the PCM. Optical sensors generate digital (on and off) signals.

**FIGURE 29–11** A light shield is being installed on an optical distributor before the rotor is attached.

**FIGURE 29–12** The firing order is cast or stamped on the intake manifold on most engines that have a distributor ignition.

## DISTRIBUTOR IGNITION

**PURPOSE AND FUNCTION** The purpose of a distributor is to distribute the high-voltage spark from the output terminal of the ignition coil to the spark plugs for each cylinder. A gear or shaft drives the distributor that is connected to the camshaft and is driven at camshaft speed. Most distributor ignition systems also use a sensor to trigger the ignition control module.

**OPERATION OF DISTRIBUTOR IGNITION** The distributor is used twice in most ignition systems that use a distributor:

- First, to trigger the ignition control module by the use of the rotating distributor shaft
- Second, by rotating the rotor to distribute the high-voltage spark to the individual spark plugs

**FIRING ORDER** **Firing order** means the order that the spark is distributed to the correct spark plug at the right time. The firing order of an engine is determined by crankshaft and camshaft design. The firing order is determined by the location of the spark plug wires in the distributor cap of an engine equipped with a distributor. The firing order is often cast into the intake manifold for easy reference. ● **SEE FIGURE 29–12.**

Service information also shows the firing order and the direction of the distributor rotor rotation as well as the location of the spark plug wires on the distributor cap.

CAUTION: Ford V-8s use two different firing orders depending on whether the engine is high output or standard. Using the incorrect firing order can cause the engine to backfire and could cause engine damage or personal injury. General Motors V-6 engines use different firing orders and different locations for cylinder 1 between the 60-degree V-6 and the 90-degree V-6. Using the incorrect firing order or cylinder number location chart could result in poor engine operation or a no start. Firing order is also important for waste-spark-type ignition systems. The spark plug wire can often be installed on the wrong coil pack, which can create a no-start condition or poor engine operation.

# WASTE-SPARK IGNITION SYSTEMS

**PARTS INVOLVED** Waste-spark ignition is another name for distributorless ignition system (DIS) or electronic ignition. Waste-spark ignition was introduced in the mid-1980s and uses the ignition control module (ICM) and/or the powertrain control module (PCM) to fire the ignition coils. A 4-cylinder engine uses two ignition coils, and a 6-cylinder engine uses three ignition coils. Each coil is a true transformer because the primary winding and secondary winding are not electrically connected. Each end of the secondary winding is connected to a cylinder exactly opposite the other in the firing order, which is called a **companion** (paired) **cylinder.** ● SEE FIGURE 29–13.

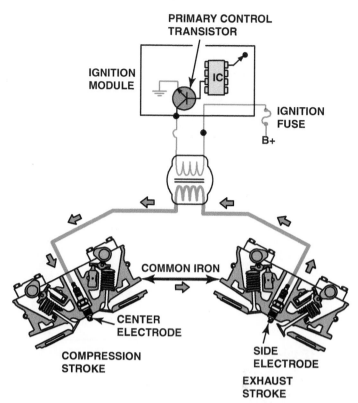

**FIGURE 29–13** A waste-spark system fires one cylinder while its piston is on the compression stroke and into paired or companion cylinders while it is on the exhaust stroke. In a typical engine, it requires only about 2 to 3 kV to fire the cylinder on the exhaust stroke. The remaining coil energy is available to fire the spark plug under compression (typically about 8 to 12 kV).

 **FREQUENTLY ASKED QUESTION**

**How Can You Determine the Companion Cylinder?**

Companion cylinders are two cylinders in the same engine that both reach top dead center (TDC) at the same time:

• One cylinder is on the compression stroke.
• The other cylinder is on the exhaust stroke.

To determine which two cylinders are companion cylinders in the engine, follow these steps:

STEP 1   Determine the firing order (such as 165432 for a typical V-6 engine).

STEP 2   Write the firing order and then place the second half under the first half:

$$\frac{165}{432}$$

STEP 3   The cylinder numbers above and below each other are companion or paired cylinders.
   In this case 1 and 4, 6 and 3, and 5 and 2 are companion cylinders.

**TECH TIP**

**Odds Fire Straight**

Waste-spark ignition systems fire two spark plugs at the same time. Most vehicle manufacturers use a waste-spark system that fires the odd number cylinders (1, 3, and 5) by straight polarity (current flow from the top of the spark plug through the gap and to the ground electrode). The even number cylinders (2, 4, and 6) are fired reverse polarity, meaning that the spark jumps from the side electrode to the center electrode. Some vehicle manufacturers equip their vehicles with platinum plugs that have the expensive platinum alloy on only one electrode, as follows:

• On odd number cylinders (1, 3, 5), the platinum is on the center electrode.
• On even number cylinders (2, 4, 6), the platinum is on the ground electrode.

Replacement spark plugs use platinum on both electrodes (double platinum) and, therefore, can be placed in any cylinder location.

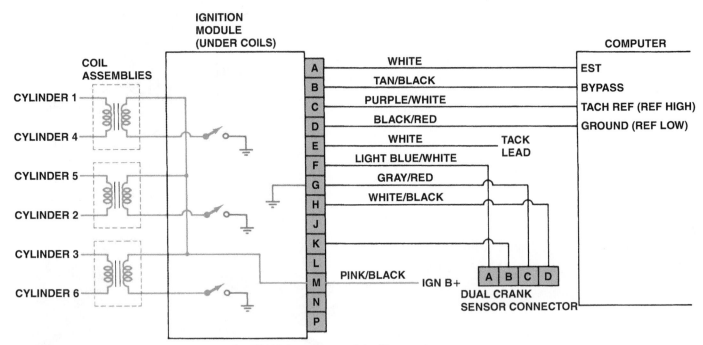

**FIGURE 29–14** Typical wiring diagram of a GM V-6 waste-spark ignition system.

**WASTE-SPARK SYSTEM OPERATION** *Both* spark plugs fire at the same time (within nanoseconds of each other):

- When one cylinder (for example, cylinder number 6) is on the compression stroke, the other cylinder (number 3) is on the exhaust stroke.
- The spark that occurs on the exhaust stroke is called the *waste spark* because it does no useful work and is only used as a ground path for the secondary winding of the ignition coil. The voltage required to jump the spark plug gap on cylinder 3 (the exhaust stroke) is only 2 to 3 kV.
- The cylinder on the compression stroke uses the remaining coil energy.
- One spark plug of each pair always fires straight polarity (center to side electrode), and the other cylinder always fires reverse polarity (side to center electrode). Spark plug life is not greatly affected by the reverse polarity. If there is only one defective spark plug wire or spark plug, two cylinders may be affected.

The coil polarity is determined by the direction the coil is wound (left-hand rule for conventional current flow) and cannot be changed.

Each spark plug for a particular cylinder always will be fired either with straight or reversed polarity, depending on its location in the engine and how the coils are wired. However, the compression and waste-spark condition flip-flops. When one cylinder is on compression, such as cylinder 1, then the paired cylinder (number 4) is on the exhaust stroke. During the next rotation of the crankshaft, cylinder 4 is on the compression stroke, and cylinder 1 is on the exhaust stroke:

**Cylinder 1** Always fires straight polarity (from the center electrode to the ground electrode), one time, requiring 10 to 12 kV, and one time, requiring 3 to 4 kV.

**Cylinder 4** Always fires reverse polarity (from the ground electrode to the center electrode), one time, requiring 10 to 12 kV, and one time, requiring 3 to 4 kV.

Waste-spark ignitions require a sensor (usually a crankshaft sensor) to trigger the coils at the correct time. ● **SEE FIGURE 29–14.**

The crankshaft sensor cannot be moved to adjust ignition timing because ignition timing is not adjustable. The slight adjustment of the crankshaft sensor is designed to position the sensor exactly in the middle of the rotating metal disc for maximum clearance.

**COMPRESSION-SENSING WASTE-SPARK IGNITION** Some waste-spark ignition systems, such as those used on Saturns and others, use the voltage required to fire the cylinders to determine cylinder position. It requires a higher voltage to fire a spark plug under compression than it does when the spark plug is being fired on the exhaust stroke. The electronics in the coil and the PCM can detect which of the two companion (paired) cylinders that are fired at the same time requires the higher voltage and therefore indicates the cylinder that is on the compression stroke. For example, a typical 4-cylinder engine equipped with a waste-spark ignition system will fire both cylinders 1 and 4. If cylinder 4 requires a higher voltage to fire, as determined by the electronics connected to the coil,

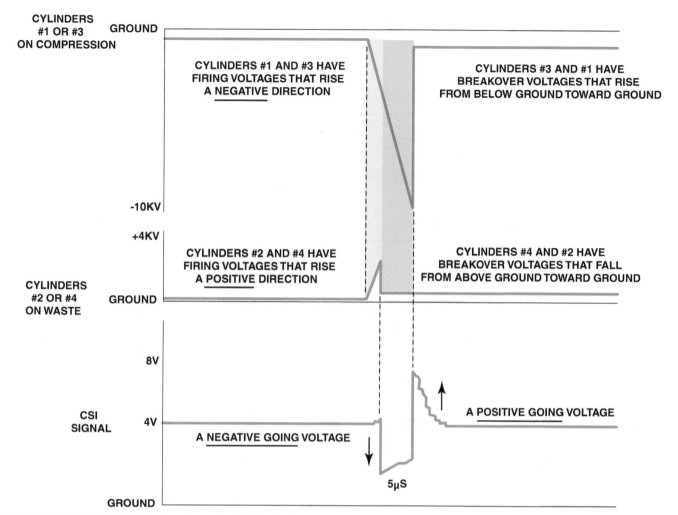

**FIGURE 29–15** The slight (5 microsecond) difference in the firing of the companion cylinders is enough time to allow the PCM to determine which cylinder is firing on the compression stroke. The compression sensing ignition (CSI) signal is then processed by the PCM which then determines which cylinder is on the compression stroke.

then the PCM assumes that cylinder 4 is on the compression stroke. Engines equipped with compression-sensing ignition systems do not require the use of a camshaft position sensor to determine specific cylinder numbers. ● **SEE FIGURE 29–15.**

## COIL-ON-PLUG IGNITION

**TERMINOLOGY** Coil-on-plug (COP) ignition uses one ignition coil for each spark plug. This system is also called *coil-by-plug, coil-near-plug,* or *coil-over-plug ignition.* ● **SEE FIGURES 29–16 AND 29–17.**

**ADVANTAGES** The COP system eliminates the spark plug wires that are often the source of electromagnetic interference (EMI) that can cause problems to some computer signals. The vehicle computer controls the timing of the spark. Ignition timing also can be changed (retarded or advanced) on a cylinder-by-cylinder basis for maximum performance and to respond to knock sensor signals.

**TYPES OF COP SYSTEMS** There are two basic types of COP ignition systems:

- **Two primary wires.** This design uses the vehicle computer to control the firing of the ignition coil. The two wires include the ignition voltage feed and the pulse ground wire, which is controlled by the computer. The ignition control module is located in the PCM, which handles all ignition timing and coil on-time control.

- **Three primary wires.** This design includes an ignition module at each coil. The three wires include the following:
  - Ignition voltage
  - Ground
  - Pulse from the computer to the built-in ignition module

Vehicles use a variety of COP-type ignition systems, including the following:

- Many General Motors V-8 engines use a coil-near-plug system with individual coils and modules for each individual cylinder that are placed on the valve covers. Short secondary ignition spark plug wires are used to connect the output terminal of the ignition coil to the

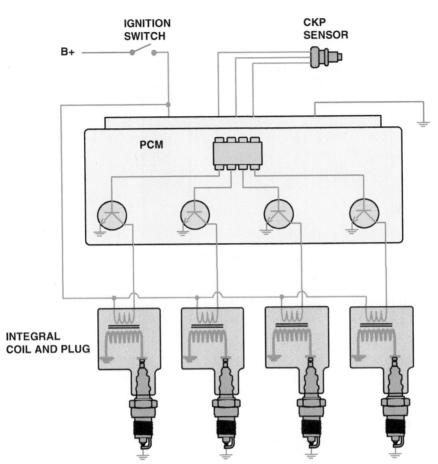

**FIGURE 29-16** A typical two wire coil-on-plug (COP) ignition system showing the triggering and the switching being performed by the PCM from input from the crankshaft position sensor.

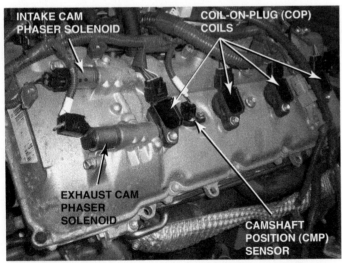

**FIGURE 29-17** An overhead camshaft engine equipped with variable valve timing on both the intake and exhaust camshafts and coil-on-plug (COP) ignition.

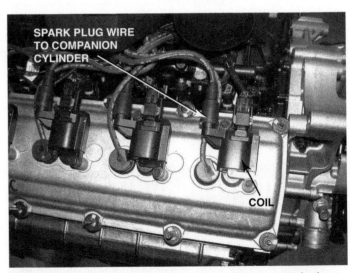

**FIGURE 29-18** A Chrysler Hemi V-8 that has two spark plugs per cylinder. The coil on top of one spark fires that plug and, through a spark plug wire, fires a plug in the companion cylinder.

spark plug, and therefore this system is called a *coil-near-plug* system.

- In a combination of COP and waste-spark systems, the systems fire a spark plug attached to the coil and use a spark plug wire attached to the other secondary terminal

of the coil to fire another spark plug of the companion cylinder. This type of system is used in some Chrysler Hemi V-8 and Toyota V-6 engines. ● **SEE FIGURE 29-18.**

Most new engines use coil-on-plug-type ignition systems. Each coil is controlled by the PCM, which can vary the ignition

timing separately for each cylinder based on signals the PCM receives from the knock sensor(s). For example, if the knock sensor detects that a spark knock has occurred after firing cylinder 3, then the PCM will continue to monitor cylinder 3 and retard timing on just this one cylinder if necessary to prevent engine-damaging detonation.

**ION-SENSING IGNITION** In an **ion-sensing ignition** system, the spark plug itself becomes a sensor. An ion-sensing ignition uses a COP design where the ignition control module (ICM) applies a DC voltage across the spark plug gap *after* the ignition event to sense the ionized gases (called plasma) inside the cylinder. Ion-sensing ignition is used in the General Motors EcoTec 4-cylinder engines. ● **SEE FIGURE 29–19.**

The secondary coil discharge voltage (10 to 15 kV) is electrically isolated from the ion-sensing circuit. The combustion flame is ionized and will conduct some electricity, which can be accurately measured at the spark plug gap. The purpose of this circuit includes the following:

■ Misfire detection (required by OBD-II regulations)

■ Knock detection (eliminates the need for a knock sensor)

■ Ignition timing control (to achieve the best spark timing for maximum power with lowest exhaust emissions)

■ Exhaust gas recirculation (EGR) control

■ Air-fuel ratio control on an individual cylinder basis

Ion-sensing ignition systems still function the same as conventional COP designs, but the engine does not need to be equipped with a camshaft position sensor for misfire detection or a knock sensor because both of these faults are achieved using the electronics inside the ignition control circuits.

**SPARK EVENT—SPARK CURRENT FLOW**

**FIGURE 29–19** A DC voltage is applied across the spark plug gap after the plug fires, and the circuit can determine if the correct air-fuel ratio was present in the cylinder and if knock occurred. The applied voltage for ion-sensing does not jump the spark plug gap but determines the conductivity of the ionized gases left over from the combustion process.

# KNOCK SENSORS

**PURPOSE AND FUNCTION** **Knock sensors** are used to detect abnormal combustion, often called **ping, spark knock,** or **detonation.** Whenever abnormal combustion occurs, a rapid pressure increase occurs in the cylinder, creating a vibration in the engine block. It is this vibration that is detected by the knock sensor. The signal from the knock sensor is used by the PCM to retard the ignition timing until the knock is eliminated, thereby reducing the damaging effects of the abnormal combustion on pistons and other engine parts.

Inside the knock sensor is a piezoelectric element that is a type of crystal that produces a voltage when pressure or a vibration is applied to the unit. The knock sensor is tuned to the engine knock frequency, which is a range from

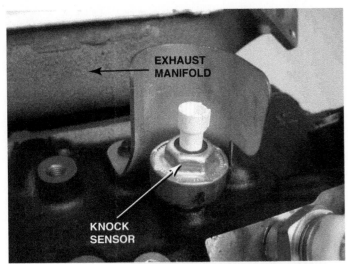

FIGURE 29–20 A typical knock sensor on the side of the block. Some are located in the "V" of a V-type engine and are not noticeable until the intake manifold has been removed.

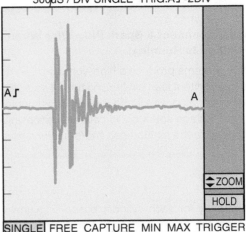

FIGURE 29–21 A typical waveform from a knock sensor during a spark knock event. This signal is sent to the computer, which in turn retards the ignition timing. This timing retard is accomplished by an output command from the computer to either a spark advance control unit or directly to the ignition module.

5 to 10 kHz, depending on the engine design. The voltage signal from the knock sensor is sent to the PCM. The PCM retards the ignition timing until the knocking stops. ● SEE FIGURE 29–20.

### DIAGNOSING THE KNOCK SENSOR
If a knock sensor diagnostic trouble code (DTC) is present, follow the specified testing procedure in the service information. A scan tool can be used to check the operation of the knock sensor, using the following procedure:

**STEP 1** Start the engine and connect a scan tool to monitor ignition timing and/or knock sensor activity.

**STEP 2** Create a simulated engine knocking sound by tapping on the engine block or cylinder head with a soft-faced mallet or small ball peen hammer.

**STEP 3** Observe the scan tool display. The vibration from the tapping should have been interpreted by the knock sensor as a knock, resulting in a knock sensor signal and a reduction in the spark advance.

A knock sensor also can be tested using a digital storage oscilloscope. ● SEE FIGURE 29–21.

NOTE: Some engine computers are programmed to ignore knock sensor signals when the engine is at idle speed to avoid having the noise from a loose accessory drive belt or other accessory interpreted as engine knock. Always follow the vehicle manufacturer's recommended testing procedure.

### REPLACING A KNOCK SENSOR
If replacing a knock sensor, be sure to purchase the exact replacement needed, because they often look the same, but the frequency range can

🚗 **REAL WORLD FIX**

**The Low-Power Toyota**

A technician talked about the driver of a Toyota who complained about poor performance and low fuel economy. The technician checked everything and even replaced all secondary ignition components. Then the technician connected a scan tool and noticed that the knock sensor was commanding the timing to be retarded. Careful visual inspection revealed a "chunk" missing from the serpentine belt, which caused a "noise" similar to a spark knock. Apparently the knock sensor was "hearing" the accessory drive belt noise and kept retarding the ignition timing. After replacing the accessory drive belt, a test drive confirmed that normal engine power was restored.

Other items that can fool the knock sensor to retard the ignition timing include the following:
- Loose valve lifter adjustment
- Engine knocks
- Loose accessory brackets such as air-conditioning compressor, power steering pumps, or alternator

vary according to engine design and location on the engine. Always tighten the knock sensor using a torque wrench and tighten to the specified torque to avoid causing damage to the piezoelectric element inside the sensor.

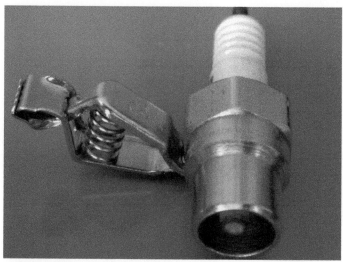

**FIGURE 29–22** A spark tester looks like a regular spark plug with an alligator clip attached to the shell. This tester has a specified gap that requires at least 25,000 volts (25 kV) to fire.

**FIGURE 29–23** A close-up showing the recessed center electrode on a spark tester. It is recessed 3/8 inch into the shell, and the spark must then jump another 3/8 inch to the shell for a total gap of 3/4 inch.

## IGNITION SYSTEM DIAGNOSIS

**CHECKING FOR SPARK** In the event of a no-start condition, the first step should be to check for secondary voltage out of the ignition coil or to the spark plugs. If the engine is equipped with a separate ignition coil, remove the coil wire from the center of the distributor cap, install a **spark tester** and crank the engine. See the Tech Tip "Always Use a Spark Tester." A good coil and ignition system should produce a blue spark at the spark tester. ● **SEE FIGURES 29–22 AND 29–23.**

If the ignition system being tested does not have a separate ignition coil, disconnect any spark plug wire from a spark plug and, while cranking the engine, test for spark available at the spark plug wire, again using a spark tester.

**NOTE: An intermittent spark should be considered a no-spark condition.**

Typical causes of a no-spark (intermittent spark) condition include the following:

1. Weak ignition coil
2. Low or no voltage to the primary (positive) side of the coil
3. High resistances, open coil wire, or spark plug wire
4. Negative side of the coil not being pulsed by the ignition module
5. Defective pickup coil or crankshaft position sensor
6. Defective ignition control module (ICM)
7. Defective main relay (can be labeled Main, EFI, ASD on Chrysler products; EEC on Ford vehicle relays)

The triggering sensor has to work to create a spark from the ignition coil(s). If there is a no-spark condition, check for triggering by using a scan tool and check for engine RPM while cranking the engine:

- If the engine speed (RPM) shows zero or almost zero while cranking, the most likely cause is a defective triggering sensor or sensor circuit fault.
- If the engine speed (RPM) is shown on the scan tool while cranking the engine, then the triggering sensor is working (in most cases).

Check service information for the exact procedure to follow for testing triggering sensors.

**IGNITION COIL TESTING USING AN OHMMETER** If an ignition coil is suspected of being defective, a simple ohmmeter check can be performed to test the resistance of the primary and secondary windings inside the coil. For accurate resistance measurements, the wiring to the coil should be removed before testing. To test the primary coil winding resistance, take the following steps: ● **SEE FIGURE 29–24.**

**STEP 1** Set the meter to read low ohms.

**STEP 2** Measure the resistance between the positive terminal and the negative terminal of the ignition coil. Most coils will give a reading between less than 1 ohm and 3 ohms. Check the manufacturer's specifications for the exact resistance values.

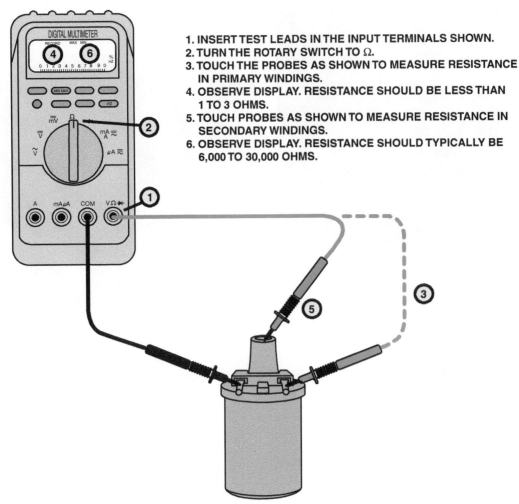

1. INSERT TEST LEADS IN THE INPUT TERMINALS SHOWN.
2. TURN THE ROTARY SWITCH TO Ω.
3. TOUCH THE PROBES AS SHOWN TO MEASURE RESISTANCE IN PRIMARY WINDINGS.
4. OBSERVE DISPLAY. RESISTANCE SHOULD BE LESS THAN 1 TO 3 OHMS.
5. TOUCH PROBES AS SHOWN TO MEASURE RESISTANCE IN SECONDARY WINDINGS.
6. OBSERVE DISPLAY. RESISTANCE SHOULD TYPICALLY BE 6,000 TO 30,000 OHMS.

**FIGURE 29–24** Checking an ignition coil using a multimeter set to read ohms.

 **TECH TIP**

### Always Use a Spark Tester

A spark tester looks like a spark plug except it has a recessed center electrode and no side electrode. The tester commonly has an alligator clip attached to the shell so that it can be clamped on a good ground connection on the engine. A good ignition system should be able to cause a spark to jump this wide gap at atmospheric pressure. Without a spark tester, a technician might assume that the ignition system is okay because it can spark across a normal, grounded spark plug. The voltage required to fire a standard spark plug when it is out of the engine and not under pressure is about 3,000 volts or less. An electronic ignition spark tester requires a minimum of 25,000 volts to jump the 3/4-inch gap. Therefore, never assume that the ignition system is okay because it fires a spark plug—always use a spark tester. *Remember that an intermittent spark across a spark tester should be interpreted as a no-spark condition.*

To test the secondary coil winding resistance, follow these steps:

**STEP 1** Set the meter to read kilohms (k ).

**STEP 2** Measure the resistance either between the primary terminal and the secondary coil tower or between the secondary towers. The normal resistance of most coils ranges between 6,000 and 30,000 ohms. Check the manufacturer's specifications for the exact resistance values.

**MAGNETIC SENSOR TESTING** Magnetic Sensor such as the pickup coil, located under the distributor cap on many electronic ignition engines, can cause a no-spark condition if defective. The sensor must generate an AC voltage pulse to the ignition module so that the module can pulse the ignition coil.

The sensor contains a coil of wire, and the resistance of this coil should be within the range specified by the manufacturer.

Some common tests for pickup coils and magnetic crankshaft position sensors include the following:

- **Resistance.** Usually between 150 and 1,500 ohms, but check service information for the exact specifications.
  ● **SEE FIGURE 29–25.**

- **Coil shorted to ground.** Check that the coil windings are insulated from ground by checking for continuity

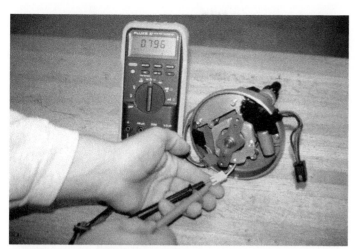

**FIGURE 29–25** Measuring the resistance of an HEI pickup coil using a digital multimeter set to the ohms position. The reading on the face of the meter is 0.796 k , or 796 ohms in the middle of the 500- to 1,500-ohm specifications.

using an ohmmeter. With one ohmmeter lead attached to ground, touch the other lead of the ohmmeter to the pickup coil terminal. The ohmmeter should read OL (over limit) with the ohmmeter set on the high scale. If the sensor resistance is not within the specified range or if it has continuity to ground, replace the pickup coil assembly.

- **AC voltage output.** The sensor also can be tested for proper voltage output. During cranking, most sensors should produce a minimum of 0.25 volt AC.

**TESTING HALL-EFFECT SENSORS** As with any other sensor, the output of the Hall-effect sensor should be tested first. Using a digital voltmeter, check for the following:

- Power and ground to the sensor
- Changing voltage (pulsed on and off or digital DC voltage) when the engine is being cranked
- Waveform, using an oscilloscope ● **SEE FIGURE 29–26.**

**TESTING OPTICAL SENSORS** Optical sensors will not operate if they are dirty or covered in oil. Perform a thorough visual inspection and look for an oil leak that could cause dirty oil to get on the LED or phototransistor. Also be sure that the light shield is securely fastened and that the seal is lightproof. An optical sensor also can be checked using an oscilloscope. ● **SEE FIGURE 29–27.**

Because of the speed of the engine and the number of slits in the optical sensor disk, a scope is one of the only tools that can capture useful information. For example, a Nissan has 360 slits, and if it is running at 2,000 RPM, a signal is generated 720,000 times per minute, or 12,000 times per second.

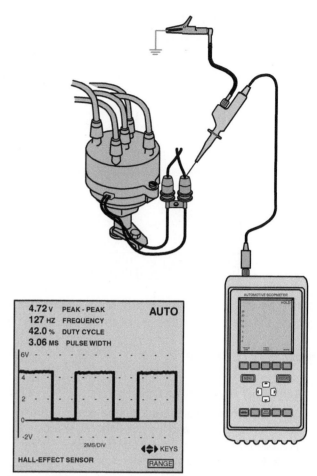

| 4.72 V | PEAK - PEAK | AUTO |
| 127 HZ | FREQUENCY | |
| 42.0 % | DUTY CYCLE | |
| 3.06 MS | PULSE WIDTH | |

HALL-EFFECT SENSOR

**FIGURE 29–26** The connection required to test a Hall-effect sensor. A typical waveform from a Hall-effect sensor.

## SPARK PLUG WIRE INSPECTION

Spark plug wires should be visually inspected for cuts or defective insulation. Faulty spark plug wire insulation can cause hard starting or no starting in rainy or damp weather conditions. When removing a spark plug wire, be sure to rotate the boot of the wire at the plug before pulling it off the spark plug. This will help prevent damaging the wire, as many wires are stuck to the spark plug and are often difficult to remove.

**VISUAL INSPECTION** A thorough visual inspection should include a look at the following items:

- Check all spark plug wires for proper routing. All plug wires should be in the factory wiring separators and be clear of any metallic object that could damage the insulation and cause a short-to-ground fault.
- Check that all spark plug wires are securely attached to the spark plugs and to the distributor cap or ignition coil(s).

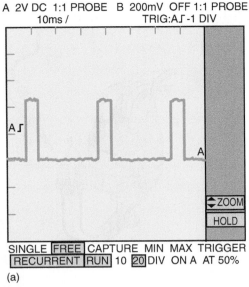

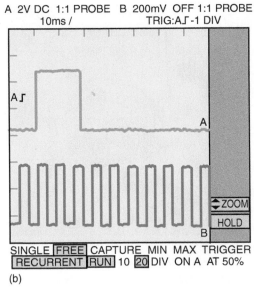

A 2V DC 1:1 PROBE  B 200mV OFF 1:1 PROBE
10ms /                    TRIG:A⌐ -1 DIV

SINGLE [FREE] CAPTURE MIN MAX TRIGGER
[RECURRENT] [RUN] 10 [20] DIV ON A AT 50%

(a)

A 2V DC 1:1 PROBE  B 200mV OFF 1:1 PROBE
10ms /                    TRIG:A⌐ -1 DIV

SINGLE [FREE] CAPTURE MIN MAX TRIGGER
[RECURRENT] [RUN] 10 [20] DIV ON A AT 50%

(b)

**FIGURE 29–27** (a) The low-resolution signal has the same number of pulses as the engine has cylinders. (b) A dual-trace pattern showing both the low-resolution signal and the high-resolution signals that usually represent 1 degree of rotation.

 **TECH TIP**

### Bad Wire? Replace the Coil!

When performing engine testing (such as a compression test), always ground the coil wire. Never allow the coil to discharge without a path to ground for the spark. High-energy ignition systems can produce 40,000 volts or more of electrical pressure. If the spark cannot spark to ground, the coil energy can (and usually does) arc inside the coil itself, creating a low-resistance path to the primary windings or the steel laminations of the coil. ● **SEE FIGURE 29–28.**

This low-resistance path is called a **track** and could cause an engine miss under load even though all of the remaining component parts of the ignition system are functioning correctly. Often these tracks do not show up on any coil test, including most scopes. Because the track is a lower resistance path to ground than normal, it requires that the ignition system be put under a load for it to be detected, and even then, the misfire may be intermittent. If a misfire was the result of an open circuit in the secondary circuit, the coil is ruined and must be replaced.

When disabling an ignition system, perform one of the following procedures to prevent possible ignition coil damage:

1. Remove the power source wire from the ignition system to prevent any ignition operation.
2. On distributor-equipped engines, remove the secondary coil wire from the center of the distributor cap and connect a jumper wire between the disconnected coil wire and a good engine ground. This ensures that the secondary coil energy will be safely grounded and prevents high-voltage coil damage.

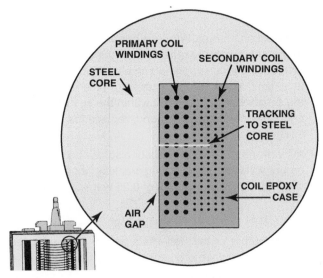

**FIGURE 29–28** A track inside an ignition coil is not a short but a low-resistance path or hole that has been burned through from the secondary wiring to the steel core.

- Check that all spark plug wires are clean and free from excessive dirt or oil. Check that all protective covers normally covering the coil and/or distributor cap are in place and not damaged.
- Carefully check the cap and distributor rotor for faults or coil secondary terminal on waste spark coils. ● **SEE FIGURE 29–29.**

Visually check the wires and boots for damage. ● **SEE FIGURE 29–30.**

Check all spark plug wires with an ohmmeter for proper resistance. Good spark plug wires should measure less than 10,000 ohms per foot of length. ● **SEE FIGURE 29–31.**

**FIGURE 29–29** Corroded terminals on a waste-spark coil can cause misfire diagnostic trouble codes to be set.

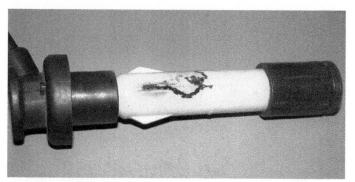

**FIGURE 29–30** This spark plug boot on an overhead camshaft engine has been arcing to the valve cover causing a misfire to occur.

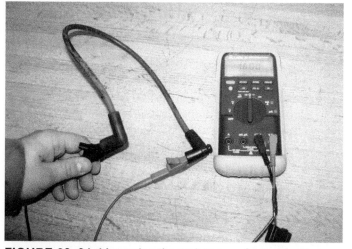

**FIGURE 29–31** Measuring the resistance of a spark plug wire with a multimeter set to the ohms position. The reading of 16.03 k (16,030 ohms) is okay because the wire is about 2 feet long. Maximum allowable resistance for a spark plug wire this long would be 20 k (20,000 ohms).

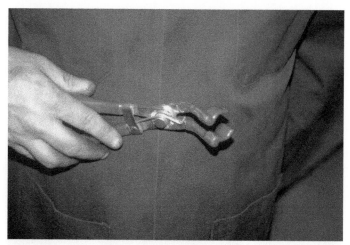

**FIGURE 29–32** This spark plug wire boot pliers is a handy addition to any tool box.

---

 **TECH TIP**

**Spark Plug Wire Pliers Are a Good Investment**

Spark plug wires are often difficult to remove. Using good-quality spark plug wire pliers, as shown in ● **FIGURE 29–32,** saves time and reduces the chance of harming the wire during removal.

---

 **TECH TIP**

**Route the Wires Right!**

High voltage is present through spark plug wires when the engine is running. Surrounding the spark plug wires is a magnetic field that can affect other circuits or components of the vehicle. For example, if a spark plug wire is routed too closely to the signal wire from a mass airflow (MAF) sensor, the induced signal from the ignition wire could create a false MAF signal to the computer. The computer, not able to detect that the signal was false, would act on the MAF signal and command the appropriate amount of fuel based on the false MAF signal.

   To prevent any problems associated with high-voltage spark plug wires, be sure to route them using all of the factory holding brackets and wiring combs. ● **SEE FIGURE 29–33.**

   If the factory method is unknown, most factory service information shows the correct routing.

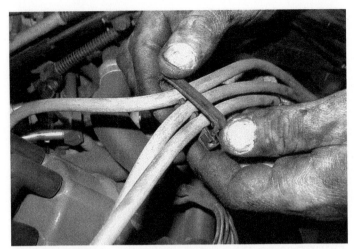

FIGURE 29–33 Always take the time to install spark plug wires back into the original holding brackets (wiring combs).

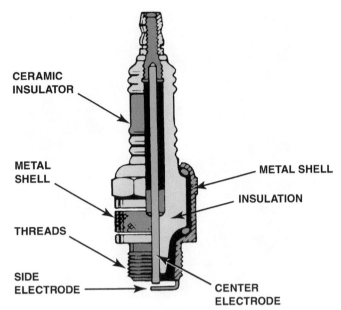

FIGURE 29–34 Parts of a spark plug.

# SPARK PLUGS

**SPARK PLUG CONSTRUCTION** **Spark plugs** are manufactured from ceramic insulators inside a steel shell. The threads of the shell are rolled and a seat is formed to create a gastight seal with the cylinder head. ● **SEE FIGURE 29–34.**

The physical differences in spark plugs include the following:

- **Reach.** This is the length of the threaded part of the plug.

- **Heat range.** This refers to how rapidly the heat created at the tip is transferred to the cylinder head. A spark plug with a long ceramic insulator path will run hotter at the tip than one that has a shorter path because the heat must travel farther. ● **SEE FIGURE 29–35.**

- **Type of seat.** Some spark plugs use a gasket, and others rely on a tapered seat to seal.

**RESISTOR SPARK PLUGS** Most spark plugs include a resistor in the center electrode, which helps to reduce electromagnetic noise or radiation from the ignition system. The closer the resistor is to the actual spark or arc, the more effective it becomes. The value of the resistor is usually between 2,500 and 7,500 ohms.

**PLATINUM SPARK PLUGS** **Platinum spark plugs** have a small amount of the precious metal platinum included on the end of the center electrode as well as on the ground or side electrode. Platinum is a gray-white metal that does not react with oxygen and, therefore, will not erode away as can occur with conventional nickel alloy spark plug electrodes. Platinum is also used as a catalyst in catalytic converters, where it is able to start a chemical reaction without itself being consumed.

**IRIDIUM SPARK PLUGS** Iridium is a white precious metal and is the most corrosion-resistant metal known. Most **iridium spark plugs** use a small amount of iridium welded onto the tip of a small center electrode, 0.0015 to 0.002 inch (0.4 to 0.6 mm)

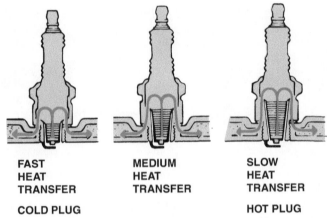

FIGURE 29–35 The heat range of a spark plug is determined by distance the heat flows from the tip to the cylinder head.

in diameter. The small diameter reduces the voltage required to jump the gap between the center and the side electrode, thereby reducing possible misfires. The ground or side electrode is usually tipped with platinum to help reduce electrode gap wear.

Spark plugs should be inspected when an engine performance problem occurs and should be replaced at specified intervals to ensure proper ignition system performance:

- Nonplatinum spark plugs have a service life of over 20,000 miles (32,000 km).

- Platinum-tipped original equipment spark plugs have a typical service life of 60,000 to 100,000 miles (100,000 to 160,000 km) or longer.

Used spark plugs should *not* be cleaned and reused unless absolutely necessary. The labor required to remove and replace (R & R) spark plugs is the same whether the spark plugs are replaced or cleaned. Although cleaning spark plugs often restores proper engine operation, the service life of cleaned spark plugs is definitely shorter than that of new spark plugs.

NOTE: Platinum-tipped spark plugs should not be re-gapped on one that has been used in an engine before. The engine heat makes the platinum brittle, and the center electrode can be easily broken if regapping the plug is attempted. Using a gapping tool can break the platinum after it has been used in an engine. Check service information regarding the recommended type of spark plugs and the specified service procedures.

## SPARK PLUG SERVICE
When replacing spark plugs, perform the following steps:

**STEP 1** **Check service information.** Check for the exact spark plug to use and the specified instructions and/or technical service bulletins that affect the number of plug to be used or a revised replacement procedure.

**STEP 2** **Allow the engine to cool before removing spark plugs.** This is true especially on engines with aluminum cylinder heads.

**STEP 3** **Use compressed air or a brush to remove dirt from around the spark plug before removal.** This step helps prevent dirt from getting into the cylinder of an engine while removing a spark.

**STEP 4** **Check the spark plug gap and correct as needed.** Be careful not to damage the tip on the center electrode if adjusting a platinum or iridium type of spark plug.

**STEP 5** **Install the spark plugs by hand.** After tightening by hand, use a torque wrench and tighten the spark plugs to factory specifications. ● **SEE FIGURES 29–36 AND 29–37.**

Spark plugs are the windows to the inside of the combustion chamber. A thorough visual inspection of the spark plugs often can lead to the root cause of an engine performance problem. Two indications on spark plugs and their possible root causes in engine performance include the following:

1. **Carbon fouling.** If the spark plug(s) has *dry black carbon* (soot), the usual causes include the following:
   ▪ Excessive idling
   ▪ Overly rich air-fuel mixture due to a fuel system fault
   ▪ Weak ignition system output

2. **Oil fouling.** If the spark plug has wet, oily deposits with little electrode wear, oil may be getting into the combustion chamber from the following:
   ▪ Worn or broken piston rings
   ▪ Worn valve guides
   ▪ Defective or missing valve stem seals

When removing spark plugs, place them in order so that they can be inspected to check for engine problems that might affect one or more cylinders. All spark plugs should be in the same condition, and the color of the center insulator should be light tan or gray. If all the spark plugs are black or dark, the engine should be checked for conditions that could cause an overly rich air-fuel mixture or possible oil burning. If only one or a few spark plugs are black, check those cylinders for proper firing (possible defective spark plug wire) or an engine condition affecting only those particular cylinders. ● **SEE FIGURES 29–38 THROUGH 29–41.**

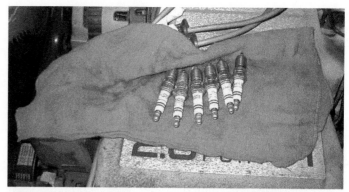

**FIGURE 29–36** When removing spark plugs, it is wise to arrange them in the order by the cylinder they were removed from so that they can be compared and any problem can be identified with a particular cylinder.

**FIGURE 29–37** A spark plug thread chaser is a low-cost tool that hopefully will not be used often but is necessary to use to clean the threads before new spark plugs are installed.

If all spark plugs are white, check for possible overadvanced ignition timing or a vacuum leak causing a lean air-fuel mixture. If only one or a few spark plugs are white, check for a vacuum leak or injector fault affecting the air-fuel mixture only to those particular cylinders.

NOTE: The engine computer "senses" rich or lean air-fuel ratios by means of input from the oxygen sensor(s). If one cylinder is lean, the PCM may make all other cylinders richer to compensate.

Inspect all spark plugs for wear by first checking the condition of the center electrode. As a spark plug wears, the center electrode becomes rounded. If the center electrode is rounded, higher ignition system voltage is required to fire the spark plug.

When installing spark plugs, always use the correct tightening torque to ensure proper heat transfer from the spark plug shell to the cylinder head. ● **SEE CHART 29–1.**

NOTE: General Motors does not recommend the use of antiseize compound on the threads of spark plugs being installed in an aluminum cylinder head because the spark plug will be overtightened. This excessive tightening torque places the threaded portion of the spark plug too far into the combustion chamber, where carbon can accumulate and result in the spark plugs being difficult to remove. If antiseize compound is used on spark plug threads, reduce the tightening torque by 40%. Always follow the vehicle manufacturer's recommendations.

**FIGURE 29–38** A normally worn spark plug that uses a tapered platinum-tipped center electrode.

**FIGURE 29–40** A spark plug from an engine that had a blown head gasket. The white deposits could be from the aluminum of the piston or from the additives in the coolant.

**FIGURE 29–39** A worn spark plug showing fuel and/or oil deposits.

**FIGURE 29–41** A platinum tipped spark plug that is fuel soaked indicating a fault with the fuel system or the ignition system causing the spark plug to not fire.

| SPARK PLUG TYPE | TORQUE WITH TORQUE WRENCH (LB-FT) | | TORQUE WITHOUT TORQUE WRENCH (TURNS AFTER SEATED) | |
|---|---|---|---|---|
| | CAST-IRON HEAD | ALUMINUM HEAD | CAST-IRON HEAD | ALUMINUM HEAD |
| Gasket | 26–30 | 18–22 | 1/4 | 1/4 |
| 14 mm | 32–38 | 28–34 | 1/4 | 1/4 |
| 18 mm | | | | |
| Tapered seat | 7–15 | 7–15 | 1/16 (snug) | 1/16 (snug) |
| 14 mm | 15–20 | 15–20 | 1/16 (snug) | 1/16 (snug) |
| 18 mm | | | | |

**CHART 29–1**

Typical spark plug installation torque.

🔧 **TECH TIP**

**Two-Finger Trick**

To help prevent overtightening a spark plug when a torque wrench is not available, simply use two fingers on the ratchet handle. Even the strongest service technician cannot overtighten a spark plug by using two fingers.

# IGNITION TIMING

**PURPOSE** **Ignition timing** refers to when the spark plug fires in relation to piston position. The time when the spark occurs depends on engine speed and, therefore, must be advanced (spark plugs fire sooner) as the engine rotates faster. The ignition in the cylinder takes a certain amount of time, usually 30 ms (30/1,000 of a second), and remains constant regardless of engine speed. Therefore, to maintain the most efficient combustion, the ignition sequence has to occur sooner as the engine speed increases. For maximum efficiency from the expanding gases inside the combustion chamber, the burning of the air-fuel mixture should end by about 10 degrees after top dead center (ATDC). If the burning of the mixture is still occurring after that point, the expanding gases do not exert much force on the piston because the gases are "chasing" the piston as it moves downward.

Therefore, to achieve the goal of having the air-fuel mixture be completely burned by the time the piston reaches 10 degrees ATDC, the spark must be advanced (occur sooner) as the engine speed increases. This timing advance is determined and controlled by the PCM on most vehicles. ● **SEE FIGURES 29–42 AND 29–43.**

If the engine is equipped with a distributor, it may be possible to adjust the base or the initial timing. The initial timing is usually set to fire the spark plug between zero degrees (TDC)

**FIGURE 29–42** Ignition timing marks are found on the harmonic balancers on engines equipped with distributors that can be adjusted for timing.

or slightly before TDC (BTDC). Ignition timing changes as mechanical wear occurs to the following:

- Timing chain
- Distributor gear
- Camshaft drive gear

**CHECKING IGNITION TIMING** To be assured of the proper ignition timing, follow exactly the timing procedure indicated on the underhood vehicle emission control information (VECI) decal. ● **SEE FIGURE 29–44.**

NOTE: The ignition timing for waste-spark and coil-on-plug ignition systems cannot be adjusted.

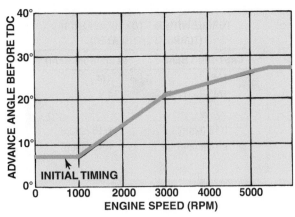

FIGURE 29–43 The initial (base) timing is where the spark plug fires at idle speed. The PCM then advances the timing based primarily on engine speed.

(a)

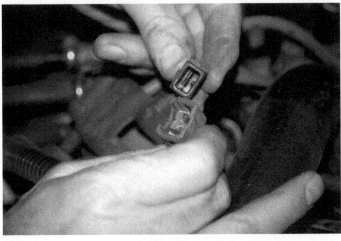

(b)

FIGURE 29–44 (a) Typical SPOUT connector as used on many Ford engines equipped with distributor ignition. (b) The connector must be opened (disconnected) to check and/or adjust the ignition timing. On DIS/EDIS systems, the connector is called SPOUT/SAW (spark output/spark angle word).

 TECH TIP

**Two Marks Are the Key to Success**

When a distributor is removed from an engine, always mark where the rotor is pointing to ensure that the distributor is reinstalled in the correct position. Because of the helical cut on the distributor drive gear, the rotor rotates as the distributor is being removed from the engine. To help reinstall a distributor without any problems, simply make another mark where the rotor is pointing just as the distributor is lifted out of the engine. Then to reinstall, simply line up the rotor to the second mark and lower the distributor into the engine. The rotor should then line up with the original mark as a double check.

TECH TIP

**Use a Water Spray Bottle to Check the Secondary Ignition Circuit**

To check for breaks in the insulation in the secondary circuit perform the following steps:

STEP 1   Start the engine and allow to reach normal operating temperature.

STEP 2   Using a water spray bottle set to mist, spray the secondary ignition components and listen for any change in operation.

STEP 3   If the engine operation is affected at all there is a break in the secondary ignition circuit insulation. Continue spraying to pinpoint the exact location.

## IGNITION SYSTEM SYMPTOM GUIDE

| Problem | Possible Causes and/or Solutions |
|---|---|
| No spark out of the coil | ▪ Open in the ignition switch circuit or theft deterrent system fault<br>▪ Defective ignition control module<br>▪ Defective triggering device (magnetic sensor, Hall-effect or optical sensor) |
| Weak spark out of the coil | ▪ High-resistance coil wire or spark plug wire<br>▪ Poor ground between the distributor or ignition control module and the engine block |
| Engine misfire | ▪ Defective (open) spark plug wire<br>▪ Worn or fouled spark plugs<br>▪ Defective ignition control module (ICM) |

## SUMMARY

1. All inductive ignition systems supply battery voltage to the positive side of the ignition coil and pulse the negative side of the coil on and off to ground to create a high-voltage spark.
2. If an ignition system uses a distributor, it is a distributor ignition system.
3. If an ignition system does not use a distributor, it is an electronic ignition system.
4. A waste-spark ignition system fires two spark plugs at the same time.
5. A coil-on-plug ignition system uses an ignition coil for each spark plug.
6. A thorough visual inspection should be performed on all ignition components when diagnosing an engine performance problem.
7. Platinum spark plugs should not be regapped after use in an engine.

## REVIEW QUESTIONS

1. How can 12 volts from a battery be changed to 40,000 volts for ignition?
2. How does a magnetic sensor work?
3. How does a Hall-effect sensor work?
4. How does a waste-spark ignition system work?
5. Why should a spark tester be used to check for spark rather than a standard spark plug?
6. How do you test a pickup coil for resistance and AC voltage output?
7. What harm can occur if the engine is cranked or run with an open (defective) spark plug wire?

## CHAPTER QUIZ

1. The primary (low-voltage) ignition system must be working correctly before any spark occurs from a coil. Which component is not in the primary ignition circuit?
   a. Spark plug wiring
   b. Ignition module (igniter)
   c. Pickup coil (pulse generator)
   d. Ignition switch

2. The ignition module has direct control over the firing of the coil(s) of an ignition system. Which component(s) triggers (controls) the module?
   a. Pickup coil
   b. Computer
   c. Crankshaft sensor
   d. All of the above

3. Distributor ignition systems can be triggered by a _____.
   a. Hall-effect sensor
   b. Magnetic sensor
   c. Spark sensor
   d. Either a or b

4. Ignition coil primary resistance is usually _____ ohms.
   a. 6,000 to 30,000
   b. 150 to 1,500
   c. Less than 1 to 3
   d. Zero

5. Coil polarity is determined by the _____.
   a. Direction of rotation of the coil windings
   b. Turn ratio
   c. Direction of laminations
   d. Saturation direction

6. A compression-sensing ignition system uses a _____ type of ignition.
   a. Distributor
   b. Coil-on-plug
   c. Waste-spark
   d. All of the above

7. The pulse generator _____.
   a. Fires the spark plug directly
   b. Signals the ignition control module (ICM)
   c. Signals the computer that fires the spark plug directly
   d. Is used as a tachometer reference signal by the computer and has no other function

8. Two technicians are discussing coil-on-plug ignition systems. Technician A says that they can be called coil-near-plug or coil-by-plug ignition systems. Technician B says that some can use ion sensing. Which technician is correct?
   a. Technician A only
   b. Technician B only
   c. Both Technicians A and B
   d. Neither Technician A nor B

9. A waste-spark-type ignition system fires _____.
   a. Two spark plugs at the same time
   b. One spark plug with reverse polarity
   c. One spark plug with straight polarity
   d. All of the above

10. Technician A says that a defective crankshaft position sensor can cause a no-spark condition. Technician B says that a faulty ignition control module can cause a no-spark condition. Which technician is correct?
    a. Technician A only
    b. Technician B only
    c. Both Technicians A and B
    d. Neither Technician A nor B

# SCAN TOOLS AND ENGINE PERFORMANCE DIAGNOSIS

**OBJECTIVES:** **After studying Chapter 30, the reader should be able to:** • Prepare for the ASE computerized engine controls diagnosis (A8) certification test content area "E." • List the steps of the diagnostic process. • Describe the simple preliminary tests that should be performed at the start of the diagnostic process. • List six items to check as part of a thorough visual inspection. • Explain the troubleshooting procedures to follow if a diagnostic trouble code has been set. • Explain the troubleshooting procedures to follow if no diagnostic trouble code has been set. • Discuss the type of scan tools that are used to assess vehicle components. • Describe the methods that can be used to reprogram (reflash) a vehicle computer.

**KEY TERMS:** Data link connector (DLC) 383 • Drive cycle 395 • Flash code retrieval 386 • Key-on—engine off test (KOEO) 387 • Key-on—engine running test (KOER) 387 • Paper test 381 • Pending code 382 • Self-test automatic readout (STAR) 387 • Smoke machine 381 • Technical service bulletin (TSB) 382 • Trip 391

## THE EIGHT-STEP DIAGNOSTIC PROCEDURE

It is important that all automotive service technicians know how to diagnose and troubleshoot engine computer systems. The diagnostic process is a strategy that eliminates known-good components or systems in order to find the root cause of automotive engine performance problems. All vehicle manufacturers recommend a diagnostic procedure, and the plan suggested in this chapter combines most of the features of these plans plus additional steps developed over years of real-world problem solving.

Many different things can cause an engine performance problem or concern. The service technician has to narrow the possibilities to find the cause of the problem and correct it. A funnel is a way of visualizing a diagnostic procedure. ● **SEE FIGURE 30–1.** At the wide top are the symptoms of the problem; the funnel narrows as possible causes are eliminated until the root cause is found and corrected at the bottom of the funnel.

All problem diagnosis deals with symptoms that could be the result of many different causes. The wide range of possible solutions must be narrowed to the most likely, and these must eventually be further narrowed to the actual cause. The following section describes eight steps the service technician can take to narrow the possibilities to one cause.

**STEP 1 VERIFY THE PROBLEM (CONCERN)** Before a minute is spent on diagnosis, be certain that a problem exists. If the problem cannot be verified, it cannot be solved or tested to verify that the repair was complete. ● **SEE FIGURE 30–2.**

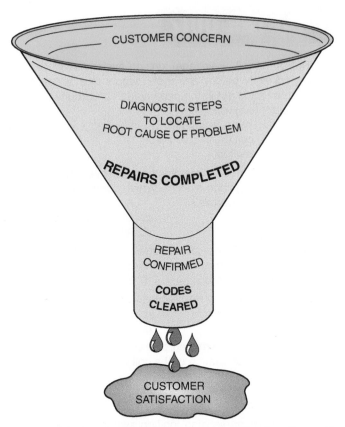

**FIGURE 30–1** A funnel is one way to visualize the diagnostic process. The purpose is to narrow the possible causes of a concern until the root cause is determined and corrected.

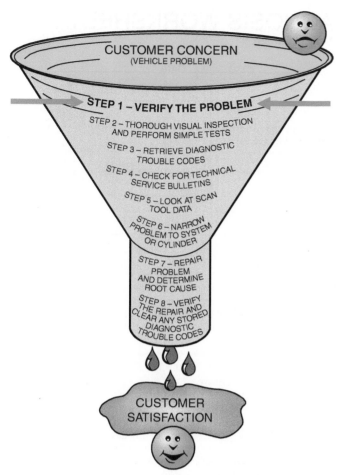

CUSTOMER CONCERN
(VEHICLE PROBLEM)

STEP 1 – VERIFY THE PROBLEM

STEP 2 – THOROUGH VISUAL INSPECTION AND PERFORM SIMPLE TESTS

STEP 3 – RETRIEVE DIAGNOSTIC TROUBLE CODES

STEP 4 – CHECK FOR TECHNICAL SERVICE BULLETINS

STEP 5 – LOOK AT SCAN TOOL DATA

STEP 6 – NARROW PROBLEM TO SYSTEM OR CYLINDER

STEP 7 – REPAIR PROBLEM AND DETERMINE ROOT CAUSE

STEP 8 – VERIFY THE REPAIR AND CLEAR ANY STORED DIAGNOSTIC TROUBLE CODES

CUSTOMER SATISFACTION

**FIGURE 30–2** Step #1 is to verify the customer concern or problem. If the problem cannot be verified, then the repair cannot be verified.

The driver of the vehicle knows much about the vehicle and how it is driven. *Before* diagnosis, always ask the following questions:

- Is the malfunction indicator light (check engine) on?
- What was the temperature outside?
- Was the engine warm or cold?
- Was the problem during starting, acceleration, cruise, or some other condition?
- How far had the vehicle been driven?
- Were any dash warning lights on? If so, which one(s)?
- Has there been any service or repair work performed on the vehicle lately?

**NOTE: This last question is very important. Many engine performance faults are often the result of something being knocked loose or a hose falling off during repair work. Knowing that the vehicle was just serviced before the problem began may be an indicator as to where to look for the solution to a problem.**

After the nature and scope of the problem are determined, the complaint should be verified before further diagnostic tests

TECH TIP

**"Original Equipment" Is Not a Four-Letter Word**

To many service technicians, an original-equipment part is considered to be only marginal, and to get the really "good stuff" an aftermarket (renewal market) part has to be purchased. However, many problems can be traced to the use of an aftermarket part that has failed early in its service life. Technicians who work at dealerships usually begin their diagnosis with an aftermarket part identified during a visual inspection. It has been their experience that simply replacing the aftermarket part with the factory original-equipment (OE) part often solves the problem.

Original equipment parts are *required* to pass quality and durability standards and tests at a level not required of aftermarket parts. The technician should be aware that the presence of a new part does not necessarily mean that the part is good.

are performed. A sample form that customers could fill out with details of the problem is shown in ● **FIGURE 30–3.**

**NOTE: Because drivers differ, it is sometimes the best policy to take the customer on the test drive to verify the concern.**

## STEP 2 PERFORM A THOROUGH VISUAL INSPECTION AND BASIC TESTS

The visual inspection is the most important aspect of diagnosis! Most experts agree that between 10% and 30% of all engine performance problems can be found simply by performing a *thorough* visual inspection. The inspection should include the following:

- **Check for obvious problems (basics, basics, basics).**
  Fuel leaks
  Vacuum hoses that are disconnected or split
  Corroded connectors
  Unusual noises, smoke, or smell
  Check the air cleaner and air duct (squirrels and other small animals can build nests or store dog food in them) ● **SEE FIGURE 30–4.**
- **Check everything that does and does not work.** This step involves turning things on and observing that everything is working properly.
- **Look for evidence of previous repairs.** Any time work is performed on a vehicle, there is always a risk that something will be disturbed, knocked off, or left disconnected.
- **Check oil level and condition.** Another area for visual inspection is oil level and condition.
  **Oil level.** Oil should be to the proper level.

# ENGINE PERFORMANCE DIAGNOSIS WORKSHEET

(To Be Filled Out By the Vehicle Owner)

Name: _____ Mileage: _____ Date: _____

Make: _____ Model: _____ Year: _____ Engine: _____

| (Please Circle All That Apply in All Categories) | |
|---|---|
| **Describe Problem:** | |
| **When Did the Problem First Occur?** | • Just Started • Last Week • Last Month<br>• Other _____ |
| **List Previous Repairs in the Last 6 Months:** | |
| **Starting Problems** | • Will Not Crank • Cranks, but Will Not Start • Starts, but Takes a Long Time |
| **Engine Quits or Stalls** | • Right after Starting • When Put into Gear • During Steady Speed Driving<br>• Right after Vehicle Comes to a Stop • While Idling • During Acceleration<br>• When Parking |
| **Poor Idling Conditions** | • Is Too Slow at All Times • Is Too Fast • Intermittently Too Fast or Too Slow<br>• Is Rough or Uneven • Fluctuates Up and Down |
| **Poor Running Conditions** | • Runs Rough • Lacks Power • Bucks and Jerks • Poor Fuel Economy<br>• Hesitates or Stumbles on Acceleration • Backfires • Misfires or Cuts Out<br>• Engine Knocks, Pings, Rattles • Surges • Dieseling or Run-On |
| **Auto. Transmission Problems** | • Improper Shifting (Early/Late) • Changes Gear Incorrectly<br>• Vehicle Does Not Move when in Gear • Jerks or Bucks |
| **Usually Occurs** | • Morning • Afternoon • Anytime |
| **Engine Temperature** | • Cold • Warm • Hot |
| **Driving Conditions During Occurrence** | • Short—Less Than 2 Miles • 2–10 Miles • Long—More Than 10 Miles<br>• Stop and Go • While Turning • While Braking • At Gear Engagement<br>• With A/C Operating • With Headlights On • During Acceleration<br>• During Deceleration • Mostly Downhill • Mostly Uphill • Mostly Level<br>• Mostly Curvy • Rough Road |
| **Driving Habits** | • Mostly City Driving • Highway • Park Vehicle Inside • Park Vehicle Outside<br>**Drive Per Day:** • Less Than 10 Miles • 10–50 • More Than 50 |
| **Gasoline Used** | **Fuel Octane:** • 87 • 89 • 91 • More Than 91<br>**Brand:** _____ |
| **Temperature when Problem Occurs** | • 32–55° F • Below Freezing (32° F) • Above 55° F |
| **Check Engine Light/ Dash Warning Light** | • Light on Sometimes • Light on Always • Light Never On |
| **Smells** | • "Hot" • Gasoline • Oil Burning • Electrical |
| **Noises** | • Rattle • Knock • Squeak • Other |

**FIGURE 30–3** A form that the customer should fill out if there is a driveablilty concern to help the service technician more quickly find the root cause.

**FIGURE 30-4** This is what was found when removing an air filter from a vehicle that had a lack-of-power concern. Obviously the nuts were deposited by squirrels or some other animal, blocking a lot of the airflow into the engine.

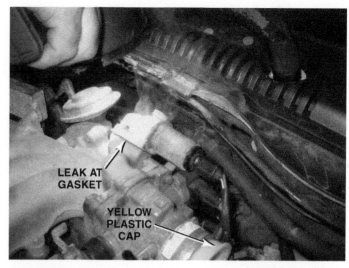

LEAK AT GASKET

YELLOW PLASTIC CAP

**FIGURE 30-5** Using a bright light makes seeing where the smoke is coming from easier. In this case, smoke was added to the intake manifold with the inlet blocked with a yellow plastic cap, and smoke was seen escaping past a gasket at the idle air control.

 **TECH TIP**

### Smoke Machine Testing

Vacuum (air) leaks can cause a variety of driveability problems and are often difficult to locate. One good method is to use a machine that generates a stream of smoke. Connecting the outlet of the **smoke machine** to the hose that was removed from the vacuum brake booster allows smoke to enter the intake manifold. Any vacuum leaks will be spotted by observing smoke coming out of the leak. ● SEE FIGURE 30-5.

**Oil condition.** Using a match or lighter, try to light the oil on the dipstick; if the oil flames up, gasoline is present in the engine oil. Drip some engine oil from the dipstick onto the hot exhaust manifold. If the oil bubbles or boils, coolant (water) is present in the oil. Check for grittiness by rubbing the oil between your fingers.

NOTE: Gasoline in the oil will cause the engine to run rich by drawing fuel through the positive crankcase ventilation (PCV) system.

■ **Check coolant level and condition.** Many mechanical engine problems are caused by overheating. The proper operation of the cooling system is critical to the life of any engine.

NOTE: Check the coolant level in the radiator only if the radiator is cool. If the radiator is hot and the radiator cap is removed, the drop in pressure above the coolant will cause the coolant to boil immediately, which can cause severe burns because the coolant expands explosively upward and outward from the radiator opening.

■ **Use the paper test.** A sound engine should produce even and steady exhaust flow at the tailpipe when

running. For the **paper test**, hold a piece of paper (even a dollar bill works) or a 3-by-5-inch card within 1 inch (2.5 cm) of the tailpipe with the engine running at idle. The paper should blow evenly away from the end of the tailpipe without "puffing" or being drawn inward toward the end of the tailpipe. If the paper is at times drawn *toward* the tailpipe, the valves in one or more cylinders could be burned. Other reasons why the paper might be drawn toward the tailpipe include the following:

1. The engine could be misfiring because of a lean condition that could occur normally when the engine is cold.

2. Pulsing of the paper toward the tailpipe could also be caused by a hole in the exhaust system. If exhaust escapes through a hole in the exhaust system, air could be drawn—in the intervals between the exhaust puffs—from the tailpipe to the hole in the exhaust, causing the paper to be drawn toward the tailpipe.

■ **Ensure adequate fuel level.** Make certain that the fuel tank is at least one-fourth to one-half full; if the fuel level is low, it is possible that any water or alcohol at the bottom of the fuel tank is more concentrated and can be drawn into the fuel system.

■ **Check the battery voltage.** The voltage of the battery should be at least 12.4 volts, and the charging voltage (engine running) should be 13.5 to 15.0 volts at 2,000 RPM on most vehicles. Low battery voltage can cause a variety of problems, including reduced fuel economy and incorrect (usually too high) idle speed. Higher-than-normal battery voltage can also cause the powertrain control module (PCM) problems and could cause damage to electronic modules.

■ **Check the spark using a spark tester.** Remove one spark plug wire and attach the removed plug wire to the spark tester. Attach the grounding clip of the spark tester

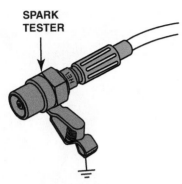

SPARK TESTER

**FIGURE 30–6** A spark tester connected to a spark plug wire or coil output. A typical spark tester will fire only if at least 25,000 volts is available from the coil, making a spark tester a very useful tool. Do not use one that just lights when a spark is present because they do not require more than about 2,000 volts to light.

to a good clean engine ground, start or crank the engine and observe the spark tester. ● **SEE FIGURE 30–6.** The spark at the spark tester should be steady and consistent. If an intermittent spark occurs, then this condition should be treated as a no-spark condition. If this test does not show satisfactory spark, carefully inspect and test all components of the primary and secondary ignition systems.

**NOTE: Do not use a standard spark plug to check for proper ignition system voltage. An electronic ignition spark tester is designed to force the spark to jump about 0.75 inch (19 mm). This amount of gap requires between 25,000 and 30,000 volts (25 to 30 kV) at atmospheric pressure, which is enough voltage to ensure that a spark can occur under compression inside an engine.**

■ **Check the fuel-pump pressure.** Checking the fuel-pump pressure is relatively easy on many port-fuel-injected engines. Often the cause of intermittent engine performance is due to a weak electric fuel pump or clogged fuel filter. Checking fuel pump pressure early in the diagnostic process eliminates low fuel pressure as a possibility.

## STEP 3 RETRIEVE THE DIAGNOSTIC TROUBLE CODES

If a diagnostic trouble code (DTC) is present in the computer memory, it may be signaled by illuminating a malfunction indicator lamp (MIL), commonly labeled "check engine" or "service engine soon." ● **SEE FIGURE 30–7.** Any code(s) that is displayed on a scan tool when the MIL is *not* on is called a **pending code**. Because the MIL is not on, this indicates that the fault has not repeated to cause the PCM to turn on the MIL. Although this pending code is helpful to the technician to know that a fault has, in the past, been detected, further testing will be needed to find the root cause of the problem.

## STEP 4 CHECK FOR TECHNICAL SERVICE BULLETINS (TSBs)

Check for corrections or repair procedures in **technical service bulletins (TSBs)** that match the symptoms. ● **SEE FIGURE 30–8.** According to studies performed by automobile manufacturers, as many as 30% of vehicles can be repaired

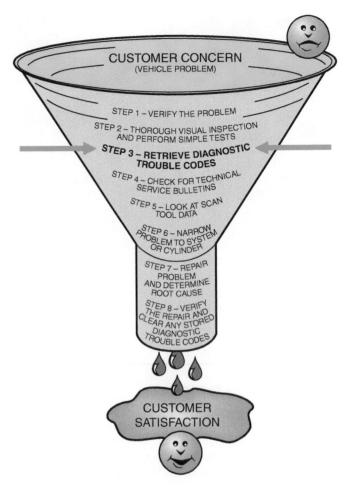

CUSTOMER CONCERN
(VEHICLE PROBLEM)

STEP 1 – VERIFY THE PROBLEM

STEP 2 – THOROUGH VISUAL INSPECTION AND PERFORM SIMPLE TESTS

STEP 3 – RETRIEVE DIAGNOSTIC TROUBLE CODES

STEP 4 – CHECK FOR TECHNICAL SERVICE BULLETINS

STEP 5 – LOOK AT SCAN TOOL DATA

STEP 6 – NARROW PROBLEM TO SYSTEM OR CYLINDER

STEP 7 – REPAIR PROBLEM AND DETERMINE ROOT CAUSE

STEP 8 – VERIFY THE REPAIR AND CLEAR ANY STORED DIAGNOSTIC TROUBLE CODES

CUSTOMER SATISFACTION

**FIGURE 30–7** Step 3 in the diagnostic process is to retrieve any stored diagnostic trouble codes (DTCs).

**FIGURE 30–8** After checking for stored diagnostic trouble codes (DTCs), the wise technician checks service information for any technical service bulletins that may relate to the vehicle being serviced.

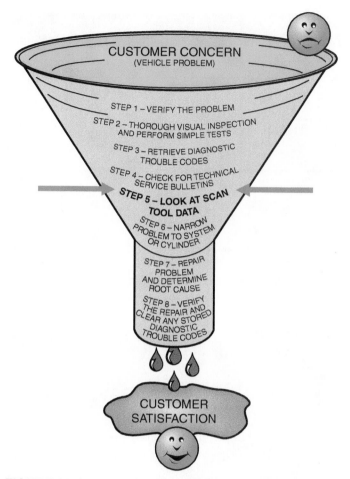

**FIGURE 30–9** Looking carefully at the scan tool data is very helpful in locating the source of a problem.

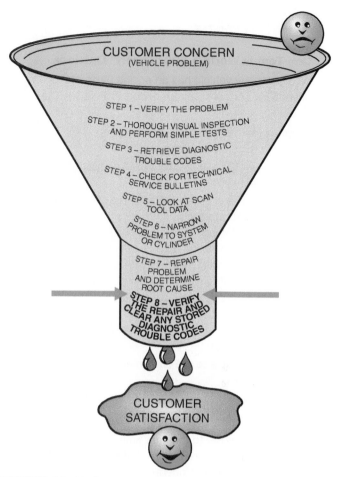

**FIGURE 30–10** Step 8 is very important. Be sure that the customer's concern has been corrected.

following the information, suggestions, or replacement parts found in a service bulletin. DTCs must be known before searching for service bulletins because bulletins often include information on solving problems that involve a stored DTC.

### STEP 5 LOOK CAREFULLY AT SCAN TOOL DATA
Vehicle manufacturers have been giving the technician more and more data on a scan tool connected to the **data link connector (DLC)**. ● **SEE FIGURE 30–9.** Beginning technicians are often observed scrolling through scan data without a real clue about what they are looking for. When asked, they usually reply that they are looking for something unusual, as if the screen will flash a big message "LOOK HERE—THIS IS NOT CORRECT." That statement does not appear on scan tool displays. The best way to look at scan data is in a definite sequence and with specific, selected bits of data that can tell the most about the operation of the engine, such as the following:

- Engine coolant temperature (ECT) is the same as intake air temperature (IAT) after the vehicle sits for several hours.

- Idle air control (IAC) valve is being commanded to an acceptable range.

- Oxygen sensor ($O_2S$) is operating properly:
  1. Readings below 200 mV at times
  2. Readings above 800 mV at times
  3. Rapid transitions between rich and lean

### STEP 6 NARROW THE PROBLEM TO A SYSTEM OR CYLINDER
Narrowing the focus to a system or individual cylinder is the hardest part of the entire diagnostic process:

- Perform a cylinder power balance test.

- If a weak cylinder is detected, perform a compression and a cylinder leakage test to determine the probable cause.

### STEP 7 REPAIR THE PROBLEM AND DETERMINE THE ROOT CAUSE
The repair or part replacement must be performed following vehicle manufacturer's recommendations and be certain that the root cause of the problem has been found. Also follow the manufacturer's recommended repair procedures and methods.

### STEP 8 VERIFY THE REPAIR AND CLEAR ANY STORED DTCS
● **SEE FIGURE 30–10.**

- Test-drive to verify that the original problem (concern) is fixed.

- Verify that no additional problems have occurred during the repair process.

- Check for and then clear all DTCs. (This step ensures that the computer will not make any changes based on a stored DTC but should not be performed if the vehicle is

**One Test Is Worth 1,000 "Expert" Opinions**

Whenever any vehicle has an engine performance or driveability concern, certain people always say the following:

"Sounds like it's a bad injector."

"I'll bet you it's a bad computer."

"I had a problem just like yours yesterday and it was a bad EGR valve."

Regardless of the skills and talents of those people, it is still more accurate to perform tests on the vehicle than to rely on feelings or opinions of others who have not even seen the vehicle. Even your own opinion should not sway your thinking. Follow a plan and perform tests, and the test results will lead to the root cause.

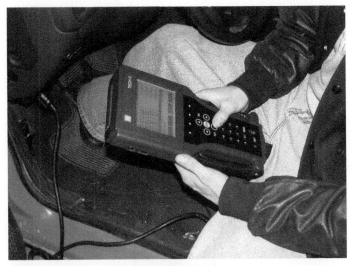

**FIGURE 30–11** A TECH 2 scan tool is the factory scan tool used on General Motors vehicles.

going to be tested for emissions because all of the monitors will need to be run and pass.)

■ Return the vehicle to the customer and double-check the following:

1. The vehicle is clean.

2. The radio is turned off.

3. The clock is set to the right time, and the radio stations have been restored if the battery was disconnected during the repair procedure.

## SCAN TOOLS

Scan tools are the workhorse for any diagnostic work on all vehicles. Scan tools can be divided into two basic groups:

1. **Factory scan tools.** These are the scan tools required by all dealers that sell and service the brand of vehicle. Examples of factory scan tools include the following:

   ■ **General Motors**—Tech 2. ● **SEE FIGURE 30–11.**
   ■ **Ford**—New Generation Star (NGS) and IDS (Integrated Diagnostic Software).
   ■ **Chrysler**—DRB III, Star Scan or wiTECH for CAN-equipped vehicles.
   ■ **Honda**—HDS or Master Tech
   ■ **Toyota**—Master Tech

All factory scan tools are designed to provide bidirectional capability, which allows the service technician the opportunity to operate components using the scan tool, thereby confirming that the component is able to work when commanded. Also, all factory scan tools are capable of displaying all factory parameters.

2. **Aftermarket scan tools.** These scan tools are designed to function on more than one brand of vehicle. Examples of aftermarket scan tools include the following:

   ■ **Snap-on** (various models including the MT2500 and Modis)

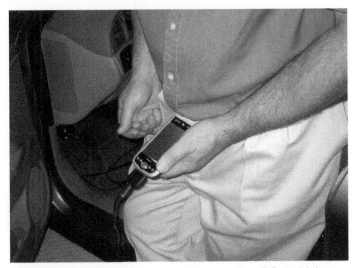

**FIGURE 30–12** Some scan tools use pocket PCs, which make it very convenient to use.

   ■ **OTC** (various models including Pegasus, Genisys and Task Master)
   ■ **AutoEnginuity** and other programs that use a laptop or handheld computer for the display

While many aftermarket scan tools can display most if not all of the parameters of the factory scan tool, there can be a difference when trying to troubleshoot some faults. ● **SEE FIGURE 30–12.**

## RETRIEVAL OF DIAGNOSTIC INFORMATION

To retrieve diagnostic information from the PCM, a scan tool is needed. If a factory or factory-level scan tool is used, then all of the data can be retrieved. If a global (generic) only type scan tool is used, only the emissions-related data can be retrieved.

To retrieve diagnostic information from the PCM, use the following steps:

**STEP 1** Locate and gain access to the data link connector (DLC).

**STEP 2** Connect the scan tool to the DLC and establish communication.

> **NOTE: If no communication is established, follow the vehicle manufacturer's specified instructions.**

**STEP 3** Follow the on-screen instructions of the scan tool to correctly identify the vehicle.

**STEP 4** Observe the scan data as well as any DTCs.

**STEP 5** Check to see that all of the monitors have run and passed. A diagnostic trouble code (DTC) will not be set unless the monitor for that system has been run.

**STEP 6** Follow vehicle manufacturer's instructions if any DTCs are stored. If no DTCs are stored, compare all sensor values with a factory acceptable range chart to see if any sensor values are out of range.

| Parameter Identification (PID) | | |
|---|---|---|
| **Scan Tool Parameter** | **Units Displayed** | **Typical Data Value** |
| Engine Idling/Radiator Hose Hot/Closed Throttle/Park or Neutral/Closed Loop/Accessories Off/Brake Pedal Released | | |
| 3X Crank Sensor | RPM | Varies |
| 24X Crank Sensor | RPM | Varies |
| Actual EGR Position | Percent | 0 |
| BARO | kPa/Volts | 65–110 kPa/ 3.5–4.5 Volts |
| CMP Sensor Signal Present | Yes/No | Yes |
| Commanded Fuel Pump | On/Off | On |
| Cycles of Misfire Data | Counts | 0–99 |
| Desired EGR Position | Percent | 0 |
| ECT | °C/°F | Varies |
| EGR Duty Cycle | Percent | 0 |
| Engine Run Time | Hr: Min: Sec | Varies |
| EVAP Canister Purge | Percent | Low and Varying |
| EVAP Fault History | No Fault/ Excess Vacuum/ Purge Valve Leak/ Small Leak/ Weak Vacuum | No Fault |
| Fuel Tank Pressure | Inches of $H_2O$/ Volts | Varies |
| $HO_2S$ Sensor 1 | Ready/Not Ready | Ready |
| $HO_2S$ Sensor 1 | Millivolts | 0–1,000 and Varying |

| **Scan Tool Parameter** | **Units Displayed** | **Typical Data Value** |
|---|---|---|
| $HO_2S$ Sensor 2 | Millivolts | 0–1,000 and Varying |
| $HO_2S$ X Counts | Counts | Varies |
| IAC Position | Counts | 15–25 preferred |
| IAT | °C/°F | Varies |
| Knock Retard | Degrees | 0 |
| Long Term FT | Percent | 0–10 |
| MAF | Grams per second | 3–7 |
| MAF Frequency | Hz | 1,200–3,000 (depends on altitude and engine load) |
| MAP | kPa/Volts | 20–48 kPa/ 0.75–2 Volts (depends on altitude) |
| Misfire Current Cyl. 1–10 | Counts | 0 |
| Misfire History Cyl. 1–10 | Counts | 0 |
| Short Term FT | Percent | 0–10 |
| Start Up ECT | °C/°F | Varies |
| Start Up IAT | °C/°F | Varies |
| Total Misfire Current Count | Counts | 0 |
| Total Misfire Failures | Counts | 0 |
| Total Misfire Passes | Counts | 0 |
| TP Angle | Percent | 0 |
| TP Sensor | Volts | 0.20–0.74 |
| Vehicle Speed | MPH/Km/h | 0 |

**Note:** Viewing the PID screen on the scanner is useful in determining if a problem is occurring at the present time

# TROUBLESHOOTING USING DTC DIAGNOSTIC TROUBLE CODES

Pinning down causes of the actual problem can be accomplished by trying to set the opposite code. For example, if a code indicates an open throttle position (TP) sensor (high resistance), clear the code and create a shorted (low-resistance) condition. This can be accomplished by using a jumper wire and connecting the signal terminal to the 5-volt reference terminal. This should set a DTC:

- **If the opposite code sets,** this indicates that the wiring and connector for the sensor is okay and the sensor itself is defective (open).

- **If the same code sets,** this indicates that the wiring or electrical connection is open (has high resistance) and is the cause of the setting of the DTC.

## METHODS FOR CLEARING DIAGNOSTIC TROUBLE CODES
Clearing DTCs from a vehicle computer sometimes needs to be performed. There are three methods that can be used to clear stored DTCs:

**CAUTION: Clearing diagnostic trouble codes (DTCs) also will clear all of the noncontinuous monitors.**

- **Clearing codes—Method 1.** The preferred method of clearing codes is by using a scan tool. This is the method recommended by most vehicle manufacturers if the procedure can be performed on the vehicle. The computer of some vehicles cannot be cleared with a scan tool.

- **Clearing codes—Method 2.** If a scan tool is not available or a scan tool cannot be used on the vehicle being serviced, the power to the computer can be disconnected:

   1. Disconnect the fusible link (if so equipped) that feeds the computer.

   2. Disconnect the fuse or fuses that feed the computer.

   **NOTE: The fuse may not be labeled as a computer fuse. For example, many Toyotas can be cleared by disconnecting the fuel-injection fuse. Some vehicles require that two fuses be disconnected to clear any stored codes.**

- **Clearing codes—Method 3.** If the other two methods cannot be used, the negative battery cable can be disconnected to clear stored DTCs.

**NOTE: Because of the adaptive learning capacity of the computer, a vehicle may fail an exhaust emissions test if the vehicle is not driven enough to allow the computer to run all of the monitors.**

**CAUTION: By disconnecting the battery, the radio presets and clock information will be lost. They should be reset before returning the vehicle to the customer. If the radio has a security code, the code must be entered before the radio will function. Before disconnecting the battery, always check with the vehicle owner to be sure that the code is available.**

## FLASH CODE RETRIEVAL ON OBD-I GENERAL MOTORS VEHICLES

The GM system uses a "check engine" or "check engine soon" MIL to notify the driver of possible system failure. Under the dash (on most GM vehicles) is a data link connector (DLC) previously called an assembly line communications link (ALCL) or assembly line diagnostic link (ALDL).

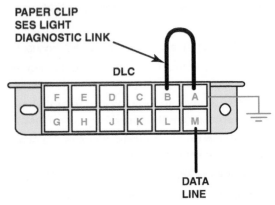

**FIGURE 30–13** To retrieve flash codes from an OBD-I General Motors vehicle, without a scan tool, connect terminals A and B with the ignition on–engine off. The M terminal is used to retrieve data from the sensors to a scan tool.

### TECH TIP

**Do Not Lie to a Scan Tool!**

Because computer calibration may vary from year to year, using the incorrect year for the vehicle while using a scan tool can cause the data retrieved to be incorrect or inaccurate.

Most General Motors DTCs can be retrieved by using a metal tool and contacting terminals A and B of the 12-pin DLC. ● **SEE FIGURE 30–13.** This method is called **flash code retrieval** because the MIL will flash to indicate DTCs. The steps are as follows:

1. Turn the ignition switch to on (engine off). The "check engine" light or "service engine soon" light should be on. If the amber malfunction indicator light (MIL) is not on, a problem exists within the light circuit.

2. Connect terminals A and B at the DLC.

3. Observe the MIL. A code 12 (one flash, then a pause, then two flashes) reveals that there is no engine speed indication to the computer. Because the engine is not running, this simply indicates that the computer diagnostic system is working correctly.

   **NOTE: Refer to service manual diagnostic procedures if the MIL is on and does not flash a code 12 when terminals A and B are connected.**

4. After code 12 is displayed three times, the MIL will flash any other stored DTCs in numeric order starting with the lowest-number code. If only code 12 is displayed another three times, the computer has not detected any other faults.

**NOTE: Trouble codes can vary according to year, make, model, and engine. Always consult the service literature or service manual for the exact vehicle being serviced. Check service information for the meaning and recommended steps to follow if a diagnostic trouble code (DTC) is retrieved.**

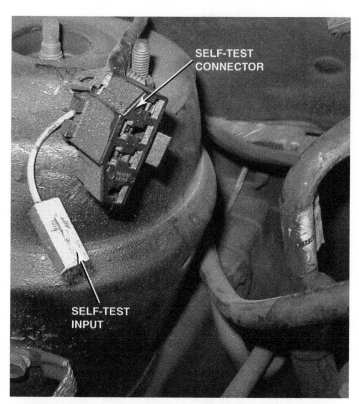

**FIGURE 30–14** A Ford OBD-I self-test connector. The location of this connector can vary with model and year of vehicle.

# RETRIEVING FORD DIAGNOSTIC CODES

The best tool to use during troubleshooting of a Ford vehicle is a **self-test automatic readout (STAR)** tester, new generation STAR (NGS), WDS (Worldwide Diagnostic System), or another scan tool with Ford capabilities. If a STAR tester or scan tool is not available, a needle (analog) type of voltmeter can be used for all OBD-I (prior to 1996) systems. See the Tech Tip "Put a Wire in the Attic and a Light in the Basement!" to obtain flash codes. The test connector is usually located under the hood on the driver's side. ● **SEE FIGURE 30–14.**

### KEY ON–ENGINE OFF TEST (ON-DEMAND CODES OR HARD FAULTS)

With the ignition key on (engine off), watch the voltmeter pulses, which should appear within 5 to 30 seconds. (Ignore any initial surge of voltage when the ignition is turned on.)

The computer will send a two-digit code that will cause the voltmeter to pulse or move from left to right. For example, if the voltmeter needle pulses two times, then pauses for 2 seconds, and then pulses three times, the code is 23. There is normally a 4-second pause between codes.

**SEPARATOR PULSE.** After all the codes have been reported, the computer will pause for about 6 to 9 seconds, then cause

the voltmeter needle to pulse once and then pause for another 6 to 9 seconds. This is the normal separation between current trouble codes and continuous memory codes (for intermittent problems). Code 11 is the normal pass code, which means that no fault has been stored in memory. Therefore, normal operation of the diagnostic procedure using a voltmeter should indicate the following if no codes are set: one pulse (2-second pause), one pulse (6- to 9-second pause), one pulse (6- to 9-second pause), one pulse (2-second pause), and, finally, one pulse. These last two pulses that are separated by a 2-second interval represent a code 11, which is the code used between current and intermittent trouble codes.

### CONTINUOUS MEMORY CODES (SOFT CODES)

Continuous memory codes are set based on information stored while the vehicle was in normal operation. These codes represent an intermittent problem and should be used only for diagnosis if the **KOEO** test results in code 11 (no faults detected). Therefore, any codes displayed after the separation pulse represent failures that have been detected but may no longer be present.

### KEY ON–ENGINE RUNNING (KOER) TEST

During the **KOER** self-test, the sensors are checked by the computer under actual operating conditions, and the output devices (actuators) are operated and checked for expected results. Start the engine and raise the speed to 2,500 to 3,000 RPM to warm the oxygen sensor within 20 seconds of starting. Hold a steady high engine

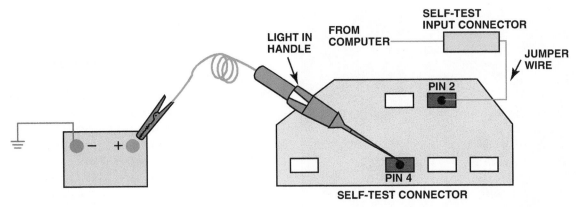

**FIGURE 30–15** To retrieve Ford DTCs using a test light and a jumper wire, turn the ignition switch on (engine off) and make the connections shown. The test light will blink out the diagnostic trouble codes (DTCs).

speed until the initial pulses appear (two pulses for a 4-cylinder engine, three pulses for a 6-cylinder, and four pulses for an 8-cylinder). These codes are used to verify the proper processor (computer) is in the vehicle and that the self-test has been entered. Continue to hold a high engine speed until the code pulses begin (10 to 14 seconds).

### STEERING, BRAKE, AND OVERDRIVE SWITCH TEST

To test the power steering pressure switch, the technician must turn the steering wheel one-half turn after the ID code has been displayed. The brake pedal and the overdrive cancel switch must also be cycled after the ID code to allow the system to detect a change of state of these switches.

**DYNAMIC RESPONSE CHECK.** The dynamic response test checks the throttle position (TP) mass air flow (MAF) and manifold absolute pressure (MAP) sensors during a brief wide-open throttle (WOT) test performed by the technician. The signal for the technician to depress the throttle briefly to wide open is a single pulse or a code 10 on a STAR tester.

If any hard (on-demand) faults appear, these should be repaired first and then any soft (continuous) codes next. Use the factory "pinpoint tests" to trace the problem. Refer to service information for a description of Ford-specific alphanumeric DTCs.

**FIGURE 30–16** A typical OBD-II data link connector (DLC). The location varies with make and model and may even be covered, but a tool is not needed to gain access. Check service information for the exact location if needed.

NOTE: **Unlike other manufacturers, most Chrysler brand vehicles equipped with OBD-II will display the P-codes on the odometer display by cycling the ignition key as previously performed on older vehicles.**

## FLASH CODE RETRIEVAL ON CHRYSLER VEHICLES

To put the computer into the self-diagnostic mode, the ignition switch must be turned on and off three times within a 5-second period (on-off-on-off-on). The computer will flash a series of fault codes. Older Chrysler brand products flash the "check engine" lamp on the dash.

## OBD-II DIAGNOSIS

Starting with the 1996 model year, all vehicles sold in the United States must use the same type of 16-pin data link connector (DLC) and must monitor emission-related components. ● **SEE FIGURE 30–16.**

**RETRIEVING OBD-II CODES** A scan tool is required to retrieve DTCs from most OBD-II vehicles. Every OBD-II scan tool will be able to read all generic Society of Automotive Engineers (SAE) DTCs from any vehicle.

## Fuel and Air Metering System

| | |
|---|---|
| P0100 | Mass or Volume Airflow Circuit Problem |
| P0101 | Mass or Volume Airflow Circuit Range or Performance Problem |
| P0102 | Mass or Volume Airflow Circuit Low Input |
| P0103 | Mass or Volume Airflow Circuit High Input |
| P0105 | Manifold Absolute Pressure or Barometric Pressure Circuit Problem |
| P0106 | Manifold Absolute Pressure or Barometric Pressure Circuit Range or Performance Problem |
| P0107 | Manifold Absolute Pressure or Barometric Pressure Circuit Low Input |
| P0108 | Manifold Absolute Pressure or Barometric Pressure Circuit High Input |
| P0110 | Intake Air Temperature Circuit Problem |
| P0111 | Intake Air Temperature Circuit Range or Performance Problem |
| P0112 | Intake Air Temperature Circuit Low Input |
| P0113 | Intake Air Temperature Circuit High Input |
| P0115 | Engine Coolant Temperature Circuit Problem |
| P0116 | Engine Coolant Temperature Circuit Range or Performance Problem |
| P0117 | Engine Coolant Temperature Circuit Low Input |
| P0118 | Engine Coolant Temperature Circuit High Input |
| P0120 | Throttle Position Circuit Problem |
| P0121 | Throttle Position Circuit Range or Performance Problem |
| P0122 | Throttle Position Circuit Low Input |
| P0123 | Throttle Position Circuit High Input |
| P0125 | Excessive Time to Enter Closed-Loop Fuel Control |
| P0128 | Coolant Temperature Below Thermostat Regulating Temperature |
| P0130 | O2 Sensor Circuit Problem (Bank 1* Sensor 1) |
| P0131 | O2 Sensor Circuit Low Voltage (Bank 1* Sensor 1) |
| P0132 | O2 Sensor Circuit High Voltage (Bank 1* Sensor 1) |
| P0133 | O2 Sensor Circuit Slow Response (Bank 1* Sensor 1) |
| P0134 | O2 Sensor Circuit No Activity Detected (Bank 1* Sensor 1) |
| P0135 | O2 Sensor Heater Circuit Problem (Bank 1* Sensor 1) |
| P0136 | O2 Sensor Circuit Problem (Bank 1* Sensor 2) |
| P0137 | O2 Sensor Circuit Low Voltage (Bank 1* Sensor 2) |
| P0138 | O2 Sensor Circuit High Voltage (Bank 1* Sensor 2) |
| P0139 | O2 Sensor Circuit Slow Response (Bank 1* Sensor 2) |
| P0140 | O2 Sensor Circuit No Activity Detected (Bank 1* Sensor 2) |
| P0141 | O2 Sensor Heater Circuit Problem (Bank 1* Sensor 2) |
| P0142 | O2 Sensor Circuit Problem (Bank 1* Sensor 3) |
| P0143 | O2 Sensor Circuit Low Voltage (Bank 1* Sensor 3) |
| P0144 | O2 Sensor Circuit High Voltage (Bank 1* Sensor 3) |
| P0145 | O2 Sensor Circuit Slow Response (Bank 1* Sensor 3) |
| P0146 | O2 Sensor Circuit No Activity Detected (Bank 1* Sensor 3) |
| P0147 | O2 Sensor Heater Circuit Problem (Bank 1* Sensor 3) |
| P0150 | O2 Sensor Circuit Problem (Bank 2 Sensor 1) |
| P0151 | O2 Sensor Circuit Low Voltage (Bank 2 Sensor 1) |
| P0152 | O2 Sensor Circuit High Voltage (Bank 2 Sensor 1) |
| P0153 | O2 Sensor Circuit Slow Response (Bank 2 Sensor 1) |
| P0154 | O2 Sensor Circuit No Activity Detected (Bank 2 Sensor 1) |
| P0155 | O2 Sensor Heater Circuit Problem (Bank 2 Sensor 1) |
| P0156 | O2 Sensor Circuit Problem (Bank 2 Sensor 2) |
| P0157 | O2 Sensor Circuit Low Voltage (Bank 2 Sensor 2) |
| P0158 | O2 Sensor Circuit High Voltage (Bank 2 Sensor 2) |
| P0159 | O2 Sensor Circuit Slow Response (Bank 2 Sensor 2) |
| P0160 | O2 Sensor Circuit No Activity Detected (Bank 2 Sensor 2) |
| P0161 | O2 Sensor Heater Circuit Problem (Bank 2 Sensor 2) |
| P0162 | O2 Sensor Circuit Problem (Bank 2 Sensor 3) |
| P0163 | O2 Sensor Circuit Low Voltage (Bank 2 Sensor 3) |
| P0164 | O2 Sensor Circuit High Voltage (Bank 2 Sensor 3) |
| P0165 | O2 Sensor Circuit Slow Response (Bank 2 Sensor 3) |
| P0166 | O2 Sensor Circuit No Activity Detected (Bank 2 Sensor 3) |
| P0167 | O2 Sensor Heater Circuit Problem (Bank 2 Sensor 3) |
| P0170 | Fuel Trim Problem (Bank 1*) |
| P0171 | System Too Lean (Bank 1*) |
| P0172 | System Too Rich (Bank 1*) |
| P0173 | Fuel Trim Problem (Bank 2) |
| P0174 | System Too Lean (Bank 2) |
| P0175 | System Too Rich (Bank 2) |
| P0176 | Fuel Composition Sensor Circuit Problem |
| P0177 | Fuel Composition Sensor Circuit Range or Performance |
| P0178 | Fuel Composition Sensor Circuit Low Input |
| P0179 | Fuel Composition Sensor Circuit High Input |
| P0180 | Fuel Temperature Sensor Problem |
| P0181 | Fuel Temperature Sensor Circuit Range or Performance |
| P0182 | Fuel Temperature Sensor Circuit Low Input |
| P0183 | Fuel Temperature Sensor Circuit High Input |

## Fuel and Air Metering (Injector Circuit)

| | |
|---|---|
| P0201 | Injector Circuit Problem—Cylinder 1 |
| P0202 | Injector Circuit Problem—Cylinder 2 |
| P0203 | Injector Circuit Problem—Cylinder 3 |
| P0204 | Injector Circuit Problem—Cylinder 4 |
| P0205 | Injector Circuit Problem—Cylinder 5 |
| P0206 | Injector Circuit Problem—Cylinder 6 |
| P0207 | Injector Circuit Problem—Cylinder 7 |
| P0208 | Injector Circuit Problem—Cylinder 8 |
| P0209 | Injector Circuit Problem—Cylinder 9 |
| P0210 | Injector Circuit Problem—Cylinder 10 |
| P0211 | Injector Circuit Problem—Cylinder 11 |
| P0212 | Injector Circuit Problem—Cylinder 12 |
| P0213 | Cold Start Injector 1 Problem |
| P0214 | Cold Start Injector 2 Problem |

## Ignition System or Misfire

| | |
|---|---|
| P0300 | Random Misfire Detected |
| P0301 | Cylinder 1 Misfire Detected |
| P0302 | Cylinder 2 Misfire Detected |
| P0303 | Cylinder 3 Misfire Detected |
| P0304 | Cylinder 4 Misfire Detected |
| P0305 | Cylinder 5 Misfire Detected |

*(continued)*

P0306   Cylinder 6 Misfire Detected
P0307   Cylinder 7 Misfire Detected
P0308   Cylinder 8 Misfire Detected
P0309   Cylinder 9 Misfire Detected
P0310   Cylinder 10 Misfire Detected
P0311   Cylinder 11 Misfire Detected
P0312   Cylinder 12 Misfire Detected
P0320   Ignition or Distributor Engine Speed Input Circuit Problem
P0321   Ignition or Distributor Engine Speed Input Circuit Range or Performance
P0322   Ignition or Distributor Engine Speed Input Circuit No Signal
P0325   Knock Sensor 1 Circuit Problem
P0326   Knock Sensor 1 Circuit Range or Performance
P0327   Knock Sensor 1 Circuit Low Input
P0328   Knock Sensor 1 Circuit High Input
P0330   Knock Sensor 2 Circuit Problem
P0331   Knock Sensor 2 Circuit Range or Performance
P0332   Knock Sensor 2 Circuit Low Input
P0333   Knock Sensor 2 Circuit High Input
P0335   Crankshaft Position Sensor Circuit Problem
P0336   Crankshaft Position Sensor Circuit Range or Performance
P0337   Crankshaft Position Sensor Circuit Low Input
P0338   Crankshaft Position Sensor Circuit High Input

## Auxiliary Emission Controls

P0400   Exhaust Gas Recirculation Flow Problem
P0401   Exhaust Gas Recirculation Flow Insufficient Detected
P0402   Exhaust Gas Recirculation Flow Excessive Detected
P0405   Air Conditioner Refrigerant Charge Loss
P0410   Secondary Air Injection System Problem
P0411   Secondary Air Injection System Insufficient Flow Detected
P0412   Secondary Air Injection System Switching Valve or Circuit Problem
P0413   Secondary Air Injection System Switching Valve or Circuit Open
P0414   Secondary Air Injection System Switching Valve or Circuit Shorted
P0420   Catalyst System Efficiency below Threshold (Bank 1*)
P0421   Warm Up Catalyst Efficiency below Threshold (Bank 1*)
P0422   Main Catalyst Efficiency below Threshold (Bank 1*)
P0423   Heated Catalyst Efficiency below Threshold (Bank 1*)
P0424   Heated Catalyst Temperature below Threshold (Bank 1*)
P0430   Catalyst System Efficiency below Threshold (Bank 2)
P0431   Warm Up Catalyst Efficiency below Threshold (Bank 2)
P0432   Main Catalyst Efficiency below Threshold (Bank 2)
P0433   Heated Catalyst Efficiency below Threshold (Bank 2)
P0434   Heated Catalyst Temperature below Threshold (Bank 2)
P0440   Evaporative Emission Control System Problem
P0441   Evaporative Emission Control System Insufficient Purge Flow
P0442   Evaporative Emission Control System Leak Detected
P0443   Evaporative Emission Control System Purge Control Valve Circuit Problem
P0444   Evaporative Emission Control System Purge Control Valve Circuit Open
P0445   Evaporative Emission Control System Purge Control Valve Circuit Shorted
P0446   Evaporative Emission Control System Vent Control Problem
P0447   Evaporative Emission Control System Vent Control Open
P0448   Evaporative Emission Control System Vent Control Shorted
P0450   Evaporative Emission Control System Pressure Sensor Problem
P0451   Evaporative Emission Control System Pressure Sensor Range or Performance
P0452   Evaporative Emission Control System Pressure Sensor Low Input
P0453   Evaporative Emission Control System Pressure Sensor High Input

## Vehicle Speed Control and Idle Control

P0500   Vehicle Speed Sensor Problem
P0501   Vehicle Speed Sensor Range or Performance
P0502   Vehicle Speed Sensor Low Input
P0505   Idle Control System Problem
P0506   Idle Control System RPM Lower Than Expected
P0507   Idle Control System RPM Higher Than Expected
P0510   Closed Throttle Position Switch Problem

## Computer Output Circuit

P0600   Serial Communication Link Problem
P0605   Internal Control Module (Module Identification Defined by J1979)

## Transmission

P0703   Brake Switch Input Problem
P0705   Transmission Range Sensor Circuit Problem (PRNDL Input)
P0706   Transmission Range Sensor Circuit Range or Performance
P0707   Transmission Range Sensor Circuit Low Input
P0708   Transmission Range Sensor Circuit High Input
P0710   Transmission Fluid Temperature Sensor Problem
P0711   Transmission Fluid Temperature Sensor Range or Performance
P0712   Transmission Fluid Temperature Sensor Low Input
P0713   Transmission Fluid Temperature Sensor High Input
P0715   Input or Turbine Speed Sensor Circuit Problem
P0716   Input or Turbine Speed Sensor Circuit Range or Performance
P0717   Input or Turbine Speed Sensor Circuit No Signal
P0720   Output Speed Sensor Circuit Problem
P0721   Output Speed Sensor Circuit Range or Performance
P0722   Output Speed Sensor Circuit No Signal
P0725   Engine Speed Input Circuit Problem
P0726   Engine Speed Input Circuit Range or Performance

| | |
|---|---|
| P0727 | Engine Speed Input Circuit No Signal |
| P0730 | Incorrect Gear Ratio |
| P0731 | Gear 1 Incorrect Ratio |
| P0732 | Gear 2 Incorrect Ratio |
| P0733 | Gear 3 Incorrect Ratio |
| P0734 | Gear 4 Incorrect Ratio |
| P0735 | Gear 5 Incorrect Ratio |
| P0736 | Reverse Incorrect Ratio |
| P0740 | Torque Converter Clutch System Problem |
| P0741 | Torque Converter Clutch System Performance or Stuck Off |
| P0742 | Torque Converter Clutch System Stuck On |
| P0743 | Torque Converter Clutch System Electrical |
| P0745 | Pressure Control Solenoid Problem |
| P0746 | Pressure Control Solenoid Performance or Stuck Off |
| P0747 | Pressure Control Solenoid Stuck On |
| P0748 | Pressure Control Solenoid Electrical |
| P0750 | Shift Solenoid A Problem |
| P0751 | Shift Solenoid A Performance or Stuck Off |
| P0752 | Shift Solenoid A Stuck On |
| P0753 | Shift Solenoid A Electrical |
| P0755 | Shift Solenoid B Problem |
| P0756 | Shift Solenoid B Performance or Stuck Off |
| P0757 | Shift Solenoid B Stuck On |
| P0758 | Shift Solenoid B Electrical |
| P0760 | Shift Solenoid C Problem |
| P0761 | Shift Solenoid C Performance or Stuck Off |
| P0762 | Shift Solenoid C Stuck On |
| P0763 | Shift Solenoid C Electrical |
| P0765 | Shift Solenoid D Problem |
| P0766 | Shift Solenoid D Performance or Stuck Off |
| P0767 | Shift Solenoid D Stuck On |
| P0768 | Shift Solenoid D Electrical |
| P0770 | Shift Solenoid E Problem |
| P0771 | Shift Solenoid E Performance or Stuck Off |
| P0772 | Shift Solenoid E Stuck On |
| P0773 | Shift Solenoid E Electrical |

\* The side of the engine where number one cylinder is located.

## OBD-II ACTIVE TESTS

The vehicle computer must run tests on the various emission-related components and turn on the malfunction indicator lamp (MIL) if faults are detected. OBD-II is an *active* computer analysis system because it actually tests the operation of the oxygen sensors, exhaust gas recirculation system, and so forth whenever conditions permit. It is the purpose and function of the PCM to monitor these components and perform these active tests.

For example, the PCM may open the EGR valve momentarily to check its operation while the vehicle is decelerating. A change in the manifold absolute pressure (MAP) sensor signal will indicate to the computer that the exhaust gas is, in fact, being introduced into the engine. Because these tests are active and certain conditions must be present before these tests can be run, the computer uses its internal diagnostic program to keep track of all the various conditions and to schedule active tests so that they will not interfere with each other.

**OBD-II DRIVE CYCLE** The vehicle must be driven under a variety of operating conditions for all active tests to be performed. A **trip** is defined as an engine-operating drive cycle that contains the necessary conditions for a particular test to be performed. For example, for the EGR test to be performed, the engine has to be at normal operating temperature and decelerating for a minimum amount of time. Some tests are performed when the engine is cold, whereas others require that the vehicle be cruising at a steady highway speed.

**TYPES OF OBD-II CODES** Not all OBD-II DTCs are of the same importance for exhaust emissions. Each type of DTC has different requirements for it to set, and the computer will turn on the MIL only for emissions-related DTCs.

**TYPE A CODES.** A type A DTC is emission related and will cause the MIL to be turned on at the *first trip* if the computer has detected a problem. Engine misfire or a very rich or lean air–fuel ratio, for example, would cause a type A DTC. These codes alert the driver to an emissions problem that may cause damage to the catalytic converter.

**TYPE B CODES.** A type B code will be stored as a pending code in the PCM, and the MIL will be turned on only after the second consecutive trip, alerting the driver to the fact that a diagnostic test was performed and failed.

**NOTE: Type A and Type B codes are emission related and will cause the lighting of the malfunction indicator lamp, usually labeled "check engine" or "service engine soon."**

**TYPE C AND D CODES.** Type C and type D codes are for use with non-emission-related diagnostic tests. They will cause the lighting of a "service" lamp (if the vehicle is so equipped).

**OBD-II FREEZE-FRAME** To assist the service technician, OBD-II requires the computer to take a "snapshot" or freeze-frame of all data at the instant an emission-related DTC is set. A scan tool is required to retrieve this data. CARB and EPA regulations require that the controller store specific freeze-frame (engine-related) data when the first emission related fault is detected. The data stored in freeze-frame can be replaced only by data from a trouble code with a higher priority, such as a trouble related to a fuel system or misfire monitor fault.

**NOTE: Although OBD-II requires that just one freeze-frame of data be stored, the instant an emission-related DTC is set, vehicle manufacturers usually provide expanded data about the DTC beyond that required. However, retrieving enhanced data usually requires the use of an enhanced or factory-level scan tool.**

The freeze-frame has to contain data values that occurred at the time the code was set (these values are provided in standard units of measurement). Freeze-frame data is recorded during the first trip on a two-trip fault. As a result, OBD-II systems record the data present at the time an emission-related code is recorded and the MIL activated. This data can be accessed and displayed on a scan tool. Freeze-frame data is one frame or one instant in time. Freeze-frame data is not updated (refreshed) if the same monitor test fails a second time.

### REQUIRED FREEZE-FRAME DATA ITEMS

- Code that triggered the freeze-frame
- A/F ratio, airflow rate, and calculated engine load
- Base fuel injector pulse width
- ECT, IAT, MAF, MAP, TP, and VS sensor data
- Engine speed and amount of ignition spark advance
- Open- or closed-loop status
- Short-term and long-term fuel trim values
- For misfire codes—identify the cylinder that misfired

NOTE: All freeze-frame data will be lost if the battery is disconnected, power to the PCM is removed, or the scan tool is used to erase or clear trouble codes.

### DIAGNOSING INTERMITTENT MALFUNCTIONS
Of all the different types of conditions that you will see, the hardest to accurately diagnose and repair are intermittent malfunctions. These conditions may be temperature related (occur only when the vehicle is hot or cold) or humidity related (occur only when it is raining). Regardless of the conditions that will cause the malfunction to occur, you must diagnose and correct the condition.

When dealing with an intermittent concern, you should determine the conditions when the malfunction occurs and then try to duplicate those conditions. If a cause is not readily apparent to you, ask the customer when the symptom occurs. Ask if there are any conditions that seem to be related to or cause the concern.

Another consideration when working on an OBD-II-equipped vehicle is whether a concern is intermittent or whether it only occurs when a specific diagnostic test is performed by the PCM. Since OBD-II systems conduct diagnostic tests only under very precise conditions, some tests may be run only once during an ignition cycle. Additionally, if the requirements needed to perform the test are not met, the test will not run during an ignition cycle. This type of on-board diagnostics could be mistaken as "intermittent" when, in fact, the tests are only infrequent (depending on how the vehicle is driven). Examples of this type of diagnostic test are HO$_2$S heaters, evaporative canister purge, catalyst efficiency, and EGR flow. When diagnosing intermittent concerns on an OBD-II-equipped vehicle, a logical diagnostic strategy is essential. The use of stored freeze-frame information can also be very useful when diagnosing an intermittent malfunction if a code has been stored.

## SERVICE/FLASH PROGRAMMING

Designing a program that allows an engine to meet strict air quality and fuel economy standards while providing excellent performance is no small feat. However, this is only part of the challenge facing engineers assigned with the task of developing OBD-II software. The reason for this is the countless variables involved with running the diagnostic monitors. Although programmers do their best to factor in any and all operating conditions when writing this complex code, periodic revisions are often required.

Reprogramming consists of downloading new calibration files from a scan tool, personal computer (PC), or modem into the PCM's electronically erasable programmable read-only memory (EEPROM). This can be done on or off the vehicle using the appropriate equipment. Since reprogramming is not an OBD-II requirement however, many vehicles will need a new PCM in the event software changes become necessary. Physically removing and replacing the PROM chip is no longer possible.

The following are three industry-standard methods used to reprogram the EEPROM:

- Remote programming
- Direct programming
- Off-board programming

REMOTE PROGRAMMING. Remote programming uses the scan tool to transfer data from the manufacturer's shop PC to the vehicle's PCM. This is accomplished by performing the following steps:

- Connect the scan tool to the vehicle's DLC. ● SEE FIGURE 30–17.
- Enter the vehicle information into the scan tool through the programming application software incorporated in the scan tool. ● SEE FIGURE 30–18.
- Download VIN and current EEPROM calibration using a scan tool.
- Disconnect the scan tool from the DLC and connect the tool to the shop PC.
- Download the new calibration from the PC to the scan tool. ● SEE FIGURE 30–19.
- Reconnect the scan tool to the vehicle's DLC and download the new calibration into the PCM.

CAUTION: Before programming, the vehicle's battery must be between 11 and 14 volts. Do not attempt to program while charging the battery unless using a special battery charger that does not produce excessive ripple voltage, such as the Midtronics PSC-300 (30 amp) or PSC-550 (55 amp) or similar as specified by the vehicle manufacturer.

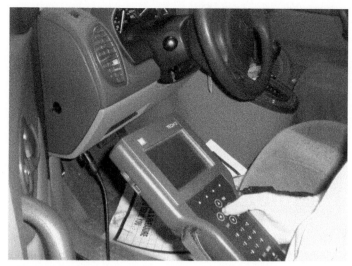

**FIGURE 30–17** The first step in the reprogramming procedure is to determine the current software installed using a scan tool. Not all scan tools can be used. In most cases using the factory scan tool is needed for reprogramming unless the scan tool is equipped to handle reprogramming.

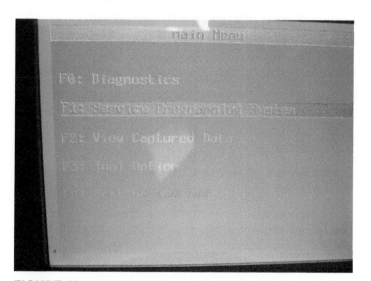

**FIGURE 30–18** Follow the on-screen instructions.

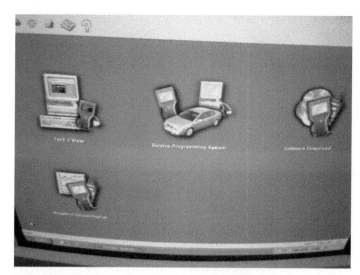

**FIGURE 30–19** An Internet connection is usually needed to perform updates, although some vehicle manufacturers use CDs that are updated regularly at a cost to the shop.

**FIGURE 30–20** Connecting cables and a computer to perform off-board programming.

**DIRECT PROGRAMMING.** Direct programming does utilize a connection between the shop PC and the vehicle DLC.

**OFF-BOARD PROGRAMMING.** Off-board programming is used if the PCM must be programmed away from the vehicle. This is preformed using the off-board programming adapter. ● **SEE FIGURE 30–20.**

**J2534 REPROGRAMMING** Legislation has mandated that vehicle manufacturers meet the SAE J2534 standards for all emissions-related systems on all new vehicles starting with model year 2004. This standard enables independent service repair operators to program or reprogram emissions-related ECMs from a wide variety of vehicle manufacturers with a single tool. ● **SEE FIGURE 30–21.** A J2534-compliant

pass-through system is a standardized programming and diagnostic system. It uses a PC plus a standard interface to a software device driver and a hardware vehicle communication interface. The interface connects to a PC and to a programmable ECM on a vehicle through the J1962 data link connector (DLC). This system allows programming of all vehicle manufacturer ECMs using a single set of programming hardware. Programming software made available by the vehicle manufacturer must be functional with a J2534-compliant pass-through system.

The software for a typical pass-through application consists of two major components, including the following:

■ The part delivered by the company that furnishes the hardware for J2534 enables the pass-through vehicle communication interface to communicate with the PC and provides

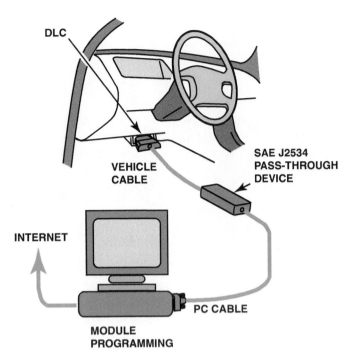

FIGURE 30–21 The J2534 pass-through reprogramming system does not need a scan tool to reflash the PCM on most 2004 and newer vehicles.

FIGURE 30–22 A typical J2534 universal reprogrammer that uses the J2534 standards.

for all Vehicle Communication Protocols as required by SAE J2534. It also provides for the software interface to work with the software applications as provided for by the vehicle manufacturers. ● **SEE FIGURE 30–22.**

■ The second part of the pass-through enabling software is provided for by the vehicle manufacturers. This is normally a subset of the software used with their original equipment manufacturer (OEM) tools, and their website will indicate how to obtain this software and under what conditions it can be used. Refer to the National Automotive Service

Task Force (NASTF) website for the addresses for all vehicle manufacturers' service information and cost, *www.NASTF.org.*

Since the majority of vehicle manufacturers make this software available in downloadable form, having an Internet browser (Explorer/Netscape) and connection is a must.

## MANUFACTURER'S DIAGNOSTIC ROUTINES

Each vehicle manufacturer has established its own diagnostic routines and they should be followed. Most include the following steps:

**STEP 1**  Retrieve DTCs.

**STEP 2**  Check for all technical service bulletins that could be related to the stored DTC.

**STEP 3**  If there are multiple DTCs, the diagnostic routine may include checking different components or systems instead of when only one DTC was stored.

**STEP 4**  Perform system checks.

**STEP 5**  Perform the necessary service or repair

**STEP 6**  Perform a road test matching the parameters recorded in the freeze-frame to check that the repair has corrected the malfunction.

**STEP 7**  Repeat the road test to cause the MIL to be extinguished.

**NOTE: Do not clear codes (DTCs) unless instructed by the service information.**

Following the vehicle manufacturer's specific diagnostic routines will ensure that the root cause is found and the repair verified. This is important for customer satisfaction.

## COMPLETING SYSTEM REPAIRS

After the repair has been successfully completed, the vehicle should be driven under similar conditions that caused the original concern. Verify that the problem has been corrected. To perform this test drive, it is helpful to have a copy of the freeze-frame parameters that were present when the DTC was set. By driving under similar conditions, the PCM may perform a test of the system and automatically extinguish the MIL. This is the method preferred by most vehicle manufacturers. The DTC can be cleared using a scan tool, but then that means that monitors will have to be run, and the vehicle may fail an emission inspection if driven directly to the testing station.

# PROCEDURES FOR RESETTING THE PCM

The PCM can be reset or cleared of previously set DTCs and freeze-frame data in the following ways:

1. **Driving the vehicle.** Drive the vehicle under similar conditions that were present when the fault occurred. If the conditions are similar and the PCM performed the noncontinuous monitor test and it passed three times, then the PCM will extinguish the MIL. This is the method preferred by most vehicle manufacturers, however, this method could be time consuming. If three passes cannot be achieved, the owner of the vehicle will have to be told that even though the check engine light (MIL) is on, the problem has been corrected, and the MIL should go out in a few days of normal driving.

2. **Clear DTCs using a scan tool.** A scan tool can be used to clear the DTC, which will also delete all of the freeze-frame data. The advantage of using a scan tool is that the check engine (MIL) will be out and the customer will be happy that the problem (MIL on) has been corrected. Do not use a scan tool to clear a DTC if the vehicle is going to be checked soon at a test station for state-mandated emission tests.

3. **Battery disconnect.** Disconnecting the negative battery cable will clear the DTCs and freeze-frame on many vehicles but not all. Besides clearing the DTCs, disconnecting the battery for about 20 minutes will also erase radio station presets and other memory items in many cases. Most vehicle manufacturers do not recommend that the battery be disconnected to clear DTCs, and it may not work on some vehicles.

# ROAD TEST (DRIVE CYCLE)

Use the freeze-frame data and test-drive the vehicle so that the vehicle is driven to match the conditions displayed on the freeze-frame. If the battery has been disconnected, then the vehicle may have to be driven under conditions that allow the PCM to conduct monitor tests. This drive pattern is called a **drive cycle.** The drive cycle is different for each vehicle manufacturer, but a universal drive cycle may work in many cases. In many cases performing a universal drive cycle will reset most monitors in most vehicles.

## UNIVERSAL DRIVE CYCLE

**PRECONDITIONING: Phase 1**

> MIL must be off.
> No DTCs present.
> Fuel fill between 15% and 85%.
> Cold start—Preferred = 8-hour soak at 68°F to 86°F.
> Alternative = ECT below 86°F.

1. With the ignition off, connect scan tool.
2. Start engine and drive between 20 and 30 mph for 22 minutes, allowing speed to vary.
3. Stop and idle for 40 seconds, gradually accelerate to 55 mph.
4. Maintain 55 mph for 4 minutes using a steady throttle input.
5. Stop and idle for 30 seconds, then accelerate to 30 mph.
6. Maintain 30 mph for 12 minutes.
7. Repeat steps 4 and 5 four times.

> Using scan tool, check readiness. If insufficient readiness set, continue to universal drive trace phase II.

**Important: (Do not shut off engine between phases).**
**Phase II:**

1. Vehicle at a stop and idle for 45 seconds, then accelerate to 30 mph.
2. Maintain 30 mph for 22 minutes.
3. Repeat steps 1 and 2 three times.
4. Bring vehicle to a stop and idle for 45 seconds, then accelerate to 35 mph.
5. Maintain speed between 30 and 35 mph for 4 minutes.
6. Bring vehicle to a stop and idle for 45 seconds, then accelerate to 30 mph.
7. Maintain 30 mph for 22 minutes.
8. Repeat steps 6 and 7 five times.
9. Using scan tool, check readiness.

## SUMMARY

1. Funnel diagnostics—Visual approach to a diagnostic procedure:
   **Step 1** Verify the problem (concern)
   **Step 2** Perform a thorough visual inspection and basic tests
   **Step 3** Retrieve the diagnostic trouble codes (DTCs)
   **Step 4** Check for technical service bulletins (TSBs)
   **Step 5** Look carefully at scan tool data
   **Step 6** Narrow the problem to a system or cylinder
   **Step 7** Repair the problem and determine the root cause
   **Step 8** Verify the repair and check for any stored DTCs

2. A thorough visual inspection is important during the diagnosis and troubleshooting of any engine performance problem or electrical malfunction.

3. If the MIL is on, retrieve the DTC and follow the manufacturer's recommended procedure to find the root cause of the problem.

4. OBD-II vehicles use a 16-pin DLC and common DTCs.

## REVIEW QUESTIONS

1. Explain the procedure to follow when diagnosing a vehicle with stored DTCs using a scan tool.

2. Discuss what the PCM does during a drive cycle to test emission-related components.

3. Explain the difference between a type A and type B OBD-II DTC.

4. List three things that should be checked as part of a thorough visual inspection.

5. List the eight-step funnel diagnostic procedure.

6. Explain why a bulletin search should be performed after stored DTCs are retrieved.

7. List the three methods that can be used to reprogram a PCM.

## CHAPTER QUIZ

1. Technician A says that the first step in the diagnostic process is to verify the problem (concern). Technician B says the second step is to perform a thorough visual inspection. Which technician is correct?
   **a.** Technician A only
   **b.** Technician B only
   **c.** Both Technicians A and B
   **d.** Neither Technician A nor B

2. Which item is *not* important to know before starting the diagnosis of an engine performance problem?
   **a.** List of previous repairs
   **b.** The brand of engine oil used
   **c.** The type of gasoline used
   **d.** The temperature of the engine when the problem occurs

3. A paper test can be used to check for a possible problem with _____.
   **a.** The ignition system (bad spark plug wire)
   **b.** A faulty injector on a multiport engine
   **c.** A burned valve
   **d.** All of the above

4. Which step should be performed *last* when diagnosing an engine performance problem?
   **a.** Checking for any stored diagnostic trouble codes (DTCs)
   **b.** Checking for any technical service bulletins (TSBs)
   **c.** Performing a thorough visual inspection
   **d.** Verify the repair

5. Technician A says that if the opposite DTC can be set, the problem is the component itself. Technician B says if the opposite DTC cannot be set, the problem is with the wiring or grounds. Which technician is correct?
   **a.** Technician A only
   **b.** Technician B only
   **c.** Both Technicians A and B
   **d.** Neither Technician A nor B

6. The preferred method to clear DTCs is to _____.
   **a.** Disconnect the negative battery cable for 10 seconds
   **b.** Use a scan tool
   **c.** Remove the computer (PCM) power feed fuse
   **d.** Cycle the ignition key on and off 40 times

7. Which is the factory scan tool for Chrysler brand vehicles equipped with CAN?
   **a.** Star Scan
   **b.** Tech 2
   **c.** NGS
   **d.** Master Tech

8. Technician A says that reprogramming a PCM using the J2534 system requires a factory scan tool. Technician B says that reprogramming a PCM using the J2534 system requires Internet access. Which technician is correct?
   **a.** Technician A only
   **b.** Technician B only
   **c.** Both Technicians A and B
   **d.** Neither Technician A nor B

9. Technician A says that knowing if there are any stored DTCs may be helpful when checking for related TSBs. Technician B says that only a factory scan tool should be used to retrieve DTCs. Which technician is correct?
   **a.** Technician A only
   **b.** Technician B only
   **c.** Both Technicians A and B
   **d.** Neither Technician A nor B

10. Which method can be used to reprogram a PCM?
    **a.** Remote
    **b.** Direct
    **c.** Off-board
    **d.** All of the above

# NATEF TASK CORRELATION CHART

For every task in Engine Performance the following safety requirement must be strictly enforced:

Comply with personal and environmental safety practices associated with clothing; eye protection; hand tools; power equipment; proper ventilation; and the handling, storage, and disposal of chemicals/materials in accordance with local, state, and federal safety and environmental regulations.

## ENGINE PERFORMANCE (A8)

| TASK | TEXTBOOK PAGE NO. | WORKTEXT PAGE NO. |
|---|---|---|
| **A. GENERAL ENGINE DIAGNOSIS** | | |
| 1. Complete work order to include customer information, vehicle identifying information, customer concern, related service history, cause, and correction. (P-1) | 4 | 4 |
| 2. Identify and interpret engine performance concern; determine necessary action. (P-1) | 378–383 | 44, 146 |
| 3. Research applicable vehicle and service information, such as engine management system operation, vehicle service history, service precautions, and technical service bulletins. (P-1) | 3–4 | 5–7, 17, 89, 95, 117, 139 |
| 4. Locate and interpret vehicle and major component identification numbers. (P-1) | 1–2 | 8–9, 1–15, 45 |
| 5. Inspect engine assembly for fuel, oil, coolant, and other leaks; determine necessary action. (P-2) | 136–137 | 34–35 |
| 6. Diagnose abnormal engine noise or vibration concerns; determine necessary action. (P-3) | 138–139 | 36 |
| 7. Diagnose abnormal exhaust color, odor, and sound; determine necessary action. (P-2) | 136 | 37 |
| 8. Perform engine absolute (vacuum/boost) manifold pressure tests; determine necessary action. (P-1) | 144–146 | 38 |
| 9. Perform cylinder power balance test; determine necessary action. (P-2) | 144 | 39 |
| 10. Perform cylinder cranking and running compression tests; determine necessary action. (P-1) | 140–143 | 40 |
| 11. Perform cylinder leakage test; determine necessary action. (P-1) | 143 | 41 |
| 12. Diagnose engine mechanical, electrical, electronic, fuel, and ignition concerns; determine necessary action. (P-1) | 378–383 | 42 |
| 13. Prepare 4 or 5 gas analyzer; inspect and prepare vehicle for test, and obtain exhaust readings; interpret readings, and determine necessary action. (P-3) | 311–315 | 118 |
| 14. Verify engine operating temperature; determine necessary action. (P-1) | 180–184 | 43 |

| TASK | TEXTBOOK PAGE NO. | WORKTEXT PAGE NO. |
|------|-------------------|-------------------|

## B. COMPUTERIZED ENGINE CONTROLS DIAGNOSIS AND REPAIR

| TASK | TEXTBOOK PAGE NO. | WORKTEXT PAGE NO. |
|------|-------------------|-------------------|
| 1. Retrieve and record diagnostic trouble codes, OBD monitor status, and freeze frame data; clear codes when applicable. (P-1) | 156–161, 382 | 147 |
| 2. Diagnose the causes of emissions or driveability concerns with stored or active diagnostic trouble codes; obtain, graph, and interpret scan tool data. (P-1) | 385–392 | 46–48, 148–149 |
| 3. Diagnose emissions or driveability concerns without stored diagnostic trouble codes; determine necessary action. (P-1) | 384–385 | 49, 119, 150 |
| 4. Check for module communication (including CAN/BUS systems) errors using a scan tool. (P-2) | 163–176 | 51 |
| 5. Inspect and test computerized engine control system sensors, powertrain/engine control module (PCM/ECM), actuators, and circuits using a graphing multimeter (GMM)/digital storage oscilloscope (DSO); perform necessary action. (P-1) | 180–236 | 52–81, 90, 96 |
| 6. Access and use service information to perform step-by-step diagnosis. (P-1) | 378 | 97–100, 151 |
| 7. Diagnose driveability and emissions problems resulting from malfunctions of interrelated systems (cruise control, security alarms, suspension controls, traction controls, A/C, automatic transmissions, non-OEM-installed accessories, or similar systems); determine necessary action. (P-3) | 378–383 | 18, 50, 91, 101–102, 152 |
| 8. Perform active tests of actuators using a scan tool; determine necessary action. (P-1) | 283–294 | 103, 153 |
| 9. Describe the importance of running all OBDII monitors for repair verification. (P-1) | 160–161 | 154–155 |

## C. IGNITION SYSTEM DIAGNOSIS AND REPAIR

| TASK | TEXTBOOK PAGE NO. | WORKTEXT PAGE NO. |
|------|-------------------|-------------------|
| 1. Diagnose ignition system related problems such as no-starting, hard starting, engine misfire, poor driveability, spark knock, power loss, poor mileage, and emissions concerns; determine necessary action. (P-1) | 367–376 | 140 |
| 2. Inspect and test ignition primary and secondary circuit wiring and solid state components; test ignition coil(s); perform necessary action. (P-1) | 367–376 | 141–144 |
| 3. Inspect and test crankshaft and camshaft position sensor(s); perform necessary action. (P-1) | 368–369 | 145 |
| 4. Inspect, test, and/or replace ignition control module, powertrain/engine control module; reprogram as necessary. (P-2) | 367 | 145 |

## D. FUEL, AIR INDUCTION, AND EXHAUST SYSTEMS DIAGNOSIS AND REPAIR

| TASK | TEXTBOOK PAGE NO. | WORKTEXT PAGE NO. |
|------|-------------------|-------------------|
| 1. Diagnose hot or cold no-starting, hard starting, poor driveability, incorrect idle speed, poor idle, flooding, hesitation, surging, engine misfire, power loss, stalling, poor mileage, dieseling, and emissions problems; determine necessary action. (P-1) | 286–295 | 104–107 |
| 2. Check fuel for contaminants and quality; determine necessary action. (P-2) | 90, 93 | 19–21 |
| 3. Inspect and test fuel pumps and pump control systems for pressure, regulation, and volume; perform necessary action. (P-1) | 248–254 | 83–87 |
| 4. Replace fuel filters. (P-2) | 248 | 88 |
| 5. Inspect throttle body, air induction system, intake manifold and gaskets for vacuum leaks and/or unmetered air. (P-2) | 209, 298 | 92, 93, 108 |
| 6. Inspect and test fuel injectors. (P-1) | 291–295 | 109–115 |
| 7. Verify idle control operation. (P-1) | 295–296 | 116 |
| 8. Inspect the integrity of the exhaust manifold, exhaust pipes, muffler(s), catalytic converter(s), resonator(s), tail pipe(s), and heat shield(s); perform necessary action. (P-1) | 347–349 | |
| 9. Perform exhaust system back-pressure test; determine necessary action. (P-1) | 346–347 | 135 |
| 10. Test the operation of turbocharger/supercharger systems; determine necessary action. (P-3) | 130–131 | |

| TASK | TEXTBOOK PAGE NO. | WORKTEXT PAGE NO. |
|---|---|---|
| **E. EMISSIONS CONTROL SYSTEMS DIAGNOSIS AND REPAIR** | | |
| 1. Diagnose oil leaks, emissions, and driveability concerns caused by the positive crankcase ventilation (PCV) system; determine necessary action. (P-2) | 336–337 | 130 |
| 2. Inspect, test and service positive crankcase ventilation (PCV) filter/breather cap, valve, tubes, orifices, and hoses; perform necessary action. (P-2) | 337–338 | 131 |
| 3. Diagnose emissions and driveability concerns caused by the exhaust gas recirculation (EGR) system; determine necessary action. (P-1) | 331–333 | 126 |
| 4. Inspect, test, service and replace components of the EGR system, including EGR tubing, exhaust passages, vacuum/pressure controls, filters and hoses; perform necessary action. (P-1) | 331–333 | 127 |
| 5. Inspect and test electrical/electronic sensors, controls, and wiring of exhaust gas recirculation (EGR) systems; perform necessary action. (P-2) | 330 | 128–129 |
| 6. Diagnose emissions and driveability concerns caused by the secondary air injection and catalytic converter systems; determine necessary action. (P-2) | 340–341, 346–347 | 132 |
| 7. Inspect and test mechanical components of secondary air injection systems; perform necessary action. (P-3) | 340–341 | 133 |
| 8. Inspect and test electrical/electronically-operated components and circuits of air injection systems; perform necessary action. (P-3) | 340–341 | 134 |
| 9. Inspect and test catalytic converter efficiency. (P-1) | 348 | 136–138 |
| 10. Diagnose emissions and driveability concerns caused by the evaporative emissions control system; determine necessary action. (P-1) | 322–323 | 120 |
| 11. Inspect and test components and hoses of the evaporative emissions control system; perform necessary action. (P-1) | 322–323 | 121–124 |
| 12. Interpret diagnostic trouble codes (DTCs) and scan tool data related to the emissions control systems; determine necessary action. (P-1) | 325, 333, 338, 341, 349 | 125 |
| **F. ENGINE RELATED SERVICE** | | |
| 7. Identify hybrid vehicle internal combustion engine service precautions. (P-3) | 404 | 157 |

**AC coupling** A selection that can be made to observe a waveform.

**AC/DC clamp-on DMM** A type of meter that has a clamp that is placed around the wire to measure current.

**Acceleration simulation mode** Uses a dynamometer that applies a heavy load on the vehicle at a steady-state speed.

**Accumulator** A temporary location for fluid under pressure.

**Actuator** An electrical or mechanical device that converts electrical energy into a mechanical action, such as adjusting engine idle speed, altering suspension height, or regulating fuel metering.

**Adjustable wrench** A wrench that has a movable jaw to allow it to fit many sizes of fasteners.

**Adsorption** Attaches the fuel vapor molecules to the carbon surface.

**AFV** Alternative-fuel vehicle.

**AGST** Aboveground storage tank, used to store used oil.

**Air–fuel ratio** The ratio of air to fuel in an intake charge as measured by weight.

**Analog-to-digital (AD) converter** An electronic circuit that converts analog signals into digital signals that can then be used by a computer.

**Annealing** A heat-treating process that takes out the brittle hardening of the casting to reduce the chance of cracking from the temperature changes.

**ANSI** American National Standards Institute.

**Antiknock Index (AKI)** The pump octane.

**API gravity** An arbitrary scale expressing the gravity or density of liquid petroleum products devised jointly by the American Petroleum Institute and the National Bureau of Standards.

**Asbestosis** A health condition where asbestos causes scar tissue to form in the lungs causing shortness of breath.

**ASD** Automatic Shutdown Relay.

**ASM 50/15 test** Places a load of 50% on the vehicle at a steady 15 mph. This load represents 50% of the horsepower required to simulate the FTP acceleration rate of 3.3 mph/sec.

**ASM** 25/25 test Places a 25% load on the vehicle while it is driven at a steady 25 mph. This represents 25% of the load required to simulate the FTP acceleration rate of 3.3 mph/sec.

**ASTM** American Society for Testing Materials.

**B20** A blend of 20% biodiesel with 80% petroleum diesel.

**Back pressure** The exhaust system's resistance to flow. Measured in pounds per square inch (PSI).

**Baffle** A plate or shield used to direct the flow of a liquid or gas.

**Bar** When air is pumped into the cylinder, the combustion chamber receives an increase of air pressure known as boost and is measured in pounds per square inch (PSI), atmospheres (ATM), or bar.

**BARO sensor** A sensor used to measure barometric pressure.

**Base timing** The timing of the spark before the computer advances the timing.

**Baud rate** The speed at which bits of computer information are transmitted on a serial data stream. Measured in bits per second (bps).

**BCI** Battery Council International.

**Bias voltage** a weak signal voltage applies to an oxygen sensor by the PCM. This weak signal voltage is used by the PCM to detect when the oxygen sensor has created a changing voltage and for diagnosis of the oxygen senor circuit.

**Binary system** A computer system that uses a series of zeros and ones to represent information.

**Biodiesel** A renewable fuel manufactured from vegetable oils, animal fats, or recycled restaurant grease.

**Biomass** Nonedible farm products, such as cornstalks, cereal straws, and plant wastes from industrial processes, such as sawdust and paper pulp, used in making ethanol.

**Block** The foundation of any engine. All other parts are either directly or indirectly attached to the block of an engine.

**BMAP sensor** A sensor that has individual circuits to measure barometric and manifold pressure. This input not only allows the computer to adjust for changes in atmospheric pressure due to weather, but also is the primary sensor used to determine altitude.

**BNC connector** A miniature standard coaxial cable connector.

**BOB** Break-out box.

**Boost** An increase in air pressure above atmospheric. Measured in pounds per square inch (PSI).

**Bore** The inside diameter of the cylinder in an engine.

**Boxer** A type of engine design that is flat and has opposing cylinders. Called a boxer because the pistons on one side resemble a boxer during engine operation. Also called a pancake engine.

**Breaker bar** A handle used to rotate a socket; also called a flex handle.

**British thermal unit** A unit of heat measurement.

**Bump cap** A hat that is plastic and hard to protect the head from bumps.

**Burn kV** Spark line voltage.

**BUS** A term used to describe a communication network.

**Bypass ignition** Commonly used on General Motors engines equipped with distributor ignition (DI), as well as those equipped with waste-spark ignition.

**Bypass valve** Allows intake air to flow directly into the intake manifold bypassing the supercharger.

**CAA** Clean Air Act. Federal legislation passed in 1970 that established national air quality standards.

**Calibration codes** Codes used on many powertrain control modules.

**California Air Resources Board** A state of California agency that regulates the air quality standards for the state.

**Cam-in-block design** An engine where the crankshaft is located in the block rather than in the cylinder head.

**Campaign** A recall where vehicle owners are contacted to return a vehicle to a dealer for corrective action.

**CAN** A type of serial data transmission.

**Cap screw** A bolt that is threaded into a casting.

**Casting number** An identification code cast into an engine block or other large cast part of a vehicle.

**CAT III** An electrical measurement equipment rating created by the International Electrotechnical Commission (IEC). CAT III indicates the lowest level of instrument protection that should be in place when performing electrical measurements on hybrid electric vehicles.

**Catalysts** Platinum and palladium used in the catalytic converter to combine oxygen ($O_2$) with hydrocarbons (HC) and carbon monoxide (CO) to form nonharmful tailpipe emissions of water ($H_2O$) and carbon dioxide ($CO_2$).

**Catalytic converter** An emission control device located in the exhaust system that changes HC and CO into harmless $H_2O$ and $CO_2$. If a three-way catalyst, $NO_x$ is also separated into harmless, separate N and O.

**Catalytic cracking** Breaking hydrocarbon chains using heat in the presence of a catalyst.

**CCM** Comprehensive Component Monitor.

**Cellulose ethanol** Ethanol produced from biomass feedstock such as agricultural and industrial plant wastes.

**Cellulosic biomass** Composed of cellulose and lignin, with smaller amounts of proteins, lipids (fats, waxes, and oils), and ash.

**Cerium** An element that can store oxygen.

**Cetane number** A measure of the ease with which the fuel can be ignited.

**CFR** Code of Federal Regulations.

**Cheater bar** A pipe or other object used to lengthen the handle of a ratchet or breaker bar. Not recommended to be used as the extra force can cause the socket or ratchet to break.

**CID** Component Identification.

**CKP** Crankshaft position sensor.

**Class 2** A type of BUS communication used in General Motors vehicles.

**Clock generator** A crystal that determines the speed of computer circuits.

**Close-end wrench** A type of hand tool that is closed at both ends.

**Closed-loop operation** A phase of computer-controlled engine operation in which oxygen sensor feedback is used to calculate air–fuel mixture.

**Cloud point** The low-temperature point at which the waxes present in most diesel fuel tend to form wax crystals that clog the fuel filter.

**CMP** Camshaft position sensor.

**CNG** Compressed natural gas.

**Coal-to-liquid** A refining process in which coal is converted to liquid fuel.

**Coil-on-plug ignition** An ignition system without a distributor, where each spark plug is integrated with an ignition coil.

**Combination wrench** A wrench that is open ended at one end and has a box end at the other end.

**Combustion chamber** The space left within the cylinder when the piston is at the top of its combustion chamber.

**Combustion** The rapid burning of the air–fuel mixture in the engine cylinders, creating heat and pressure.

**Compression ratio** The ratio of the volume in the engine cylinder with the piston at bottom dead center (BDC) to the volume at top dead center (TDC).

**Compression-sensing ignition** Does not require the use of a camshaft position sensor to determine cylinder number.

**Compressor bypass valve** This type of relief valve routes the pressurized air to the inlet side of the turbocharger for reuse and is quiet during operation.

**Connecting rod** Connects the pistons to the crankshaft.

**Continuity light** A test light that has a battery and lights if there is continuity (electrical connection) between the two points that are connected to the tester.

**Controller** A term that is usually used to refer to a computer or an electronic control unit (ECU).

**CPS** Canister purge solenoid.

**CPU** Central processor unit.

**Cracking** A refinery process in which hydrocarbons with high boiling points are broken into hydrocarbons with low boiling points.

**Cranking vacuum test** Measuring the amount of manifold vacuum during cranking.

**Crest** The outside diameter of a bolt measured across the threads.

**Cross counts** The number of times an oxygen sensor changes voltage from high to low (from low to high voltage is not counted) in 1 second (or 1.25 second, depending on scan tool and computer speed).

**CRT** Cathode ray tube.

**Cycle life** The number of times a battery can be charged and discharged without suffering significant degradation in its performance.

**Cylinder head temperature (CHT) sensor-** A temperature sensor mounted on the cylinder head and used by the PCM to determine fuel delivery.

**Cylinder leakage test** A test that involves injecting air under pressure into the cylinders one at a time. The amount and location of any escaping air helps the technician determine the condition of the engine.

**DC coupling** A selection that can be made to observe a waveform.

**DDS** Demand delivery system.

**Delta Pressure Feedback EGR sensor** This sensor measures the pressure differential between two sides of a metered orifice positioned just below the EGR valve's exhaust side.

**Detonation** A violent explosion in the combustion chamber created by uncontrolled burning of the air–fuel mixture; often causes a loud, audible knock. Also known as spark knock or ping.

**DI** Distributor ignition.

**Diagnostic executive** Software program designed to manage the operation of all OBD-II monitors by controlling the sequence of steps necessary to execute the diagnostic tests and monitors.

**Diesel oxidation catalyst** Consists of a flow-through honeycomb-style substrate structure that is washcoated with a layer of catalyst materials, similar to those used in a gasoline engine catalytic converter.

**Diesohol** Standard #2 diesel fuel combined with up to 15% ethanol.

**Digital computer** A computer that uses on and off signals only. Uses an A to D converter to change analog signals to digital before processing.

**Direct injection** A fuel-injection system design in which gasoline is injected directly into the combustion chamber.

**DIS** Distributorless ignition system. Also called direct-fire ignition system.

**Displacement** The total volume displaced or swept by the cylinders in an internal combustion engine.

**Distillation** The process of purification through evaporation and then condensation of the desired liquid.

**Distillation curve**   A graph that plots the temperatures at which the various fractions of a fuel evaporate.

**Distributor cap**   Provides additional space between the spark plug connections to help prevent crossfire.

**Division**   A block.

**Divorced coil**   Used by most waste-spark ignition coils to keep both the primary and secondary winding separated.

**DMM**   Digital multimeter. A digital multimeter is capable of measuring electrical current, resistance, and voltage.

**Double-layer technology**   Technology used to build ultracapacitors. Involves the use of two carbon electrodes separated by a membrane.

**DPS**   Differential pressure sensor.

**Drive size**   The size in fractions of an inch of the square drive for sockets.

**DSO**   Digital storage oscilloscope, takes samples of the signals that can be stopped or stored.

**Dual overhead camshaft**   An engine design with two camshafts above each line of cylinders—one for the exhaust valves and one for the intake valves.

**Dump valve**   Features an adjustable spring design that keeps the valve closed until a sudden release of the throttle. The resulting pressure increase opens the valve and vents the pressurized air directly into the atmosphere.

**Duty cycle**   Refers to the percentage of on-time of the signal during one complete cycle.

**DVOM**   Digital volt-ohm-millimeter.

**Dwell section**   The amount of time that the current is charging the coil from the transistor-on point to the transistor-off point.

**Dwell**   The number of degrees of distributor cam rotation that the points are closed.

**Dynamic compression test**   A compression test done with the engine running rather than during engine cranking as is done in a regular compression test.

**E & C**   Entertainment and comfort.

**E10**   A fuel blend of 10% ethanol and 90% gasoline.

**E2PROM**   Electrically erasable read-only memory.

**E85**   A fuel blend of 85% ethanol and 15% gasoline.

**ECA**   Electronic Control Module. The name used by Ford to describe the computer used to control spark and fuel on older-model vehicles.

**ECM**   Electronic control module on a vehicle.

**ECT**   Engine coolant temperature.

**ECU**   Electronic control unit on a vehicle.

**E-diesel**   Standard #2 diesel fuel combined with up to 15% ethanol. Also known as diesohol.

**EECS**   Evaporative Emission Control System.

**EEPROM**   Electronically erasable read-only memory.

**EGR valve position**   A linear potentiometer on the top of the EGR valve stem indicates valve position for the computer.

**Electrolysis**   The process in which electric current is passed through water in order to break it into hydrogen and oxygen gas.

**Electromagnetic interference**   An undesirable electronic signal. It is caused by a magnetic field building up and collapsing, creating unwanted electrical interference on a nearby circuit.

**Electronic air control**   The idle air control valve.

**Electronic ignition**   General term used to describe any of the various types of ignition systems that use electronic instead of mechanical components, such as contact points.

**Electronic returnless fuel system**   A fuel delivery system that does not return fuel to the tank.

**Electronic spark timing**   The computer controls spark timing advance.

**Enable criteria**   Operating condition requirements.

**Energy carrier**   Any medium that is utilized to store or transport energy. Hydrogen is an energy carrier because energy must be used to generate hydrogen gas that is used as a fuel.

**Energy density**   A measure of the amount of energy that can be stored in a battery relative to the volume of the battery container. Energy density is measured in terms of watt-hours per liter (Wh/L).

**Engine fuel temperature (EFT)**   sensor- A temperature sensor located on the fuel rail that measures the temperature of the fuel entering the engine.

**Engine mapping**   A computer program that uses engine test data to determine the best fuel–air ratio and spark advance to use at each speed of the engine for best performance.

**EPA**   Environmental Protection Agency.

**Ethyl alcohol**   See *ethanol*.

**Ethyl tertiary butyl ether**   An octane enhancer for gasoline. It is also a fuel oxygenate that is manufactured by reacting isobutylene with ethanol. The resulting ether is high octane and low volatility. ETBE can be added to gasoline up to a level of approximately 13%.

**Ethanol**   Grain alcohol that is blended with gasoline to produce motor fuel. Also known as ethyl alcohol.

**Exhaust gas recirculation**   An emission control device to reduce $NO_x$ (oxides of nitrogen).

**Extension**   A socket wrench tool used between a ratchet or breaker bar and a socket.

**External trigger**   Occurs when the trace starts when a signal is received from another (external) source.

**Eye wash station**   A water fountain designed to rinse the eyes with a large volume of water.

**False air**   A term used to describe air that enters the engine without being measured by the mass air flow sensor.

**False lean indication**   Occurs when an oxygen sensor reads low as a result of a factor besides a lean mixture.

**False rich indication**   A high oxygen sensor voltage reading that is not the result of a rich exhaust. Some common causes for this false rich indication include a contaminated oxygen sensor and having the signal wire close to a high voltage source such as a spark plug wire.

**FCHV**   Fuel-cell hybrid vehicle.

**FCV**   Fuel-cell vehicle.

**Filter basket**   A fine mesh screen filter located in the top of a fuel injector.

**Fire blanket**   A fireproof wool blanket used to cover a person who is on fire and smother the fire.

**Fire extinguisher classes**   The types of fires that a fire extinguisher is designed to handle are referred to as fire classes.

**Firing line**   The leftmost vertical (upward) line.

**Firing order**   The order that the spark is distributed to the correct spark plug at the right time.

**Flare**   An increase and then decrease in engine speed.

**Flare-nut wrench** A type of wrench used to remove fuel, brake, or air-conditioning lines.

**Flash point** The temperature at which the vapors on the surface of the fuel will ignite if exposed to an open flame.

**Flex fuel** Flex-fuel vehicles are capable of running on straight gasoline or gasoline/ethanol blends.

**Flow gauge** Tests for proper airflow in the EVAP system.

**Flyback voltage** The inductive kick created when the primary field collapses is used by the PCM to monitor secondary ignition performance.

**Formaldehyde** Formed when RFG is burned, and the vehicle exhaust has a unique smell when reformulated gasoline is used.

**Freeze-frame** A snapshot of all of the engine data at the time the DTC was set.

**Frequency** The number of times a waveform repeats in one second, measured in hertz (Hz), frequency band.

**FTD** Fischer-Tropsch diesel.

**FTP** Federal Test Procedure.

**Fuel cell** An electrochemical device that converts the energy stored in hydrogen gas into electricity, water, and heat.

**Fuel compensation sensor** A sensor used in flex-fuel vehicles that provides information to the PCM on the ethanol content and temperature of the fuel as it is flowing through the fuel delivery system.

**Fuel-cell stack** A collection of individual fuel cells, which are stacked end-to-end into one compact package.

**Functionality** Refers to PCM inputs checking the operation of the outputs.

**Gang fired** Pulsing injectors in groups.

**Gasoline direct injection** A fuel-injection system design in which gasoline is injected directly into the combustion chamber.

**Gasoline** Refined petroleum product that is used primarily as a motor fuel. Gasoline is made up of many different hydrocarbons and also contains additives for enhancing its performance in an ICE.

**Gas-to-liquid** A refining process in which natural gas is converted into liquid fuel.

**GAWR** Gross axle weight rating. A rating of the load capacity of a vehicle and included on placards on the vehicle and in the owner's manual.

**Gerotor** A type of positive displacement pump that is often used in engine oil pumps. It uses the meshing of internal and external gear teeth to pressurize the fuel.

**Glow plug** A heating element that uses 12 volts from the battery and aids in the starting of a cold engine.

**GMLAN** GM local area network. A type of serial data transmission by General Motors.

**GMM** Graphing multimeter. A cross between a digital meter and a digital storage oscilloscope.

**Grade** The strength rating of a bolt.

**Grain alcohol** See *ethanol*.

**Graticule** The grid lines on the scope screen.

**GVWR** Gross vehicle weight rating. The total weight of the vehicle including the maximum cargo.

**Hall-effect switch** A semiconductor moving relative to a magnetic field, creating a variable voltage output. Used to determine position. A type of electromagnetic sensor used in electronic ignition and other systems. Named for Edwin H. Hall, who discovered the Hall effect in 1879.

**Hangers** Made of rubberized fabric with metal ends that hold the muffler and tailpipe in position so that they do not touch any metal part. This helps to isolate the exhaust noise from the rest of the vehicle.

**Heat of compression** Air is compressed until its temperature reaches about 1000°F.

**Helmholtz resonator** Used on the intake duct between the air filter and the throttle body to reduce air intake noise during engine acceleration.

**HEPA vacuum** High-efficiency particulate air filter vacuum used to clean brake dust.

**Hertz** The measurement of frequency.

**HEUI** Hydraulic Electronic Unit Injection.

**High Energy Ignition** General Motors' name for their electronic ignition.

**High-impedance meter** Measures the total internal resistance of the meter circuit due to internal coils, capacitors, and resistors.

**High-pressure common rail** Diesel fuel under high pressure, over 20,000 PSI (138,000 kPa), is applied to the injectors, which are opened by a solenoid controlled by the computer. Because the injectors are computer controlled, the combustion process can be precisely controlled to provide maximum engine efficiency with the lowest possible noise and exhaust emissions.

**Homogeneous charge compression ignition** A low-temperature combustion process that involves air–fuel mixtures being burned without the use of spark ignition.

**HV cables** Vehicle cables that carry high voltage.

**HV** High voltage. Applies to any voltage above 50 volts.

**Hydraulic power assist** A hybrid vehicle configuration that utilizes hydraulic pumps and accumulators for energy regeneration.

**Hydrocracking** A refinery process that converts hydrocarbons with a high boiling point into ones with low boiling points.

**Hydrokinetic pump** This design of pump rapidly moves the fuel to create pressure.

**I/M 240 test** It is a portion of the 505-second FTP test used by the manufacturers to certify their new vehicles. The "240" stands for 240 seconds of drive time on a dynamometer.

**IAC** Idle air control.

**ICE** Internal combustion engine.

**IEC** International Electrotechnical Commission.

**Igniter** Ignition Control Module.

**Ignition coil** An electrical device that consists of two separate coils of wire: a primary and a secondary winding. The purpose of an ignition coil is to produce a high-voltage (20,000 to 40,000 volts), low-amperage (about 80 mA) current necessary for spark ignition.

**Ignition control module** Controls (turns on and off) the primary ignition current of an electronic ignition system.

**Ignition control** Igniter.

**Ignition timing** The exact point of ignition in relation to piston position.

**Inches of Mercury** A measurement of vacuum; pressure below atmospheric pressure.

**Indirect injection** Fuel is injected into a small prechamber, which is connected to the cylinder by a narrow opening. The initial combustion takes place in this prechamber. This has the effect of slowing the rate of combustion, which tends to reduce noise.

**Inductive ammeter** A type of ammeter that is used a Hall-effect sensor in a clamp that surrounds a conductor carrying a current.

**Inductive reactance**  An opposing current created in a conductor whenever there is a charging current flow in a conductor.

**Inert**  Chemically inactive.

**Inertia switch**  Turns off the electric fuel pump in an accident.

**Initial timing**  Where the spark plug fires at idle speed. The computer then advances the timing based off engine speed and other factors.

**Injection pump**  Delivers fuel to the injectors at a high pressure and at timed intervals. Each injector sprays fuel into the combustion chamber at the precise moment required for efficient combustion.

**Input conditioning**  What the computer does to the input signals to make them useful; usually includes an analog to digital converter and other electronic circuits that eliminate electrical noise.

**Input**  Information on data from sensors to an electronic controller is called input. Sensors and switches provide the input signals.

**Intercooler**  Similar to a radiator, wherein outside air can pass through, cooling the pressurized heated air.

**Intermediate oscillations**  Also called the "ringing" of the coil as it is pulsed.

**Inverter**  An electronic device used to convert DC (direct current) into AC (alternating current).

**Iridium spark plugs**  Use a small amount of iridium welded onto the tip of a small center electrode 0.0015 to 0.002 inch (0.4 to 0.6 mm) in diameter. The small diameter reduces the voltage required to jump the gap between the center and the side electrode, thereby reducing possible misfires. The ground or side electrode is usually tipped with platinum to help reduce electrode sap wear.

**ISC**  Idle speed control motor.

**KAM**  Keep-alive memory.

**Keyword**  A type of network communications used in many General Motors vehicles.

**Kilo**  Means 1,000; abbreviated k or K.

**Knock sensor**  A sensor that can detect engine spark knock.

**Leak defection pump**  Chrysler uses an electric pump that pressurizes the fuel system to check for leaks by having the PCM monitor the fuel tank pressure sensor.

**Lean indicator**  Oxygen.

**LED test light**  Uses an LED instead of a standard automotive bulb for a visual indication of voltage.

**Lift pump**  The diesel fuel is drawn from the fuel tank by the lift pump and delivers the fuel to the injection pump.

**Linear air–fuel ratio sensor**  See lean air–fuel ratio sensor.

**Linear EGR**  Contains a stepper motor to precisely regulate exhaust gas flow and a feedback potentiometer that signals to the computer the actual position of the valve.

**Linesman's gloves**  Type of gloves worn by technicians when working around high-voltage circuits. Usually includes a rubber inner glove rated at 1,000 volts and a protective leather outer glove when used for hybrid electric vehicle service.

**Liquefied petroleum gas**  Sold as compressed liquid propane that is often mixed with about 10% of other gases such as butane, propylene, butylenes, and mercaptan to give the colorless and odorless propane a smell.

**Logic probe**  A type of tester that can detect either power or ground. Most testers can detect voltage but some cannot detect if a ground is present without further testing.

**Low-grade heat**  Cooling system temperatures that are very close to the temperature of the ambient air, resulting in lowered heat transfer efficiency.

**LP-gas**  See *liquefied petroleum gas*.

**M85**  Internal combustion engine fuel containing 85% methanol and 15% gasoline.

**Magnetic pulse generator**  The pulse generator consists of a trigger wheel (reluctor) and a pickup coil. The pickup coil consists of an iron core wrapped with fine wire, in a coil at one end and attached to a permanent magnet at the other end. The center of the coil is called the pole piece.

**Magnetic sensor**  Uses a permanent magnet surrounded by a coil of wire. The notches of the crankshaft (or camshaft) create a variable magnetic field strength around the coil. When a metallic section is close to the sensor, the magnetic field is stronger because metal is a better conductor of magnetic lines of force than air.

**Magnetic-resistive sensor**  A sensor that is similar to a magnetic sensor but, instead of producing an analog voltage signal, the electronics inside the sensor itself generate a digital on/off signal or an output.

**Malfunction indicator lamp**  This amber, dashboard warning light may be labeled check engine or service engine soon.

**MAP sensor**  A sensor used to measure the pressure inside the intake manifold compared to a perfect vacuum.

**Married coil**  Also called a tapped transformer.

**Mass air flow sensor**  Measures the density and amount of air flowing into the engine, which results in accurate engine control.

**Mechanical returnless fuel system**  A returnless fuel delivery system design that uses a mechanical pressure regulator located in the fuel tank.

**Mega**  Million. Used when writing larger numbers or measuring a large amount of resistance.

**Membrane electrode assembly**  The part of the PEM fuel cell that contains the membrane, catalyst coatings, and electrodes.

**Mercury**  A heavy metal.

**Meter accuracy**  The accuracy of a meter measured in percent.

**Meter resolution**  The specification of a meter that indicates how small or fine a measurement the meter can detect and display.

**Methanol**  Typically manufactured from natural gas. Methanol content, including cosolvents, in unleaded gasoline is limited by law to 5%.

**Methanol-to-gasoline**  A refining process in which methanol is converted into liquid gasoline.

**Methyl alcohol**  See *methanol*.

**Methyl tertiary butyl ether**  A fuel oxygenate that is permitted in unleaded gasoline up to a level of 15%.

**Metric bolts**  Bolts manufactured and sized in the metric system of measurement.

**Micro (μ)**  One millionth of a volt or ampere.

**Micron**  Equal to 0.000039 in.

**Milli (m)**  One thousandth of a volt or ampere.

**Millisecond sweep**  The scope will sweep only that portion of the pattern that can be shown during a 5- or 25-ms setting.

**MSDS**  Material safety data sheet.

**MTHF**  Methyltetrahydrofuron. A component of P-series nonpetroleum-based fuels.

**Multiplexing**  A process of sending multiple signals of information at the same time over a signal wire.

**Mutual induction**  The generation of an electric current due to a changing magnetic field of an adjacent coil.

**Naturally (normally) aspirated**  An engine that uses atmospheric pressure for intake.

**NEDRA**   National Electric Drag Racing Association.

**Negative back pressure**   An EGR valve that reacts to a low pressure area by closing a small internal valve, which allows the EGR valve to be opened by vacuum.

**Negative temperature coefficient**   Usually used in reference to a temperature sensor (coolant or air temperature). As the temperature increases, the resistance of the sensor decreases.

**Network**   A communications system used to link multiple computers or modules.

**NGV**   Natural gas vehicle.

**NiMH**   Nickel-metal hydride. A battery design used for the high-voltage batteries in most hybrid electric vehicles.

**Node**   A module and computer that is part of a communications network.

**Noid light**   Designed to electrically replace the injector in the circuit and to flash if the injector circuit is working correctly.

**Nonchecking**   Some General Motors throttle-body units that do not hold pressure.

**Non-methane hydrocarbon**   The standard by which exhaust emission testing for hydrocarbons is evaluated.

**Nonprincipal end**   Opposite the principal end and is generally referred to as the front of the engine, where the accessory belts are used.

**Nonvolatile RAM**   Computer memory capability that is not lost when power is removed. See also *read-only memory (ROM)*.

**OBD**   On-board diagnostic.

**Octane rating**   The measurement of a gasoline's ability to resist engine knock. The higher the octane rating, the less prone the gasoline is to cause engine knock (detonation).

**Oil galleries**   An oil pump, which is driven by the engine, forces the oil through the oil filter and then into passages in the crankshaft and block.

**OL**   Open circuit.

**Opacity**   The percentage of light that is blocked by the exhaust smoke.

**Open-end wrench**   A type of wrench that allows access to the flats of a bolt or nut from the side.

**Open-loop operation**   A phase of computer-controlled engine operation where air–fuel mixture is calculated in the absence of oxygen sensor signals. During open loop, calculations are based primarily on throttle position, engine RPM, and engine coolant temperature.

**Optical sensors**   Use light from a LED and a phototransistor to signal the computer.

**Organic**   A term used to describe anything that was alive at one time.

**ORVR**   Onboard refueling vapor recovery.

**OSC**   Oxygen storage capacity.

**Oscilloscope (scope)**   A visual volt meter.

**OSHA**   Occupational Safety and Health Administration.

**Oxygen sensor**   A sensor in the exhaust system to measure the oxygen content of the exhaust.

**Oxygenated fuels**   Fuels such as ETBE or MTBE that contain extra oxygen molecules to promote cleaner burning. Oxygenated fuels are used as gasoline additives to reduce CO emissions.

**Ozone**   Oxygen-rich ($O_3$) gas created by sunlight reaction with unburned hydrocarbons (HC) and oxides of nitrogen ($NO_x$); also called smog.

**Palladium**   A catalyst that starts a chemical reaction without becoming a part of, or being consumed in, the process.

**Pancake engine**   See *boxer*.

**Paper test**   Hold a piece of paper or a 3 × 5 index card (even a dollar bill works) within 1 inch (2.5 centimeters) of the tailpipe with the engine running at idle. The paper should blow out evenly without "puffing." If the paper is drawn toward the tailpipe at times, the exhaust valves in one or more cylinders could be burned.

**Parameter identification**   The information found in the vehicle data stream as viewed on a scan tool.

**PCM**   The onboard computer that controls both the engine management and transmission functions of the vehicle.

**PCV**   Pressure control valve.

**Peripheral pump**   Turbine pump.

**Petrodiesel**   Another term for petroleum diesel, which is ordinary diesel fuel refined from crude oil.

**Petroleum**   Another term for crude oil. The literal meaning of petroleum is "rock oil."

**PFE sensor**   Pressure feedback EGR.

**PHEV**   Plug-in hybrid electric vehicle.

**Pickup coil**   A simple and common ignition electronic switching device in the magnetic pulse generator system.

**Piezoresistivity**   Change in resistance due to strain.

**Pinch weld seam**   A strong section under a vehicle where two body panels are welded together.

**Ping**   Secondary rapid burning of the last 3% to 5% of the air–fuel mixture in the combustion chamber causes a second flame front that collides with the first flame front causing a knock noise. Also called detonation or spark knock.

**Piston stroke**   A one-way piston movement between the top and bottom of the cylinder.

**Pitch**   The pitch of a threaded fastener refers to the number of threads per inch.

**Platinum spark plug**   A spark plug that has a small amount of the precious metal platinum welded onto the end of the center electrode, as well as on the ground or side electrode. Platinum is a grayish-white metal that does not react with oxygen and therefore, will not erode away as can occur with conventional nickel alloy spark plug electrodes.

**Platinum**   A catalyst that starts a chemical reaction without becoming a part of, or being consumed in, the process.

**Plenum**   A chamber, located between the throttle body and the runners of the intake manifold, used to distribute the intake charge more evenly and efficiently.

**Polarity**   The condition of being positive or negative in relation to a magnetic pole.

**Polymer electrolyte fuel cell**   Another term for PEM fuel cell.

**Pop tester**   A device used for checking a diesel injector nozzle for proper spray pattern. The handle is depressed and pop off pressure is displayed on the gauge.

**Port fuel-injection**   Uses a nozzle for each cylinder and the fuel is squirted into the intake manifold about 2 to 3 inches (70 to 100 mm) from the intake valve.

**Positive back pressure**   An EGR valve that is designed with a small valve inside that bleeds off any applied vacuum and prevents the valve from opening.

**Positive displacement**   All of the air that enters is forced through the roots-type supercharger.

**Power balance test**   Determines if all cylinders are contributing power equally. It determines this by shorting out one cylinder at a time.

**PPO**   Pure plant oil.

**Preconverter**   A small, quick heating oxidation converter.

**Pressure differential**   A difference in pressure from one brake circuit to another.

**Pressure relief valve**   A valve located in a power steering pump that uses a check ball, which unseats and allows fluid to return to the reservoir if pressure exceeds a certain volume.

**Pressure vent valve**   A valve located in the fuel tank to prevent overpressure due to the thermal expansion of the fuel.

**Prevailing torque nut**   A special design of nut fastener that is deformed slightly or has other properties that permit the nut to remain attached to the fastener without loosening.

**Primary ignition circuit**   The ignition components that regulate the current in the coil primary winding by turning it on and off.

**Principal end**   The end of the engine that the flywheel is attached to.

**Programmable controller interface (PCI)**   A type of serial data transmission used by Chrysler.

**PROM**   Programmable read-only memory.

**Propane**   See *liquified petroleum gas*.

**Proton exchange membrane**   A low-temperature fuel cell known for fast starts and relatively simple construction.

**Pulse train**   A DC voltage that turns on and off in a series of pulses.

**Pulse width**   A measure of the actual on-time measured in milliseconds.

**Pup converter**   See *preconverter*.

**Pushrod engine**   Uses one camshaft for the intake valves and a separate camshaft for the exhaust valves. When the camshaft is located in the block, the valves are operated by lifters, pushrods, and rocker arms.

**PWM**   Pulse-width modulation.

**R & R**   Remove and replace.

**RAM**   Random-access memory.

**Range**   The distance a vehicle can travel on a full charge or full-fuel tank without recharging or refueling. Range is measured in miles or kilometers.

**Raster**   Stacked.

**Rationality**   Refers to a PCM comparison of input value to values.

**RCRA**   Resource Conservation and Recovery Act.

**Recall**   A notification to the owner of a vehicle that a safety issue needs to be corrected.

**Reformulated gasoline**   RFG has oxygenated additives and is refined to reduce both the lightest and heaviest hydrocarbon content from gasoline in order to promote cleaner burning.

**Regeneration**   A process of taking the kinetic energy of a moving vehicle and converting it to electrical energy and storing it in a battery.

**Reid vapor pressure**   A method of determining vapor pressure of gasoline and other petroleum products. Widely used in the petroleum industry as an indicator of the volatility of gasoline.

**Reluctor**   A notched metal wheel used with a magnetic sensor to trigger crankshaft or camshaft position.

**Residual check valve**   A valve in the outlet end of the master cylinder to keep the hydraulic system under a light pressure on drum brakes only.

**Residual or rest pressure**   Prevents vapor lock and hot-start problems on these systems.

**Restricted exhaust**   The engine will be low on power, yet smooth.

**Rhodium**   A catalyst that starts a chemical reaction without becoming a part of, or being consumed in, the process.

**Right-to-know laws**   Laws that state that employees have a right to know when the materials they use at work are hazardous.

**RMS**   A method of calculating surface roughness using the square root of the average readings squared.

**Roller cell**   Vane pump.

**ROM**   Read-only memory.

**Roots-type**   Named for Philander and Francis Roots, two brothers from Connersville, Indiana, who patented the design in 1860 as a type of water pump to be used in mines. Later it was used to move air and is used today on two-stroke cycle Detroit diesel engines and other supercharged engines. The roots-type supercharger is called a positive displacement design because all of the air that enters is forced through the unit.

**Rotary engine**   Operates on the four-stroke cycle but uses a rotor instead of a piston and crankshaft to achieve intake, compression, power, and exhaust stroke.

**Rotary vane pump**   The pump consists of a central impeller disk, several rollers or vanes that ride in notches in the impeller, and a pump housing that is offset from the impeller centerline.

**Rotor gap**   Measures the voltage required to jump the gap (0.030 to 0.050 in. or 0.8 to 1.3 mm) between the rotor and the inserts (segments) of the distributor cap.

**Running compression test**   A test that can inform a technician of the relative compression of all the cylinders.

**SAE**   Society of Automotive Engineers.

**Saturation**   The point of maximum magnetic field strength of a coil.

**Schmitt trigger**   Converts the analog signal into a digital signal.

**Secondary ignition circuit**   The components necessary to create and distribute the high voltage produced in the secondary windings of the coil.

**Secondary winding**   A winding that has about 100 times the number of turns of the primary winding, referred to as the turns ratio (approximately 100:1).

**Self-induction**   The generation of an electric current in the wires of a coil created when the current is first connected or disconnected.

**Sequential fuel injection**   A fuel injection system in which injectors are pulsed individually in sequence with the firing order.

**Serial communications interface (SCI)**   A type of serial data transmission used by Chrysler.

**Serial data**   Data that is transmitted by a series of rapidly changing voltage signals.

**Side-channel pump**   Turbine pump.

**Single overhead camshaft**   When one overhead camshaft is used.

**SIP**   State Implementation Plan.

**Smog**   The term used to describe a combination of smoke and fog. Formed by $NO_x$ and HC with sunlight.

**Socket adapter**   An adapter that allows the use of one size of driver (ratchet or breaker bar) to rotate another drive size of socket.

**Socket**   A tool that fits over the head of a bolt or nut and is rotated by a ratchet or breaker bar.

**Solvent**   Usually colorless liquids that are used to remove grease and oil.

**Spark ignition direct injection**   GM's name for GDI system.

**Spark knock**   See *Detonation*.

**Spark line**   A short horizontal line immediately after the firing line.

**Spark output**   The term that Ford used to describe the OBD-II terminology for the output signal from the PCM to the ignition system that controls engine timing.

**Spark tester**   Looks like a spark plug except it has a recessed center electrode and no side electrode. The tester commonly has an alligator clip attached to the shell so that it can be clamped on a good ground connection on the engine.

**Specific energy**   The energy conteat of a battery relative to the mass of the battery. Specific energy is measured in watt-hours per kilogram (Wh/kg).

**Speed density**   The method of calculating the amount of fuel needed by the engine.

**Splice pack**   A central point where many serial data lines jam together, often abbreviated SP.

**Spontaneous combustion**   A condition that can cause some materials, such as oily rags, to catch fire without a source of ignition.

**SST**   Special service tools.

**Standard corporate protocol (SCP)**   A network communications protocol used by Ford.

**State of health (SOH)**   A signal sent by a module to all of the other modules in the network indicating that it is well and able to transmit.

**Stoichiometric ratio**   The ideal mixture or ratio at which all of the fuel combines with all of the oxygen in the air and burns completely.

**Straight vegetable oil**   Vegetable oil, a triglyceride with a glycerin component joining three hydrocarbon chains of 16 to 18 carbon atoms each.

**Stud**   A short rod with threads on both ends.

**Supercharger**   Forces the air–fuel mixture into the cylinder for even greater power.

**Superimposed**   A position used to look at differences in patterns between cylinders in all areas except the firing line.

**SWCAN**   An abbreviation for single wire CAN (Controller Area Network).

**Switchgrass**   A feedstock for ethanol production that requires very little energy or fertilizer to cultivate.

**Switching**   Turning on and off of the primary circuit.

**Syncrude**   A product of a process where coal is broken down to create liquid products. First the coal is reacted with hydrogen ($H_2$) at high temperatures and pressure with a catalyst.

**Syn-gas**   Synthesis gas generated by a reaction between coal and steam. Syn-gas is made up of mostly hydrogen and carbon monoxide and is used to make methanol. Syn-gas is also known as town gas.

**Synthetic fuel**   Fuels generated through synthetic processes such as Fischer-Tropsch.

**Tap test**   Involves tapping (not pounding) on the catalytic converter using a rubber mallet.

**Tapped transformer**   See *married coil*.

**Task manager**   A term Chrysler uses to describe the software program that is designed to manage the operation of all OBD-II monitors by controlling the sequence of steps necessary to execute the diagnostic tests and monitors.

**TBI**   Throttle-body injection.

**Tensile strength**   The maximum stress used under tension (lengthwise force) without causing failure.

**Terminating resistors**   Resistors placed at the end of a high-speed serial data circuit to help reduce electromagnetic interference.

**Tertiary-amyl methyl ether**   An oxygenate added to gasoline that is flammable and can form explosive mixtures with air. It is slightly soluble in water, very soluble in ethers and alcohol, and soluble in most organic solvents including hydrocarbons.

**Test light**   A light used to test for voltage. Contains a light bulb with a ground wire at one end and a pointed tip at the other end.

**Tetraethyl lead**   A liquid added to gasoline in the early 1920s to reduce the tendency to knock.

**Throttle body temperature (TBT)**   sensor- A temperature sensor that is mounted on the throttle body and measures the temperature of the air entering the engine.

**Throttle position sensor**   The sensor that provides feedback concerning the position of the throttle plate.

**TID**   Test identification.

**Time base**   Setting how much time will be displayed in each block.

**Top dead center**   The highest point in the cylinder that the piston can travel. The measurement from bottom dead center (BDC) to TDC determines the stroke length of the crankshaft.

**Transistor**   A semiconductor device that can operate as an amplifier or an electrical switch.

**Transmission fluid temperature (TFT)**   sensor- A sensor located inside an automatic transmission/transaxle that measures the temperature of the fluid.

**Trigger level**   The start of the display.

**Trigger slope**   The voltage direction that a waveform must have in order to start the display.

**True transformer**   See *divorced coil*.

**TSB**   Technical service bulletin.

**Turbine pump**   Turns at higher speeds and is quieter than the other electric pumps.

**Turbo lag**   The delay between acceleration and turbo boost.

**Turbocharger**   An exhaust-powered supercharger.

**TWC**   Three-way converter.

**Twisted pair**   A pair of wires that are twisted together from 9 to 16 turns per foot of length. Most are twisted once every inch (12 per foot) to help reduce electromagnetic interference from being induced in the wires as one wire would tend to cancel out any interference pickup up by the other wire.

**UART**   Universal Asynchronous Receive/Transmit; a type of serial data transmission.

**UBP**   UART-based protocol.

**UCG**   Underground coal gasification.

**Ultracapacitor**   A specialized capacitor technology with increased storage capacity for a given volume.

**UNF**   Unified national fine.

**Universal joint**   A joint in a steering or drive shaft that allows torque to be transmitted at an angle.

**Up-integrated ignition**   Ignition control where all timing functions are interpreted in the PCM, rather than being split between the ignition control module and the PCM.

**Used cooking oil**   A term used when the oil may or may not be pure vegetable oil.

**Used oil**   Any petroleum-based or synthetic oil that has been used.

**Vacuum test**   Testing the engine for cranking vacuum, idle vacuum, and vacuum at 2,500 RPM.

**Vacuum**   Any pressure less than atmospheric pressure (14.7 PSI).

**VAF**   Vane air flow.

**Vapor lock**   A lean condition caused by vaporized fuel in the fuel system.

**Variable fuel sensor**   See *fuel compensation sensor*.

**Variable reluctance sensor**   Magnetic sensor.

**VECI**   Vehicle emission control information. This sticker is located under the hood on all vehicles and includes emission-related information that is important to the service technician.

**VIN**   Vehicle identification number.

**Virtual-flexible fuel vehicle**   The virtual-flexible fuel vehicle can operate on pure gasoline, E10, E85, or any combination.

**VOC**   Volatile organic compound.

**Volatility**   A measurement of the tendency of a liquid to change to vapor. Volatility is measured using RVP, or Reid vapor pressure.

**Volumetric efficiency**   The ratio between the amount of air–fuel mixture that actually enters the cylinder and the amount that could enter under ideal conditions expressed in percent.

**Wankel engine**   Rotary engine.

**Washcoat**   A porous aluminum material which makes the surface rough.

**Waste vegetable oil**   This oil could include animal or fish oils from cooking.

**Wastegate**   A valve similar to a door that can open and close. The wastegate is a bypass valve at the exhaust inlet to the turbine. It allows all of the exhaust into the turbine, or it can route part of the exhaust past the turbine to the exhaust system.

**Waste-spark ignition**   Introduced in the mid-1980s, it uses the on-board computer to fire the ignition coils.

**Water-fuel separator**   Separates water and fuel in a diesel engine.

**Wet compression test**   A test that uses oil to help seal around the piston rings.

**WHMIS**   Workplace Hazardous Materials Information Systems.

**Wide-band oxygen sensor**   An oxygen sensor design that is capable of detecting actual air–fuel ratios. This is in contrast to a conventional oxygen sensor that only changes voltage when a stoichiometric air–fuel ratio has been achieved.

**Wind farms**   A group of windmills.

**Wood alcohol**   See *methanol*.

**World wide fuel charter**   A fuel quality standard developed by vehicle and engine manufacturers in 2002.

**Wrench**   A hand tool used to grasp and rotate a threaded fastener.

# SPANISH GLOSSARY

**Absorción de calor a bajas temperaturas**   El enfriamiento de una temperatura sistémica que se aproxima a la temperatura ambiente, lo cual resulta en una transferencia de calor de menor eficiencia.

**Aceite de cocina usado**   Un término utilizado para designar aquel aceite que puede o no ser aceite vegetal puro.

**Aceite usado**   Cualquier aceite de base petrolero o sintético que ha sido usado.

**Aceite vegetal de residuos**   Esta clasificación de aceite incluye los aceites de cocina animales y de en base a pescado entre otros.

**Aceite vegetal no modificado para combustible o "directo"**   Un triglicérido de glicerol que une tres cadenas hidrocarbonadas cuya longitud oscila entre 16 y 22 átomos de carbono.

**Acoplamiento de corriente alterna**   Una función que se puede seleccionar para observar la forma de una onda.

**Acoplamiento de corriente directa**   Una señal que transmite tanto el componente de corriente alterna como el componente de corriente directa al medidor.

**Actuador**   Un aparato eléctrico o mecánico que convierte la energía eléctrica en una acción mecánica. A modo de ejemplo, puede ajustar la velocidad de marcha mínima, alterar la altura de la suspensión o regular la dosificación del combustible.

**Acumulador**   Un depósito o recipiente temporal para fluidos bajo presión.

**Adaptador de buje o casquillo**   Un instrumento utilizado para adaptar un tamaño de un propulsor de bujes o dados para ser usado con otro propulsor de bujes o dados de distinto tamaño tal como un maneral o barra rompedora.

**Administrador de Funciones o *Task Manager***   Un término utilizado por la empresa Chrysler para describir el programa de computación diseñado para manejar la operación de todos los monitores OBD-II lo cual logra controlando la secuencia de pasos necesaria para ejecutar las pruebas diagnósticas y los monitores.

**Adsorción**   Proceso fisicoquímico mediante el cual las moléculas del vapor de combustibles son atraídas y retenidas en la superficie del carbón.

**AFV**   Siglas en inglés para vehículo de combustible alternativo.

**AGST**   Siglas en inglés para tanque de almacenamiento no subterráneo, utilizado para almacenar combustible usado.

**Aire falso**   Un término utilizado para describir el aire que ingresa a un motor y que no ha sido medido por el sensor de flujo de aire.

**Alcohol de grano**   *Véase* Etanol.

**Alcohol de madera**   *Véase* Metanol.

**Alcohol etílico**   *Véase* Etanol.

**Alcohol metilo**   *Véase* Metanol.

**Alto voltaje**   Se define como cualquier voltaje que excede los 50 voltios.

**Amperímetro inductivo**   Un tipo de amperímetro que utiliza un sensor de efecto Hall en una tenaza que se usa para envolver un conductor que transporta una corriente.

**Anchura de pulso**   Duración del tiempo de encendido/funcionamiento de un inyector de combustible electrónico.

**ANSI**   Siglas en inglés para Instituto Nacional Estadounidense de Estándares.

**Árbol de levas de configuración OVH sencilla**   Un diseño en el cual se coloca un árbol de levas dentro de la culata del cilindro.

**Árbol de levas doble en culata**   Un diseño de motor con dos árboles de leva que se ubican encima de cada línea de cilindros, una para las válvulas de agotamiento y otra para las válvulas de entrada.

**Asbestosis**   Condición médica en la que el asbesto produce la formación de cicatrices en los pulmones, lo cual causa falta de aliento.

**ASD**   Siglas en inglés para relé de cierre automático.

**ASTM**   Siglas en inglés para la Sociedad Estadounidense para Prueba de Materiales.

**Auto inducción**   Cuando una corriente comienza a fluir hacia una bobina, una corriente opuesta se genera en el embobinado de la bobina.

**Autoencendido o picado de las bielas**   *Véase* Detonación.

**Avance inicial**   El avance de la chispa a velocidad ralentí. Seguidamente, la computadora regula el avance de la chispa de acuerdo a la velocidad del motor y tomando en cuenta otros factores.

**Ayuda hidráulica de propulsión**   Configuración en vehículos híbridos que utiliza bombas hidráulicas y botellas acumuladoras para la regeneración de energía.

**B20**   Una mezcla de 20% de biodiesel con 80% de petrodiesel.

**Bar**   Cuando el aire es bombeado al interior del cilindro, la cámara de combustión recibe un incremento de la presión del aire conocido como sobrepresión que se mide en libras por pulgadas cuadradas (*PSI*), atmósferas (*ATMs*), o bar.

**Barra articulada**   Una herramienta que se utiliza para la propulsión del dado. También llamada mango articulado.

**Barra de alargue**   Una barra utilizada en una llave para incrementar la torción que se puede aplicar a un sujetador. No se recomienda su uso.

**BCI**   Siglas en inglés para Consejo Internacional de Baterías.

**Biodiesel**   Un combustible renovable producido a partir de aceites vegetales, grasas animales o grasa reciclada de restaurante.

**Biomasa de celulosa**   Compuesta principalmente de celulosa y lignina con pequeñas cantidades de proteínas, lípidos (grasas, ceras y aceites) y cenizas.

**Biomasa**   Productos agrícolas no comestibles tales como: tallos de maíz, pajas de cereal y deshechos botánicos de procesos industriales, tales como el aserrín y la pulpa de papel utilizadas en la elaboración del etanol.

**Bloque de motor**   La base de cualquier motor. Todas las demás partes están directa o indirectamente adheridas al bloque del motor.

**BOB**   Siglas en inglés para caja de desconexión.

**Bobina con tomas**   También conocida como transformador con tomas.

**Bobina de chispa perdida**   El tipo de bobina utilizado por la mayoría de sistemas de encendido estático de "chispa perdida" para mantener tanto el bobinado primario como el secundario, separado el uno del otro.

**Bobina del encendido**   Artefacto eléctrico que consta de dos bobinas distintas de alambre: un bobinado primario y un secundario. El objetivo de un encendido es producir una corriente de alto voltaje (de entre 20,000 y 40,000 V) y amperaje suficientemente bajo (cerca de 80 mA) como para que se produzca el encendido de la chispa.

**Bobina doble** *Véase* Bobina de chispa perdida.

**Bobina exploradora** Un interruptor electrónico del encendido común y sencillo que se encuentra en el sistema de generador de pulsos magnéticos.

**Bobinado secundario** Un bobinado que tiene aproximadamente cien veces más vueltas que un bobinado primario o un ratio de giro de aproximadamente 100:1.

**Bomba de canal lateral** Una bomba de turbina.

**Bomba de detección de fuga** La empresa *Chrysler* utiliza una bomba eléctrica que presuriza el sistema de combustible para detectar la presencia de fugas de combustible a través de un monitoreo por parte del monitor del módulo de control del tren de fuerza del tanque de combustible por medio del sensor de presión.

**Bomba de elevación (de aceleración o de pique)** El combustible diésel es extraído del tanque de combustible por una bomba de presión para, de esta manera, hacer llegar el combustible a la bomba de inyección.

**Bomba de inyección** La bomba de inyección bombea combustible a los inyectores a alta presión y a intervalos predeterminados. Cada inyector inyecta combustible en la cámara de combustión en el momento preciso requerido para una combustión eficiente.

**Bomba de paleta oscilante** Bomba de paleta.

**Bomba de paletas rotativa** Esta bomba consiste en un disco del rodete central, varias aspas o paletas que viajan en las ranuras del rodete en una carcasa de bomba que está descentrada en relación al eje central del rodete.

**Bomba de turbina** Una bomba eléctrica que gira a mayor velocidad y es menos ruidosa que otras bombas eléctricas.

**Bomba hidráulica con gerotor** Un tipo de bomba de desplazamiento positivo que a menudo se utiliza en bombas de aceite de motor. Hace uso del contacto de los dientes del gerotor con la pista del engrane rotor para generar la presión necesaria para bombear el aceite a presión.

**Bomba hidrocinética** Este diseño de bomba permite que el combustible se bombee rápidamente a fin de generar la presión necesaria.

**Bomba periférica** Una bomba de turbina.

**Bujía de incandescencia** (bujía de encendido) Pequeño calentador eléctrico, localizado en el interior del cilindro de un motor diesel, para precalentar el aire y ayudar al arranque del motor.

**Bujía de platino o platinos** Son bujías que contienen una pequeña cantidad del metal precioso denominado platino soldado a la punta de un diminuto electrodo central así como al final del electrodo lateral o de tierra. El platino es un metal blanco, grisáceo que no reacciona ante la presencia del oxígeno, por lo tanto no se oxida como en el caso de los electrodos de una bujía convencional de aleación de níkel.

**Bujías de iridio** Son bujías que contienen una pequeña cantidad de iridio soldado a la punta de un diminuto electrodo central, de entre 0.4 y 0.6 mm (0.0015 a 0.002 pulgadas) de diámetro. El reducido diámetro de este electrodo reduce el voltaje requerido para acortar la distancia entre el electrodo central y el lateral, lo cual reduce el potencial de rateos o fallos en el encendido. El electrodo puesto a tierra o el lateral usualmente termina en una punta de platino a fin de reducir el desgaste del electrodo.

**Bus de datos** Término utilizado para describir una red de comunicación.

**CAA** Siglas en inglés para *Clean Air Act*. Legislación federal adoptada en 1970 que introdujo estándares de calidad de aire a nivel nacional.

**Cables de alto voltaje** Cables vehiculares que transportan cargas de energía de alto voltaje.

**Calibrado de velocidad por densidad** Un método utilizado para calcular la cantidad de combustible que un motor necesita.

**Calibrador de flujo** Un dispositivo que mide el nivel de circulación de aire apropiado en el sistema de control de evaporación de combustibles.

**Calibre** El diámetro interior de un cilindro en un motor.

**Calor de compresión** El aire es comprimido hasta que la temperatura alcanza aproximadamente los 1000 grados Fahrenheit.

**Cámara de aire** Una cámara localizada entre el cuerpo de la mariposa y las varillas deslizantes del múltiple de entrada, usada para distribuir la carga de entrada de una manera más uniforme y eficiente.

**Cámara de combustión** El espacio que queda en el interior de un cilindro de motor cuando un pistón se encuentra en lo más alto de su cámara de combustión.

**Campaña** 1. Una llamada efectuada a los dueños de los vehículos para devolver el vehículo a la concesionaria y repararlo. 2. Una notificación efectuada al dueño de un vehículo que le informa que se debe atender y corregir algún asunto que está atentando contra la seguridad vehicular.

**CAN** Siglas en inglés para red de control de área. Un tipo de transmisión de datos en serie.

**Canasta de filtro** Filtro final.

**Carbón a líquido (CAL) o liquefacción de carbón** Un proceso de refinación mediante el cual el carbón se convierte en combustible líquido.

**Carrera del pistón o embolada** Movimiento del pistón de una vía entre la parte superior e inferior (culata y piso) del cilindro.

**Casquillo** Un instrumento que encaja por encima de un perno o tuerca y que es girado por un maneral o barra rompedora.

**CAT III** Una medida para equipos de medición eléctrica creada por la Comisión Electrotécnica Internacional (*IEC* por sus siglas en inglés). El modelo CAT III indica el nivel más bajo de protección instrumental que debería estar implementada cuando se realizan medidas electrónicas en vehículos eléctricos híbridos.

**Catalizador** Platino y paladio utilizado en el convertidos catalítico para combinar oxígeno ($O_2$) con hidrocarburos (HC) y monóxido de carbono (CO) para formar emisiones de escape inocuas compuestas de agua ($H_2O$) y dióxido de carbono ($CO_2$).

**Catalizador oxigenado de diésel** Consiste en una estructura alveolar de flujo continuo que está enchapado con una capa de material catalítico similar a la utilizada por los convertidores catalíticos en un motor de gasolina.

**CCM** Siglas en inglés para monitor de componente integral.

**Célula combustible con membrana de intercambio de protones** Una célula combustible de bajas temperaturas conocida por su arranque rápido y su construcción relativamente sencilla.

**Célula combustible de polímero de electrolito (*PEFC* por sus siglas en inglés)** Otro término para la célula combustible de membrana de intercambio de protones (véase *PEM*).

**Célula de combustible o energética** Un dispositivo electroquímico que convierte la energía almacenada en gas hidrógeno a electricidad, agua y calor.

**Cerio** Un elemento que puede almacenar oxígeno.

**CFR** Siglas en inglés para código de regulaciones federales.

**Ciclo de duración** Porcentaje de tiempo en el que una señal se mantiene encendida.

**Ciclo de vida** El número de veces que una batería puede ser cargada y descargada sin sufrir una disminución significativa en su desempeño.

**CID** Siglas en inglés para identificación de componente.

**Circuito de encendido primario** El componente de encendido que regula la corriente en el embobinado primario al encenderlo y apagarlo.

**Circuito de encendido** secundario Componentes necesarios para producir y distribuir electricidad de alto voltaje para encender la mezcla de combustible y aire al interior del motor.

**CKP** Siglas en inglés para sensor de la posición del cigüeñal del motor.

**Clase 2** Un tipo de protocolo de comunicación BUS utilizado por los vehículos de *General Motors*.

**CMP** Siglas en inglés para sensor de posicionamiento de árbol de levas.

**CNG** Siglas en inglés para gas natural comprimido.

**Códigos de calibración** Códigos utilizados en muchos de los módulos de control del tren de fuerza.

**Coeficiente de temperatura negativa** Una medida que usualmente se usa en referencia a un sensor de temperatura (ya sea este un sensor de temperatura ambiente o del refrigerante). A medida que la temperatura aumenta, la resistencia al sensor se reduce.

**Colas** Hechas de tela engomada con terminaciones de metal que soportan el silenciador y el tubo de escape en posición de modo que no toquen ninguna parte de metal. Esto ayuda a aislar cualquier ruido producido en el escape del resto del vehículo.

**Combustibles oxigenados** Combustibles tales como el ETBE o el MTBE que contienen moléculas de oxígeno extras para promover un quemado mas limpio. Los combustibles oxigenados se usan como aditivos de la gasolina para reducir las emisiones de dióxido de carbono.

**Combustibles sintéticos** Combustibles creados a través de productos sintéticos tales como el proceso Fischer-Tropsch.

**Combustión** La ignición rápida de una mezcla de aire y combustible en los cilindros del motor que genera calor y presión al interior del motor.

**Combustión espontánea** Un fenómeno por el cual un incendio comienza espontáneamente en trapos llenos de aceite o grasa.

**Computadora digital** Una computadora que solamente utiliza señales de encendido y apagado. Utiliza un convertidor A a D para convertir las señales analógicas en señales digitales antes de procesarlas.

**Conductor doble retorcido** Un par de cables trenzados en una ratio de 9 a 16 vueltas por pie longitudinal. La mayoría de estos cables se trenzan una vez cada pulgada (12 vueltas por cada pie longitudinal) para reducir la interferencia electromagnética que podría resultar al ser inducida en el alambrado, ya que un alambre tendería a cancelar la interferencia inducida en.

**Conector BNC** Un mini conector de entrada estándar de tipo coaxial.

**Conmutación** Encender y apagar el circuito primario.

**Conteo o frecuencia de cambio de voltaje** El número de veces que un sensor de oxígeno cambia de voltaje a la baja (el alza de voltaje no cuenta en el conteo) en un segundo (o 1.25 segundos, dependiendo de la velocidad de la computadora o sonda que se utiliza).

**Contrapresión** La resistencia al flujo del sistema de escape que se mide en libras por pulgada cuadrada (*PSI*).

**Contrapresión negativa** Una válvula EGR que reaccionan a un área de baja presión cerrando una pequeña válvula interna lo cual permite que la válvula EGR se abra al vacío.

**Contrapresión positiva** Una válvula EGR diseñada con una válvula interior que sangra cualquier residuo de vacío y previene que la válvula principal se abra.

**Controlador** Un término utilizado para referirse a una computadora vehicular o unidad de control electrónico (*ECU* por sus siglas en inglés).

**Controlador de Interconexión Programable (*PCI* por sus siglas en inglés)** Un tipo de protocolo de comunicación de red utilizado en vehículos marca *Chrysler*.

**Convenio mundial de combustibles** Un estándar de calidad de combustible desarrollado por fabricantes de motores y vehículos en el año 2002.

**Convertidor** Aparato electrónico que se usa para convertir CD (corriente directa) en CA (corriente alterna).

**Convertidor catalítico** Un mecanismo de control de emisiones ubicado en el sistema de escape que convierte el HC y el CO en $H_2O$ y $CO_2$ inocuos. En un catalizador de tres vías, el NOx también se divide en nitrógeno (N) y oxígeno (O).

**Convertidor de análogo a digital (*AD* por sus siglas en inglés)** Un circuito electrónico que convierte las señales análogas a señales digitales que pueden ser usadas por una computadora.

**Convertidor Pup *Véase*** Preconvertidor.

**CPS** Siglas en inglés para solenoide de purga del cánister (filtro de carbón activo).

**CPU** Siglas en inglés para unidad central de procesamiento.

**Cresta** El diámetro externo de un tornillo medido de rosca a rosca.

**Cristal oscilante** Un cristal que determina la velocidad de los circuitos electrónicos.

**Criterios de Operación** Prerrequisitos de operación.

**CRT** Siglas en inglés para tubo de rayo catódico.

**Crudo sintético** Un derivado del proceso pott-Broche o licuefacción directa del carbono mediante el cual se descompone el carbón usando un proceso químico para convertirlo en una mezcla de hidrocarburos líquidos. Este proceso comienza con un proceso termoquímico en el que el carbono reacciona con el hidrogeno ($H_2$) a altas temperaturas y bajo una presión elevadísima cuando se usa un catalizador.

**Cuadrícula** Conjunto de cuadrados en la cara de un osciloscopio.

**Curva de destilación** Una grafica que grafica las temperaturas a las cuales se evaporan las diferentes fracciones de un combustible.

**DDS** Siglas en inglés para sistema de provisión por demanda.

**Densidad de la energía** Una medida de la cantidad de energía que puede ser almacenada en una batería relativa al volumen del contenedor de la batería. La densidad de la energía es medida en términos de Watts por hora por litro (Wh/L).

**Desintegración catalítica** Un proceso de refinación donde los hidrocarburos con puntos de ebullición altos se desintegran y forman hidrocarburos con puntos de ebullición bajos.

**Desplazamiento (cilindrada)** El volumen total barrido en cada carrera del pistón en su movimiento dentro del cilindro al interior de un motor de combustión.

**Desplazamiento positivo** Cuando todo el aire que ingresa es forzado a pasar por un turbocargador o súpercargador enraizado.

**Destilación** Es el proceso de purificación a través de la evaporación y luego condensación del líquido deseado.

**Detonación** Una explosión violenta en la cámara de combustión creada por una incineración incontrolada de la mezcla aire y combustible; generalmente causa un golpeteo fuerte y audible. También conocido como golpeteo o ping.

**DI** Siglas en inglés de sistema de encendido con distribuidor.

**Diferencial de presión**   Una diferencia en la presión de un circuito de frenos a otro.

**DIS**   Siglas en inglés para sistema de encendido sin distribuidor. También llamado sistema de ignición estática.

**Diseño de varillaje en bloque**   Un motor donde el cigüeñal está ubicado en el bloque y no en el cabezal.

**Diseño enraizado**   Nombrado en honor a los hermanos Philander y Francisco Roots originarios de Coneersville, Indiana quienes patentaron el diseño enraizado en 1860 en la forma de una bomba de agua para ser usada en la industria minera. Posteriormente este diseño fue utilizado para circular el aire y hoy en día se lo utiliza en los motores *Detroit* de diésel a dos tiempos. El diseño enraizado utilizado en los supercargadores o supercompresores es considerado un diseño de desplazamiento positivo porque todo el aire que ingresa es forzado a pasar a través de la unidad.

**Disparador *Schmitt***   Un dispositivo que convierte las señales análogas en digitales.

**Dispositivo de encendido**   Sinónimo de ignitor.

**Distancia entre roscas**   El número de roscas por pulgada de un sujetador enroscado.

**División**   Un bloque.

**DMM**   Siglas en inglés para multímetro digital. Un multímetro digital tiene la capacidad de medir simultáneamente la corriente eléctrica, la resistencia y el voltaje.

**DPS**   Siglas en inglés para sensor de presión diferencial.

**DSO**   Siglas en inglés para osciloscopio de almacenamiento digital.

**DVOM**   Siglas en inglés para un miliamperímetro de voltios ohmios digital.

**E & C**   Siglas en inglés para entretenimiento y confort.

**E-10**   Una mezcla de combustible compuesta de 10% de etanol y 90% de gasolina.

**E2PROM**   Siglas en inglés para una memoria de sólo lectura que puede ser eléctricamente lectura borrable y programable.

**E-85**   Una mezcla de combustible compuesta de 85% de etanol y 15% de gasolina.

**ECA**   Siglas en inglés para módulo de control electrónico. El nombre utilizado por *Ford* para describir la computadora utilizada para controlar el abastecimiento de combustible y el encendido en los modelos de vehículos más antiguos.

**ECM**   Siglas en inglés para módulo de control electrónico en un vehículo.

**ECT**   Siglas en inglés para temperatura del refrigerante del motor.

**ECU**   Siglas en inglés para unidad de control electrónico en un vehículo.

**E–diésel**   Diésel estándar, grado 2, que contiene hasta 15% de etanol. También conocido como diesohol fuera de los Estados Unidos.

**EECS**   Siglas en inglés para sistema de control de evaporación de emisiones.

**EEPROM**   *Véase* E2PROM.

**Eficiencia volumétrica**   El ratio o relación entre la cantidad de mezcla aire-combustible que en realidad ingresa al cilindro y la cantidad que potencialmente podría ingresar si se diesen las condiciones ideales y que es expresado en un porcentaje.

**EGR lineal**   Contiene un motor de etapas que regula con precisión el flujo de escape de gases y que contiene un potenciómetro de retroalimentación que informa a la computadora mediante señales en relación a la posición actual exacta de la válvula.

**Ejecutor de Diagnóstico**   Un programa de computación diseñado para manejar todos los monitores OBD-II al controlar la secuencia de pasos necesarias para llevar a cabo las pruebas de diagnóstico y manejar los monitores.

**Electrólisis**   El proceso mediante el cual la corriente eléctrica pasa a través del agua para convertirse en hidrógeno y oxígeno gaseoso.

**Emisiones de hidrocarburo no-metano**   El estándar bajo el cual se evalúan las pruebas de emisión para detectar hidrocarburos.

**Encendido de desviación o de modo de desviación**   Un tipo de encendido comúnmente utilizado en motores de *General Motors* que están equipados con encendido de distribuidor (o *DI* por sus siglas en inglés), así como aquellos motores equipados con sistemas de encendido estático de "chispa perdida."

**Encendido integral mejorado**   Un control de encendido mediante el cual todas las funciones de sincronización son interpretadas por el módulo de control del tren de fuerza en vez de estar divididas entre el módulo de control del tren de fuerza y el modulo de control de ignición.

**Encendido por compresión de carga homogénea**   Un proceso de combustión a bajas temperaturas que consiste en la quema de la mezcla estequiométrica sin el uso del encendido por chispa.

**Energía específica**   El contenido de energía de una batería en relación a la masa de la batería. La energía específica se mide en  vatio-horas por kilogramo (Vh/kg).

**Ensamblaje de empalme**   Un término utilizado por *General Motors* para describir la interconexión de los módulos en una red. A menudo se abrevia SP.

**Ensamblaje o montaje del electrodo de la membrana (*MEA* por sus siglas en inglés)**   El componente de la célula combustible de membrana electrolítica de polímetro (PEM po r sus siglas en inglés) que contiene la membrana, las capas catalíticas y los electrodos.

**Entretuerca**   Un tipo de tuerca que tiene fuerza de torción; también llamada tuerca de seguridad.

**EPA**   Siglas en inglés para Agencia de Protección Ambiental.

**Esmog**   Polución del aire formada por NOx y HC con incidencia de la luz solar. Una combinación de los términos en inglés para "humo" y "niebla."

**Espárrago o perno prisionero**   Vara corta con roscas de tornillo a ambos extremos.

**Espinterómetro**   Un aparato que mide el voltaje requerido para recorrer la distancia entre el rotor y los segmentos de la capa del distribuidor (entre 0.8 a 1.3 mm o 0.030 a 0.050 pulgadas).

**Estación de lavado de ojos**   Una unidad dispensadora de agua que dirige chorros de agua hacia los ojos.

**Etanol**   Alcohol de grano que se mezcla con la gasolina para producir un combustible vehicular. También conocido como alcohol etílico.

**Etanol de celulosa**   Etanol producido a partir de cargas de alimentación de biomasa tales como residuos vegetales agrícolas e indústriales.

**ETBE**   éter butil etil terciario. El ETBE es un combustible oxigenado que es producido haciendo reaccionar isobutileno con etanol. El éter que resulta tiene un alto contenido de octano y baja volatilidad. El ETBE puede utilizarse como un aditivo de la gasolina hasta un nivel de 13% aprox.

**Éter metil terciario amil**   Un combustible oxigenado que es utilizado como un aditivo de la gasolina para aumentar sus características inflamables.

**Extensión**   Barras de acero con puntales hembra y macho que se utilizan para extender el campo de acción de una matraca o mango articulado a fin de rotar una llave de cubo o dado.

**Extinguidor de fuego, tipos de incendios** Tipos de fuegos que un extinguidor de fuego está diseñado para manejar, se refiere a tipos de incendios.

**Extremo no principal** El extremo de un motor opuesto a la terminación principal, generalmente denominado parte frontal del motor donde se utilizan las correas.

**Extremo principal** El extremo del motor al cual se adhiere el volante.

**FCHV** Siglas en inglés para vehículo híbrido de célula de combustible.

**FCV** Siglas en inglés para vehículo de pila de combustible o "vehículo impulsado por célula energética."

**Fenolformaldehida** Se forma cuando se quema la gasolina reformulada. El tubo de escape presenta un olor muy peculiar cuando se utiliza gasolina reformulada.

**Fidelidad de medición** El porcentaje de precisión o exactitud de un medidor.

**Filtro APEE** Tipo de filtro de aire particulado de elevada eficiencia utilizado para filtrar el polvo de los frenos.

**Frazada para incendios** Una frazada de lana a prueba de fuego que se utiliza para apagar el fuego al envolverla alrededor de una víctima.

**Frecuencia** El número de veces que se repite una onda en un segundo, medido en Hertz (Hz), frecuencia de banda.

**FTP** Siglas en inglés para Procedimiento Federal de Evaluaciones.

**Fulgor** Un incremento seguido de una rebaja en la velocidad de marcha de un motor.

**Función de barrido en milisegundos** En este modo el osciloscopio solo llevará a cabo el barrido electrónico de la porción del patrón que se puede visualizar mientras el osciloscopio se encuentra en la función de 5 a 25 milisegundos.

**Funcionalidad** Se refiere al proceso mediante el cual las señales de entrada del módulo de control del tren de fuerza revisan el funcionamiento de las señales de salida.

**Funcionamiento *Closed Loop*** Una fase en la operación del motor por medios electrónicos en la cual los datos del sensor de oxígeno se utilizan para calcular el nivel de la mezcla aire-combustible.

**Galería de aceite** Una bomba de aceite accionada por el motor que empuja el motor a través de un filtro de aceite y posteriormente a los ductos que se encuentran al interior del árbol de levas y del bloque del motor.

**Gas licuado de petróleo** Se comercializa como propano líquido que a menudo contiene una mezcla de 10% de otros gases tales como butano, propileno, butileno y etil mercaptan a fin de que este gas incoloro e inodoro sea odorizado por razones de seguridad.

**Gasolina** Producto de petróleo refinado que es utilizado principalmente como combustible vehicular. La gasolina está compuesta de una variedad de hidrocarburos y también contiene aditivos para aumentar su rendimiento en un ICE.

**Gasolina reformulada (*RFG* por sus siglas en inglés)** La gasolina reformulada tiene aditivos oxigenados y ha sido refinada con el propósito de reducir tanto el contenido de los hidrocarburos más pesados como el de los más livianos de la gasolina a fin de promover una combustión más limpia de la misma.

**GAWR** Siglas en inglés para peso bruto nominal por eje. Una calificación de la capacidad de carga de peso de un vehículo y que se incluye en las señalizaciones del vehículo así como en el manual de operaciones.

**Generador magnético de impulsos** Un interruptor generador de señales que crea un pulso de voltaje a medida que el flujo magnético cambia alrededor de la bobina captadora.

**GLP** *Véase* Gas licuado de petróleo.

**GMLAN** Siglas en inglés para red de área local de *General Motors*. Un término utilizado por la *General Motors* para describir la red bus CAN usada en vehículos GM.

**GMM** Siglas en inglés para multímetro gráfico.

**Golpeteo** Quemado rápido secundario de los últimos 3% a 5% de la mezcla de aire/combustible en la cámara de combustión que causa un segundo frente de llama que colinda con el primer frente de flama causando un ruido de golpeteo. También llamado detonación o ping.

**Gorra de seguridad** Casco de plástico duro que protege la cabeza de los golpes.

**Granja de viento** Un área de terreno destinada a la instalación de plantas de energía eólica.

**Gravedad *API*** Una escala de medición arbitraria que mide la densidad o peso específico de los productos líquidos derivados del petróleo, desarrollada en forma conjunta entre el Instituto Estadounidense de Petróleo (*API* por sus siglas en inglés) y el Colegio Nacional de Estándares.

**Guantes de goma *Lineman*** Tipo de guantes usados por técnicos al trabajar alrededor de circuitos de alto voltaje. Usualmente incluyen un guante interior forrado de goma que se clasifica para 1.000 voltios y un guante exterior protector de cuero cuando se usan para trabajar en vehículos eléctricos híbridos.

**GVWR** Siglas en inglés para nivel de peso total del vehículo.

**HEI** Siglas en inglés para la marca de encendido de alta energía utilizada en los vehículos de *General Motors Corporation*.

**Hertzio** Unidad de medida de la frecuencia, abreviada Hz.

**HEUI** Siglas en inglés para unidad de inyección electrónica hidráulica.

**Hidrocraqueo** Proceso de refinamiento que convierte los hidrocarburos con alto punto de ebullición en otros con bajo punto de ebullición.

**IAC** Siglas en inglés para control de aire de ralentí.

**ICE** Siglas en inglés para motor de combustión interna.

**IEC** Siglas en inglés para Comisión Electrotécnica Internacional.

**Ignitor** El módulo de encendido electrónico.

**Imagen de Pantalla** Un muestreo o una instantánea de todos los datos del motor en el momento exacto en que se configuró el DTC.

**Indicación falsa de presencia de mezcla fina** Ocurre cuando un sensor de oxígeno proporciona una lectura baja en el índice lambda por causa de algún factor que no tenga que ver con la presencia de una mezcla fina de combustible.

**Indicación falsa de presencia de mezcla rica en gasolina** Una lectura de voltaje alta en el índice lambda del sensor de oxígeno que se produce por algún factor que no tenga que ver con la presencia de una mezcla rica en el sistema de escape. Algunas de las causas comunes de esa falsa lectura son, que el sensor de oxígeno esté contaminado y que tenga un cable de señalización demasiado cerca a una fuente de alto voltaje tal como un embobinado de bujía.

**Índice antidetonante (*AKI* por sus siglas en inglés)** El octanaje que se exhibe en las gasolineras.

**Índice de cetano (cetanaje)** Medida de las características antidetonantes de un combustible diésel.

**Índice de octano** Medida de las características antidetonantes de un combustible motor. Cuanto más alto es el octanaje menos proclividad tiene la gasolina a detonarse.

**Inducción mutua** La generación de una corriente eléctrica a lo largo y ancho del embobinado en ambos lados.

**Inerte** Químicamente inactivo.

**Intercambio en serie de datos** Datos transmitidos en serie por medio de señales de voltaje altamente variable.

*Intercooler* Un dispositivo similar a un radiador en el que el aire externo puede circular en su interior con la finalidad de enfriar el aire recalentado por causa de la presión.

**Interfaz de comunicación serial (*SCI* por sus siglas en inglés)** Un tipo de transmisión de datos en serie utilizado por la marca *Chrysler*.

**Interferencia electromagnética** Una señal electrónica indeseada, causada por la expansión y colapso de un campo magnético, lo cual genera una interferencia eléctrica no deseada en un circuito eléctrico cercano.

**Interruptor de energía hacia la bomba de gasolina** Un interruptor de energía hacia la bomba de gasolina, también conocido como "interruptor de inercia" tiene la función de apagar la bomba de gasolina del vehículo en caso de un accidente.

**Interruptor o sensor de efecto Hall** Un semiconductor moviéndose en relación a un campo magnético, creando así una salida de voltaje variable. Utilizado para determinar una posición. Un tipo de sensor electromagnético utilizado en el encendido electrónico y otros sistemas. Llamado así en honor a Edwin H. Hall, el descubridor del efecto Hall en 1879.

**Inyección de Combustible Simultánea** Cuando los inyectores son pulsados en grupo.

**Inyección de puerto de combustible** Un sistema de inyección que utiliza una tobera para cada cilindro y en el cual el combustible se inyecta al múltiple de admisión a una distancia aproximada de 70 a 100 mm (2 a 3 pulgadas) de la válvula de admisión.

**Inyección directa de gasolina** Diseño del sistema de inyección de combustible en el cual se inyecta la gasolina directamente a la cámara de combustión.

**Inyección directa por encendido de chispa** El nombre mediante el cual *General Motors* designa a un sistema *GDI*.

**Inyección directa** Un diseño de inyección de combustible mediante le cual el combustible se inyecta directamente al cilindro.

**Inyección indirecta** El combustible es inyectado a una pequeña antecámara que es conectada al cilindro por una apertura delgada. La combustión inicial se lleva a cabo en esta antecámara. Esto tiene el efecto de reducir la velocidad de la combustión, lo cual tiende a reducir el nivel de ruido.

*ISC* Siglas en inglés para control de velocidad de marcha mínima.

**Junta de recursos atmosféricos de California (*CARB* por sus siglas en inglés)** Agencia gubernamental estatal del estado de California que regula los estándares de calidad de aire para el estado de California.

*KAM* Siglas en inglés para memoria siempre activa.

**Kilo** Significa 1,000; se abrevia "k'' o "K''.

**Laguna de aceleración** La demora entre la aceleración y la sobrepresión.

**Lámpara de prueba *Noid*** Una lámpara de prueba diseñada para reemplazar la función eléctrica del inyector en el circuito y para centellear si es que el circuito de inyección esta funcionando correctamente.

**Lámpara indicadora de mal funcionamiento** Luz de advertencia que alerta al conductor de una falla que puede afectar las emisiones o el funcionamiento del tren de fuerza.

**Leyes de derecho de saber** Leyes que requieren que los negocios exhiban hojas de datos sobre la seguridad de materiales para que todos sepan cuáles materiales peligrosos se utilizan en ese edificio.

**Línea de Chispa** Una línea en la forma de onda de la bobina secundaria en el gráfico del módulo de ignición que precede la línea de disparo.

**Línea de disparo** La línea más vertical izquierda en la forma de onda de la bobina secundaria en el gráfico del módulo de ignición.

**Llave** Una herramienta manual utilizada para sostener, apretar y girar objetos tales como pernos, tuercas o remaches.

**Llave combinada** Un tipo de llave que tiene un extremo abierto y el otro en forma de estría.

**Llave de boca abierta** Un tipo de llave que permite el acceso lateral a la parte plana de una tuerca o tornillo.

**Llave de boca ajustable** Llave con una quijada móvil que le permite adaptarse a diferentes tipos de medida de sujetadores de tuerca.

**Llave de cabeza cerrada** Una herramienta manual con cabeza cerrada que sirve para ejercer la torsión necesaria para aflojar tornillos o pernos.

**Llave para tuercas cónicas** Un tipo de llave utilizada para retirar líneas de combustible, de frenos o del aire acondicionado.

**Luz de prueba** Una luz utilizada para comprobar el nivel de voltaje. Contiene un foco conectado, en un extremo, a un cable puesto a tierra y a un puntal en el otro extremo.

**Luz de prueba de continuidad** Una luz de prueba que contiene una batería y que se enciende si detecta la presencia de la continuidad (corriente eléctrica) entre los dos polos que están conectados al probador.

**Luz de prueba tipo LED** Una luz de prueba usada por técnicos y electricistas para probar el voltaje que tiene una impedancia alta y que utiliza diodos fotoemisores con un resistor de 470 ohmios para controlar la corriente que fluye a través de un probador.

**M85** Un combustible de motor de combustión interna que contiene 85% de metanol y 15 % de gasolina.

**Mapeo de motor** Un programa de computadora que utiliza la información de las pruebas de motor para determinar la mejor relación aire/combustible y la velocidad apropiada de avance de chispa para el desempeño ideal del motor.

**Medida dinámica del estado de salud (*SOH* por sus siglas en inglés)** Una señal enviada por uno de los módulos a los demás módulos en la red, informándoles que está funcionando correctamente y que mantiene su habilidad de transmitir señales.

**Medidor de alta impedancia** Mide el total de resistencia interna del circuito métrico causadas por espirales internas, capacitores y resistores.

**Medidor de tobera de inyección de diésel o *Pop Tester*** Un dispositivo que se usa para analizar la tobera de inyección de diésel para asegurarse que tiene un patrón de chorro apropiado. Cuando la manija se libera aparece la tobera de inyección en la pantalla.

**Mega millón (M)** Utilizado para describir números sumamente grandes o para medir una gran cantidad de resistencia.

**Mercurio** Un metal pesado que a temperatura ambiente se encuentra en estado líquido.

**Metanol** Alcohol típicamente elaborado a base de gas natural. El contenido de cosolventes en el metanol está limitado por ley al cinco por ciento (5%).

**Metanol a gasolina** Un proceso de refinación mediante el cual el metanol es transformado en gasolina.

**Methyl tertiary butyl ether** (*MTB*: metil-terbutil-éter). Combustible oxigenado que se permite en la gasolina sin plomo hasta un nivel de 15%.

**Método *Reid* de presión de vapor** Un método para determinar la presión del vapor de la gasolina y otros hidrocarburos. Este método es ampliamente usado en la industria petrolera como un indicador de la volatilidad de la gasolina.

**Mezcla etanol-diésel** Véase E-diésel. Combustible diésel estándar #2 combinado con hasta un 15% de etanol.

**Micro (μ)** Una millonésima parte de un voltio o un amperio.

**Micrón** Una unidad de medida equivalente a 0.000039 pulgadas.

**Mijo** Una planta o carga de alimentación usado en la producción de etanol que requiere muy poca energía o fertilizante para su cultivo.

**Mili (m)** Una milésima parte de un voltio o un amperio.

**Modo de ondas sobrepuestas** Una posición de un sensor u osciloscopio de ignición utilizado para observar la diferencia entre patrones de ondas de los cilindros en todas las áreas excepto la línea de disparo.

**Modo de simulación de aceleración** Utiliza un dinamómetro que aplica una carga pesada sobre el vehículo a una velocidad constante.

**Módulo de control del tren de fuerza (PCM por sus siglas en inglés)** La computadora de manejo del motor que controla el motor y las funciones de la transmisión.

**Módulo de encendido electrónico** Dispositivo que controla (enciende y apaga) la corriente primaria de encendido de un sistema de encendido electrónico.

**Motor empujador de válvula** Utiliza una leva para la válvula de ingreso y una leva diferente para las válvulas de escape. Cuando el árbol de levas está ubicado al interior del bloque del motor, las válvulas son operadas por empujadores de levas, elevadores o brazos de control.

**Motor radial** Véase Motor tipo Boxeador.

**Motor rotativo** Un motor que opera a cuatro tiempos pero que utiliza un rotor en vez de un ensamblaje de pistón y cigüeñal para lograr los cuatro tiempos incluyendo la admisión, la compresión, la potencia y la descarga.

**Motor tipo boxeador** Un tipo de diseño de motor que es plano y tiene cilindros opuestos. Se llama boxeador porque los pistones de un lado se asemejan a un boxeador durante la operación del motor. También llamado motor radial.

**Motor Wankel** Véase Motor rotativo.

**MSDS** Siglas en inglés para hoja de datos de seguridad física.

**Multímetro digital de corriente alterna y continúa con sujetador** Un tipo de medidor que tiene una pinza que se sujeta al cable para medir la corriente.

**Multiplexación** Un sistema en que se conectan varias computadoras de tal manera que puedan compartir información entre sí utilizando solo un cable.

**Naturalmente aspirado** Se refiere a un motor de combustión interna que no es ni súper ni turbocargado.

**NEDRA** Siglas en inglés para Asociación Nacional de los Arranque de Vehículos Eléctricos.

**NiMH** Hidruro de níquel y metal. Diseño de baterías de alto voltaje que se usan en la mayoría de los vehículos eléctricos híbridos.

**Nivel de disparo** El nivel de voltaje al cual debe llegar una configuración de onda para activar la visualización en la pantalla.

**Nodo** Un módulo y una computadora que forman parte de una red de comunicaciones.

**Nonchecking** Nombre que la empresa General Motors usa para sus sistemas o kit de admisión directa o sistemas TBI que deben mantener un vacío en su interior.

**Número de identificación de vehículo (VIN por sus siglas en inglés).**

**Número de metal moldeado** Una serie de números y/o letras moldeadas en el bloque del motor u otros componentes principales de metal forjado de un vehículo.

**OBD** Siglas en inglés para diagnóstico a bordo.

**OL** Siglas en inglés para circuito abierto.

**Opacidad** El porcentaje de luz que ha sido bloqueada por el humo del escape.

**Operación de circuito abierto** Fase de la operación computarizada del motor en la que la mezcla de aire y combustible se calcula en la ausencia de las señales del sensor de oxígeno. Durante esta fase, los cálculos se basan principalmente en la posición del acelerador, las RPM del motor y la temperatura del refrigerante del motor.

**Orden de encendido** La orden para que la chispa sea distribuida a la bobina de encendido correcta y en el momento preciso.

**Orgánico** Un término que se utiliza para describir algo que alguna vez haya gozado de vida.

**ORVR** Siglas en inglés para sistemas de diagnóstico a bordo y recuperación de vapores.

**OSC** Siglas en inglés para capacidad de almacenamiento de oxígeno.

**Oscilaciones intermedias** También conocidas como el efecto oscilatorio o *ringing* de la bobina cuando se la pulsa.

**Osciloscopio (sonda)** Un medidor que muestra una visualización de los niveles de voltaje en una pantalla.

**OSHA** Siglas en inglés para Administración de Seguridad y Salud Ocupacionales.

**Ozono** (O3) Gas rico en oxígeno formado por la combinación de hidrocarburos (HC) y óxidos de nitrógeno (NOx) en la presencia de la luz del sol. También llamado niebla tóxica (esmog).

**Palabra clave** Un tipo de comunicación en red usada en muchos vehículos de General Motors.

**Paladio** Un catalizador que comienza una reacción química permaneciendo este elemento inalterado por el proceso.

**Parámetro de identificación** La información que se encuentra en el flujo de datos en serie vehicular y que se visualiza en un instrumento de medición electrónico.

**PCV** Siglas en inglés para válvula de control de la presión.

**Pendiente de disparo** Dirección de voltaje que una onda debe tener para comenzar visualización en la pantalla. Una pendiente positiva requiere que el voltaje se aumente mientras cruza el nivel del disparado; una pendiente negativa requiere que el voltaje se disminuya.

**Pernos métricos** Pernos que se fabrican y diseñan según el sistema métrico.

**Petrodiésel** Otro término para el diésel de petróleo, que es el combustible diésel ordinario refinado del crudo de petróleo.

**Petróleo** Otro término para el crudo de petróleo. El significado literal de petróleo es "aceite de piedra".

**PHEV** Siglas en inglés para un vehículo eléctrico híbrido con conexión de clavija o vehículo híbrido-eléctrico que se enchufa.

**Piezoresistividad** Un cambio en la resistencia debido a la fatiga.

**Pila electroquímica** Un conjunto de celdas de combustible individuales apiladas y concatenadas, de principio a fin, en un paquete compacto.

**Platino** Un elemento que actúa como catalizador que comienza una reacción química permaneciendo este elemento inalterado sin ser transformado por el proceso.

**Plomo tetra etílico** El TEL fue utilizado como un aditivo antidetonante en la gasolina. El TEL fue remplazado por aditivos más benignos tales como el etanol.

**Polaridad** La condición positiva o negativa en relación con un polo magnético.

**PPO**   Siglas en inglés para aceite de planta puro.

**Preconvertidor**   Un pequeño convertidor de oxígeno de calentamiento rápido.

**Presión residual o estática**   Previene la traba de vapor y problemas de arranque caliente del vehículo en estos sistemas.

**Probador de chispa**   Un dispositivo que parece una bujía excepto por el hecho de que no tiene electrodos laterales y, más bien, contiene un electrodo central hundido. Este aparato usualmente tiene una pinza cocodrilo o de contacto adherida a su exterior a fin de que el aparato pueda sujetarse firmemente a varilla de puesto a tierra de un motor.

**Procesamiento de datos o información**   Los cambios que una computadora ejecuta sobre las señales de entrada a fin de convertirlas en información útil. Estos procesos usualmente requieren un convertidor de analógico a digital y otros circuitos electrónicos que eliminan la interferencia.

**Proceso de refinación de diésel (FTD por sus siglas en inglés)**   Véase *Fischer-Tropsch*.

**PROM**   Siglas en inglés para memoria de sólo lectura programable.

**Propano**   *Véase* GLP.

**Protocolo SCP**   Un protocolo de red utilizado por *Ford*.

**Prueba de compresión dinámica**   Un tipo de prueba de compresión que se lleva a cabo mientras el motor está encendido al contrario de la mayoría de las pruebas de compresión que se realizan con el motor en arranque.

**Prueba de compresión en húmedo**   Una prueba de compresión que utiliza el aceite para facilitar el sellado alrededor de los aros de los pistones.

**Prueba de craqueo de vacío**   La medición o determinación de la cantidad de vacío del múltiple de admisión durante la desintegración catalítica.

**Prueba de equilibrio de potencia**   Una prueba para determinar si todos los cilindros están contribuyendo la misma cantidad de potencia. Se determina esto acortando la carrera de un cilindro a la vez.

**Prueba de golpecitos fuerte**   Involucra dar golpecitos (no golpes fuertes) en el convertidor catalítico usando una maleta de goma.

**Prueba de I/M 240**   Es la porción del Procedimiento de Evaluación Federal (*FTP* por sus siglas en inglés) utilizado por los fabricantes de vehículos para certificar sus nuevos vehículos. El rótulo "240" representa los 240 segundos de manejo que debe indicar el dinamómetro.

**Prueba de papel**   Sujete un pedazo de papel o una tarjeta de 30 × 50 cms. (un billete de dólar funciona para estos propósitos) a una distancia de 2.5 cms. del tubo de escape, mientras el motor está funcionando en marcha mínima. El pedazo de papel debería oscilar de una manera uniforme. Si el papel tiende a ser atraído hacia el tubo de escape, las válvulas de escape en uno o más cilindros podrían estar quemadas.

**Prueba de pérdida de presión del cilindro**   Una prueba que consiste en inyectar aire bajo presión a los cilindros, uno a la vez. La cantidad y ubicación de cualquier aire que se escapa de los mismos ayuda a un técnico automotriz determinar el estado en que se encuentra el motor.

**Prueba de vacío**   Una prueba que consiste en probar el motor para verificar si existe un vacío al intentar arrancar el vehículo, vacío en relación a la marcha mínima y vacío cuando se alcanzan 2,500 rpm.

**Prueba modo de simulación de aceleración 25/25**   Prueba de esmog mediante la cual se coloca 25% de carga sobre un vehículo que marcha a una velocidad constante de 25 millas por hora. Esta carga representa el 25% de los caballos de fuerza que se requieren para simular un ratio de aceleración FTP de 3.3 millas por hora por segundo.

**Prueba modo de simulación de aceleración 50/15**   Prueba de esmog mediante la cual se coloca 50% de carga sobre un vehículo que marcha a una velocidad constante de 15 millas por hora. Esta carga representa el 50% de los caballos de fuerza que se requieren para simular un ratio de aceleración FTP de 3.3 millas por hora por segundo.

**Prueba operativa de compresión**   Una prueba que puede indicar al mecánico o técnico de servicio automotriz el nivel de compresión relativa de todos los cilindros.

**Pulgadas de mercurio**   Unidad de medida utilizada para medir un vacío.

**Punto de inflamabilidad**   Es la temperatura en la que los vapores de la superficie del combustible pueden encenderse si están expuestos a la llama.

**Punto de nube (punto de enturbiamiento)**   La temperatura en que la cera que se encuentra en la mayoría de los combustibles de tipo diésel tiende a formar cristales que enturbian el filtro de combustible.

**Punto muerto superior**   El punto más elevado del avance o recorrido de un pistón en el cilindro de un motor de combustión interna.

**PWM**   Siglas en inglés para modulación del ancho de pulso.

**R&R**   Siglas en inglés para retirar y reemplazar.

**Racionalidad**   Se refiere a la comparación del módulo de control del tren de fuerza entre valores de entrada.

**RAM**   Siglas en inglés para memoria de acceso aleatorio.

**RAM de memoria volátil**   La cualidad de una memoria electrónica que no se pierde cuando se corta el flujo de energía a la computadora. Véase también *ROM*.

**Rango**   La distancia que un vehículo puede recorrer con una carga completa o tanque lleno sin recargar o reabastecerse de combustible. El rango se mide en millas o kilómetros.

**Ranura de soldadura de pinza**   Una sección en la parte inferior del vehículo donde dos paneles del cuerpo del automóvil se juntan y se enroscan para posteriormente soldarse.

**Raster**   Malla uniforme de celdas u otros objetos apilados unos sobre otros sobre en un área o perímetro determinado.

**Ratio de Compresión (RC)**   El ratio del volumen del motor de cilindro con el pistón en punto muerto inferior (BDC) al volumen en punto muerto superior (TDC).

**Ratio estequiométrico**   El ratio de mezcla o nivel de mezclado en el cual la totalidad del combustible se combina con la totalidad del oxígeno disponible en el aire y se quema por completo.

**RCRA**   Siglas en inglés para Ley de Conservación y Recuperación de Recursos Naturales.

**Reactancia inductiva**   Una corriente opuesta que se genera por un conductor de electricidad cuando existe una carga de corriente que fluye por dicho conductor de electricidad.

**Recocido**   Tratamiento térmico que elimina las superficies duras de una fundición metálica con la finalidad de reducir las potenciales fisuras que se producen en el metal con los cambios de temperatura.

**Red**   Un sistema de comunicaciones utilizado para conectar múltiples computadoras o módulos entre sí.

**Regeneración**   El proceso de tomar la energía cinética de un vehículo en movimiento para convertirla en energía eléctrica y almacenarla en una batería.

**Relación aire/combustible**   La relación entre aire y combustible en una entrada de combustible determinada por el peso.

**Reluctor**   Anillo dentado que rota y se usa para vigilar la velocidad o la posición de un componente que rota.

**Reposo de leva** Medición en grados, de la rotación de la leva o flecha del distribuidor en el cual los puntos descritos por el punto trazador están cerrados.

**Resistencia** La calificación de fuerza de una tuerca.

**Resistencia extensible** El estrés máximo usado bajo tensión (fuerza longitudinal) sin causar rotura.

**Resistor terminal** Un resistor colocado en el extremo de un circuito de transmisión de datos en serie de alta velocidad a fin de reducir la interferencia electromagnética.

**Resolución del medidor** Las especificaciones de un medidor que indican a qué grado de precisión puede llegar la detección y visualización de una medida por parte de un medidor.

**Resonador Helmholtz** Un dispositivo usado en el ducto de entrada, entre el filtro de aire y la carcasa de la admisión, para reducir el ruido provocado por el ingreso de aire durante la aceleración del motor.

*RMS* Siglas en inglés para raíz cuadrada promedio al cuadrado. Un método para calcular la aspereza o rugosidad de una superficie utilizando la raíz cuadrada del promedio de las lecturas cuadradas.

**Rodio** Un elemento que actúa como catalizador que comienza una reacción química sin ser consumido o alterado en el proceso.

*ROM* Siglas en inglés para memoria de sólo lectura.

*SAE* Siglas en inglés para la Sociedad de Ingenieros Automotrices.

**Saturación** El punto en que el máximo nivel de fuerza de un campo magnético es alcanzado.

**Selector de modo de disparo exterior** Un selector de modo de disparo exterior se usa en un osciloscopio activando la señal de un circuito externo para iniciar o activar la forma de la onda.

**Sensor BARO** Un sensor utilizado para medir la presión barométrica.

**Sensor *BMAP*** Un sensor que contiene circuitos individuales para medir la presión de admisión así como la presión barométrica. Este dispositivo no sólo permite a la computadora realizar los ajustes necesarios en relación a la presión atmosférica del tiempo, sino que también constituye el sensor principal a la hora de determinar la altura.

**Sensor de combustible variable** *Véase* Sensor de composición del combustible.

**Sensor de compensación del combustible** Un sensor utilizado en vehículos *flex-fuel* que proporciona información del contenido de etanol al módulo de control del tren de fuerza y la temperatura del combustible a medida que va pasando a través del sistema de distribución del combustible.

**Sensor de flujo de sangrado** Una válvula que monitorea el flujo correcto de sangrado.

**Sensor de golpeteo** Sensor que puede detectar el golpeteo de chispa del motor.

**Sensor de la temperatura del cuerpo de la mariposa (*TBT* por sus siglas en inglés) o de la carcasa de admisión** Un sensor de temperatura montado sobre la carcasa de admisión que mide la temperatura del aire que ingresa al motor.

**Sensor de la válvula *EGR*** Un potenciómetro lineal en la parte superior del vástago de la válvula *EGR* que indica la posición de la válvula en la computadora.

**Sensor de oxígeno de banda ancha** Un diseño de sensor de oxígeno capaz de detectar ratios actuales y reales de aire-combustible, a diferencia de los sensores de de oxígeno convencionales que solamente cambian de voltaje cuando el ratio estequiométrico ha sido alcanzado.

**Sensor de oxígeno** Un sensor localizado en el sistema de escape capaz de detectar el contenido de oxígeno del escape.

**Sensor de posicionamiento de la mariposa del embrague** El sensor que proporciona información de datos sobre la posición de la placa de la mariposa de embrague del motor de combustión interna.

**Sensor de reluctancia variable** Un tipo de sensor magnético.

**Sensor de temperatura de cabezal de cilindro (*CHT* por sus siglas en inglés)** Un sensor de temperatura montado sobre el cabezal de cilindro y utilizado por el módulo de control del tren de fuerza para determinar la provisión del combustible.

**Sensor de temperatura del combustible del motor (sensor *EFT* por sus sigla en inglés)** Un sensor de la temperatura ubicado en el riel de inyectores de combustible que mide la temperatura del combustible que ingresa al interior del motor.

**Sensor de temperatura del fluido de la transmisión (sensor *TFT* por sus siglas en inglés)** Un sensor ubicado al interior de un eje transversal o de la transmisión que mide la temperatura del fluido de la transmisión.

**Sensor del Flujo de la Masa de Aire** Mide la cantidad y la densidad de aire que fluye al motor, lo cual incide en un control eficiente del motor.

**Sensor detector de presión absoluta en la aspiración** Detecta la carga del motor a través de la medición de la presión al interior del múltiple de admisión.

**Sensor *EGR* de Retroalimentación de Presión Delta o Sensor *DPFE*** Este sensor mide la presión diferencial entre dos lados de un orificio colocado justo debajo del lado de escape de la válvula EGR.

**Sensor lineal de ratio de aire combustible** *Véase* Sensor de ratio de mezcla pobre de aire combustible.

**Sensor magnético resistente** Un sensor similar al sensor magnético pero que, a diferencia de aquél, no produce en sí mismo una señal de voltaje análoga sino, más bien, son los componentes electrónicos en su interior que generan una señal de salida o una señal de encendido/apagado.

**Sensor magnético** Sensor que consiste de un imán permanente y una bobina. Las ranuras del cigüeñal del motor (o árbol de levas) crean un campo de fuerza magnética a lo largo de la bobina. Cuando una sección metálica se acerca al sensor, el campo magnético se expande porque el metal es un mejor conductor de las líneas de fuerza magnéticas que el aire.

**Sensor PFE** Sensor de retroalimentación de presión EGR.

**Sensores ópticos** Utilizan la luz de un LED y de un fototransistor para mandar señales a la computadora.

**Señales de entrada** Información que los sensores proporcionan al controlador electrónico. Los sensores y los interruptores proporcionan las señales de entrada.

**Separador agua-combustible** Un dispositivo que separa el agua y el combustible en un motor a diesel.

**Sincronización de base** El tiempo de encendido antes de que la computadora sincronice el avance de ignición.

**Sincronización electrónica de chispa** El control del avance de la sincronización de chispa que se lleva a cabo por medio de la computadora.

*SIP* Siglas en inglés para Plan de Implementación Estatal.

**Sistema binario** Un sistema de computadora que usa una serie compuesta de ceros y unos para representar la información.

**Sistema de** *common-rail*, o conducto común Sistema de inyección de combustible mediante el cual el combustible diésel se aplica a los inyectores bajo una altísima presión de más de 20.000 PSI (138.000 kPa) los cuales se abren por medio de un solenoide controlado por la computadora vehicular. Debido a que los inyectores son controlados electrónicamente, el proceso de combustión interna puede ser controlado con gran precisión a fin de proveer la máxima eficiencia motriz por parte del motor y al mismo tiempo contar con los niveles de emisión gases y ruido de escape más bajos posibles.

**Sistema de encendido de bobina en bujía**  Un sistema de encendido sin distribuidor (estático) en el cual cada bobina de encendido está integrada con un bobinado de encendido.

**Sistema de encendido de sensor de compresión**  Sistema de encendido que no requiere un sensor de árbol de levas para determinar el número de cilindros.

**Sistema de encendido electrónico**  Es el término general para describir cualquiera de los múltiples tipos de sistema de ignición o encendido que utilizan componentes electrónicos, no mecánicos tales como puntos de encendido o de contacto.

**Sistema de escape restringido**  Si el sistema de escape es restrictivo o restringido, el motor tendrá baja potencia pero su funcionamiento será muy suave.

**Sistema de inyección secuencial de combustible**  Un sistema de inyección de combustible mediante el cual, con la orden de disparo se pulsan los inyectores secuencialmente, en forma individual.

**Sistema electrónico de combustible sin retorno**  Un sistema de provisión de combustible que no devuelve el combustible al tanque.

**Sistema mecánico de combustible sin retorno**  Un diseño de sistema de provisión de combustible que no devuelve el combustible al tanque, que utiliza un regulador de presión mecánico localizado en el tanque de combustible.

**Sistema para la recirculación de los gases de escape**  (*EGR* por sus siglas en inglés) Un dispositivo de reducción de emisiones vehiculares utilizado para reducir la formación de NOx (óxidos de nitrógeno).

**Sistemas de encendido estático de "chispa perdida"**  Un sistema de encendido introducido al mercado a mediados de los años ochenta que utiliza una computadora vehicular para disparar las bobinas de ignición.

**Sobrepresión**  Un incremento de la presión del aire por encima de la atmosférica. Se mide en libras por pulgada cuadrada (*PSI*).

**Solvente**  Líquido, usualmente incoloro, que se utiliza para quitar el aceite y la grasa.

**Sonda Lambda**  Sensor de oxígeno.

**Sonda Lógica**  Un tipo de medidor que puede detectar tanto la presencia de energía eléctrica o su ausencia en base a un puesto a tierra. La mayoría de los medidores de corriente pueden detectar el voltaje pero algunos no pueden detectar la presencia de un puesto a tierra sin la necesidad de llevar a cabo pruebas adicionales.

**Spark Output**  El término utilizado por *Ford* para describir la señal de salida del módulo de control del tren de fuerza al sistema de ignición que controla el tiempo de encendido del motor de acuerdo a la terminología utilizada por el OBD II.

**SST**  Siglas en inglés para herramientas de servicios especiales.

**Supercargador**  Un compresor de gas que inyecta más mezcla de aire y combustible al cilindro para generar mayor potencia en el motor.

**SWCAN**  Siglas en inglés de alambre sencillo de protocolo de comunicaciones CAN o CAN bus (siglas en inglés para *controller area network*).

**Syn gas**  Gas sintético creado como resultado de una reacción química entre el vapor y el carbón. El gas sintético está principalmente compuesto de hidrogeno y monóxido de carbono y se utiliza para crear metanol. El Syn gas también es conocido como gas artificial.

**Tabique deflector**  Una placa o pantalla utilizada para dirigir el flujo de un líquido o de un gas.

**Tamaño de casquillo**  El tamaño de los casquillos medido en fracciones de pulgada cuadrada.

**Tapa del distribuidor**  Proporciona un espacio adicional entre las conexiones de las bobina de encendido para evitar el fuego cruzado.

**TBI**  Siglas en inglés para inyección de cuerpo de la mariposa/ válvula de admisión.

**Tecnología de doble capa**  Un tipo de tecnología utilizada para fabricar ultracapacitadores, que consiste en el uso de dos electrodos de carbono separados por una membrana.

**Tecnología gas a líquido o *GTL* por sus siglas en inglés**  Un proceso de refinación mediante el cual el gas natural se liquifica.

**Tensión de polarización negativo de grilla**  Una señal de voltaje débil que se aplica a un sensor de oxígeno por el módulo de control del tren de fuerza. Esta señal de voltaje débil es utilizada por el módulo de control del tren de fuerza para detectar el momento en el cual el sensor de oxígeno ha generado un cambio de voltaje y para el diagnóstico del circuito del sensor de oxígeno.

**Termofraccionación catalítica de las cadenas hidrocarburíferas**  La desintegración de cadenas hidrocarburíferas utilizando el calor en presencia de un catalizador.

**Tetrahidrofurano (MeTHF)**  Un componente de los combustibles alternativos de serie P.

**TID**  Siglas en inglés para identificación de trabajo.

**Tiempo base/unidad de tiempo**  La cantidad fija de tiempo por división cuando se regula un osciloscopio.

**Tiempo de carga del bobinado**  El tiempo de carga de una bobina medido desde el punto de encendido del transistor hasta el punto de apagado del transistor.

**Tiempo de encendido**  Punto exacto del encendido con relación a la posición de émbolo.

**Tiempo de quemado Kv**  Voltaje de la línea de chispa.

**Tornillo de tope**  Un perno que se enrosca en una fundición.

**Traba de vapor**  Combustible vaporizado, usualmente en las líneas de combustible, que previene o aplaza la provisión del combustible a los cilindros.

**Transformador con tomas**  *Véase* Bobina con tomas.

**Transistor**  Dispositivo semiconductor que puede funcionar como un relé o un amplificador.

**Transportador eléctrico**  Cualquier medio que es utilizado para almacenar o transportar energía. Por ejemplo, el hidrógeno es un transportador de energía porque la energía debe ser utilizada para generar gas hidrógeno el cual es usado como combustible.

**Tren de pulso**  Voltaje de corriente directa que se conecta y se desconecta en una serie de pulsos.

**TSB**  Siglas en inglés de Boletín de Servicio Técnico.

**Turbocargador**  Un sobrecargador que toma su fuerza del escape.

**TWC**  Siglas en inglés de convertidor de convertidor catalítico de tres vías.

**UART**  Siglas en inglés de Receptor-Transmisor Asíncrono Universal. Un tipo de transmisión de datos en serie.

**UBP**  Siglas en inglés de protocolo basado en UART.

**UCG**  Gasificación subterránea de carbón.

**Ultra capacitador**  Una tecnología de capacitador especializado con capacidad de almacenamiento aumentada para un volumen dado.

**UNF**  Siglas en inglés de estándar de lámina fina (delgada) del tornillo.

**Unidad térmica británica (*British Thermal Unit* o *BTU*)**   Una unidad de medida de calor.

**Unión universal**   Una unión o junta en un eje de propulsión o transmisión que permite que se transmita fuerza de torsión en un ángulo.

**Vacío**   Cualquier presión menor a la presión atmosférica (14.7 PSI).

***VAF***   Siglas en inglés de circulación de aire por efecto de aspas o paletas.

**Válvula de alivio**   Una válvula en cualquier componente hidráulico que se abre para liberar la presión excesiva cuando la presión del fluido está demasiado alta. En un sistema con dirección asistida se puede usar una válvula de alivio en la bomba y/o en el mecanismo de dirección.

**Válvula de cierre ajustable**   Tiene un diseño de espiral ajustable que mantiene la válvula cerrada hasta que se produzca una repentina liberación de la mariposa.

**Válvula de desvío**   Permite que el aire que ingresa por la toma de aire fluya directamente al múltiple de admisión sin necesidad de pasar por el súpercompresor.

**Válvula de desvío de compresión**   Este tipo de válvula de escape canaliza el aire presurizado a la toma de aire del turbocargador para su reutilización y opera silenciosamente.

**Válvula de puerto de ventilación a presión**   Una válvula ubicada en el tanque de combustible para prevenir una sobrepresión debido a la expansión térmica del combustible.

**Válvula de retención residual**   Una válvula que se encuentra en el extremo de salida del cilindro maestro y cuya función consiste en mantener una pequeña presión estática y constante únicamente en los frenos de tambor del sistema hidráulico.

**Válvula electrónica de control de aire**   Válvula de control de la marcha mínima.

**Varilla conector**   Una varilla que conecta el cigüeñal de un motor de vehículo a un pistón.

***VECI***   Siglas en inglés para información de control de emisiones de vehículos. Esta etiqueta o calcomanía se encuentra debajo del capó de todos los vehículos e incluye aquella información relativa al control de emisiones importante para el mecánico o técnico automotriz.

**Vehículo de combustible flexible virtual**   Un vehículo de combustible flexible virtual puede operar con gasolina pura, con combustible E-10, combustible E85 o cualquier combinación de aquellos combustibles.

**Vehículos bicombustibles o vehículos *flex***   Los vehículos que son capaces de moverse con gasolina pura o con una mezcla de gasolina y etanol.

**Velocidad de línea en baudios**   La velocidad a la que se transmiten bits de información en un flujo de datos en serie. Se mide en bits por segundo (bps).

**VGN**   Vehículo a gas natural.

***VOC***   Siglas en inglés de compuesto orgánico volátil.

**Volatilidad**   La medida de la tendencia de un líquido para pasar al estado gaseoso. La volatilidad se mide usando el método Reid de presión de vapor y su medida el RVP.

**Voltaje *Flyback***   La fuerza o resistencia inductiva creada cuando la señal primaria colapsa y que es utilizado por el módulo de control del tren de fuerza para monitorear el desempeño del encendido secundario.

***Washcoat***   Un material poroso de aluminio.

***Wastegate***   Una válvula que tiene un diseño similar al de una puerta que puede abrirse y cerrarse de la misma manera. El wastegate es una válvula de desvío que se encuentra en la admisión de escape de la turbina. Permite que todo el escape ingrese a la turbina, en su defecto, puede dirigir parte del escape al sistema de escape saltando la turbina.

***WHMIS***   Siglas en inglés para sistema de información sobre materiales peligrosos en el lugar de trabajo.

# INDEX

## A

Aboveground storage tanks (AGST), 38
Absolute pressure, 197
Acceleration simulation mode (ASM), 309
Accelerator pedal position (APP) sensor, 68–69, 277
  cable-operated system, 278
  calibration steps, 280
  location, 278
  two sensors, 278
  voltage signals shown, 278
AC coupling, 74
Accumulator, 247
AC generator, cutaway view, 96
AC ripple current test procedure, 98
AC ripple voltage check
  principles, 97
  testing procedure, 97–98
Activated charcoal granules, 317
Acura, battery replacement, 89
AC voltage output, 369
AC volts (ACV), ripple voltage, 74
Adapter for testing backpressure, 347
Additives, gasoline, 87–88
  ethanol, 88
  octane improver, 87
  oxygenated, 88
Adjustable wrenches, 8
Adsorption, 318
AF (air-fuel) sensor, 229
AFR (air-fuel ratio) sensor, 229
Aftermarket parts
  air filters, 121
  catalytic converter, dimensions, 349
  catalytic converter, 348, 349
    failure of, 379
    installation, 348
Aftermarket scan tools, 384
  retrieving global OBD II, 47
After Top Dead Center (ATDC), 375
AFVs (alternative-fuel vehicles), 97–100
AGST (aboveground storage tanks), 38
Ah (Ampere-hour), 81
AIR (air-injection reaction) system, 339
Airbag, byteflight BUS system, 173
Airbag disposal, 42
Airbag lamp, resetting, 87
Air charge cooler, 69, 126
  cooling compressed air, 70
  cutaway view, 127
  superchargers, 126
AIR check valve, back pressure testing, 147
Air-conditioning compressor operation, 191, 233
Air-conditioning condensate, color or leak, 137
Air-conditioning systems, service, 404
Air distribution manifolds and nozzles, 339
Air filter restriction indicators, 114
  GM, 114
Air filters
  aftermarket, 121
  clogged, 131
  construction, 113
  debris deposited, 115
  debris from squirrels, 381
  dust trapped, 114
  elements, 113
  housing location, 114
  inspection, 115
  remotely mounted, 114
  replacement, 114
Air filter service, 404
Airflow requirements, 123
  factors for calculating, 123
Airflow sensors, 205
  false air, 209
  PCM uses, 207–208
  vane airflow (VAF) sensor, 205

Air-fuel mixture, MAP sensor signals, 200–201
Air-fuel ratios, 84–85
  diesel engines, 61–62
  visualizing, 85
Air hose safety, 27
Air-injection reaction (AIR) system, 339
Air intake ducts, dog food in, 314
Air intake filtration
  air filter elements, 113
  air filter restriction indicator, 114
  filter replacement, 114
  need for, 113
  remotely mounted air filters and ducts, 114
Air operated tools, 19–21
AIR pump, 339
  belt-driven, 340
  diagnosis, 340–341
  electric motor-driven, 340
  typical belt-driven, 339
Air ratchets, 20
Air reference chamber, 232
Air supply pumps, in fuel-cell vehicles, 414
Air vane sensors, fuel shutoff in case of accident, 240
AKI (antiknock index), 86
ALCL (assembly line communications link), 386
Alcohol-based gasoline additives, 87, 88
  engine operation impact, 90
  higher than 10%, 88
  phase separation, 88
  testing for alcohol content, 90, 93
ALDI (assembly line diagnostic link), 386
Alternative fuels
  comparison chart, 104
  safety procedures, 106
Alternative-fuel vehicles (AFVs), 97–100
Alternator
  AC ripple voltage check, 97–98
  battery drain, 89
  battery role, 80
  carbon pile test, 101
  construction, 95
  housing, 95
  stator winding overheating, 81
  troubleshooting low or no output, 98
  two-minute repair, 100
Alternator output test, carbon pile test, 101
Altitude
  barometric pressure, inverse relation, 201
  horsepower and, 59
  MAP sensor vacuum readings, 200
  MAP sensor voltage chart, 201
  MAP sensor voltage effects, 200
  mountainous driving, 200
  speed-density-type fuel injection, 200
Ambient air electrode, 231
Ambient side electrode, 231
American National Standards Institute (ANSI), 397
American Society for Testing and Materials (ASTM), 83, 397
  diesel fuel grades, 108
  safety gloves, 397
Ampere-hour (Ah), 81
Amplified hash, 222–223
Analog MAF sensor
  digital MAF sensor compared, 206
  grams per second/voltage chart, 208
Analog scopes, 72
  glitches missed, 77–78
Aneroid bellows, 196
Anhydrous ethanol, 96
Anode, 412
ANSI (American National Standards Institute), 397

Antifreeze
  color of leak, 137
  coolant disposal, 40
Antifreeze (ethylene glycol) contamination, 226
Antifreeze-water mixture, 236
Antiknock index (AKI), 86
API gravity, 109
  comparison chart, 110
  levels, 81
APP (accelerator pedal position) sensor, 68–69
Aromatic hydrocarbons, 87
Asbestos, 36–37
Asbestosis, 37
ASD (automatic shutdown), 245
Ash loading, 73
Asian vehicles, OBD-II data link connector, 176
ASM (acceleration simulation mode), 309
ASM 25/25 test, 309
ASM 50/15 test, 309
ASM test, 309
Asphyxiation, 101
Assembly line communications link (ALCL), 386
Assembly line diagnostic link (ALDI), 386
ASTM (American Society for Testing and Materials), 83
  founding, 397
  grades of diesel fuel, 108
  safety gloves, 397
ATDC (After Top Dead Center), 375
AT-PZEV (advanced technology partial zero-emission vehicle), 307
Audi, direct fuel injection, 270
Audio system. See Radio
AutoEnginuity scan tools, 384
Automatic shutdown (ASD), 245
Automatic transmission fluid (ATF)
  color of leak, 137
  vacuum gauge readings, 146
Automatic transmission shift points, 191, 233
Auxiliary battery
  locations of, 399, 400, 405
  testing and service, 405
Auxiliary air bypass, 266
Aviation snips, 15

## B

B20 biodiesel blend, 111
Back pressure, 147
  testing with pressure gauge, 147
  testing with vacuum gauge, 147
Back pressure adaptor, how to make, 147
Back pressure tool, construction, 347
Baffle, 238
BARO (barometric pressure) sensor, 201
  DTCs, 203
  pulse width, 259
Barometric manifold absolute pressure (BMAP) sensor, 201
  pulse width, 259
Barometric pressure, altitude, inverse relation, 201
Barometric pressure (BARO) sensor, 201, 203, 259
Base brakes, service, 405
Batteries
  battery ratings, 80–81
  battery voltage test, 82–83
  corrosion
    causes, 82
    through insulation, 86
    warning signs, 85
  cranking circuit, 89–90
  explosions, causes, 81
  jump starting safety, 27
  low voltage effects, 81
  purpose and function, 80
  service, 86

service safety, 81
  storage, 81
  visual inspection, 81–82
  weak or discharged, 81
    symptoms, 85
Battery cables
  corrosion on, 85
    through insulation, 86
  when to replace, 95
Battery charger
  connecting, safe method, 86
  set up, 86
Battery charging, 85–86
  charging time, 86
  fast-charging impact, 86
Battery Council International (BCI), 41
Battery discharging, brake pedal trick, 395
Battery disconnect, 395
Battery electrical drain test, 86–88
  battery drain and reserve capacity, 87
  finding source of drain, 89
  memory saver, 87
  procedure, 88–89
  reset all memory functions, 89
  what to do if it still exists, 89
Battery load testing, 83–84
  electronic battery tester, 84
  typical hookup, 84
Battery module switch, 30
Battery ratings
  Ampere-hour (Ah), 81
  cold-cranking amperes, 80
  cranking amperes (CA), 81
  marine cranking amperes (MCA), 81
  reserve capacity, 81
Battery terminals, corrosion, 90
Battery testing
  electrical drain test, 86–88
  ignition off draw (IOD) test, 86–87
  parasitic load test, 87
  troubleshooting, 89
Battery voltage
  dead rat smell test, 96
  scope display, 78
  scope usage, 77–78
  state of charge (chart), 83
Battery voltage correction factor, 81
  definition, 266
Battery voltage measurements, simple tester for, 97
Battery voltage tests, 82–83
  one-minute test, 84
  recommendations, 381
BCI (Battery Council International), 41
BDC (bottom dead center), 49
Beam-type torque wrenches, 10
Bear Automotive starting and charging tester, 84
Belt-driven air pumps, 339, 340
  operation shown, 340
Bench grinders, 21–22
Bias voltage, 215
  CCD BUS, 169, 170
Bin numbers
  air pollution score, 307
  Tier 2 emission limits, 307
Biodiesel, 110–111
  blends, 111
  definition, 110
  features of, 111
  vegetable oil compared, 111
Biomass, 101
  cellulosic biomass, 96
Black exhaust smoke, 75
  causes, 135
  IAT sensor defective, 185
Block, 46
Blowby, 335
Blowby gases, crankcase vent hose, 136
Blow-off valve (BOV), 130
  flow diagnosis, 131

Blue exhaust smoke, 75
  oil leaks, 135
BMAP (barometric manifold absolute
    pressure) sensor, 201
BMW, direct fuel injection, 270
BNC connector, 77
Bolts, 4–5
  simple engine testing, 140
Boost, 123
  compression ratios, 124–125
  result of restriction, 129
Bores, 54
Borrowing tools, 18
Bosch, modes of operation, 272–273
Bosch L-Jetronic, vane airflow
    sensor, 205
Bosch-Siemens-Temic (BST) BUS
    communication, 172
Bottom dead center (BDC), 49
BOV (blow-off valve), 130
  flow diagnosis, 131
Box-end wrenches, 8
Boxer engine design, 49
Brake, braking system service, 405
Brake dust, 37
Brake fluid, color of leak, 137
Brake pedal trick, 395
Brand names, tools, 15
Brazil, 95, 104
Breaker bars, 9
Breakout box (BOB)
  European vehicles, 173
  testing BUS, 173
  TP sensor testing, 234
British thermal unit (BTU), 84
Broadband oxygen sensor, 229
BST (Bosch-Siemens-Temic) BUS
    communication, 172
BTU (British thermal unit), 84
Bump caps, 21
Burn kV, 135
BUS, 165
BUS communication, 165
  differential type, 162
  General Motors, 176
  multiplexing, 162–163
  parallel type, 162
  serial data type, 162
  typical system schematics, 166
Butane-powered soldering irons, 18
"BXX" bioethanol blends, 111
Bypass (tan/black) wire, 116
Bypass ignition control, 116
Bypass mode, 174
Bypass regulator for fuel line
    pressure, 263
Bypass valves, 126
  bypass actuator shown, 126
Byteflight BUS communication, 173

C
CA (cranking amperes), 81
CAA (Clean Air Act), 36
Calibration codes, 2
California Air Resources Board
    (CARB), 153
  OBD-II objectives, 153–154
California emission standards, 306
Cam-in-block design, 51
Campaigns, 4
Cam retard value, 132
Camshaft overlap, 124
Camshaft position (CMP) sensor
  CKP sensor relationship, 131
  distributor indexing, 131–132
  worn distributor drive gear, 132
Camshafts, valve and camshaft
    number and location, 51
CAN (controller area network), 165
  background, 170
  BUS connected to accessories and
    systems, 171
  Class A, B, and C, 170–171
  diagnostic systems, P0440, 324
  differential module
    communication, 171
  features, 170
  CAN A, 170–171
  CAN B, 170–171
  CAN C, 170–171

CANDi (CAN diagnostic interface)
    module, 168
  green LED flashing, 168
CAN H circuit, 175
Canister purge (CANP) valve/
    solenoid, 320
Canister purge system pressure test, 323
Canister vent valve, 320
CAN L circuit, 175
Capacity test, 83
Capless system, 318
Cap screws, 4, 5
CARB (California Air Resources
    Board), 153
Carbon balls in EGR valves, 332
Carbon cleaning, 275
Carbon dioxide ($CO_2$)
  exhaust analysis, 311
  as measure of efficiency, 313
  measuring, 313
Carbon dioxide ($CO_2$) fire
    extinguishers, 27–28
Carbon fouling, 128, 373
  shown, 129, 374
Carbon issues, 275
Carbon knock, simple engine testing, 140
Carbon monoxide (CO)
  CO as meaning "clogged oxygen", 313
  CO too high, 312–313
  dizzy feeling or headache, 314
  dog food in air intake ducts, 314
  exhaust analysis, 311
  high, cause and correction, 315
  same as O2 reading, 313
Carbon pile test, 101
Casting numbers, 2–3
Catalyst efficiency test, GM, 51
Catalysts, 343
Catalytic converter, 343
  acceptable exhaust emissions, 312
  clogged, 146
  construction, 343
  converter-damaging conditions, 346
  defective, 346, 349
  diagnosis, 346–348
  light-off temperature, 344
  location, 343
  monolithic substrate shown, 344
  OBD-II catalytic converter
    performance, 345–346
  operation, 344, 350–351
  oxygen sensor signals, 212–213
  replacement, 348, 348–349
    guidelines, 348–349
  usage, 344–345
Catalytic converter diagnosis
  defective, 346, 349
  DTCs, 349
  efficiency tests, 348
  tap test, 346
  testing backpressure
    with pressure gauge, 346–347
    with vacuum gauge, 347–348
  testing for temperature rise, 348
Catalytic converter monitor, 216
Catalytic cracking, 82
Cathode, 412
Cathode ray tube (CRT) oscilloscope, 72
CAT III-rated digital multimeter, 398
CAT ratings for high voltage, 398
Cavalier convertible story, 201
CBV (compressor bypass valve), 130
CCA (cold-cranking amperes), 80
CCD multiplex networks
  "collision", meaning of term, 169
  plus and minus signals, 169
CCM (comprehensive component
    monitor), 154
Cellulose ethanol, 96
Cellulosic biomass, 96
Central port fuel injection, 265
  diagram, 265
  factory replacement unit, 266
Centrifugal supercharger, 126
Ceramic capacitor diaphragm, 196
Cerium, 344
  in aftermarket catalytic converter, 348
Cetane number, 108
  for E-diesel, 112
CFR (Code of Federal Regulations), 35
Channel Locks, 13

Charcoal canister, 17, 92
  location, 318
Charge density, 123
Charge indicator light, checking
    voltage, 96
Charging battery, 85–86
Charging circuit, 80
  generator output test, 100–101
  voltage drop test voltmeter hookup, 93
Charging methods (EV), 421
  conductive, 421
  inductive, 421
Charging rise time, 119
Charging stations, 421
Charging system
  voltage drop testing, 99–100
  voltage specifications, 96
  voltage test procedure, 96
Chassis, floating ground for, 400
Cheater bars, 11
Check engine light
  shown, 153
  visual inspection, 296
Check gas cap indication lamp, 322
Check valves, 240, 339
  failure, 339
  location, 339
Chemical poisoning, 39
Chemical tester, head gaskets
    diagnosis, 147
Chevrolet Blazer, EVRV
    replacement, 332
Chevrolet Cobalt, no-start story, 176
Chevrolet Corvette
  catalytic converter location, 343
  SAI pump, 340
Chevrolet Equinox, schematic with
    GMLAN BUS, 177
Chevrolet four-cylinder, start/stall/
    start/stall problem, 101
Chevrolet HHR, hard-to-start, 123
Chevrolet pickup, two-minute
    alternator repair, 100
Chevrolet pickup story, 214
Chevrolet Silverado, 31
Chevrolet V-6, dual nozzle TBI unit, 267
Chevrolet V-6 pickup, cam retard
    value, 132
Chevrolet V-8
  dual turbocharger system, 131
  no start condition, 122
Chisels, 16
Chrysler
  5-volt reference of oxygen sensor, 217
  battery or system voltage scan
    tool, 83
  bias voltage, 169, 170
  ceramic disc MAP sensor, 199
  combined BARO and IAT sensor
    (older models), 202
  communication protocols, 169–170
  distributor indexing, 132
  ECT sensor without pull-up
    resistor, 182
  ECT sensor with pull-up resistor, 182
  ECT sensor with pull-up resistor
    switched by PCM, 182
  electric fuel pumps, 245–246
  electronic conductance tester, 84
  ETC warning lamp, 282
  flash code retrieval, 388
  Flex Fuel vehicles, 99
  how to read VIN, 100
  ignition coil circuit design, 132
  injector resistance table, 291
  leak detection pump (LDP), 321
  MAP sensor chart, 199
  OBD-II data link connector, 170
  pressure-type Karman Vortex
    sensor, 207
  scan tools, 46, 384
  SCI (serial communications
    interface), 169
  SCI and CCD module
    communication, 169–170
  stepped ECT circuits, 179
  task manager, 154
  transaxle sensor temperature to
    resistance, 186
  transmission fluid temperature
    sensor, 187

Chrysler Collision Communication
    (CCD), 169
Chrysler Hemi V-8, 113, 364
CHT (cylinder head temperature)
    sensor, 187
CID (component identification), 47, 160
CIP (constant differential injector
    pressure), 263
Clacking noises, 138, 139
Class 2 communications, 165
  diagnosis circuit check, 173–174
  no-start story, 176
Clatter, possible causes, 139
Clean Air Act (CAA, 1990), 36, 154
Clean Air Act Amendments (CAAA), 306
  exhaust analysis testing, 308
Cleaning machine, fuel-injection
    service, 298
Clear flood mode, 191, 233
Clicker-type torque wrenches, 10
Clicking noises, 139
Clogged oxygen, 313
Clogged-end wrenches, 8
Closed-loop operation, 214
  wide-band oxygen sensor, 230
Cloud point of diesel fuel, 108
Clunking noise, possible causes, 139
CNG (compressed natural gas), 102–103
$CO_2$ (carbon dioxide) fire
    extinguishers, 27–28
Coal to liquid (CTL) fuel, 105–106
Coast-down stall, ETC performance
    issues, 283
Code of Federal Regulations (CFR), 35
Coil-on-plug (COP) ignition, 355
  adjusting ignition timing, 130, 375
  advantages, 112, 363
  ion-sensing ignition, 114, 365
  overhead camshaft engine, 113
  scope-testing, 137–138
  system, 104
  terminology, 111, 363
  types of systems, 112–114, 363–365
  typical system, 113, 364
Coil-on-plug (COP) ignition coils, 107, 357
Coil-over-plug-type ignition systems,
    113–114, 364–365
Coil primary wiring, tachometer trick,
    109, 358
Coked oil, 128
Cold chisels, 16
Cold climate electric vehicle
    concerns, 420–421
Cold-cranking amperes (CCA), 80
Cold-start warm-up, 274
Combination wrenches, 8
Combustion, 46
  diesel engine, 60, 62–63
  three phases, 62–63
Combustion by-products, 335
Combustion chamber, 46
  pressure differential diagram, 113
Combustion chamber volume, 58
Commutator bars, 98
Compact disc player, 235
Companion cylinder, 110, 361
  determining, 110, 361
Component identification (CID), 47, 160
  hexadecimal coding, 160
Comprehensive component monitor
    (CCM), 154
  number of times for fault detection, 160
  operation, 155
Compressed natural gas (CNG), 102–103
  amount equal to in gasoline, 103
  CNG label on vehicles, 102
  composition, 102–103
  ethyl mercaptan ("skunk") for leak
    detection, 102
  fuel systems, 103
  refueling a vehicle, 103
  refueling station pressures, 103
  vehicle design, 102–103
Compression gauge
  compression testing, 75
  readings, 141
Compression gauge set, 141
Compression ratio (CR), 55, 57
  boost, 124–125
  changing, 57–58
  formula for calculating, 57

Compression-sensing waste-spark
    ignition systems, 111, 362–363
  firing diagram, 112, 363
Compression test, 140–143
  compression gauge, 75
  cranking, 141
  diesel engines, 75
  grounding ignition coil wire, 125
  step by step, 149–150
  wet compression test, 142
Compressor bypass valve (CBV), 130
Computer-controlled diesel engine
    fuel injectors, 66
Computer-controlled purge, 318
Computer-controlled starting, 101
Computer data line circuit schematic, 176
Computer systems, scope control, 76
  See also Electronic entries
Conductance tester, 84–85
  checking battery, 91
Conductive charging, 421
Connecting rod, 49
Constant rail pressure (CRP), 263
Construction overview, 46–47
Contact points, 345
Contaminants, 38
Continuous memory codes (soft), 387
Continuous monitors, 154–155
Continuous running monitors, 155
Controlled combustion, 63
Conventional O2S review
  construction, 231
  heater circuits, 231
  narrow band, 230
  planar design, 231–232
Conversion, engine size, 55
Converter light-off temperature, 344
Coolant, cooling system service, 404
Coolant bubbles, head gaskets
    diagnosis, 148
Coolant disposal, 40
Coolant heaters, 100–101
Coolant level and condition
  diagnostic process, 381
  visual inspection, 136–137
Coolant temperature gauge, 184
Coolant temperature light, 148
Coolant temperature sensor/gauge,
    faults, 148
Cooling fan, ECT sensor testing, 180
Cooling methods, 52
Cooling system
  described, 47
  thermostat to control, 47
Cooling system service, 404
COP (coil-on-plug) ignition system
  coil-near-plug system, 112, 364
  three primary wires, 112, 363
  two primary wires, 112, 363
  variety of systems, 112–114,
    363–365
Corroded terminals, 371
Corrosion
  battery terminals, 90
  through insulation, 86
  warning signs, 85
Corrosive materials, 35
Counterclockwise (CC), 53
CR (compression ratio), 55, 57
  changing, 57–58
  formula for calculating, 57
Cracking, 82
Crankcase vacuum test, 338
Crankcase ventilation
  orifice-controlled PCV
    systems, 336
  PCV valves, 335–336
  separator systems, 336
Crankcase ventilation filter, 335
Cranking amperes (CA), 81
Cranking circuit, 80
Cranking vacuum test, 144–145
Crankshaft, 49
Crankshaft position sensor
  checking fowring of ignition control
    module, 132
  CMP sensor relationship, 131
  Hall-effect sensor, 108, 357
  magnetic sensor testing, 122
  tachometer trick, 109, 358
Cross counts, 217–218
CRP (constant rail pressure), 263

Crude oil
  low-gravity and high-gravity, 81
  "sweet" and "sour", 81
  types of, 81
Cubic inch displacement, 56
  formula, 55
Cummins diesel engine
  calibration number for injector, 78
  Dodge pickup, 61
  precaution gauge on lift pump, 77
  rod/piston assembly, 61
  troubleshooting chart, 76
  turbocharger, 69
Cup design for oxygen sensor, 231
Current draw, 253
Current ramping ignition coils, 119
  faults shown, 121
  good coil pattern, 121
  ignition cool ramp times, 121
  test procedure, 120
Cutters, 15
Cycle, 49
Cylinder
  arrangement, 49, 51
  operation, 49
Cylinder head gaskets, white
    steam, 136
Cylinder heads, described, 46–47
Cylinder head temperature (CHT)
    sensor, 187
Cylinder leakage test, 143
  handheld tester, 143
  step by step, 143
Cylinder power balance test, 144

**D**

D2B (domestic digital BUS)
    communication system, 173
Dampening chamber, 305
Dash charge indicator light, checking
    voltage, 96
Dash warning lights
  coolant temperature light, 148
  oil (engine) light, 148
Data link connector (DLC), 383
  pin layout, 167
  retrieving information, 385
  typical OBD-II, 388
DC coupling, 74
Dead-blow hammers, 13
Dead rat smell test, 96
Decarboning, engine assembly, 298
Deceleration detection, MAP sensor
    voltage, 200
Deep well sockets, 9
DEF (diesel exhaust fluid), 74
  storage, 74
Default position, 279
Defective computer, 288
DE housing, 95
Delivery system, 238
  DDS, 263
  direct-injection, 271–272
  See also Fuel delivery system
Delta pressure feedback EGR (DPFE)
    sensor, 331
  diagram, 331
Demand delivery system (DDS), 263
Density, 123
  high and low, 124
Detonation, 85–86, 114–115
  EGR system, 328
  knock sensors, 365–366
  octane rating related, 88
DI (distributor ignition), 103, 355
  firing order, 360
  operation, 360
  parts involved, 354
  purpose and function, 360
Diagnosis procedures, 403
Diagnostic circuit check, 173
Diagnostic executive, 154
  enabling criteria, 156–157
Diagnostic procedure, eight-step
  verify concern, 378–379
  visual inspection and basic tests,
    379, 381
  retrieve DTCs, 382
  ad check technical service
    bulletins, 382–383

  scan tool data, 382
  narrow the problem, 383
  repair the problem, 383
  verify the repair, 383–384
Diagnostic process
  engine performance diagnosis
    worksheet, 380
  retrieval of diagnostic information,
    384–385
  scan tools, 384
  seen as funnel, 378
  visual inspection, 379, 381
Diagnostic trouble codes (DTCs)
  BARO sensor, 203
  before service bulletins, 383
  catalytic converter, 349
  Chrysler vehicles, 388
  clearing, 383–384
    automatic, 158
    Ford, 387
    methods, 386
    with scan tool, 395
  diagnostic process, 382
  EGR-related OBD-II, 333
  emission-related, 156–157, 158
  EVAP system-related, 325
  for exact vehicle, 386
  IAT sensor, 185
  individual cylinder misfires, 155
  knock sensor, 114, 366
  listed, 388–391
  MAF-related, 210
  major categories, 157, 157–158
  manufacturer's diagnostic
    routines, 394
  MAP sensor, 203
    Cavalier convertible, 201
  multiple cylinder misfire, 154
  non-emission-related, 158
  numbering explanation, 157
  OBD-II diagnosis, 388–391
  opposite code, 385–386
  oxygen sensor, 222, 227
  PCV-related, 338
  P0100, 210
  P0101, 210, 338
  P0102, 210
  P0103, 210
  P0106, 203
  P0107, 203
  P0108, 203
  P0112, 188
  P0113, 188
  P0117, 188
  P0118, 188
  P0121, 194
  P0122, 194
  P0123, 194
  P0131, 227
  P0132, 227
  P0133, 227
  P0300, 296
  P0336, 123
  P0400, 333
  P0401, 333
  P0402, 333
  P0410, 341
  P0422, 349
  P0440, 324, 325
  P0441, 324
  P0442, 324, 325
  P0446, 325
  P0505, 338
  priority (0 through 4), 158
  SAI-related, 341
  same code, 386
  temperature sensors, 188
  for TP sensor, 194
  troubleshooting with,
    385–386
  Type A codes, 158
  Type B codes, 158
  Type C and D codes, 158
  types of, 157–158
Diagonal pliers, 13
Diamond-like carbon (DLC), 98
Die grinders, 20
Diesel emission testing, 78
  opacity test, 78
Diesel engine
  fuel tank and lift pump, 63
  injection pump, 63

Diesel engines
  accelerator pedal position (APP)
    sensor, 68–69
  advantages/disadvantages, 60–61
  air-fuel ratios, 61–62
  compression testing, 75
  construction, 61
  diesel exhaust particulate filter, 71
  diesel exhaust smoke diagnosis, 75
  diesel fuel heaters, 68
  diesel fuel ignition, 62
  diesel injector nozzles, 66–67
    operation, 66–67
    parts involved, 66
  diesel oxidation catalyst, 71
  diesel particulate matter (PM), 71
  engine-driven vacuum pump, 67–68
  exhaust gas recirculation (EGR), 70
  fundamentals, 60
  gasoline engine compared, 60–61
  glow plug resistance balance
    test, 75, 77
  glow plugs, 67
  HEUI system, 64–66
  how combustion occurs, 60
  indirect and direct injection, 62
  injector pop testing, 77
  particulate matter (PM), 71
  performance diagnosis, 75
  three main fuels, 111
  three phases of combustion, 62–63
  turbochargers, 69–70
Diesel engine turbochargers, 69–70
  air charge cooler, 69
  turbocharged diesels, 69
  variable turbocharger, 69–70
Diesel exhaust, aftertreatment of, 71–72
Diesel exhaust fluid, 74
Diesel exhaust fluid (DEF), 74
  storage, 74
Diesel exhaust particulate filters
    (DPFs), 71–73
  ash loading, 73
  diesel particulate filter regeneration, 73
  DPF differential pressure sensor, 72
  DPF regeneration process, 73
  DPF regeneration types, 73
  exhaust gas temperature sensors, 72
  operation, 72
  purpose and function, 71–72
Diesel exhaust smoke diagnosis, 75
  performance diagnosis, 75
Diesel fuel
  color of, 108
  colors, 67
  features, 108
  gasoline accidentally added to, 109
  gasoline compared, 67
  grades of, 108
  heaters, 109, 110
  requirements, 108
  specific gravity testing for, 109
  sulfur content, 108
  ultra-low-sulfur, 110
Diesel fuel heaters, 68, 109, 110
Diesel oxidation catalyst (DOC), 71
  chemical reaction with, 72
Diesel performance diagnosis, sensor
    value chart, 76
Diesel, Rudolf, 60
Diesohol (E-diesel), 112
Differential form of BUS
    communication, 162
Differential signaling, 171
Diffusion chamber, 232
Digital EGR valve, 330
Digital MAF sensor, analog MAF
    sensor compared, 234
Digital MAP sensor, 198
  scope waveform shown, 199
Digital multimeter (DMM) displays,
    MIN/MAX feature, 87
Digital multimeters (DMM), 18
  TP sensor testing, 192
Digital multimeters (DMMs)
  AC ripple voltage check, 98
  battery electrical drain test, 87
  checking BUS for voltages, 175
  ECT sensor testing, 180
  fuel injector pulse readings, 290
  for high-voltage testing, 398
  MAF sensor testing, 208–209

Digital multimeters (DMMs) (cont.)
MAP sensor testing, 200
mini-clamp battery tester, 88
Min/Max function, for TP sensors, 235
open-circuit voltage of battery, 82
oxygen sensor testing, 216
MIN/MAX function, 217
TP sensor testing procedure, 234
typical waveform, 234
wide-band oxygen sensor testing, 234
Digital oscilloscope, 72
Digital storage oscilloscope (DSO), 72
BUS circuit faults, 175
connecting to oxygen sensor signal
wire, 218
display, 74
fuel injector connection, 294
fuel injector testing, 294–295
fuel pressure test, 287
oxygen sensor (good) waveform, 233
TP sensor testing, 192, 234
Digital voltmeter
Hall-effect sensor testing, 369
for testing TP sensor, 234
Dikes, 13
Direct injection (DI) diesel engine, 62
combustion chamber, 62
Direct-injection fuel delivery system
fuel pressure regulator, 272
fuel rail, 272
high-pressure pump, 271–272
low-pressure supply pump, 271
two pumps shown, 271
Direct methanol fuel cells, 413
Direct programming, 393
Dirty MAF sensor story, 208
Dispersant, 275
Displacement, 55
cubic inch displacement formula, 55
Display (parade) position of ignition
oscilloscopes, 135
reading, 135
Disposal
air bags, 42
air-conditioning refrigerant oil, 42
brake dust and brake shoes, 37
brake fluid, 38
coolant, 40
HV batteries, 402–403
shop cloths, 23, 24
used tires, 42
waste chart, 43
Distillation, 81–82
Distillation curve, 83
typical, 84
Distillation index, 83
Distributed system interface (DSI)
BUS protocol, 172
Distributor
indexing, 131–132
pickup coils, AC coupling, 74
reinstallation, 130, 376
Distributor cam, 354
Distributor ignition (DI), 103, 355
dwell variation, 137
firing order, 109, 360
magnetic sensor testing, 122
operation, 107, 360
parts involved, 354
purpose and function, 107, 360
rotor gap voltage, 137
Distributor injection pump, 64
typical, 63
Division, 73
Divorced coils, 355
DLC (data link connector), 383
pre-CAN Acura, 172
retrieving information, 385
typical OBD-II, 388
DMM (digital multimeters), 18
DOC (diesel oxidation catalyst), 71
chemical reaction with, 72
Dog food, in air intake ducts, 314
DOHC (double overhead camshaft)
design, 51
direct valve operation, 52
four camshafts, 52
Dome light, brightness and starter
problems, 92
Domestic digital BUS (D2B) system, 173
Double cut files, 15
Double-layer technology, 415

Double overhead camshaft (DOHC)
design, 51
direct valve operation, 52
four camshafts, 52
DPF differential pressure sensor, 72
DPFE (delta pressure feedback EGR)
sensor, 331
diagram, 331
DPF regeneration
active, 73
passive, 73
DPFs (diesel exhaust particulate
filters), 71–73
ash loading, 73
diesel particulate filter
regeneration, 73
DPF differential pressure sensor, 72
exhaust gas temperature sensors, 72
operation, 72
purpose and function, 71–72
Drag cars, electric, 422
Driveability, 135
Driveability index (DI), 83
Driveability problem
engine performance diagnosis
worksheet, 380
O2S rich with low pulse width, 315
Drive belts
hand cleaner trick, 98
noise from, 138
simple engine testing, 140
slipping, 98
Drive-by-wire, 277
Drive cycle, 156, 395
universal, 395
Drive-end (nose) housing, 95
Drive-end housing, alternator, 95
Drive-on ramps, 26
Driver as resource
engine condition diagnosis, 136
questions for, 379
test drive, 379
Drive sizes, 9
Dry chemical fire extinguishers, 28
Dry system (N₂O), 132
DSI (distributed system interface)
BUS protocol, 172
DSO (digital storage oscilloscope), 72
TP sensor testing, 234
DTCs
BARO sensor, 203
before service bulletins, 383
catalytic converter, 349
Chrysler vehicles, 388
clearing, 383–384
automatic, 158
Ford, 387
methods, 386
with scan tool, 395
diagnostic process, 382
EGR-related OBD-II, 333
emission-related, 156–157, 158
EVAP system-related, 325
for exact vehicle, 386
IAT sensor, 185
individual cylinder misfires, 155
knock sensor, 114, 366
listed, 388–391
MAF-related, 210
major categories, 157, 157–158
manufacturer's diagnostic routines, 394
MAP sensor, 203
Cavalier convertible, 201
multiple cylinder misfire, 154
non-emission-related, 158
numbering explanation, 157
OBD-II diagnosis, 388–391
opposite code, 385–386
oxygen sensor, 222, 227
PCV-related, 338
P0100, 210
P0101, 210, 338
P0102, 210
P0103, 210
P0106, 203
P0107, 203
P0108, 203
P0112, 188
P0113, 188
P0117, 188
P0118, 188
P0121, 194

P0122, 194
P0123, 194
P0131, 227
P0132, 227
P0133, 227
P0300, 296
P0336, 123
P0400, 333
P0401, 333
P0402, 333
P0410, 341
P0422, 349
P0440, 324, 325
P0441, 324
P0442, 324, 325
P0446, 325
P0505, 338
priority (0 through 4), 158
SAI-related, 341
same code, 386
temperature sensors, 188
for TP sensor, 194
troubleshooting with, 385–386
Type A codes, 158
Type B codes, 158
Type C and D codes, 158
types of, 157–158
Dual-cell planar-type wide-band
oxygen sensor
construction and operation, 232
diagnosis, 234
stoichiometric, 232–233
testing equipment shown, 235
Dual turbocharger system, 130
Chevrolet V-8, 131
Dump valve, 130
Dust, brake, 37
Duty cycle, 75
on-time, 75
Dwell, 75
current-limiting hump, 137
definition, 134
Dwell period, ignition coil testing, 119
Dwell section of ignition scope test, 134
Dwell variation, 137
Dynamic compression test, 142
procedure, 143
Dynamic pressure test, 142–143, 250
Dynamic response check, 388

E

E & C (entertainment and comfort)
communication, 165
E10 (ethanol blend gasoline), 88
E85, 96–97
in cold climate tests, 97
fuel economy of, 97
fuel system requirements, 97–98
EAC (electronic air control) valve, 267
E coil, 105, 355
steel lamination, 105, 355
ECT circuits, 179–180
schematic, 180
ECT sensor
construction, 179
location, 179
pulse width, 259
purpose and function, 179
troubleshooting with DTCs, 183–184
two sensors, 184
voltage curve reading versus, 180
ECT sensors, stepped ECT circuits,
179–180
ECT sensor testing, 180–181
E-diesel (diesohol), 112
EEPROM (electronically erasable
programmable read-only
memory), reprogramming,
392–393
Effective compression ratio, 124
boost pressure compared, 125
Efficiency check, 58
Efficiency tests, catalytic converter, 348
EFI injector
described, 259
solenoid-operated injector, 259, 260
EFT (engine fuel temperature)
sensor, 187
EGR (exhaust gas recirculation), 70
exhaust gas coolers, 118
passages, 118

EGR (exhaust gas recirculation)
system, 327
benefits, 328
Blazer story, 332
blower-type exhaust hose use, 332
carbon balls, 332
carbon removal procedure, 333
computer-controlled, 329
digital EGR valves, 330
EGR valve position (EVP) sensors, 329
EVP sensors, 329
exhaust and intake manifolds, 327
Ford delta pressure, 51
Ford tests, 51
linear EGR, 330
MAP sensor signal, 200
NOx formation and control, 327
OBD-II DTCs, 333
operation, 328
positive and negative backpressure
EGR valves, 328–329
symptoms of defective, 331–333
testing procedures, 332
visual inspection, 332
EGR (exhaust gas recirculation)
temperature sensor, 187
EGR valve position sensor, 329,
329–330
location, 330
replacement checks, 330
EGR valves
back pressure testing, 147
carbon balls in, 332
digital, 330
pintle diagram, 331
vacuum-operated, 329
EI (electronic ignition), 103–104
acceleration check, 137
dwell variation, 137
Electrical cord safety, 26
Electrical hand tools, 18
Electrical heater wire, 67, 69
Electrical insulation tester, 398
Electrically operated tools, 19–21
Electrical test, 160
Electrical work hand tools, 18
Electric fuel pumps
control circuits, 245–246
ear test, 249
gerotor, 245
hydrokinetic flow pump, 244
modular fuel sensor assembly,
244–245
no danger of fire, 243
no-start condition, 250
positive displacement pump, 243–244
pulsators, 247
pump pulsation dampening, 247
replacement, 251
removing the bed for access, 251
roller cell (vane) pump, 243, 244
symptoms of low fuel volume,
252–253
testing, 253
turbine pump, 244
variable speed pumps, 247–248
Electric motor-driven air pump, 340
Electric power steering (EPS) system,
service, 405
Electric shock potential, 399
de-powering the HV system, 399, 401
locations of auxiliary batteries,
399, 400
Electric soldering guns, 18
Electric soldering pencils, 18
Electric vehicle charging station, 421
Electric vehicles (EV)
charging methods, 421
cold-weather concerns, 420–421
future for, 420–422
hot-weather concerns, 421
recharging methods and
concerns, 421
Electrolysis, 410
Electrolyte, 412
Electromagnetic induction (EMI), 104,
355–356
Electromagnetic interference (EMI), 112
"Electronic accelerator pump", 191
Electronic air control (EAC) valve, 267
Electronic brake control module
(EBCM), 190

Electronic components, battery
   electrical drain, 87–88
Electronic conductance testing, 84–85
Electronic fuel-injection systems
   diagnosis using visual inspection, 287
   ignition primary pulse, 289
   operation, 256
   speed-density fuel-injection
      system, 256–258
   types of, 256
Electronic ignition (EI), 103–104, 355
   acceleration check, 137
   "hump" in dwell section, 137
Electronic ignition spark tester, 119
Electronic ignition systems, 103–104,
   354–355
Electronic load detector (ELD), 101
Electronic odometer, 260–1311
Electronic returnless fuel system
   (ERFS), 262–263
   diagram, 262
Electronic service information, 3
Electronic spark timing (EST), 115
Electronic throttle actuator
   (servomotor), 277
Electronic throttle control (ETC), 277
   accelerator pedal position sensor, 278
   diagnosis, 281–282
   ETC throttle follower test, 283
   normal operation, 277–278
   parts involved, 277
   performance issues, 283
   schematic, 280
   service, 283–284
   throttle body assembly, 278–279
   throttle position (TP) sensor, 280–281
   warning lamp, 281
Electronic throttle control (ETC) diagnosis
   diagnostic procedure, 282
   fault mode, 281
   scan tool data, 282
   vacuum leaks, 282
Electronic throttle control (ETC)
   systems, advantages, 277
Electronic vacuum regulator valve
   (EVRV), 332
EMI (electromagnetic induction), 355–356
EMI (electromagnetic interference), 112
Emission control
   air-fuel ratios and, 85
   catalytic converter diagnosis, 346–348
   catalytic converter related DTCs, 349
   catalytic converter replacement,
      348–349
   catalytic converters, 343–351
   EGR systems, 327–330
      diagnosing defective, 331–333
      OBD-II monitoring, 330–331
      related DTCs, 333
   enhanced EVAP system, 319–320
   EVAP diagnosis, 322–323
   EVAP DTCs, 325
   EVAP monitor, 323–324
   EVAP system, 317–318
   leak detection pump system, 321
   nonenhanced EVAP system, 318–319
   OBD-II EGR monitoring strategies,
      330–331
   onboard refueling vapor recovery
      (ORVR), 321
   PCV system diagnosis, 336–338
      related DTCs, 338
   secondary air-injection, 339–341
      diagnosis, 340–341
      related DTCs, 341
Emissions
   gasoline, diesel, and HCCI
      compared, 420
   well-to-wheel emissions, 420
Emissions standards, 118
   age of vehicle and passing the
      test, 312
   California, 306–307
   Europe, 308
   exhaust analysis testing, 308–310
   federal bin number, 307
   federal Tier 1 and Tier 2, 306–307
   smog emission information, 307
   United States, 306–308
Emission tester, nitrogen gas
   pressurization, 323
Emission tests, Toyota example, 314

Emission tests, diesel engine
   opacity test, 78
   rolling acceleration test, 78
   snap acceleration test, 78
   stall acceleration test, 78
Enable criteria, 156–157, 157
Enabling conditions or criteria, 158–159
   conflict, 159
   pending, 158
   rationality test, 159
   suspend, 159
Enabling criteria
   MIL condition: FLASHING, 157
   MIL condition: OFF, 157
   MIL condition: ON STEADY, 157
   trip, 157
   warm-up cycle, 157
Energy carrier, 410
Energy density, 413
Engine
   cutaway view, 51
   energy and power, 46
   purpose and function, 46
   when it stops, 54
Engine analyzers, typical hookup
   shown, 133
Engine classification and construction
   characteristics, 49, 51–53
   rotation direction, 53
Engine condition diagnosis
   back pressure testing
      with pressure gauge, 147
      with vacuum gauge, 147
   compression test, 140–143
      step by step, 149–150
   compression testing, 140–143
   cylinder leakage test, 143
   driver as resource, 136
   engine noise, 138–139
   engine smoke diagnosis, 135
   exhaust restriction test, 146
   head gasket failure diagnosis,
      147–148
   keep it simple, 140
   oil pressure testing, 139–140
   oil pressure warning lamp, 140
   paper test, 141
   power balance test, 144
   running (dynamic) compression
      test, 142–143
   simple engine testing, 140
   typical complaints, 135
   vacuum tests, 144–145
   visual inspection, 136–138
   wet compression test, 142
Engine condition monitoring, MAP
   sensor signals, 200–201
Engine construction
   block, 46
   cylinder heads, 46–47
   rotating assembly, 46
Engine coolant temperature (ECT)
   sensor, 179
   construction, 179
   location, 179
   pulse width, 259
   stepped ECT circuits, 179–180
   troubleshooting with DTCs, 188
   two sensors, 184
   voltage curve reading versus, 180
Engine coolant temperature (ECT)
   sensor testing, 180–181
   digital meter set to DC volts, 184
   multimeter, 180
   quick and easy test, 185
   scan tool, 183–184
   visual inspection, 180
   when to test, 180
Engine-driven vacuum pump, 67–68
Engine fuel temperature (EFT)
   sensor, 187
Engine knock, 85–86
Engine measurement
   bore, 54
   calculating cubic inch
      displacement, 55
   displacement, 55
   engine size conversion, 55
   stroke, 54
Engine misfire tests
   Ford, 50
   individual cylinder misfires, 50

percentage conversion, 50
   Type A misfire codes, 50
   Type B misfire codes, 50
Engine misfiring, ignition system
   symptom guide, 138, 376
Engine noise
   cost related, 139
   diagnosis, 138–139
Engine off natural vacuum, 323
   test, 52
Engine oil
   feeds, 128
   turbochargers, 127, 128
Engine oil temperature sensor, 188
Engine parts and system
   cooling system, 47
   fuel system and ignition system, 48
   intake and exhaust manifolds, 47
   lubrication system, 48
Engine performance diagnosis
   worksheet, 380
Engine smoke diagnosis, 135
Engine start system, 274–275
Engine warning lights, 148
Enhanced emission test, 309
   clogged EGR passages, 333
Enhanced evaporative control (Evap)
   systems, 319–320
Environmental Protection Agency
   (EPA), 35, 37
   catalytic converter replacement,
      348–349
Enzymes, 95
EOBD (European on-board
   diagnosis), 47
EPA (Environmental Protection
   Agency), 35, 37, 154, 306
Equal resistance test, 292
EST (electronic spark timing), 115
EST (ignition control) (white) wire, 116
ETC throttle follower test, 283
ETC warning lamp, 281
Ethanol (ethyl alcohol), 95
   described, 88
   E10, 88
   environmental impact, 95
   as octane improver, 87
   production of, 95–96
   splash blending, 89
   switchgrass as base of, 96
Ethyl alcohol, 95
Ethyl mercaptan ("skunk"), 102
Ethyl tertiary butyl ether (ETBE), 88
European Bosch, ECT sensor, 183
European emission standards, 308
European on-board diagnosis
   (EOBD), 47
European vehicles
   BUS communications, 172–173
   OBD-II data link connector, 176
EVAP monitor, 323–324
   running, 324–325
   tests, 340
Evaporate emissions control (EVAP),
   monitors, 156
Evaporative (EVAP) emission control
   system, 317
   dash display, 322
   diagnosis, 322–323
   diagram, 318
   DTCs, 325
   EVAP monitor, 324
   monitor, 323–324
   nonenhanced, 318–319
   operation, 317–318
   pressure buildup causes, 318
   pressure conversion chart, 320
   purpose and function, 317
   schematic, 319
   state tests, 322
Evaporative system monitor, 323–324
   engine-off natural vacuum, 323
EVAP system, 317
   diagram, 318
   enhanced, 319–320
   nonenhanced, 318–319
   operation, 317–318
   pressure buildup causes, 318
   purpose and function, 317
   schematic, 319
   state tests, 322
   tests for GM CAN, 52

EVAP system diagnosis
   DTCs, 325
   locating leaks, 322–323
   symptoms, 322
EVP sensor, 329–330
EVRV (electronic vacuum regulator
   valve), 332
EWMA (exponentially weighted
   moving average) monitors, 156
Exhaust, two outlets, diesel engine, 74
Exhaust air cooler, 74
Exhaust analysis
   acceptable emission levels (chart), 312
   air/fuel ratio by weight shown, 312
   burning or watery eyes, 314
   checking for leaks, 313
   combustion efficiency and, 311
   CO too high, 312–313
   dizziness or headache, 314
   finding leaks in system, 313
   HC too high, 312
   measuring oxygen ($O_2$) and carbon
      dioxide ($CO_2$), 313
   portable exhaust analyzer, 314
   strong exhaust smell, 314
Exhaust analysis testing, 308–310
   acceleration simulation mode
      (ASM), 309
   five-gas equipment, 311
   FTP (Federal Test Procedure), 308
   hole (diagram), 313
   I/M 240 test, 310
   I/M test programs, 309
   loaded mode test, 309
   OBD-II testing, 310
   one-speed and two-speed idle
      test, 309
   precautions with clearing codes, 386
   random roadside testing, 310
   remote sensing, 310
   summary chart, 315
   visual tampering checks, 309
Exhaust camshaft timing, 314
Exhaust check valves, 339
Exhaust cooler, cutaway view, 70
Exhaust gas analyzer, 341
   head gasket diagnosis, 147
Exhaust gas coolers, 118
   typical long gasoline, 118
Exhaust gas recirculation (EGR), 70
   passages, 118
Exhaust gas recirculation (EGR) system
   benefits, 328
   exhaust and intake manifolds, 327
   Ford tests, 51
   introduction, 327
   NOx control, 327
   NOx formation, 327
   operation, 328
   oxygen sensor response, 215
   positive and negative backpressure
      EGR valves, 328–329
   temperature sensor, 187
Exhaust gas recirculation (EGR)
   temperature sensor, 187
Exhaust gas recirculation (EGR) valves
   exhaust gas coolers, 118
   purpose and function, 118
Exhaust gas recirculation passages, 118
Exhaust gas temperature sensors, 72
Exhaust leak in front of the O2S, 225
Exhaust manifold gaskets, 119–120
   typical laminated, 120
Exhaust manifolds
   construction, 118–120
   cracked, and performance, 119
   cracked Ford V-8, 139
   exhaust manifold gaskets, 119–120
   gas direction diagram, 118
   header-type, 120
   operation, 47
   purpose and function, 118
   spreader tools, 120
   visibility of cracks, 119
Exhaust manifold spreader tool, 120
Exhaust restriction test, 146
Exhaust side electrode, 231
Exhaust systems
   exhaust gas recirculation
      passages, 118
   exhaust manifolds, 118–120
   mufflers, 120–121

Exhaust valve overlap, 124
Exhaust valves, 49
Exponentially weighted moving average (EWMA) monitors, 156
Extensions, 9
External air manifold, 339
External combustion engine, 46
External triggers, 76
Eye protection, 399
Eye wash stations, 28–29

**F**

Factory original-equipment (OE), 379
Factory scan tools, generic OBD-II scan tool air-fuel ratios compared, 234
Fail-safe position, 281
Failure recorders, 158
False air, 209
False lean indication, 225
False rich indication, 225
Farads (F), in ultracapacitors, 415
Fasteners, 4–7
Fast fill method, 103
FCHV (fuel-cell hybrid vehicle), 411
FCHV (fuel cell hybrid vehicle), 411
FCV (fuel-cell vehicle), 411
Federal Test Procedure (FTP), 308
    OBD-II standards, 154
Fender covers, 23
FFV (flexible fuel vehicle), 97
Fiberglass pole, for high-voltage servicing, 399
Files, 15
Filler tubes, 239
    ground strap shown, 239
    three-piece assembly, 239
Filter basket, 249
Filter sock, 239
Finger design for oxygen sensor, 231
Fire blankets, 28
Fire extinguisher classes, 27–28
Firing line, 133
Firing line, spark line relationship, 137
Firing order, 109, 360
    on intake manifold, 109, 131, 360
    in service manuals, 131
First aid kits, 28–29
Fischer-Tropsch synthetic fuel, 104–105
Fitting wrenches, 8
5-volt reference, testing sensors, 193
Flare, 267
Flare-nut wrenches, 8
Flash code retrieval, 386
Flash codes, 385
Flat-head engine, 47
Flat-tip screwdrivers, 11
Flex Fuels, 97
    components and materials of, 97–98
    sensorless system, 98
    vehicle identification, 98–99
Flexible fuel lines, 241
Flexible-fuel vehicles (FFVs), 97
Flex plate, noise from cracked, 138
FlexRay BUS serial communication system, 173
Floating ground, 400
Fluctuating vacuum, 145–146
    readings, 145–146
Fluorescent lights, 19
Flushing, fuel-injection service, 297–298
Foot powder spray trick, 138
Forced induction system, 124
    boost and compression ratios, 124–125
    purpose and function, 123–124
Ford
    capacitor-capsule MAP sensor, 198
    clearing DTCs, 387
    Delta pressure for EGR flow test, 51
    demonstration fuel-cell vehicle, 410
    diagnostic executive, 154
    DPFE sensor and related components, 331
    ECT sensor, 182
    EGR sensor, 51
    electronic conductance tester, 84
    engine misfire tests, 50
    ETC warning lamp, 281
    fuel injectors, 264
    gas camp fuel recommendation, 91

inertia switch, 240, 246–247
    cutaway view, 241
    schematic, 247
injector resistance table, 291
MAF sensors, 206
MAP/BARO altitude chart, 202
MAP sensor green signal wire, 199
MAP sensor vacuum readings, 200
network communication protocols, 168–169
OBD-1 diagnostic link connector, 168
OBD-I Ford vehicles, 168
OBD-II data link connector, 176
OBD-I self-test connector, 387
oxygen sensor Mode $06 test, 50
retrieving DTCs, 387, 388
scan tools, 384
SPOUT (spark output), 115, 116, 376
STAR tester, 387
supercharger cutaway view, 127
throttle position (TP) sensor chart, 233
TP sensor chart, 191
transmission fluid temperature, 187
UBP module communications, 168
vane airflow sensor, 205
Ford diesel engines, oil changes, 66
Ford Escape
    EV reading, 400
    jump start button, 401
Ford Escort, poor engine operation, 216
Ford Motor Company
    Flex Fuel vehicles, 99
    how to read VIN, 100
Ford PowerStroke diesel engine, O-ring location, 65
Ford V-8
    COP systems, triple-strike secondary spark event, 138
    cracked exhaust manifold, 139
    firing order, 109, 361
    supercharger, 124
Forged pistons, 125
Formaldehyde, 105
Four-channel scope, 76
Four-cylinder engines
    3 X 5 card test, 337–338
    cubic inch displacement chart, 56
    no crank story, 91
Four-gas exhaust analysis, 341
Four-stroke cycle operation
    720-degree cycle, 49
    operation, 49, 50
    principles, 49
Four-wire oxygen sensor, 213
Fractional bolts, 4
Freeze-frame
    data, 391–392
    items listed, 158
    OBD-II vehicles, 154, 158
    required items listed, 392
Freeze-frame data
    items listed, 158
    OBD-II vehicles, 154, 158
Frequency, definition, 75
Frequency of the oxygen sensor, 221
    normal frequency shown, 222
Friction materials, 36
FRP (fuel-rail pressure) sensor, 203
FTD (Fischer-Tropsch diesel), 104–105
FTP (Federal Test Procedure), 308
Fuel cell, 410
    benefits, 410–411
    challenges, 411
    types of, 412
Fuel-cell hybrid vehicle (FCHV), 411
    fuel-cell traction motors, 415–416
    power control units, 416–417
    systems, 413–419
    transaxles, 416
    ultracapacitors, 414–415
Fuel-cell stack, 412
Fuel-cell traction motors, 415–416
Fuel cell vehicle (FCV), 411
Fuel-cell vehicle systems
    air-supply pumps, 414
    fuel-cell cooling systems, 413–414
    humidifiers, 413
Fuel compensation sensor, 97
    General Motors exception, 89
Fuel control, PCM uses of oxygen sensor, 200
"Fuel crossover," 413

Fuel delivery system
    electric fuel pumps, 243–248
    fuel filters, 248
    fuel lines, 240–243
    fuel pump current draw test, 253
    fuel pump replacement, 254
    fuel pump testing, 248–253
    fuel tanks, 238
    leakdown, 250
    scan tool diagnostics, 299
    stratified change mode, 274
    symptom guide, 254
    two "Must-Dos", 257
Fuel economy
    checking base brakes, 405
    E85 use and, 97
    EVAP system problems, 322
    grade of gasoline related, 88
    greenhouse gas score, 308
    IAT sensor defective, 185
    postinjection impulses, 73
    tire pressure related, 405
    Toyota knock sensor problem, 115, 366
Fuel fill pipe, restricted, shown, 321
Fuel filters, 248
    inline, 248
    installation, 248
    useful life, 248
Fuel-injection components and operation
    electronic, 256
    electronic returnless fuel system, 262–263
    fuel-pressure regulator, 261–262
    mass airflow, 258
    mechanical returnless fuel system, 263
    port-fuel, 258–260
    speed density, 256–258
    throttle-body, 258
    vacuum-biased fuel-pressure regulator, 262
Fuel-injection modes of operation
    acceleration enrichment, 266
    clear flood, 266
    closed-loop, 266
    deceleration enleanment, 266
    fuel shutoff, 266
    open-loop, 266
    starting, 266
Fuel-injection system
    airflow information, sources, 210
    air-fuel ratio, 84–85
    clamp recommendations, 241
    filters, 248
    fittings and nylon lines, 242
    fuel injector cleaning, 303–304
    fuel lines, 241
    Honda Civic GX, 102
    hoses, 241
    idle control, 266–267
    modes of operation, 266
    O-ring seals, 242
    pressure-drop balance test, 293
    scan tool diagnostics, 299
    service, 296–299
    spring-lock connectors, 242
    symptom chart, 299
Fuel-injection system diagnosis and service, 286
    cleaning, 298–299, 303–304
    flushing, 297–298
    fuel-injection symptom chart, 299
    fuel injector cleaning, 303–304
    fuel-injector resistance checking, 291
    fuel-pump relay circuit diagnosis, 300–302
    idle air speed control diagnosis, 295
    injector-voltage drop tests, 293–294
    port fuel-injection, 286, 288
    pressure-drop balance test, 293
    resistance of grouped injectors, measuring, 291–292
    resistance of individual injectors, measuring, 292
    scan tool diagnostics, 299
    scan tool vacuum leak diagnosis, 288
    scope-testing fuel injectors, 294–295
    service, 296–299
    testing for an injector pulse, 289–290
    visual inspection, 287

Fuel-injection system testing
    scan tool vacuum leak diagnosis, 288
    stethoscope fuel-injection test, 288
    vacuum leak diagnosis, 288
Fuel-injector resistance, 292
    checking, 291
        connections and settings, 291
    grouped, 291–292
    individual, 292, 293
Fuel injectors
    check at "bends and ends", 298
    checking resistance, clogged injector, 293
    cleaning, 298, 303–304
    computer controlled, diesel engine, 66
    Ford, 264
    GDI, 272
    injector sizing formula, 265
    multiport, 265
    pulse readings, 290
    pulse width, 75, 259
    reconditioned shown, 295
    replacement of all six, 295
    solenoid-operated, 264
    spray pattern, 264, 265
Fuel-injector screens, flushing, 297–298
Fuel injector testing
    balance test, 293
    checking resistance, 291
    injector voltage-drop tests, 293–294
    measuring resistance
        equal resistance test, 292
        grouped, 291–292
        harness wiring, 292
        individual, 292
    peak-and-hold type, 294–295
    quick and easy leak test, 288
    saturated switch type, 294
    scope-testing, 294–295
Fuel inlet location, 239
Fuel levels
    problems after refueling, 321
    recommendations, 381
Fuel line mounting, 241
    clips shown, 241
Fuel lines
    construction and operation, 240
    flexible, 241
    fuel-injection fittings and nylon lines, 242
    fuel-injection lines and clamps, 242
    layout, 242–243
    rigid lines, 241
Fuel outlet check valve, 243
Fuel pickup tube
    filter sock, 239
    view of assembly, 240
Fuel-pressure gauge, 252
    port fuel-injection system diagnosis, 289
    testing fuel-pump volume, 297
Fuel-pressure graph, 287
Fuel-pressure regulator, 261–262, 272
    10-micron filter, 260
    checking, 288
    clogged filter shown, 260
    defective, signs of, 315
    flushing, 297–298
    testing, 296–297
    vacuum-biased fuel-pressure regulator, 262
    vacuum hose removal, 251
    vacuum pressure diagram, 261
Fuel-pressure sensor, fuel-temperature sensor together with, 262
Fuel-pressure test
    instruments used, 287
    pressure transducer, 287
Fuel-pressure tester, fuel pump testing, 296
Fuel pulsator
    diagram, 247
    pump pulsation dampening, 247
Fuel pump current draw test, 253
    hookup, 253
    type of fuel injection (chart), 253
Fuel pump modules
    modular fuel sender assembly, 244–245
    spring loaded, 245
    Fuel-pump relay circuit diagnosis, 300–302

Fuel pumps
checking, 288
checking pressure and volume, 296
fuel recirculated, 242
GDI fuel rail shown with, 272
relay circuit diagnosis, 300–302
replacement, 254
testing for fuel volume, 251–252
Fuel pump testing, 248–253
dynamic pressure test, 250
ear test, 249
fuel pump volume testing, 251–252
quick and easy, 252
fuel returning to tank, 258
pressure chart, 249
pressure testing, 248–249
rest pressure test, 250
Fuel pump volume testing, 251–252, 296, 297
symptoms of low fuel volume, 252–253
Fuel rail, 264
cleaning, 299
definition, 264
direct-injection, 272
flushing, 297–298
rectangular-shaped, 264
shown with pump assembly, 272
Fuel-rail pressure (FRP) sensor, 203
Fuel return line, checking, 288
Fuel safety and storage, 41
Fuel systems
components, 48
E85 requirements, 97–98
Fuel system tester, 252
Fuel tank, 238
diesel engine, 63
importance of not running out of fuel, 66
filler tube, 239
fuel levels and EVAP monitor, 325
fuel pickup tube, 239–240
location and mounting, 239
overfilling or running out, 88, 91, 92
pressure vacuum filler caps, 239
regulator inside, 286
rollover leakage protection, 240
tank venting requirements, 240
typical installation, 238
VOC emission concerns, 243
Fuel tank cap
dash display, 322
loose, 322
testing, 322
tightening screw-type, 324
tightening until click, 324
Fuel tank filler caps
capless system (Ford), 318
EVAP systems, 317
Fuel tank fillups, pump clicking off, 317
Fuel tank pressure (FTP) sensor, 323
location, 324
Fuel temperature sensor, ice bath test, 63
Fuel trim monitor, 155
Fuel type, 52
Functionality tests, 155
example, 159
Fungible, 82

G
Gang fired, 259
Gas analyzer, 288
Gas line freeze-up, 91
Gasoline, 81
accidentally added to diesel fuel, 109
additives, 87–88
alcohol content, testing for, 90, 93
antiknock ratings, 86
blending, 89
chemical composition, 81
cold-weather driveability, 83
filling containers with, 92
general recommendations, 91–92
grades and octane number, 86
for high altitudes, 87
normal and abnormal combustion, 85–86
octane rating, 86
overfilling or running out, 88, 92
phase separation, 88
refining, 81
reformulated, 89–90

reformulated (RFG), 89–90
seasonal blending, 83
shipping, 82
sniff test, 91
testing for alcohol content, 90, 93
"top-tier", 91
volatility, 83–84
weight compared to water, 89
winter-blend, 83, 84
Gasoline blending, 89
in-line, 89
sequential, 89
splash blending, 89
Gasoline combustion process, 84–85
Gasoline containers, 92
Gasoline direct-injection (GDI) systems, 270
advantages/disadvantages, 270
diagram, 270
direct fuel injection, 270
engine start system, 274–275
fuel injectors, 272
Lexus port- and direct-injection systems, 274
NOx catalyst shown, 271
piston top designs, 273
port fuel-injection compared, 273
service, 275
Gasoline direct-injection (GDI) system service
carbon issues, 275
noise issues, 275
Gasoline direct-injection fuel injectors, 272
Gasoline engine, diesel engine compared, 60–61
Gasoline stabilizer, 91
Gasoline testing kits, 83
Gas smell, EVAP leaks, 322
Gas to liquid (GTL) technology, 105
Gateway module, 176
GAWR (gross axle weight rating), 2
General Motors
air filter restriction indicator, 114
airflow sensors (older), 206
avoid resetting fuel compensation, 89
battery or system voltage scan tool, 83
bypass ignition control, 116
CAN oxygen sensor Mode $06 test, 50–51
catalyst efficiency test, 51
central port injection, 265
coil-near-plug system, 112, 363–364
communication protocols, 165–168
diagnostic executive, 154
distributor indexing, 132
DTCs, 386
ECT sensor
with pull-up resistor, 182
without pull-up resistor, 180
electric fuel pumps, 246
electric vehicle, 420
electronic conductance tester, 84
engine oil temperature sensor, 188
EST (electronic spark timing), 115
ETC warning lamp, 281
EVAP test (CAN), 52
failure recorders, 158
flash code retrieval, 386
Flex Fuel vehicles, 99
fuel-cell vehicle, 416
gasoline direct injection (GDI), 270
GMLAN versions, 165–166
how to read VIN, 89
hybrid electric vehicle safety, 29–31
Hydrogen3, 418
injector resistance table, 291
Keyword 81, 82, and 2000 serial data, 165, 167
linear EGR valve, 330
MAP sensor vacuum readings, 200
MAP sensor voltage, 198
MAP sensor voltage (good reading), 198
M-terminal, 386
nonchecking throttle body units, 262
nylon fuel lines, 242
OBD-II data link connector, 176
oxygen sensor heater Mode $06 test, 50
oxygen sensor problem diagnosis, 218

primary winding location, 105, 356
scan tools, 384
"Skateboard concept", 416
Spark Ignition Direct Injection (SIDI), 270
spark plug overtightening, 129, 373
spark plugs and antiseize compound, 129, 373
splice packs, 163–164
stepped ECT circuits, 179
TBI fuel-injection systems, 250
Tech 2 scan tool, 174
transaxle sensor temperature to resistance, 186
UART, 165
General Motors CPI truck, fuel pump current draw, 253
General Motors Duramax
diesel troubleshooting chart, 76
injector internal parts, 67
priming pump location, 66
General Motors Ecotec, 114, 365
General Motors HEI system
bumps in scope testing, 134
"hump" in dwell section, 137
General Motors pickup, electric fuel pump replacement, 252
General Motors V-6
firing order, 109, 361
IAT sensor location, 185
Schrader valve location, 250
Generator (alternator), 81
construction, 95
dead rat smell test, 96
horsepower requirements, 96
scope patterns shown, 101
testing with a scope, 101
testing with voltmeter, 96–97
Generator output ("BAT") terminal, 101
Generator output test, 100–101
Generic OBD II, 46
Gerotor, 244
exploded view, 245
Gerotor-type fuel pump, 239
Glasses, safety, 21
Glitches, 72
Global OBD II, 160
accessing, 47
cartridge shown, 47
defined, 46
global (generic) scan tool modes, 160
hexadecimal numbers, 46–47, 160
modes, 46–47
purposes and functions, 46
Gloves, 21–22
Glow plugs, diesel engine, 67
assortment shown, 67
circuit schematic, 68
heated inlet air, 67
operation, 67
purpose and function, 67
resistance balance test, 75, 77
GMCAN, Class 2 communications, 165, 167
GMLAN (GM local area network), 165–166
GMM (graphing multimeter), 78
fuel pressure test, 287
Grades, bolt, 5
Grades of gasoline, 86
Grain alcohol, 95
Graphing multimeter (GMM), 78
fuel pressure test, 287
Graphing scan tools, 78
Graticules, 72
Gray exhaust smoke, 75
Greenhouse gases (GHG), 96
Greenhouse gas score, 234
Gross axle weight rating (GAWR), 2
Gross vehicle weight rating (GVWR), 2
Ground (black/white) wire, 116
Ground fault monitor, 400
Grove, Sir William, 410
GTL diesel, 105

H
Hacksaws, 16
Hall effect, 106
switch for ignition, 357
TP sensors, 281

Hall-effect sensor
camshaft reference sensor, 108, 359
crankshaft reference sensor, 108, 357
on-off voltage signal, 107, 359
testing, 122–123, 369
testing connection, 124, 369
typical waveform, 369
Hall-effect switch, 106–107, 357–358
Hammers, 12–13
claw, 12
Hand cleaner trick, 98
Hand safety, 39
Hand tools, 7–17
basic list, 16–17
electrical, 18
maintenance, 18–19
sets and accessories, 17–18
See also Specific tools
Hangers, 120–121
Hard faults, 388
Hash
background information, 221–222
causes, 222
class 1 (amplified and significant), 222–223
class 2 (moderate), 223
class 3 (severe), 223
misfires, types of, 223–224
Hazardous Materials Identification Guide (HMIG), 43–44
Hazardous waste materials, 35
H-bridge circuit, 279
shown, 280
HC (unburned hydrocarbons), 335
HCCI (Homogeneous Charge Compression Ignition), 419
shown, 420
Header-type exhaust manifolds, 120
Head gasket failure, diagnosing, 147–148
Headlights, battery strength related, 82–83
Hearing protection, 21
Heated inlet air, 67
Heated oxygen sensor (HO2S), 345, 346
Heat energy, 84
of E85, 97
Heater circuits, 231
Heat of compression, 60
Heat shield, 66
HEI pickup, measuring resistance with DM, 122
Helmholtz, Herman L. F., 115
Hemholtz resonator, 115
location, 115
HEPA (high-efficiency particulate air) vacuum, 37
Hertz (Hz), 75
HEUI (hydraulic electronic unit)
components, 64
operation, 65–66
O-ring grooves, 65
HEV (hybrid electric vehicles), 29–31
Hexadecimal, global OBD-II, 46–47, 160
Hexadecimal numbers, 46–47, 160
charts to translate, 48–49
High altitude, oxygenated fuels, 87
High-authority sensors, 208
High-efficiency particulate air (HEPA) vacuum, 37
High-performance exhaust system, 329
High-pressure common rail (HPCR) fuel delivery, 64
overview diagram, 65
High-pressure compressed hydrogen, 417–418
High-pressure leaks, diesel engine, 78
High-pressure lock-off, 103
High-pressure pumps, 271–272
camshaft-driven, 272
High-pressure regulator, 103
High-voltage (HV) batteries, 29
disposal of, 402–403
removing, 402–403
storing, 402
High-voltage (HV) cables, 397
High-voltage (HV) circuits, 397
High-voltage cable color identification, 397
High-voltage insulated safety gloves, 397

High-voltage safety equipment, 397–399
  CAT III-rated digital multimeter, 398
  eye protection, 399
  fiberglass pole, 399
  insulation tester, 398
  rubber gloves, 397, 406–407
  safety cones, 399
High-voltage system
  de-powering, 399, 401, 402
  discharge levels and timing, 400
  service precautions, 402
HMIG (Hazardous Materials
  Identification Guide), 43–44
Hoisting a hybrid vehicle, 402
Hoisting vehicles, 23–25
  hoist pad adapters, 25
  lift location, 24
  step by step, 32–33
Homogeneous Charge Compression
  Ignition (HCCI), 419
  shown, 420
Homogeneous knock protection
  mode, 273
Homogeneous lean mode, 273
Homogeneous mode, 272
Homogeneous stratified mode, 273
Honda
  BUS communications, 172
  ECT sensor (resistance chart), 183
  ECT sensor (voltage chart), 183
  FCX fuel-cell vehicle, 414
  fuel-cell hybrid vehicle
    ultracapacitor, 415
  hybrid electric vehicle safety, 30
  scan display, 172
  scan tool, 46, 173, 384
  toque wrench calibration, 10
Honda Civic GX
  CNG storage tank, 102
  fuel injectors, 102
Horizontally opposed engine design, 51
Horsepower
  altitude and, 59
  formula, 55
  fuel flow and, 87
  generator requirements, 96
  power related, 55
Hose trick, 142
Hot film mass airflow sensor, 205–206
  sensing wire, 206
Hot wire mass airflow sensor,
  206–207
HPA (Hydraulic Power Assist), 419
HPCR (high-pressure common rail)
  fuel delivery, 64, 65
HV (high-voltage), 397
HV (high-voltage) circuits, 397
HVAC (heating, ventilation, and
  air-conditioning), 235
HV cables, 397
HV gloves, 397
  use of, 406–407
Hybrid electric vehicles (HEV), 29–31
Hybridization, 414
Hybrid Synergy Drive (HSD), in
  FCHV, 411
Hydraulic electronic unit injection
  (HEUI)
  components, 64
  operation, 65–66
  O-ring grooves, 65
Hydraulic hybrid storage system, 419
Hydraulic Power Assist (HPA), 419
Hydrocarbons (HC)
  exhaust analysis, 311
  HC too high, 312
  high, cause and correction, 314
  non-methane hydrocarbon
    (NMHC), 311
  strong exhaust smell, 314
Hydrocracking, 82
Hydroelectric power, 422–423
Hydrogen, 410
  no carbon in fuel, 419
Hydrogen storage, 417–418
  high-pressure compressed gas,
    417–418
  liquid hydrogen, 418
Hydrokinetic flow pump, 244
Hydro-lock fault in engine, 91
Hydrometer, for diesel fuel testing, 109
Hydrostatic lock, 142

**I**

IAC (idle air control), 295
  airflow shown, 296
  cleaning passages, 298
  diagnosis, 295
  housing, 296
  typical, 296
IAC (idle air control) valve, 267
  milliamperes, 270
IAC counts, 288
  scan tool, 289
IAT sensor
  DTCs, 185
  in intake manifold, 184
  location, 185
  performance and driveability, 185
  pulse width, 259
  purpose and function, 184–185
  testing, 186
  troubleshooting with DTCs, 188
IC (ignition control), 115
ICM (ignition control module, or
  igniter), 356
IDI (indirect injection diesel) engine, 62
  prechamber and glow plug, 62
Idle air control (IAC), 295
  airflow shown, 296
  cleaning passages, 298
  diagnosis, 295
  housing, 296
  typical, 296
Idle air control (IAC) counts, 288
  scan tool, 289
Idle air control (IAC) valve, 267
  milliamperes, 270
Idle air control passages, cleaning, 298
Idle control, port fuel-injection systems,
  auxiliary air bypass, 267
Idle controls strategy, 191
Idle control strategy, 233
Idle speed control (ISC) motor, 268
Idle vacuum test, 145
IEC (International Electrotechnical
  Commission), voltage
  standards, 398
Ignitable materials, 35
Ignition
  diesel fuel ignition, 62
  external trigger, 76
  ion-sensing, 365
Ignition coil, 355–356
Ignition coil circuits
  bypass control system, 116
  terminology, 115
Ignition coils, 355
  bad wire, 125
  construction, 105, 355
  operation, 48, 104, 119
  precaution with sparks, 104
Ignition coil testing
  current ramping ignition coils, 119
  current ramping test procedure, 120
  magnetic pickup tool test, 119
  magnetic sensor testing, 368–369
  using an ohmmeter, 119, 367–368
Ignition control (IC), 115
Ignition control (IC) signal, 115
Ignition control circuits, up-integrated
  ignition, 116
Ignition control module (ICM, or igniter)
  ignition coil operation, 105,
    355–356
  operation, 48
  tachometer trick, 109, 358
Ignition delay, 62
Ignition misfire, 223
  false lean indication, 225
  hash pattern, 223–224
Ignition modules, pulse width, 75
Ignition off draw (IOD) test, 86–87
Ignition primary (pickup coil or crank
  sensor) pulse, 289
Ignition scope testing
  converting between units (chart), 136
  dwell section, 134
  firing line, 133
  intermediate oscillations, 134, 136
  pattern selection, 134–135
  spark line, 133–134
  technician's toughie story, 135
  terminology, 133
  transistor-on point, 134

typical scope hookups, 133
  typical secondary pattern, 133
Ignition sensors, operation, 48
Ignition switch
  column-mounted, 90
  cranking circuit, 89
  location, 260
Ignition switching and triggering,
  105–107, 356–358
  primary circuit operation, 106–107,
    357–358
  switching, 105–106, 356–357
  triggering, 106, 357
Ignition systems
  background, 103–104, 354–355
  coil-on-plug ignition, 111–114,
    363–365
  components, 48
  DI, 107, 109, 354, 355, 360
  diagnosis, 118–120, 367–369
  disabling, precautions, 141, 370
  Homogeneous Charge Compression
    Ignition (HCCI), 419
  ignition coil, 104–105, 355–356
  knock sensors, 114–115, 365–366
  power balance test, 144
  purpose and function, 103, 354
  switching and triggering, 105–107,
    356–358
  symptom guide, 138, 376
  testing, 118–120, 367–369
  waste-spark ignition systems,
    110–111, 355, 361–363
Ignition system testing
  checking for spark, 118, 367
  ignition coil testing, 119–120, 367–368
  magnetic sensor testing, 119, 120,
    368–369
Ignition timing, 375
  checking, 130, 375
  initial (base) timing chart, 130, 376
  marks on harmonic balancers,
    130, 376
  purpose, 130, 375
ILEV (inherently low emission
  vehicle), 307
IM 240 test, 310
  OBD-II vehicles, 154
Impact screwdrivers, 12
Impact socket, 20
Impact wrenches, 19–20
Impeller (compressor) wheel, 127
  diagram, 128
I/M test programs, 309
Incandescent lights, 19
Inches of mercury (in. Hg), 144
Inches-of-water manometer
  (gauge), 338
  gauge shown, 338
Indicator ring, fuel-injection lines, 242
Indirect injection diesel (IDI) engine, 62
  prechamber and glow plug, 62
Inductive ammeters, battery electrical
  drain test, 88
Inductive charging, 421
Inert, 327
Inertia switch, 240
  cutaway view, 241
  schematic, 247
Infection control precautions, 29
Infrared thermometer (pyrometer), 348
In. Hg (inches of mercury), 144
Injection pump, diesel engine, 60
  distributor injection pump, 64
  high-pressure common rail, 64
  need for high-pressure, 63
  schematic of Standadyne
    assembly, 64
Injector body, diesel engine, 66
Injector flow rate, 87
Injector pop testing, 77
Injector pressure chamber, diesel
  engine, 66
Injector pulse, testing for, 289–290
Injector pulse width (PW), 258
Injector pump, diesel fuel-injection
  system, 61
Injectors, diesel engine
  calibration number, 78
  precautions about switching, 78
Injector voltage-drop tests, 293–294
Inlet manifold, 115

Inline engines, 49
  exhaust gas control, 327
In-line gasoline blending, 89
Inspection/Maintenance (I/M)
  testing, 310
  age of vehicle and, 312
  evaporative emission system, 322
Instrument panel (IP) electrical center,
  E & C (entertainment and
  comfort) communication, 165
Insulated tools, 403
Insulation tester, 398
Intake air speeds, 115–116
Intake air temperature (IAT), resistance
  and voltage drop versus, 186
Intake air temperature (IAT) sensor
  GM V-6 location, 185
  in intake manifold, 184
  location, 185
  performance and driveability, 185
  pulse width, 259
  purpose and function, 184–185
  testing, 186
Intake air temperature (IAT) sensor
  testing, 186
Intake manifold pressure, how altitude
  affects, 201
Intake manifold runners, sonic
  tuning, 116
Intake manifolds
  airflow, 117
  clogged EGR passages, 333
  inlet manifold, 115
  long or short runners, 116
  plastic intake, 116–117
  upper and lower, 117
  variable, 116
Intake manifold vacuum
  calculating, 197
  fuel pressure related (chart), 262
Intake regulator, DDS, 264
Intake systems
  air intake infiltration, 113–115
  port fuel-injection intake manifolds,
    116–117
  throttle-body injection intake
    manifolds, 115–116
Intake valve overlap, 124
Intake valves, 49
  carbon deposits, 275
Integrated starter alternator (ISA), 29
Integrated starter generator (ISG), 29
Intercooler, 129
  Subaru, 129
Interior protection, 23
Intermediate oscillations, 134
  reading, 136
Intermittent malfunctions,
  diagnosing, 392
Intermittent spark, 382
Internal air manifold, 339
Internal combustion engine, 46
  air pressure related, 196
International Automotive Technicians
  Network, 210
International Electrotechnical
  Commission (IEC), voltage
  standards, 398
Internet, 3
Inverters, fuel-cell hybrid vehicle, 416
Ion-sensing ignition, 114–115, 365
  applied voltage for ion-sensing, 114
"IR" drop. See Voltage drop
Iridium spark plugs, 127, 372
ISA (integrated starter alternator), 29
ISC (idle speed control) motor, 268
ISG (integrated starter generator), 29
Isooctane, 86
Isuzu, Flex Fuel vehicles, 99

**J**

J2534 reprogramming, 393–394
  setup, 394
  view of typical, 394
Jacks, 25–26
Japanese vehicles, vane airflow
  sensor, 205
Jeep, distributor indexing, 132
Jump starting, 27, 85, 401
  cable usage guide, 84
  ground for, 85
  preventing cables from touching, 85

## K

KAM (long-term memory), 155
Karman Vortex air flow sensor
  basic designs, 207
  schematic, 207
Keep it simple engine testing, 140
Key-on—engine off (KOEO) test, 387
  oxygen sensor test, 220
Key-on—engine-running (KOER) test, 387–388
Keyword 81, 82, and 2000 serial data, 165, 167
Knives, utility, 15
Knocks, diagnosing, 138–139
Knock sensor (KS)
  diagnosing, 114–115, 366
  items that can fool, 115
  loose accessory drive belt, 115
  purpose and function, 114, 365–366
  replacing, 115
  typical location, 115
  typical waveform, 115, 366
Knock sensors, 365–366
KOEO (ignition key off, engine off), 96
KOEO test, on-demand codes or hard faults, 387
KOER (ignition key off, engine running), 96
  self-test, 387–388

## L

LAF (lean air-fuel) sensor, 229
Lambda, rich and lean exhaust readings, 226
Lambda sensor, 226
  calculating lambda, 227
Laser-calibrated potentiometer, 205
Latency period, 37
Latex surgical gloves, 22
Laughing gas, 132
LDP (leak detection pump), 321
Lead-acid battery waste, 41
Leak detection pump (LDP), 321
Leak detection pump system
  operation, 321
  purpose and function, 321
Leaks, diesel engine, 78
Leak tester, EVAP system, 322
Lean air-fuel (LAF) sensor, 229
Lean exhaust, 233
  lambda higher than 1.00, 226
  positive current, 233
Lean indicator, 313
LED (light-emitting diode), 19
LEV (low emission vehicle), 306
Lexus
  D4s system, 274
  direct fuel injection, 270
  GDI, 274
  intake valve deposits, 275
  port- and direct injection, 274
Lift points, 402
Lift pump, 63
Light-emitting diode (LED), 19
Lighter plug trick, 97
Light-off converters (LOCs), 345
Light-off temperature (LOT), 344
Light-off time (LOT), 231
Light shield, 109, 360
Limp home mode, 281
LIN (local interconnect network), 173
Lincoln, Town Car speedometer, 260
Linear EGR valve, 330
  General Motors, 330
Lineman's gloves, 398
Lineman's pliers, 13
Line wrenches, 8
Liquefied natural gas (LNG), 103
Liquid hydrogen, 418
  refueling with, 418
  solid state of hydrogen, 418
Liquid petroleum gas (LPG), 101
Liters to cubic inches chart, 57
LNG (liquefied natural gas), 103
Load detection, MAP sensor signals, 201
Loaded mode test, 309
Load response control (LRC), 101
Load test, 83
Local interconnect network (LIN), 173
Lock box for ignition keys, 402
Locking pliers, 14

LOCs (light-off converters), 345
Longitudinal mounting, 49, 51
Long-term memory (KAM), 155
Loose gas cap, 322
Loud knocking sounds, diagnosing, 138–139
Low-authority sensors, 208
Low emission vehicle (LEV), 306
Low-grade heat, in fuel-cell cooling systems, 414
Low-pressure lock-off, 103
Low-pressure regulator, 103
LPG (liquefied petroleum gas or propane), 101
LP-gas, 101
Lubrication system
  diagram, 48
  operation, 48
Lung cancer, 37

## M

M85, 101
MAF (mass airflow) sensors, 205
  analog versus digital, 206
  burn-off circuit, 207
  checking hose, 209
  contamination, 209–210
  dirty MAF sensor story, 208
  DTCs, 210
  false air, 209
  five-wire unit shown, 206
  high-authority sensors, 208
  PCM uses, 207–208
  testing, 208–209
  types, 205–207
  unplug it test, 209
MAF sensor contamination, 209–210
Magnetic crankshaft position sensors, 106, 357
  AC coupling, 74
  variable field strength, 107, 358
Magnetic crankshaft sensors, AC coupling position, 74
Magnetic field, 355
Magnetic pickup tool, 119, 120
Magnetic pulse alternator, 106, 357
  operational diagram, 106, 357
Magnetic sensor, 106, 357
  testing, 119, 120, 122, 368–369
Magnetic vehicle speed sensors, AC coupling, 74
Magnetic wheel speed sensors, AC coupling, 74
Main-bearing knock noise, 139
Malfunction indicator lamp (MIL), 153
  code 12, 386
  DTCs, 382
Mallets, 12–13
Manifold absolute pressure (MAP) sensor, 196
  altitude impact, 200
  barometric pressure changes with altitude, 202
  ceramic disc MAP sensor, 199
  construction, 196–199
  defective vacuum hose, 202
  DTCs, 203
  fuel delivery, 257
  high vacuum, applying, 202
  PCM uses, 199–201
  showing three wires, 198
  voltage chart showing altitude, 202
Manifold absolute pressure (MAP) sensor testing
  using a DMM or scope, 202
  using scan tool, 202
Manufacturer's diagnostic routines, 394
MAP (manifold absolute pressure) sensor, 196
  altitude impact, 200
  capacitor-capsule MAP sensor, 198
  ceramic disc MAP sensor, 199
  construction, 196–199
  defective vacuum hose, 202
  DTCs, 203
  fuel delivery, 257
  high vacuum, applying, 202
  PCM uses, 199–201
  showing three wires, 198
  silicon diaphragm strain gauge map sensor, 198
  for training purposes, 197

as vacuum gauge, 200
  voltage chart showing altitude, 202
MAP (manifold absolute pressure) sensor testing
  types of test instruments, 202
  using a DMM or scope, 202
  using a scan tool, 202
Marine cranking amperes (MCA), 81
Married coils, 355
Martensite steel, 6
Mass, 234
Mass airflow (MAF) sensors, 206
  air cleaner housing, 114
  analog versus digital, 206
  burn-off circuit, 207
  checking hose, 209
  contamination, 209–210
  dirty MAF sensor story, 208
  DTCs, 210
  false air, 209
  five-wire unit shown, 206
  high-authority sensors, 208
  PCM uses, 207–208
  types, 205–207
    hot film sensor, 205–206
    hot wire sensor, 206–207
  unplug it test, 209
Mass airflow (MAF) sensor testing
  digital meter test, 208–209
  output test, 208
  tap test, 208
  visual inspection, 208
Mass airflow fuel-injection system, 258
  formula, 258
Master Tech, 47
  display shown, 48
Material safety data sheets (MSDS), 36
Maximum duty cycle, fuel injector, 265
Mazda
  direct fuel injection, 270
  Flex Fuel vehicles, 99
  how to read VIN, 100
MCA (marine cranking amperes), 81
MEA (Membrane Electrolyte Assembly), 412
Mechanical compression ratio, 124
Mechanical force, 46
Mechanical power, 46
Mechanical-related complaints, 135
Mechanical returnless fuel system (MRFS), 263
  diagram, 263
Mechanic's gloves, 22
Media oriented system transport (MOST) BUS communication, 172
Membrane Electrode Assembly (MEA), 412
Memory, after battery electrical drain test, 87
Memory saver, 87
Mercaptan, 101
Mercedes
  direct fuel injection, 270
  ECT sensor, 183
Mercedes-Benz
  B-Class fuel-cell car, 411
  Flex Fuel vehicles, 99
  how to read VIN, 100
Mercury (element), 42, 43
Mercury, Flex Fuel vehicles, 99
Mercury Mariner, 30
Mesothelioma, 37
Metallic compound, 878
Methanol (methyl alcohol), 100–101
  as "carbon-neutral," 414
  described, 87
  direct methanol fuel cells, 413
  energy density, 413
  M85, 101
  as octane improver, 87
  production of, 90
Methanol to gasoline (MTG), 105
Methyl alcohol. See Methanol
Methylcyclopentadienyl manganese tricarbonyl (MMT), 87
Methyl hydrate (methanol), 100
Methyl tertiary butyl ether (MTBE), 88
Metric bolts, 4–5
MI (Motorola interconnect) BUS protocol, 172
Micron, 113

MID (Monitor Identification), 47
MIL (malfunction indicator lamp), 153
  code 12, 386
  DTCs, 382
  OBD-I requirements, 153
MIL condition: FLASHING, 157
MIL condition: OFF, 157
MIL condition: ON STEADY, 157
Millisecond (ms) sweep, 136
Milliseconds, 73
Mini clamp-on DMM, AC current check, 98
Mini converter, 345
MIN/MAX oxygen sensor test chart, 218
Misfire diagnosis, 148
Misfire monitor, 154–155
Misfires, MIL on steady, 157
Misfire type A, 155
Misfire type B, 155
Missing Ford Escort story, 216
Mitsubishi
  direct fuel injection, 270
  smart idle stop system (SISS), 274–275
  Start-Stop system, 274
MMT (methylcyclopentadienyl manganese tricarbonyl), 87
Mode $06
  data display, 48
    Chart 1, 48–49
    Chart 2, 49
  definition, 48
  diagnosing problems with, 47, 161
  reading data, 48
  replacing oscilloscope, 51
  select monitor (results), 48
  service information websites, 52
  using, 48
  where to find more information, 52
Moderate hash defined, 223
Modular fuel sender assembly, 244–245
  spring loaded, 245
Module communications
  advantages, 162
  configuration, 163
  need for network, 162
  network fundamentals, 162–163
Module current limits, 119
Module status test, 173–174
Monitor Identification (MID), 47
Monitors, 154–155
  CCM, 154, 155
  continuous, 154–155
  continuous running, 155
  enabling criteria, 156–157
  exponentially weighted moving average (EWMA), 156
  misfire, 154–155
  noncontinuous, 155
  once per trip, 155–156
Monolithic converters, 343
Most (media oriented system transport) BUS communication, 172
Motorola interconnect (MI) BUS protocol, 172
Moving a hybrid vehicle in the shop, 402
MSDS (material safety data sheets), 36
Mufflers
  clogged or restricted, 146
  construction, 120–121
  hole location, 121
  holes in, 121
  passage diagram, 120
  purpose and function, 120
Multigroove adjustable pliers, 13
Multimeters, CAT III-rated digital multimeter, 398
Multiplexing, 162
  advantages, 162–163
Multiport fuel injector, 265
Muscle car engine, 339

## N

Narrow band oxygen sensor, 230
NASTF (National Automotive Service Task Force), service information, 161
NASTF (National Automotive Service Task Force) website, 52
NASTF website, 394

National Automotive Service Task
Force (NASTF), service
information sites, 161
National Automotive Service Task
Force (NASTF) website, 52, 394
National Electric Drag Racing
Association (NEDRA), 422
Naturally aspirated, 53, 123
airflow requirements, 123
volumetric efficiency, 123
NEDRA (National Electric Drag Racing
Association), 422
Needle nose pliers, 14
Negative backpressure, 328
Negative O2S voltage, 224–225
causes, 225
Negative slope, 76
Negative temperature coefficient
(NTC), 179
Negative temperature coefficient
(NTC) sensor, 186
Negative temperature coefficient
(NTC) thermistor, 184
Nernst cell, 232
Nernst, Walter, 232
Network, 162
diagnosis, 173–175
fundamentals, 162–163
module communications, 163
types of, 162–163
Neutral position, 279
Neutral safety switch, 90
New Zealand, 105
NGVs, 102
Nickel-metal hydride (NiMH) batteries
disposal of, 402–403
paint oven damage to, 403
storing, 403
NiMH (nickel-metal hydride) batteries
disposal of, 402–403
paint oven damage to, 403
storage, 403
Nippondenso fuel injectors, 264
Nissan
ECT sensor, 183
Flex Fuel vehicles, 99
how to read VIN, 100
optical sensor testing, 124
Nitrile gloves, 22
Nitrogen gas pressurization, 323
emission tester, 323
Nitrogen oxides (NOx), formation and
control, 327
Nitrous bottles
angles for, 132
electric warming blankets for, 132, 133
Nitrous oxide (N₂O), 132
engine changes needed, 133
engine power adder, 132
pressure and temperature, 132
system installation and
calibration, 133
temperature/pressure chart, 132
wet and dray system, 132
Nitrous oxide injection system,
precautions, 133
NMHC (non-methane hydrocarbon), 311
No crank story, 91
Node, 162
communicate with other
modules, 163
Noid, use of term, 290
Noid light, 289–290
precautions with, 290
Noise, engine, 138–139
Noise issues, GDI systems, 275
Nonchecking, 262
Noncontinuous monitors, 155
Nonenhanced evaporative (EVAP)
control systems, 318–319
Non-methane hydrocarbon
(NMHC), 311
Nonprincipal end, 53
Nonsynchronized throttle-body
fuel-injection, 258
Northeast Ozone Transport Region, 308
No-spark (intermittent spark)
condition
causes, 118, 367
spark tester, 368
symptom guide, 138, 376

No-start condition
Chevrolet pickup V-8, 122
diagnosis, 132
electronic fuel-injection systems, 289
ignition system diagnosis, 118, 367
inoperative electric fuel pump, 250
radio shorted-to-ground, 176
tachometer trick, 109, 358
NOx. See Oxides of nitrogen
NTC (negative temperature
coefficient) thermistor, 184
Nuts, 6

O

OBD (on-board diagnosis), 153
OBD Generation I (OBD-I), 153
OBD-I
California requirements, 153
General Motors vehicles, 386
self-test connector (Ford), 387
OBD-I Ford, 168
data link connector, 168
OBD-II (onboard diagnosis second
generation)
16 pin DLC, 176
active tests, 391–392
background, 153
catalytic converter performance,
345–346
data link connector, view
of typical, 388
diagnosis, 388–391
DLC (data link connector), 176
DTC numbering designation, 157–158
enhanced evaporative control
systems, 319–320
freeze-frame, 391–392
freeze frame data, 154, 158
global, 160
location of terminals, 173
monitor information, 155–156
objectives, 153–154
oxidation and reduction sections, 345
testing, 310
OBD-II EGR monitoring strategies
delta pressure feedback EGR
(DPFE) sensor, 331
MAP sensor as EGR monitor, 331
OBD-II active test, 332
oxygen in exhaust, 331
purpose and function, 331–332
OBD-II scan tool, dual cell
diagnosis, 234
Occupational Health and Safety Act
(OSHA), 35, 37
safety gloves, 397
Octane improver additives, 87
Octane rating, 86
antiknock properties, 85
high-altitude, 87
Off-board programming, 393
connecting cables and
computer, 393
Offset left aviation snips, 15
Offset right aviation snips, 15
Offset screwdrivers, 11–12
Ohmmeter
coil shorted to ground, 122,
368–369
ignition coil testing, 119, 367–368
measuring injector resistance, 291
measuring pickup coil resistance, 368
setup for testing ignition coil, 120, 368
Oil burning, simple engine testing, 140
Oil change
Ford diesel engines, 66
procedures, 404
Oil condition, diagnostic process,
379, 381
Oil drain back holes, 337
Oil filter disposal, 39
Oil fouling, 128, 373
Oil galleries, 48
Oil leaks
black light to spot, 138
blue exhaust smoke, 135
checking with engine off, 337
fluorescent dye, 138
foot powder spray trick, 138
visual inspection, 137–138
where they appear, 138

Oil level and condition, visual
inspection, 136
Oil pan gaskets, leak, 137
Oil pressure gauge, fabrication, 139
Oil pressure sending (sender) unit
location, 140
Oil pressure testing, 140–141
gauge use, 140
Oil pressure warning lamp, 140
Oil return (drain) line, clogged, 131
Oil, used, 38–39
Oil/vapor separator, 335
Oil/water separator, 335
On-board diagnosis (OBD), 153
On-Board Diagnostics (OBDs), 153
Onboard diagnosis second
generation. See OBD-II
Onboard refueling vapor recovery
(ORVR), 239, 321
reduced-size fill tube, 239
Once per trip monitors, 155–156
One-minute test, 84
One-speed and two-speed idle
test, 309
One-wire oxygen sensor, 213
Opacity, 78
Opacity test, 78
Open-circuit battery voltage test, 82
Open-end wrenches, 8
Open-loop operation, 214
Optical distributors, 107, 358
cutaway view, 108, 360
light shield installation, 109, 360
one-degree slits, 108, 360
Optical sensors, 107, 358
testing, 122–123, 369
visual inspection, 122–123, 369
Orange-colored cables, 397
Orifice-controlled PCV systems, 336
Original equipment, 379
O-rings, 65–66
location on Ford PowerStroke
diesel engine, 65
symptoms of trouble, 66
ORVR (onboard refueling vapor
recovery), 239, 321
reduced-size fill tube, 239
OSC (oxygen storage capacity), 345
Oscilloscopes
COP system, 137–138
definition, 72
display grid, 72
fuel injector testing, 294–295
Hall-effect sensor testing,
122–123
MAP sensor testing, 202
Mode $06 replacing, 51
number of channels, 75–76
optical sensor testing, 124
setup and adjustments, 73–74
TP sensor testing, 234
triggers, 76
types of, 72
using, 77–78
waste-spark system, 137
OSHA (Occupational Health and
Safety Act), 35, 37
safety gloves, 397
OTC Genisys, 47
OTC scan tools, 384
Otto, Nickolaus, 49
Output test, MAF sensor, 208
Overhead camshaft engine, 364
Overhead valve (OHV), 51
cutaway of V-8 engine, 52
Overheating, diagnostic process, 381
Overlap, 124
Oxides of nitrogen (NOx)
burning or watery eyes, 314
catalytic converter role, 348
clogged EGR passages, 333
EGR control of, 327
emission control, 327
excessive, causes of, 314
exhaust analysis, 311
high, causes and correction, 315
specifications, 314
testing for, 314
Oxygen (O2)
exhaust analysis, 311
measuring, 313

Oxygenated fuels, 88
storage life, 100
Oxygen level test, 348
Oxygen sensor (O2S), 212
closed loop and open loop, 214
construction and operation, 212–213
conventional O2S review, 230–232
diagnosis, 215–218
different designs, 213
DTCs, 227
DTC troubleshooting, 227
exhaust system back pressure, 147
false rich indication, 225
front and rear connector
switched, 214
fuel trim, 215
GM CAN Mode 406 test, 50–51
high O2S readings, 225
how voltage is generated (view), 213
as lambda sensor, 226
location, 212
low O2S readings, 225
with low pulse width, 315
metal shield missing, 225
numbering and location, 214, 215
pending monitor, 158
poor ground connection, 230
pulse width, 259
stoichiometric air-fuel ratio
response, 213
visual inspection, 226–227
volts per division (V/div), 74
wide-band, 229
Oxygen sensor (O2S) testing
false rich signal, 230
KOEO, 220
KOEO test, 220
propane oxygen sensor test, 220
using a digital voltmeter, 215–217
using a scan tool, 217–218
using a scope, 232
using MIN/MAX method, 217
Oxygen sensor cross counts,
217–218
Oxygen sensor heater, Mode $06
test, 50
Oxygen sensor Mode $06 test,
Ford, 50
Oxygen sensor waveform analysis,
218, 221
with DSO, 219
frequency, 221
good reading, 233
hash, 221–224
negative O2S voltage, 224–225
other rules concerning hash, 224
rapid switching, 232, 233–234
Oxygen storage capacity (OSC), 345
Ozone, 313

P

Palladium, 344
Pancake engine design, 49
Paper test, 141, 381
shown, 141
Parameter identification (PID), 160
Parameter identification (PID)
display, 46
chart, 385
Parasitic draw, 174
Parasitic load test, 87
Parasitic load tool, 88
Particulate matter (PM)
definition, 71
relative size, 71
standards, 71
PASS fire extinguisher procedure, 28
PCI (programmable controller
interface), 170
PCM (powertrain control module)
air-fuel ratio sensing, 128
coil-over-plug-type ignition
systems, 113–114, 364–365
determination of faults chart, 159
differential "delta" pressure, 72
drive cycle, 156
drive the light out, 395
E85 fuel system requirements, 98
EGR valve, 70
EGT 1 and EGT 2 use, 72
EGT sensor signals, 72

fuel trim, 215
General Motors exception, 100
glow plugs, 67
HEUI system, 65
MAP sensor uses, 199–201
procedures for resetting, 395
retrieving diagnostic information,
384–385
signal from knock sensors, 114,
365–366
spring test, 279
TP sensor uses, 191, 233
transmission fluid temperature
signal, 187
uses of oxygen sensor, 214–215
in virtual flexible fuel vehicle, 98
PCV (positive crankcase ventilation)
system, 335–338
checking oil leaks, 337
PCV (positive crankcase ventilation)
system diagnosis
3 X 5 card test, 337–338
crankcase vacuum test, 338
DTCs, 338
PCV monitor, 338
rattle test, 324
snap-back test, 338
symptoms, 336–337
system performance check, 337
PCV (pressure control valve), 263
PCV inlet air filter, 335
PCV monitor, 338
PCV valve with fastener, 338
PCV system, 335–338
PCV system performance check, 337
PCV valves, 335–336
airflows, 336
backfire operation shown, 336
crankcase ventilation, 335–336
ice blockage prevention, 338
spring-operated plunger, 336
whistling engine noise, 336
wires at, 338
Peak-and-hold fuel-injector
waveforms, 294–295
Pedestal-mounted grinders, 21–22
Peen, 12
PEFC (Polymer Electrolyte Fuel
Cell), 412
PEM (Proton Exchange Membrane), 412
fuel cell, 412–413
PEM fuel cells, 412–413
direct current (DC) electricity from, 412
"five nines" purity, 412
humidifier role in, 413
Pending, 158
Pending codes, 382
scan tools, 158
Performance problems
aftermarket air filter, 121
cracked exhaust manifold, 119
EVAP system problems, 322
racing manifolds, 116
smaller diameter pulley, 126
Toyota, 115, 366
Peripheral pump, 244
Permanent magnet (PM)
sensors, 260
Personal protective equipment (PPE),
21–22, 35
Petrodiesel, 111
Petroleum, 81
Petroleum diesel, 111
PFE sensor, 329
PHEV (plug-in hybrid electric
vehicle), 420
Phillips screwdrivers, 11
Photochemical smog formation, 313
Pickup coil, 106, 357
AC voltage output, 122, 369
magnetic sensor testing, 119,
120, 369
showing how waveform created, 122
tachometer trick, 109, 358
waveforms and speed related, 123
PID (parameter identification), 160
PID (parameter identification)
display, 46
Piezoresistive crystal, 196
Piezoresistivity, 198
Pillar post, 2
Pinch weld seams, 24

Ping, 85–86
EGR system, 328
knock sensors, 114–115, 365–366
octane rating related, 88
Ping modules, 173–174
Pinpoint tests, 388
Pipelines, 82
Piping, damaged or defective, 146
Piston pin knock, 138
Piston rings, friction and engine
speed, 55
Pistons, bore and stroke shown, 54
Piston slap, 138
Piston stroke, 49
compression stroke, 49, 50
exhaust stroke, 49, 50
intake stroke, 49, 50
power stroke, 49, 50
Piston top designs, 273
Pitch, 4
Planar design, 231
dual cell, 232
Planar design zirconia oxygen sensor,
schematic, 232
Plantinum electrodes, conventional
oxygen sensor, 231
Plasma, 114, 365
Plastic intake manifolds, 116–117
construction, 116
Plastic optical fiber (POF), 173
Platinum, 344
Platinum electrodes, zirconia oxygen
sensor, 232
Platinum spark plugs, 127, 372
Plenum, 117
Pliers, 13–15
Plug-in hybrid electric vehicle
(PHEV), 420
PM (particulate matter)
definition, 71
relative size, 71
standards, 71
PM (permanent magnet)
sensors, 260
PM10, 71
PM.25, 71
POF (plastic optical fiber), 173
Poisoning, chemical, 39
Polyglycol, 38
Polymer electrolyte fuel cell (PEFC), 412
Polysaccharides, 96
Polyurethane gloves, 22
Pop tester, 77
typical, 77
Portable exhaust analyzer, 314
Port fuel-injection systems, 256
advantages, 258–259
air cleaner housing, 114
checking fuel-injector resistance, 291
diagnosis, 289
diagram, 267
fuel-pressure regulator shown, 261
fuel pump current draw, 253
gasoline direct-injection
compared, 273
grouped double-fire, 259
location of various components, 257
manifold runners, 260
nozzle assembly, 260
oxygen sensor reading, 221, 222
plastic intake manifolds, 116–117
pressure regulator diagnosis, 286
sequential fuel injection (SFI),
259, 260
simultaneous double-fire, 259
terminology, 116
two injectors per cylinder, 260
upper and lower intake manifolds, 117
variable intakes, 116
Positive backpressure, 328
Positive crankcase ventilation (PCV)
systems, 335–338
plugged, 131
Positive crankcase ventilation (PCV)
valve
checking, 287
clogged, 287
Positive displacement design, 126
Positive displacement fuel pump,
243–244
detail shown, 244
Positive slope, 76

Post-catalytic converter sensor
testing, 226
Postinjection impulses, 73
Potentiometer, 190
laser-calibrated, 205
throttle position signal voltage, 190
TP sensors, 280
typical mount, 190
Pounding tools, 13
Pour point for diesel fuel, 108
Power, definition, 58
Power adder, 132
Power balance test, 144
procedure, 144
Power control unit (PCU), fuel-cell
hybrid vehicle, 416–417
Power steering fluid, color of leak, 137
Powerstroke troubleshooting chart, 76
Powertrain control modules (PCMs)
air-fuel ratio sensing, 128
coil-over-plug-type ignition
systems, 113–114, 364–365
determination of faults chart, 159
differential "delta" pressure, 72
drive cycle, 156
drive the light out, 395
E85 fuel system requirements, 98
EGR valve, 70
EGT 1 and EGT 2 use, 72
EGT sensor signals, 72
fuel trim, 215
General Motors exception, 100
glow plugs, 67
HEUI system, 65
MAP sensor uses, 199–201
procedures for resetting, 395
retrieving diagnostic information,
384–385
signal from knock sensors, 114,
365–366
spring test, 279
TP sensor uses, 191, 233
transmission fluid temperature
signal, 187
uses of oxygen sensor, 214–215
in virtual flexible fuel vehicle, 98
PPE (personal protective equipment),
21–22, 35
PPO (pure plant oil), 111
Pre-combustion chamber, 67
Preconverter, 345
Pressure control valve (PCV), 263
Pressure differential, 196
Pressure-drop balance test, 293
Pressure feedback EGR (PFE)
sensor, 329
Pressure gauge
testing back pressure, 147
testing backpressure with,
346–347
Pressure regulator
diagnosis, 286
gasoline in vacuum hose, 286
Pressure sensors, principles of, 196
Pressure transducer, 287
Pressure-type Karman Vortex
sensor, 207
Pressure vacuum filler cap, 239
Pressure vent valve (PVV), 263
Prevailing torque nuts, 7
Priestly, Joseph, 37
Primary ignition circuit, 106–107, 356
diagram, 106, 357
operation, 106–107, 357–358
Primary winding
connections, 105, 355
definition, 105
location, 105, 355
waveform showing primary current
flow, 120
Princeton University P-series fuel,
103–104
Principal end, 53
Programmable controller interface
(PCI), 170
Propane, 101
Propane oxygen sensor test, 220
fuel rich reading, 221
shut off reading, 221
Protocol, 165
Proton Exchange Membrane (PEM), 412
PEM fuel cells, 412–413

P-series fuels, 103–104
composition of, 104
Pulse alternator (pick-up coil), 357
Pulse train, 74–75
definition, 74
frequency, 75
Pulse width
definition, 75
injector on-time shown, 294
Pulse-width modulated type of
injector drive circuit, 295
Pulse-width modulation (PWM), 75
Pump cell, 232
Punches, 15–16
warning, 16
Pup (mini) converter, 345
Pure plant oil (PPO), 111
Purge valve, 321
problems after refueling, 321
Pushrod engines, 51
PVV (pressure vent valve), 263
PWM (pulse-width modulated) signal,
throttle plate motor, 279
Pyrometer (infrared thermometer), 348
Pyrotechnic devices, 42
PZEV (partial zero-emission vehicle), 307

Q
Quick and easy ECT test, 185
Quick and easy fuel volume test, 252
Quick-connector separator tool, 242

R
Racing manifolds, 116
Radiator cap, testing ECT sensor, 180
Radiators, coolant level check
precautions, 136
Radio
battery replacement issues, 87
E & C (entertainment and comfort)
communication, 165
no-start story, 176
security code to unlock, 87, 386
Radioactive materials, 35
Ramps, drive-on, 26
Random roadside testing, 310
Range, on a full battery charge, 421
Rapid combustion phase, 62–63
Raster (stacked) position of ignition
oscilloscopes, 135
Ratchets, 9, 10–11
Rationality tests, 155
enabling monitor, 159
MAP and MAF sensors, 191
Rattle noise, 139
Rattle test, 337
RCRA (Resource Conservation and
Recovery Act), 36
Reactive materials, 35
Rear main seal, 135
Recalls, 4
Red lightning bolt symbol, 282
Reduced power warning light, 281
Reference electrodes, 232
Reference voltage, 232
Refining
cracking, 82
crude oil types, 81
distillation, 81–82
major steps and processes, 82
shipping, 82
Reformulated gasoline (RFG), 89–90
Refueling, problems after, 321
Regeneration
diesel particulate filter, 73
process, 73
types of DPFs, 73
Regenerative braking, 417
service, 405
Reid vapor pressure (RVP), 83
Relearn onboard computer, after fuel-
injector service, 298
Reluctor wheel, damaged, 123, 124
Remote programming, 392
Remote sensing, 310
Repairs
completing, 394
previous, as indicator in diagnosis, 379
Reprogramming, 171, 392–393
first step shown, 393
J2534 reprogramming, 393–394

Reserve capacity, 81
    battery drain and, 87
Residual (rest) pressure, 243
Resistance
    ECT sensor measurement, 181
    ECT testing with multimeter, 180
    pickup coils, 122
    voltage drop test for determining, 92
Resistance values, 180
Resistor spark plugs, 127, 372
Resistors, terminating, 174
Resonance tube, 115
Resonators, 120
Resource Conservation and Recovery
    Act (RCRA), 36
Rest pressure test, 250
Restricted exhaust, 146
Revolutions per minute (RPM),
    frequency, 75
RFG (reformulated gasoline), 89–90
Rhodium, 344
Rich exhaust, 233
    lambda less than 1.00, 226
    negative current, 233
Rich indicator, 312
Right-to-know laws, 36
Rigid fuel lines, 241
Ring link networks, 163, 164
Ring/star hybrid networks, 165
Ripple voltage, 74
Road test, 395
Robertson screwdrivers, 12
Rochester Multec fuel injectors, 264
Rocker cover gaskets, checking for
    leaks, 137
Rod-bearing noise, 139
Roller cell (vane) fuel pump, 243
Rolling acceleration test, 78
Rollover leakage protection, 240
    check valve, 240
    inertia switch, 240
Roots, Philander and Francis, 126
Roots supercharger, 126
    blower and intercooler, 127
    two lobes, 126
Rotary engine, 52
    rotor use, 53
Rotary vane fuel pump, 243–244
    action shown, 244
Rotating assembly, 46
    V-8 engine, 47
Rotation direction, 53
Rotation speed, 55
Rotor gap voltage, 137
Rubber gloves, for high-voltage
    safety, 398
Rubber mallet trick, 250
Running (dynamic) compression test,
    142–143
    procedure, 143
RVP (Reid vapor pressure), 83

S

SAE (Society of Automotive
    Engineers), 157
Safety
    air hose, 27
    alternative fuels, 106
    battery service, 81
    chisel, 16
    cutter, 15
    file, 15
    hacksaw, 16
    hammer, 13
    hand, 39
    hybrid electric vehicle, 29–31
    infection control precautions, 29
    lifting vehicles, 23–25
    mallet, 13
    plier, 15
    precautions list, 22
    punch, 16
    ratchet, 10–11
    screwdriver, 12
    shop cloth disposal, 23
    socket, 10–11
    wrench, 8–9
Safety cones, for high-voltage
    servicing, 399
Safety glasses, 21
Safety gloves, 397
    HV gloves, 406–407

Safety stands, 24, 25–26
SAI (secondary air-injection) system
    air distribution manifolds and
        nozzles, 339
    belt-driven air pumps, 340
    diagnosis, 340–341
    electric motor-driven air pumps, 340
    exhaust check valves, 339
    operation chart, 341
    parts and operation, 339
    purpose and function, 339
    typical components, 339
    visual inspection, 340–341
SAI pump, 339
    electric motor-driven, 340
Sampling rates, 72
Saran resin, 240
Saturated switch-type injector-driven
    circuit, 294
Saturation, 294
Saturn, waste-spark ignition system,
    111, 362
Scan tool data (PID), 234
Scan tools, 384
    aftermarket, 384
    battery or system voltage, 83
    bias voltage, 215
    checking battery voltage, 83, 84
    data link connector (DLC), 172, 383
    drive cycle, 156
    dual cell diagnosis, 234
    ECT sensor testing, 183–184
    engine speed in RPM, 83
    engine testing procedure, 232
    erasing DTCs, 158
    ETC readings, 282
    EVAP system, 318
    factory versus generic, 160
    Ford SCP BUS, 168
    fuel-system diagnostics, 299
    generator testing, 97
    global OBD-II, 160
    global OBD II modes, 46
    global versus factory, 46
    GM Tech 2 scan tool, 174
    Honda, 173
    Honda/Toyota communications, 172
    how to use data, 383
    IAC counts, 289
    incorrect vehicle year, 386
    MAP sensor testing, 202
    oxygen sensor testing, 231–232
    parameter identification (PID), 385
    ping modules, 173–174
    retrieving diagnostic information,
        384–385
    single cell wide-band oxygen
        sensor, 235, 236
    starter testing, 91–92
    TP sensor testing, 193, 234
    vacuum leak diagnosis, 288
Schematics, computer data line
    circuit schematic, 176
Schematic symbols
    BUS systems, 166
    memory saver, 87
Schmitt trigger, 107, 358
Schrader valve, 250
    fuel pressure gauge with, 289
    location in GM V-6, 250
SCI (serial communications
    interface), 170
Scope test leads, 77
SCP (standard corporate protocol), 168
SCR (selective catalytic reduction), 74
    advantages/disadvantages, 74
Screwdrivers, 11–12
Screw heads, 4
Sealed Housing for Evaporative
    Determination (SHED) test, 308
Secondary air-injection (SAI) system, 339
    air distribution manifolds and
        nozzles, 339
    belt-driven air pumps, 340
    diagnosis, 340–341
    DTCs, 341
    electric motor-driven air pumps, 340
    exhaust check valves, 339
    operation chart, 341
    parts and operation, 339
    purpose and function, 339
    visual inspection, 340–341

Secondary battery, in fuel-cell hybrid
    vehicle, 415
Secondary ignition circuit, 105, 356
Secondary winding, 355
Security code to unlock radio, 87, 386
Selective catalytic reduction (SCR),
    advantages/disadvantages, 74
Self-test automatic readout (STAR)
    tester, 387
Sensorless Flex-Fuel systems, 98
Separator pulse, 387
Separator systems, 336
Sequential fuel injection (SFI), 259, 260
    color of wires, 260
Sequential gasoline blending, 89
Serial communications interface
    (SCI), 170
Serial data, 162
Service/flash programming, 392–394
Service information, 3
Service information (SI)
    BUS circuit faults, 175
    computer data line circuit
        schematic, 176
    network communication protocol
        to use, 173
Service manuals, 3
Service plug in HV system, 401
Service procedures, routine, 403–405
    air-conditioning service, 404
    air filter service, 404
    auxiliary battery testing and
        service, 405
    braking system service, 405
    caution with READY indicator, 400
    cooling system service, 404
    diagnosis, 403
    oil change, 404
    steering system service, 405
    tires, 405
Servomotor, 279
720-degree cycle, 49
Severe hash defined, 223
SHED test, 308
Shipping of gasoline, 82
Shoes, disposal, 37
Shoes, steel-toed safety, 21
Shop cloth disposal, 23, 24
Shut-off tool for batteries, 88
Shutoff valves
    fuel system procedure, 289
    shown, 290
Side-channel pump, 244
Side cuts, 13
Side-post batteries, 86
Side post battery adaptors, 86
SIDI (Spark Ignition Direct
    Injection), 270
Signal electrode, 231
Significant hash, definition, 223
Silica contamination, 226
Silica deposits, 226
Silicon diaphragm strain gauge map
    sensor, 198
Silicon spray, precautions with, 227
Silicon wafer, 198
Single cell wide-band oxygen sensors
    construction, 234–235
    four wires shown, 236
    testing with millimeter, 235
    testing with scan tool, 235, 236
Single-channel scope, 75
Single cut files, 15
Single overhead camshaft (SOHC)
    design, 51
Single-wire CAN (SWCAN), 166
SIP (State Implementation Plan), 308
SISS (smart idle stop system), 274–275
Six-cylinder engines, cubic inch
    displacement chart, 56
"Skateboard concept", 416
Skewed, 193
Slip-joint pliers, 13
Slip-ring-end (SRE) housing, 95
Smart idle stop system (SISS), 274–275
Smart regulator, 263
Smog, 313
Smog pump, 339
Smoke machine, 381
    checking for leaks in exhaust
        system, 313
    testing, vacuum (air) leaks, 381

Smoke machine testing
    bright light for, 381
    leak detection, 322
    unit shown, 322
Snake trick, 333
Snap acceleration test, 78
Snap-back test, 338
Snap-On 2500, 47
Snap-On Modis, 47
Snap-on scan tool, 384
Snap-On Solus, 47
Snap-ring pliers, 14
Snap-throttle test, 348
Sniff test for gasoline, 91
Snips, 15
Society of Automotive Engineers
    (SAE), 157
    communication, classes of, 165
    distributor ignition (DI), 103
    electronic ignition, 103–104
Socket adapters, 11
Sockets, 9, 10–11
Soft codes, 387
SOHC (single overhead camshaft)
    design, 51
    additional components, 52
Soldering guns, 18
Solenoid-operated starters,
    typical, 90
Solvents, 37, 39–40
Solvent spray, 37
Soot, 71
    in DPF passages, 72
    very small particles, 71
Sound system. See Radio
Spark Ignition Direct Injection
    (SIDI), 270
Spark, intermittent, 118, 367
Spark knock, 85–86, 114–115, 328
    clogged EGR passages, 333
    EGR system, 328
    knock sensors, 365–366
    octane rating related, 88
Spark line, 133–134
    firing line relationship, 137
    length guidelines, 136
    length of, 135, 136
    reading, 135–136
    slope, 136
    upward-sloping, 136
Spark output (SPOUT), 115, 376
Spark plug boot, 126, 371
Spark plugs, 372
    carbon fouling, 128, 129, 373
    clipped side (ground) electrode,
        128, 374
    construction, 126–127, 372
    heat range, 126–127, 372
    heat transfer diagram, 127, 372
    inspecting for wear, 128, 373
    installation, 127, 128, 372, 373
    installation (hose trick), 142
    iridium, 127, 372
    misfire, 225
    normal wear shown, 128, 374
    operation, 48
    overtightening, 129, 373
    parts diagram, 127, 372
    platinum, 127, 372
    polarity, 110–111, 361
    reach, 126, 372
    removal procedure, 128, 373
    resistor type, 127, 372
    seat type, 127, 372
    service, 127, 373
    typical installation torque (chart),
        129, 375
    typical wear shown, 129, 374
Spark plug thread chaser, 128, 373
Spark plug wire boot pliers, 125, 371
Spark plug wire pliers, 125, 371
Spark plug wires
    high voltage problems, 131
    inspection, 125–126, 369–370
    maximum allowable resistance,
        126, 371
    original wiring brackets, 131
    precautions with disconnecting,
        112, 132, 365
    track, 125, 370
    visual inspection, 125, 369–370
    water spray bottle for testing, 126

Spark tester, 367
  with alligator clip, 118, 367
  always use, 119, 368
  diagnosis, 118, 367
  diagnostic process, 367
  recessed center close-up, 119, 367
Special service tools (SST), 19
Specific energy, of hydrogen, 410
Specific gravity, diesel fuel
  testing, 109
Speed density, 199
Speed-density fuel-injection system,
  256–258
  central port injection, 265
  demand delivery system, 263
  fuel injectors, 264
  idle control, 266–267
  MAP sensor values, 199–200
  modes of operation, 266
  stepper motor operation, 267
Splash gasoline blending, 89
Splice pack (SP), 163
Spontaneous combustion, 23
SPOUT (spark output), 115, 376
Spray-guided combustion, 273
  diagram, 273
Spreader tool, reinstallation of
  exhaust manifold, 120
Spring-lock connectors, 242
  quick-connect shown, 243
  tool for disassembly, 242
"Spring test," 279
Sprinter, troubleshooting chart, 76
SRE housing, 95
SST (special service tools), 19
Stall acceleration test, 78
Standadyne assembly, schematic, 64
Standard corporate protocol (SCP), 168
STAR (self-test automatic readout)
  tester, 387
Star link networks, 163–164
Starter amperage test, 91
Starter diagnosis chart, 94
Starter drives, cranking circuit, 89
Starter drive-to-flywheel clearance,
  94–95
  checking for proper clearance, 95
  procedure for proper clearance,
    94–95
  shims needed, 95
  touch test, 95
Starter motors
  avoid hitting, 92
  battery condition, 89
  cranking circuit, 89
  diagnosing using visual
    inspection, 90
  diagnosis chart, 94
Starter ring gear, 54
Starter solenoid (relay)
  cranking circuit, 89
  source of battery drain, 89
Starter testing
  check battery, 91
  connections (SUN VAT 45), 91
  starter amperage test, 91
  using scan tool, 91–92
Starting and charging tester, typical
  hookup, 100
Start/stall/start/stall problem, 101
State Implementation Plan (SIP), 308
State of health (SOH), 174
Static electricity, 92
Steam
  blown cylinder head gaskets, 136
  excessive exhaust head gasket
    failure, 148
  possible causes, 135
Steering, brake, and overdrive switch
  test, 388
Steering system service, 405
Steering wheel controls, E & C
  communication, 235
Stepped ECT circuits, 179–180
Stepper motor operation, 267
  disadvantage for ETC, 279
  schematic, 267
Step-up resistor, 179
Stethoscope fuel-injection test, 288
  fuel returning, 288
  lack of sound, 288
Stoichiometric, 232–233

Stoichiometric air-fuel ratio, 85
  CNG, 102
Stone wheels, 21
Straight blade screwdrivers, 11
Straight cut aviation snips, 15
Straight vegetable oil (SVO) as
  fuel, 111
Stratified catalyst heating mode, 273
Stratified mode, 272, 273
Stroke, 54
  how it is determined, 54
Strokes, number of, 49
Studs, 4
Subaru, intercooler, 129
Substrate, 343
SULEV (super ultra low emission
  vehicle), 306–307
Sulfur, 108
SUN VAT 45 starter tester, 91
Supercharged engines, MAP sensor
  calibration, 196
Supercharger, 125
  boost control, 126, 129–130
  centrifugal, 126
  Ford cutaway view, 127
  Ford V-8, 124
  induction pressure, 53
  pressurizing air, 124
  roots type, 126
  service, 126
  types of, 126
  volumetric efficiency, 123
Supercharger boost control, 126,
  129–130
  boost control factors, 129
  bypass valve, 126
  purpose and function, 129
  relief valves, 130
  wastegate, 129–130
Superimposed position of ignition
  oscilloscopes, 134
Surface charge, 82
SVO (straight vegetable oil) as
  fuel, 111
SWCAN (single-wire CAN), 166
Swirl combustion, 273
  diagram, 274
Switchgrass, 96
Switching, 356–357
  ignition system, 105–106
Synchronized throttle-body fuel-
  injection, 258
Syncrude, 105
Syn-gas (synthesis gas), 101
Synthetic engine oil, 126
Synthetic fuels, 104–105
  coal to liquid (CTL), 105
  Fischer-Tropsch, 104–105
  future of, 105
  methanol-to-gasoline (MTG), 105

**T**

TAC (Throttle Actuator Control)
  module, 278
Tachometer trick, 109, 358
Tach reference (purple/white)
  wire, 116
Tailpipe outlet exhaust, precautions, 74
Tap test, 208
  catalytic converters, 346
Target idle speed, TP sensor, 233
Target speed idle, 191
Task manager, 154
  enabling criteria, 156
TBT (throttle-body temperature), 185
TDC (top dead center), 49
TDMA (time division multiple access)
  protocol, 173
Tech 2 scan tool, 384
  bypass mode, 174
  DTC P0336, 123
  pinging, 173–174
  retrieving global OBD II, 47
  zero RPM while engine running, 122
Technical service bulletins (TSBs), 3,
  382–383
Technical service information bulletins
  (TSIB), 3
Technician's toughie story, 233
Techron®, 275
TEL (tetraethyl lead), 86

Temperature sensors
  DTCs, 188
  fuel delivery, 258
Tensile strength, 6
Tensioners, noise from, 138
Terminating resistors, 174
Tertiary-amyl methyl ether (TAME), 88
Tertiary butyl alcohol (TBA), 87
Test Identification (TID), 47
  hexadecimal coding, 160
Testing, basic tests, 379
Test lights, 18
Tetraethyl lead (TEL), 86
TFT (transmission fluid temperature)
  sensor, 186–187
Thermactor pump, 339
Thermal stress, 119
Thermal vacuum valves, leaking, 148
Thermostat
  cooling system, 47
  normal operating temperatures, 183
Thimble design for oxygen sensor, 231
Threaded fasteners, 4–7
Threads, 4
3 X 5 card test, 337–338
Three Cs, 4
Three-way catalytic converter
  (TWC), 344
Three-wire oxygen sensor, 213
Throttle Actuator Control (TAC)
  module, 278
Throttle body, removal for cleaning, 298
Throttle body assembly, 278–279
  cleaning procedure, 283
  electronic throttle body motor, 279
  precautions with, 283
  throttle plate and spring, 279
Throttle body cleaning, 283
Throttle-body fuel-injection
  systems, 256
  Chevrolet V-6, 257
  fuel pressure regulator shown, 258
  fuel pump current draw, 253
  nonsynchronized, 258
  rich-lean switching frequencies, 221
  synchronized, 258
Throttle-body injection intake manifolds
  intake air speeds, 115–116
  terminology, 115
Throttle-body injection unit, on GM
  V-6, 116
Throttle-body injector
  purpose, 115
  shorted, 115
Throttle body relearn procedure, 284
Throttle-body temperature (TBT), 185
Throttle-body temperature sensor, 185
  PCM uses for, 191
Throttle control assembly, corrosion
  shown, 283
Throttle plate motor
  H-bridge circuit, 279
  shown, 280
Throttle plates, 279
  cleaning, 298
  default position shown, 279
  fail safe position, 279
  neutral position, 279
  normal and abnormal operation, 282
  staying where it is moved, 282
Throttle position (TP) sensors, 190,
  277, 280–281
  5-volt reference, 193
  backing up other sensors, 233
  computer input functions,
    191, 233
  DTCs, 194, 236
  fuel delivery, 257
  Hall-effect, 281
  location, 278
  open on DTC, 385
  opposite voltage signals, 280
  PCM uses for, 233
  potentiometers, 190
  pulse width, 259
  skewed, 193
  testing, 192–193, 234–236
    with multimeter, 192
    using Min/Max function, 193
    using scan tool, 193
  three-wire potentiometer, 280
  three wires, 190

  voltage at idle, 190
  waveform, 74
Throttle-position (TP) sensor testing,
  234–235
  using Min/Max function, 193
  using scan tool, 193
Throttling losses, 61
TID (test identification), 47, 160
Time base, 73
Time division multiple access (TDMA)
  protocol, 173
Time per division, 74–75
Timing chain, noise, 138
Tin snips, 15
Tire pressure, service, 405
Tires, disposal, 42
Titania (titanium oxide) oxygen
  sensor, 214
TLEV (transitional low emission
  vehicle), 306
Tool sets and accessories, 17–18
Top dead center (TDC), 49
Top-tier gasoline, 91
Torque, 58
  ft-lb or lb-ft, 58
Torque converter
  clutch engagement and release, 233
  engine noise diagnosis, 138
Torque converter clutch, 191
Torque wrenches, 10
Total suspended particulate (TSP), 71
Touch test, 95
Towing, 401–402
Toxic materials, 35
Toyota
  airflow sensors, 210
  battery replacement issues, 87
  BUS communications, 172
  clearing DTCs, 386
  combination spark plug system,
    113, 364
  direct fuel injection, 270
  EGR temperature sensor, 187
  failed emission test, 210, 314
  fuel cap, tightening, 324
  hybrid vehicles, 30
  low engine power problem, 115, 366
  scan tools, 46, 384
  scan tools compared for air-fuel
    ratio, 234
  turbocharger, 124
Toyota Camry
  high idle, 282
  smog emissions label, 308
Toyota FCHV, 411, 414, 416, 417
Toyota HEV, closed loop operation, 230
Toyota Prius, jump starting, 401
TP (throttle position) sensors
  backing up other sensors, 233
  computer input functions, 233
  fuel delivery, 257
  PCM uses for, 233
  pulse width, 259
  testing, 234–236
T-pin, 192
TP sensors
  computer input functions, 191
  PCM uses for, 191
  potentiometers, 190
  three wires, 190
  voltage at idle, 190
Track, 370
  definition, 125
  diagram, 125, 370
Transaxles, fuel-cell hybrid
  vehicles, 416
Transformers, 355
Transistor, 106, 357
Transmission fluid temperature (TFT)
  sensor, 186–187
Transmission oil temperature (TOT)
  sensor, 186–187
Transverse mounting, 49
  shown, 51
Tri-fuel vehicles, 104
Trigger level, 76
Triggers, 76, 106, 357
Trigger slope, 76
Trip, 391
  definition, 157
Trouble codes, U codes, 169
Trouble lights, 19

Troubleshooting
battery testing, 89
using DTCs, 385–386
TSBs (technical service bulletins), 3, 382–383
TSIB (technical service information bulletins), 3
TSP (total suspended particulate), 71
Tube-nut wrenches, 8
Tumble combustion, 273
diagram, 274
Turbine fuel pump, 244
cutaway view, 246
Turbine wheel, 127
diagram, 128
expanding exhaust gases, 127
Turbocharged diesels, 69–70
variable, 69–70
Turbocharged engines
fuel pump current draw, 253
MAP sensor calibration, 197
Turbocharger failures
preventing, 131
symptoms, 130–131
Turbochargers, 127
air cleaner housing, 114
failures, 130–131
heat energy use, 127
induction pressure, 53
liquid-cooled, 128
operation, 127–128
pressurizing air, 124
separator systems, 336
size and response time, 128–129
Toyota, 124
turbine wheel and impeller wheel, 128
two are better, 130
volumetric efficiency, 123
Turbo lag, 128–129
Turns ratio, 105, 355
TWC (three-way catalytic converter), 344
Twisted pair, 162
reducing interference, 167, 168
Two-channel scope, 75
Two-finger trick, 129, 375
Two-lobed epitrochoid, 52
Two-step sensor (narrow band), 230
Two-wire oxygen sensor, 213
Type A codes, 391
Type B codes, 391
Type C and D codes, 391

U

UART (universal asynchronous receive and transmit), 165
UART-based protocol (UBP), 165, 167
Ford, 168
UBP module communications, 169
UCO (used cooking oil) as fuel, 111
U diagnostic trouble codes, 169
ULEV (ultra low emission vehicle), 306
ULEV II (ultra low emission vehicle), 306
ULSD (ultra-low-sulfur diesel), 110
pump decal for, 111
Ultracapacitors, 414–415
Ultra-low-sulfur diesel (ULSD) fuel, 110
pump decal for, 111
Ultrasonic Karman Vortex air flow sensors, 207
Unburned hydrocarbons (HC), 335
UNC (unified national coarse), 4, 5
Underground coal gasification (UCG), 105
Underground storage tanks (UST), 38
UNF (unified national fine), 4, 5
Unified national coarse (UNC), 4, 5
Unified national fine (UNF), 4, 5
Unison ring, 69
Universal drive cycle, 156, 395
Universal joints, 9
Unplug it test, 209
Up-integrated ignition, 116

Upper and lower intake manifolds, 117
Urea, 75
injection, 75
Used cooking oil (UCO) as fuel, 111
Used oil, 38–39
UST (underground storage tanks), 38
Utility knives, 15

V

V-6 engine
burning oil, 337
grouped fuel injectors, 292
waste-spark ignition wiring diagram, 111, 362
V-8 engine, cubic inch displacement chart, 56
Vacuum, 196
air pressure related, 196
diagram of process, 197
Vacuum-biased fuel-pressure regulator, 262
Vacuum gauge
MAP sensor as, 200
testing back pressure, 147
testing backpressure with, 347–348
Vacuum hose
checking, 202
pressure levels, 286
Vacuum leaks
ETC system, 282
smoke machine testing, 381
Vacuum lock, fuel tanking venting, 240
Vacuum pump, 60
diesel engine-driven, 67–68
hand operated, 202, 203
for pressure regulator diagnosis, 286
Vacuum-referenced regulator, 250
Vacuum tests, 144–145
cranking vacuum test, 144–145
fluctuating vacuum, 145–146
idle vacuum test, 145
low and steady vacuum, 145
Valves, clicking, 138, 139
Vane airflow (VAF) sensor, 205
with cover removed, 206
cutaway view, 205
DTCs, 210
Vane position control solenoid valve, 69
Van Karman, Theodore, 207
Vapor lock, 83–84
fuel lines, 240
fuel tank layout, 242–243
Vapor purging, 318
Vapor vent lines, 241
Variable fuel sensor, 97
location of, 97
Variable resistance sensor, 190
Variable speed fuel pumps, 247–248
Variable turbochargers, 69–70
VECI (vehicle emissions control information), 2
Vegetable oil, as fuel, 111
Vehicle communication protocols, 394
Vehicle emissions control information (VECI), 2
Vehicle identification, 1–2
for Flex Fuel vehicles, 98–99
Vehicle identification number (VIN), 1
how to read, 100
Vehicle protection, 23
Vehicle safety certification label, 2
Vent valve, 130, 321
V-FFV (virtual flexible fuel vehicle), 98
VIN (vehicle identification number), 1
Vinyl gloves, 22
Virtual flexible fuel vehicle (V-FFV), 98
Vise Grips, 14
Visual inspection
batteries, 81–82
electrolyte level, 82, 85
coolant level and condition, 136–137
diagnostic process, 379, 381
EGR testing, 332

electronic fuel-injection problems, 287
engine condition diagnosis, 344–346
intermittent "check engine" light, 296
mass airflow sensors, 208
oil leaks, 137–138
optical sensors, 122–123, 369
oxygen sensor, 226–227
SAI systems, 340–341
spark plug wires, 125, 369–370
starter problems, 90
testing ECT sensor, 180
Visual tampering checks, 309
Volatile organic compound (VOC), fuel tank layout, 243
Volatility, 83
distillation curve, 83, 84
Reid pressure vapor (RVP), 83
related problems, 83–84
seasonal blending, 83
Voltage
BUS operation checks, 174
ripple voltage, 74
Voltage drop
ECT measurement with PCM, 180, 181
ECT testing with multimeter, 180
proportional to resistance, 92
Voltage-drop tester, 293
typical, 294
Voltage drop testing, 92–94
charging system, 96–97, 99–100
procedure, 92–94
purpose, 92
results of excessive voltage drop, 92
test procedure, 92–94
voltmeter hookups, 93
Voltmeters
battery electrical drain test, 88
battery voltage and headlights, 82–83
charging system voltage drop test, 93
charging system voltage test procedure, 224
testing MAP sensor, 202
Volts per division (V/div), 74
Volumetric efficiency, 123
turbochargers/superchargers, 123
Vref, 191
V-type engines, 49
exhaust gas control, 327
two turbochargers for, 130

W

"Wait to start" lamp, 67
Wall-guided (swirl) combustion, 273
diagram, 274
Wankel engine, 52
Wankel, Felix Heinrich, 52
Warm-up cycle, 157
Warning lamp, oil pressure, 140
Washcoat, 343
Washers, 7
Waste chart, 43
Wastegate, 129–130
computer-controlled valve, 130
definition, 129
operation, 129–130
Waste-spark ignition system, 104
Waste-spark ignition systems, 355
adjusting ignition timing, 130, 375
compression-sensing, 111, 362–363
corroded terminals, 126, 371
dual trace scope pattern, 138, 370
firing order, 131
odds fire straight, 111, 361
operation, 110–111, 355
parts involved, 110, 361
schematic, 121, 362

scope-testing, 137
typical engine, 110
V-6 wiring diagram, 111, 362
Waste-spark system, 355
Waste vegetable oil (WVO), 111
Water fire extinguishers, 28
Water-fuel separator, 63
Water, precautions with lubricating diesel engine, 63
Water pump pliers, 13
Weak spark condition, ignition system symptom guide, 138, 376
Well-to-wheel emissions, 420
Wet compression test, 142
Wet system ($N_2O$), 132
Wheel dollies, 402
Wheel motors, 416
Wheels
stone, 21
wire brush, 21
Whine, possible causes, 139
Whistle stop, 143
White (steam) exhaust smoke
blown cylinder head gaskets, 136
causes, 135
White exhaust smoke (steam), 75
WHMIS (Workplace Hazardous Materials Information Systems), 36
Wide-band oxygen sensors (O2S)
closed loop, 230
dual cell, 232–234
dual cell planar, 232–233
need for, 229
pattern failures, 236
purpose and function, 229
single cell, 234–235
terminology, 229
Wide-range oxygen sensors (O2S), 229
Wind farms, 422, 423
Wind power, 422, 423
Winter-blend gasolines (high-RVP fuel), 83, 84
Wire brush wheels, 21
Wiring, ignition system, 48
Wood alcohol (methanol), 100
Work lights, 19
Work orders, 4
Workplace Hazardous Materials Information Systems (WHMIS), 36
World Wide Fuel Charter (WWFC), 91
WRAF (wide-range air-fuel) sensor, 229
Wrenches, 7–9, 10
impact, 19–20
Wrench symbol warning lamp, 281
WVO (waste vegetable oil), 111
WWFC (World Wide Fuel Charter), 91

Y

Yellow jaundice, 39

Z

ZEV (zero emission vehicle), 307
Zirconia oxygen sensors, 213–214
conventional, cup-type design, 231
conventional, narrow band, 230
conventional, reset limits, 229
conventional, voltage value shown, 230
cross-sectional view, 213
KOEO oxygen sensor test, 234
lean mixture, 214
O2S voltage above 450 mV, 214
O2S voltage below 450 mV, 214
platinum electrodes, 231
reset limits, 229
rich mixture, 214
typical view, 214
Zirconium dioxide ($ZRO_2$), 212

Taken from:
*Advanced Engine Performance Diagnosis*, Fifth Edition
by James D. Halderman

# chapter
# 4

# GLOBAL OBD II
# AND MODE $06

**OBJECTIVES:** After studying Chapter 4, the reader will be able to: • Access global OBD II on a scan tool. • Identify mode $06 diagnostic steps. • Describe how mode $06 can be used to identify a problem. • Explain how to convert raw numbers to usable data.

**KEY TERMS:** CID 47 • Generic OBD II 46 • Global OBD II 46 • MID 47 • Mode $06 48 • PID 46 • TID 47

## WHAT IS GLOBAL OBD II?

**Global OBD II,** also called **generic OBD II,** is the standardized format of on-board diagnostics, following SAE standard J1962. Global OBD II was designed for engineers: when OBD II was first introduced, it was not intended to be used by service technicians.

### PURPOSES AND FUNCTIONS
The purposes and functions of Global OBD II include:

1. It can check the powertrain control module (PCM) to determine what it has detected about a failure.

2. It can be used by service technicians to verify a repair.

3. It can check the test results performed by the PCM to see if the results are close to a failure level. This information will show what is at fault even though no diagnostic trouble codes are set.

4. Since the data displayed is very technical, it often needs to be converted to give the service technician usable information.

5. An estimated 80% of the PCM DTCs can be diagnosed using the global OBD II function of the scan tool.

6. All global OBD-II functions are standardized, which is not the case when looking at original equipment manufacturer (OEM) data.

7. Some DTCs may be displayed using the global OBD-II function of the scan tool that is not displayed on an OEM, or by using the enhanced mode OBD-II function of the scan tool.

## GLOBAL OBD II MODES

All OBD-II vehicles must be able to display data on a global (generic) scan tool under nine different modes of operation. These modes include:

| MODE ONE | Current powertrain data (parameter identification display or **PID**) |
|---|---|
| MODE TWO | Freeze-frame data |
| MODE THREE | Diagnostic trouble codes |
| MODE FOUR | Clear and reset diagnostic trouble codes (DTCs), freeze-frame data, and readiness status monitors for noncontinuous monitors only |
| MODE FIVE | Oxygen sensor monitor test results |
| MODE SIX | Onboard monitoring of test results for noncontinuous monitored systems |
| MODE SEVEN | Onboard monitoring of test results for continuously monitored systems |
| MODE EIGHT | Bidirectional control of onboard systems |
| MODE NINE | Module identification |

### HEXADECIMAL NUMBERS
Generic (global) data is used by most state emission programs. Generic OBD-II displays often use hexadecimal numbers, which use 16 numbers instead of 10. The numbers 0 to 9 (zero counts as a number) make up

**FREQUENTLY ASKED QUESTION**

**How Can You Tell Global from Factory?**

When using a scan tool on an OBD-II equipped vehicle, if the display asks for make, model, and year, then the factory or enhanced part of the PCM is being accessed. This is true for most scan tools except the Chrysler DRB III and Star Scans being used on a Chrysler vehicle. These scan tools can determine vehicle information from the PCM and do not need to be entered by the service technician. If the global or generic part of the PCM is being scanned, then there is no need to know the vehicle details.

the first 10 and then capital letters A to F complete the 16 numbers. To help identify the number as being in a hexadecimal format, a dollar sign ($) is used in front of the number or letter. See the following conversion chart:

| Decimal Number | Hexadecimal Code |
|:---:|:---:|
| 0 | $0 |
| 1 | $1 |
| 2 | $2 |
| 3 | $3 |
| 4 | $4 |
| 5 | $5 |
| 6 | $6 |
| 7 | $7 |
| 8 | $8 |
| 9 | $9 |
| 10 | $A |
| 11 | $B |
| 12 | $C |
| 13 | $D |
| 14 | $E |
| 15 | $F |

Hexadecimal coding is also used to identify tests (**Test Identification [TID]** and **Component Identification [CID]**). CAN-equipped vehicles use **monitor identification (MID)** and TID.

## DIAGNOSING PROBLEMS USING MODE $06

Mode $06 information can be used to diagnose faults by following three steps:

**STEP 1** Check the monitor status before starting repairs. This step will show how the system failed.

**STEP 2** Look at the component or parameter that triggered the fault. This step will help pin down the root cause of the failure.

**STEP 3** Look to the monitor enable criteria, which will show what it takes to fail or pass the monitor.

## ACCESSING GLOBAL OBD II

Global (generic) OBD II is used by inspectors where emission testing is performed. Aftermarket scan tools are designed to retrieve global OBD II; however, some original equipment scan

**FIGURE 4–1** Global OBD II can be accessed from the main menu on all aftermarket and some original equipment scan tools.

tools, such as the Tech 2 used on General Motors vehicles, are not able to retrieve the information without special software. Global OBD II is accessible using ISO-9141-2, KWP 2000, J1850 PWM, J1850 VPW, and CAN. ● **SEE FIGURE 4–1.**

**SNAP-ON 2500** An older Snap-on scan tool, often called "the brick" that was used in the aftermarket for many year.

**SNAP-ON SOLUS** From the main menu select "Generic OBD II/EOBD" and then follow the on-screen instructions to select the desired test.

**SNAP-ON MODIS** Select the scanner using the down arrow key and then select "Global OBD II." Follow on-screen instructions to get to "start communication" and then to the list of options to view.

**OTC GENISYS** From the main menu select "Global OBD II" and then follow the on-screen instructions. Select "special tests" to get access to mode $06 information and parameters.

**MASTER TECH** From the main menu, select "Global OBD II." At the next screen, select "OBD II functions," then "system tests," and then "other results" to obtain mode $06 data. ● **SEE FIGURE 4–2.**

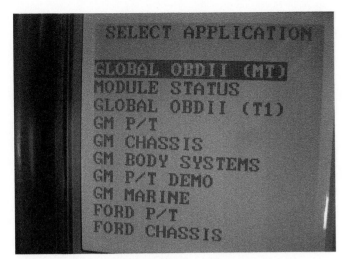

**FIGURE 4–2** A photo of a Master Tech display, showing where to select global OBD II from the menu.

## MODE $06

Mode $06 is used by service technicians to monitor the PCM test results of various systems. While other modes are used for monitoring other functions, mode $06 is used to maintain all continuous and noncontinuous monitors and pending DTCs. The continuous monitors include fuel system monitors, misfire monitors, and comprehensive component monitors (CCM). The noncontinuous monitors include catalyst efficiency, EGR, EVAP, oxygen sensor monitors, oxygen sensor heater, secondary air injection (SAI), and thermostats.

**USING MODE $06**   Mode $06 is used to monitor all of the tests of the system and components. Mode $06 allows the service technician to view what the computer is doing and see the results of all of the tests that are being performed. Mode $06 can be used for the following:

- **See test results that are close to failing.** This means that a diagnostic trouble code may be set in the future because results of the test are close to the set limit, which would cause a DTC to set. Therefore, by looking at mode $06 data, the technician can be forewarned of a problem; in that case the customer can be told that a "check engine" light may come on and why.

- **Verify a repair.** By looking at mode $06 test results, the service technician can determine whether or not the repair that caused the check engine light to come on was in fact repaired correctly. If the test results are close to the upper or lower limit allowed, the repair was not completed successfully. If, however, the test results are far from the upper or lower limit, the repair was successful

and the vehicle can be returned to the owner with the satisfaction of knowing that the check engine light will not come on again due to the same concern.

**READING MODE $06 DATA**   Some scan tools translate the raw hexadecimal data into English, such as Auto Enginuity scan tool software, which is used with a PC. However, the data is difficult to read. In addition, data from Ford vehicles needs to be multiplied by a conversion factor to achieve a usable value.

**SELECT MONITOR**   The first step is to select the monitor (fuel trim, misfire, catalyst, etc.). There could be three results:

- **Incomplete.** This means that the computer has not yet completed the test for the selected monitor.

- **Pass.** This means that the monitor was tested to completion and that the test passed. This pass could have been close to failing; looking at the test results will indicate how close it came to failing.

- **Fail.** The monitor test failed. Checking the test results will help the service technician determine why it failed and by how much, which will help in diagnosing the root cause.

**DATA DISPLAY**   The test data displayed often includes upper limit and/or lower limit (often not both), test results, and units.

The "unit" may be just a number. However, by looking at the upper and lower limits, the technician can judge how close the test results were to failing the test. Many scan tools display component and test information in plain English while others just display the hexadecimal number. If just the hexadecimal number is shown, it has to be translated into English to show which component or test is being displayed. Check service information for the exact translation or refer to the following charts for a typical example.

### Chart 1

| | |
|---|---|
| $03 | Fuel System 1 |
| $03 | Fuel System 2 |
| $04 | Calculated Load Percentage |
| $05 | Engine Coolant Temp Sensor (Celsius) |
| $06 | Short-Term Fuel Trim Bank 1 (%) |
| $07 | Long-Term Fuel Trim Bank 1 (%) |
| $08 | Short-Term Fuel Trim Bank 2 (%) |
| $09 | Long-Term Fuel Trim Bank 2 (%) |
| $0A | Fuel Pressure Gauge (KPA) |
| $0B | Intake MAP (KPA) |
| $0C | Engine Speed (1/min) |
| $0D | Vehicle Speed (km/h) |
| $0E | Ignition Timing Advance (degrees) |
| $0F | Intake Air Temperature (Celsius) |
| $10 | Air Flow Rate (g/s) |
| $11 | Absolute Throttle Position (%) |

| | |
|---|---|
| $12 | Commanded Secondary AIR Status |
| $13 | O2S Bank 1-Sensor 1 |
| $13 | O2S Bank 1-Sensor 2 |
| $13 | O2S Bank 1-Sensor 3 |
| $13 | O2S Bank 1-Sensor 4 |
| $13 | O2S Bank 2-Sensor 1 |
| $13 | O2S Bank 2-Sensor 2 |
| $13 | O2S Bank 2-Sensor 3 |
| $13 | O2S Bank 2-Sensor 4 |
| $14 | O2S Voltage Bank 1-Sensor 1 (V) |
| $14 | Short-Term Fuel Trim Bank 1-Sensor 1 (%) |
| $15 | O2S Voltage Bank 1-Sensor 2 (V) |
| $15 | Short-Term Fuel Trim Bank 1-Sensor 2 (%) |
| $16 | O2S Voltage Bank 1-Sensor 3 (V) |
| $16 | Short-Term Fuel Trim Bank 1-Sensor 3 (%) |
| $17 | O2S Voltage Bank 1-Sensor 4 (V) |
| $17 | Short-Term Fuel Trim Bank 1-Sensor 4 (%) |
| $18 | O2S Voltage Bank 2-Sensor 1 (V) |
| $18 | O2S Voltage Bank 3-Sensor 1 (V) |
| $18 | Short-Term Fuel Trim Bank 2-Sensor 1 (%) |
| $18 | Short-Term Fuel Trim Bank 3-Sensor 1 (%) |
| $19 | O2S Voltage Bank 2-Sensor 2 (V) |
| $19 | O2S Voltage Bank 3-Sensor 2 (V) |
| $19 | Short-Term Fuel Trim Bank 2-Sensor 2 (%) |
| $19 | Short-Term Fuel Trim Bank 3-Sensor 2 (%) |
| $1A | O2S Voltage Bank 2-Sensor 3 (V) |
| $1A | O2S Voltage Bank 4-Sensor 1 (V) |
| $1A | Short-Term Fuel Trim Bank 2-Sensor 3 (%) |
| $1A | Short-Term Fuel Trim Bank 4-Sensor 1 (%) |
| $1B | O2S Voltage Bank 2-Sensor 4 (V) |
| $1B | O2S Voltage Bank 4-Sensor 2 (V) |
| $1B | Short-Term Fuel Trim Bank 2-Sensor 4 (%) |
| $1B | Short-Term Fuel Trim Bank 4-Sensor 2 (%) |
| $1C | OBD Requirements |
| $1D | O2S Bank 1-Sensor 1 |
| $1D | O2S Bank 1-Sensor 2 |
| $1D | O2S Bank 2-Sensor 1 |
| $1D | O2S Bank 2-Sensor 2 |
| $1D | O2S Bank 3-Sensor 1 |
| $1D | O2S Bank 3-Sensor 2 |
| $1D | O2S Bank 4-Sensor 1 |
| $1D | O2S Bank 4-Sensor 2 |
| $1E | Power Take Off Status |
| $1F | Time Since Engine Start(s) |
| $21 | Distance While MIL Active (km/miles) |
| $22 | Relative Fuel Pressure (kPa) |
| $23 | Fuel Pressure Gauge (kPa) |
| $24 | Equivalence Ratio Bank 1-Sensor 1 (:1) |
| $25 | Equivalence Ratio Bank 1-Sensor 2 (:1) |
| $26 | Equivalence Ratio Bank 1-Sensor 3 (:1) |
| $27 | Equivalence Ratio Bank 1-Sensor 4 (:1) |
| $28 | Equivalence Ratio Bank 2-Sensor 1 (:1) |
| $28 | Equivalence Ratio Bank 3-Sensor 1 (:1) |
| $29 | Equivalence Ratio Bank 2-Sensor 2 (:1) |
| $29 | Equivalence Ratio Bank 3-Sensor 2 (:1) |
| $2A | Equivalence Ratio Bank 2-Sensor 3 (:1) |

| | |
|---|---|
| $2A | Equivalence Ratio Bank 3-Sensor 3 (:1) |
| $2B | Equivalence Ratio Bank 2-Sensor 4 (:1) |
| $2B | Equivalence Ratio Bank 3-Sensor 4 (:1) |
| $2C | Commanded EGR (%) |
| $2D | EGR Error (%) |
| $2E | Commanded Evaporative Purge (%) |
| $2F | Fuel Level Input (%) |
| $30 | Number of Warm-Ups Since DTCs Cleared |
| $31 | Distance Since DTCs Cleared |
| $32 | EVAP System Vapor Pressure (Pa) |
| $33 | Barometric Pressure (kPa) |
| $34 | O2S Current Bank 1-Sensor 1 (ma) |
| $35 | O2S Current Bank 1-Sensor 2 (ma) |
| $36 | O2S Current Bank 1-Sensor 3 (ma) |
| $37 | O2S Current Bank 1-Sensor 4 (ma) |
| $38 | O2S Current Bank 2-Sensor 1 (ma) |
| $38 | O2S Current Bank 3-Sensor 1 (ma) |
| $39 | O2S Current Bank 2-Sensor 2 (ma) |
| $39 | O2S Current Bank 3-Sensor 2 (ma) |
| $3A | O2S Current Bank 2-Sensor 3 (ma) |
| $3A | O2S Current Bank 3-Sensor 3 (ma) |
| $3B | O2S Current Bank 2-Sensor 4 (ma) |
| $3B | O2S Current Bank 3-Sensor 4 (ma) |
| $3C | Catalyst Temperature Bank 1-Sensor 1°C |
| $3D | Catalyst Temperature Bank 2-Sensor 1°C |
| $3E | Catalyst Temperature Bank 1-Sensor 2°C |
| $3F | Catalyst Temperature Bank 2-Sensor 2°C |
| $42 | Control Module Voltage |
| $43 | Absolute Load Value (%) |
| $44 | Commanded Equivalence Ratio |
| $45 | Relative Throttle Position (%) |
| $46 | Ambient Air Temperature °C |
| $47 | Absolute Throttle Position B (%) |
| $48 | Absolute Throttle Position C (%) |
| $49 | Accelerator Pedal Position D (%) |
| $4A | Accelerator Pedal Position E (%) |
| $4B | Accelerator Pedal Position F (%) |
| $4C | Commanded Throttle ACT. Control (%) |
| $4D | Engine Run Time with MIL Active (min.) |
| $4E | Time Since DTCs Cleared (min.) |

## Chart 2

| Test ID | Numbers (oxygen sensor) |
|---|---|
| $01 | Rich to Lean Sensor Threshold |
| $02 | Lean to Rich Sensor Threshold |
| $03 | Low Sensor Voltage for Switch Time Calculation |
| $04 | High Sensor Voltage for Switch Time Calculation |
| $05 | Rich to Lean Sensor Switch Time |
| $06 | Lean to Rich Sensor Switch Time |
| $07 | Minimum Sensor Voltage for Test Cycle |
| $08 | Maximum Sensor Voltage for Test Cycle |
| $09 | Time Between Sensor Transitions |
| $0A | Sensor Period |

# OXYGEN SENSOR HEATER MODE $06 TEST (GENERAL MOTORS)

This fault can set a P0141 DTC for bank 1, sensor 1 (B1S1). Checking service information indicates the following enable criteria for the code to set:

1. Cold engine start
2. Engine at idle speed
3. Engine operating temperature below 150°F (66°C)

The following monitors are suspended:

1. EVAP
2. Oxygen sensor performance
3. Catalyst

Mode $06 data for B1S1 heater circuit in TID-06, CID-41:

1. The maximum limit—186
2. Measure value = 33
3. Minimum limit = -----
4. Result = passed

Note that the technician cannot determine what is being measured nor what the number 186 indicates. Also note that there is no minimum limit and the measured value of 33 is far below the maximum limit of 186. This means that the oxygen sensor heater test easily passed.

# ENGINE MISFIRE TESTS (FORD)

A misfire fault can set a random misfire DTC of P0300 or one or more individual misfire DTCs P0301 through P0310 for cylinders one through 10. The enable criteria for these codes to set include:

1. Time since engine start 5 seconds
2. Engine coolant temperature 20°F (−7°C) to 250°F (121°C)
3. RPM range from idle to redline or fuel cutoff
4. Fuel level 15% minimum

Test ID is used to identify several related tests including:

$50—Total engine misfire (updated every 1,000 revolutions)
$53—Cylinder specific misfire

For example, a Ford being checked using mode $06 for TID-50 had the following results:

Maximum limit = 1,180
Measured value = 0

Minimum value = -----
Result = passed

What is the percentage of misfire allowed? The value shown for maximum has to be converted to get the actual percentage.

According to service information, to get the actual percentage of misfire the value has to be multiplied by 0.000015. Therefore, the raw value for maximum misfire was 1,180 × 0.000015, which equals 1.7%. In other words, the maximum allowable misfire before a DTC is set is 1.7%. By looking at mode $06 data, the technician can determine how close the engine is to failing the misfire monitor.

For individual cylinder misfires, check test ID $53. For example, if a value of 17,482 is displayed, the test failed. Multiplying the test results (17,482) by the conversion factor (0.000015) shows a misfire of 26%.

Type A misfire codes are those that can cause damage to the catalytic converter. The misfire usually ranges from 40% at idle to about 4% at high engine speeds.

Type B misfire codes are set if the misfire exceeds 2% to 4%, depending on the engine, make, model, and year.

# FORD OXYGEN SENSOR MODE $06 TEST

Ford and other companies have many tests performed on the oxygen sensor, including voltage amplitude. For example, Ford TID $01, CID $21 for HO2S1 shows:

Minimum value = 512
Maximum value = N/A
Current value = 794

According to Ford service information, the numbers have to be converted into volts by multiplying the value by 0.00098. Therefore, the current value is 0.778 volts, which is above the minimum allowable voltage of 0.50 (512 × 0.0098 = 0.50)

# GENERAL MOTORS CAN OXYGEN SENSOR MODE $06 TEST

One of the oxygen sensor tests performed on a General Motors vehicle equipped with CAN (GMCAN) is the rich-to-lean sensor switch time. Typical test results show:

Monitor ID (MID) $01
Test ID $05

Maximum limit = 0.155 sec.

Measured value = 0.030 sec.

Minimum value = 0.000 sec.

Result = passed

This mode $06 test clearly shows that the oxygen sensor is able to reset very quickly to a change in air-fuel mixture from rich to lean by reacting in 30 ms (0.030 sec.). Normally this information can only be determined by a service technician using a scope of the waveform who forces the system lean and watches the reaction time on the scope display. Using mode $06 and a scan tool, especially on vehicles equipped with CAN, is a fast and easy way to determine oxygen sensor health without having to do time-consuming tests.

## FORD EGR TESTS

Ford checks many functions of the exhaust gas recirculation (EGR) system, including flow testing and tests of the sensor used to check the flow of exhaust gases. The duty cycle of the EGR solenoid can be checked using mode $06 by looking at the following:

TID $4B

CID $30

Maximum limit = 26,214

Measured value = 14,358

Minimum value = -----

Test results = passed

These results at the limits, like many other Ford mode $06 data, must be converted to give usable values. Multiply the measured set limit value by 0.0000305 to get the duty cycle as a percentage (%).

Maximum limit = 26,214 × 0.0000305 = 80%

Measured value = 14.358 × 0.0000305 = 43%

### FORD DELTA PRESSURE FOR EGR FLOW TEST  In this test, the following occurred on a test vehicle:

TID 4A

CID 30

Maximum limit =

Measured value = 2,226

Minimum limit = 768

Result = passed

The values shown need to be compared and corrected as follows:

- If the value is greater than 32,767, the value is negative.

**Mode $06 Replaces a Scope**

Mode $06 data, especially when used on CAN-equipped vehicles, reduces the need to use an oscilloscope to view oxygen sensor reaction time in milliseconds. In the past, the only way to test an oxygen sensor for reaction time was to force the sensor lean or rich while viewing the reaction on a scope. Then, the reaction time could be determined using the cursors. Mode $06 data now includes oxygen sensor reaction time so that all that is needed to determine oxygen sensor condition is a scan tool and mode $06 data.

- If the value is less than 32,767, the value is positive.

- Multiply the value by 0.0078 to get inches of water.

The value was 2,226 × 0.0078 = 17.7 inches of water (in. $H_2O$) of vacuum (negative pressure).

## GENERAL MOTORS CATALYST EFFICIENCY TEST

The scan tool displays data that does not need to be converted, although the units are often unknown. The service technician can, however, see how close the test results come to either the maximum or the minimum limits. For example, a General Motors idle catalyst efficiency test could have the results following:

TID 0C

CID 60

Maximum limit = 33,234

Measured value = 17,708

Minimum limit = -----

Result = passed

What do the numbers represent? The numbers are created as a result of the test and cannot be determined by the technician. However, it is clear by the reading and the maximum limit that the catalyst efficiency test easily passed. This is an excellent test to check if the efficiency of the catalytic converter needs to be determined.

## GENERAL MOTORS EVAP TEST (CAN)

One of the evaporative (EVAP) system tests that can be monitored using a scan tool and mode $06 data is the engine off, natural vacuum test. An example of a typical result includes:

MID EVAP – 0.020

TID 201

Minimum value = 0.000

Maximum value = 0.601

Current value = 0.023

The values do not need to be converted, although the units are unknown. However, it is clear from the test results that the current value is not even close to the maximum limit, which means that the EVAP system being tested by the natural vacuum method is free from faults.

## WHERE TO GET MODE $06 INFORMATION

Many scan tools display all of the parameters and information needed so that additional mode $06 data is not needed. Many vehicle manufacturers post mode $06 information on the service information websites. This information is often free, unlike other service information. Refer to the National Automotive Service Task Force (NASTF) website for the website address of all vehicle manufacturers' service information sites (*www.NASTF.org*)

Two examples include:

*http://service.gm.com* (free access to mode $06 information)

*www.motorcraftservice.com* (search for mode $06 free access)

## SUMMARY

1. Global OBD II can be used by a service technician to do the following:
   a. Check the PCM regarding what it has detected as a fault
   b. Verify a repair
   c. Check if the test results are close to failure, which could trigger the MIL
2. Global OBD II has nine modes, each covering a certain aspect of the diagnostic system.
3. Mode $06 is the most commonly used mode of global OBD II because it includes data on the noncontinuous monitored system.
4. Most aftermarket scan tools and some original equipment scan tools can access global OBD II data.
5. Many Ford mode $06 data requires that the displayed number be converted to show usable values.

## REVIEW QUESTIONS

1. What are the nine modes of global (generic) OBD II?
2. How do hexadecimal numbers differ from base 10 numbers?
3. Why does some mode $06 data need to be translated into plain English?
4. Where can mode $06 data information be obtained?

## CHAPTER QUIZ

1. What is global (generic) OBD II?
   a. A standardized format that meets SAE standard J1962
   b. A format originally designed for engineers
   c. The same for all numbers and models of vehicles
   d. All of the above
2. Mode $06 can be used to verify a repair by checking _____.
   a. The component system test passed
   b. DTCs
   c. Sensor values
   d. A captured freeze-frame
3. Mode $06 is the mode that checks which systems?
   a. Oxygen sensors
   b. Continuously monitored systems
   c. Noncontinuously monitored systems
   d. Current powertrain data (PIDs)
4. The hexadecimal number for 12 is _____.
   a. 12
   b. $A
   c. $B
   d. $C

5. Technician A says that by looking at the mode $06 data, the technician can determine how close a component or system came to passing the onboard test. Technician B says that the data shown may have to be converted to obtain values that are meaningful to the technician. Which technician is correct?
   a. Technician A only
   b. Technician B only
   c. Both Technicians A and B
   d. Neither Technician A nor B

6. The data display usually shows what information?
   a. Upper limit and lower limit
   b. Upper limit or lower limit
   c. Test results
   d. Both b and c

7. An oxygen sensor switch time from rich to lean is identified as test identification (TID) _____.
   a. $05
   b. $0A
   c. $02
   d. $09

8. Type A misfire codes are those that can damage the catalytic converter and usually have misfires that range from _____ at idle to _____ at high engine speeds.
   a. 10%, 20%
   b. 40%, 4%
   c. 25%, 25%
   d. 2%, 4%

9. A General Motors vehicle is being checked using mode $06 for the proper operation of the oxygen sensor. The rich-to-lean sensor switch time is 0.030 seconds. Technician A says that this indicates a slow reacting oxygen sensor. Technician B says that the oxygen sensor is reacting correctly and is okay. Which technician is correct?
   a. Technician A only
   b. Technician B only
   c. Both Technicians A and B
   d. Neither Technician A nor B

10. Mode $06 information can be accessed at _____.
   a. http://service.gm.com
   b. www.motorcraftservice.com
   c. www.nastf.org
   d. All of the above

# FUEL TRIM DIAGNOSIS

**OBJECTIVES:** **After studying Chapter 17, the reader will be able to:** • Explain the purpose and function of fuel trim. • Discuss the difference between speed density and mass air flow fuel control. • Describe how knowing the volumetric efficiency of the engine can help diagnose engine performance concerns. • Explain how to tell if a volumetric efficiency concern in an engine is due to a mechanical or an airflow measurement problem.

**KEY TERMS:** Alpha 230 • Base Pulse Width 225 • Equivalence Ratio (ER) 224 • Fuel Trim 225 • Fuel Trim Cells 228 • Lambda 224 • Long-Term Fuel Trim (LTFT) 228 • Short-Term Fuel Trim (STFT) 227 • Stoichiometric 224 • Volumetric Efficiency (VE) 230

## FUEL TRIM

**PURPOSE AND FUNCTION** The powertrain control module (PCM) does not measure or check the air-fuel mixture entering the cylinders. Instead, the PCM measures the air mass, and then calculates the amount of fuel needed. Fuel trim provides a method that is capable of changing the amount of fuel delivered to the engine based on feedback from the oxygen sensors. The primary purpose of the fuel trim is to keep the air-fuel mixture as close to 14.7:1 as possible. When the air-fuel ratio is kept at 14.7:1, the efficiency of the catalytic converter is the highest, which results in the lowest possible exhaust emissions. ● **SEE FIGURE 17–1.**

**LAMBDA** **Lambda** is a Greek letter used to represent ratio, as in air-fuel ratio. If an engine is operating at exactly 14.7:1, the air-fuel ratio on gasoline, the ratio is called **stoichiometric** and is assigned a lambda of 1.0.

- Air-fuel ratios lower than 1.0 indicate a rich mixture.
- Air-fuel ratios higher than 1.0 indicate a lean mixture.

To determine the air-fuel ratio if lambda is given, multiply lambda times 14.7.

### Example 1:

A lambda of 1.05 means that the engine is operating 5% lean and has an air-fuel mixture of 15.4:1 (14.7 × 1.05 = 15.4).

### Example 2:

A lambda of 0.97 means that the engine is operating 3% rich and has an air-fuel mixture of 14.3:1 (0.97 × 1.47 = 14.28).

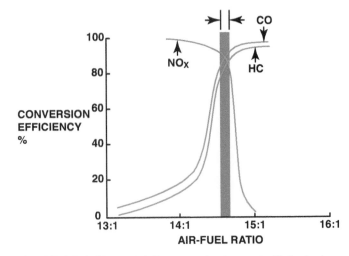

**FIGURE 17–1** The catalytic converter is most efficient when the exhaust ratio is closest to 14.7:1.

The usual lambda limits include:

- 0.9 lambda (13.2:1) is 10% rich and results in maximum power.
- 1.15 lambda (16.9:1) is 15% lean; in this case, a lean misfire is likely to occur.

Most newer vehicles are designed to operate between 0.98 and 1.02 lambda or, stated another way, within 2% of stoichiometric.

**EQUIVALENCE RATIO** The **equivalence ratio (ER)** is the inverse of lambda, with 1.0 equal to 1.0 lambda; however, 0.9 ER is equal to 1.1 lambda. Equivalence ratio (ER) = 1/λ (lambda), which is the inverse of lambda.

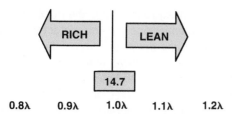

**FIGURE 17–2** Shown is lambda. The equivalence ratio is opposite lambda.

Therefore, a rich air-fuel mixture has an equivalence ratio of greater than 1 and a lean mixture less than 1. ● **SEE FIGURE 17–2.**

NOTE: **Engineers and many technical articles of fuel trim use equivalence ratios instead of lambda.**

# BASE PULSE WIDTH

**PURPOSE AND FUNCTION**   The **base pulse width** is the injector pulse width that is calculated by the PCM using information from sensors before the oxygen senor(s) is operating and supplying air-fuel ratio information. The PCM uses information from the following sensors to determine the base pulse width for the fuel injectors.

- RPM (engine speed)
- Load
- Intake air temperature (IAT)
- Engine coolant temperature (ECT) (used mostly when the engine is cold)
- Amount of exhaust gas recirculation
- Canister purge flow amount
- Manifold absolute pressure
- BARO (altitude)
- Volumetric efficiency calculation

**MASS AIR FLOW VERSUS SPEED DENSITY**   All throttle-body injected engines and some port fuel-injected engines use the speed density method for fuel control. The speed density uses the MAP sensor as the high authority sensor to determine the amount of fuel that will be needed. Although a speed density system can compensate for altitude, it is not as accurate as an engine equipped with a Mass Air Flow sensor that measures the actual amount of air entering the engine.

**SPEED DENSITY MODIFIER**   Besides the MAP sensor, other sensors are used to fine tune or modify the mathematical calculations needed to determine the injector pulse width. The

input sensors that affect fuel trim in a speed density system include:

**BARO.**  The BARO sensor or MAP sensor reading at key on determines the atmospheric pressure.

**IAT.**  The intake air temperature (IAT) sensor measures the temperature of the air entering the engine. The PCM uses this information to calculate the density of the air.

**RPM.**  All speed density calculations need the speed of the engine to calculate injector pulse width.

**EGR.**  The PCM needs to determine the amount of exhaust gases being recirculated into the intake manifold to make an accurate measurement of air mass entering the cylinders. Various vehicle designs are used for this calculation and include one or more of the following:

- EGR valve pintle position
- EGR passage temperature sensor
- Pressure differential in the EGR passage
- ECT. The engine coolant temperature is used to add fuel when the engine is cold but has little effect on

### Is There less Oxygen in the Air at High Altitude?

No. At altitudes above sea level, the atmospheric pressure and air density are lower but the amount of oxygen (21%) remains the same at all altitudes. Three basic altitude-related factors are:

- **Physical altitude.** This is the altitude measured above sea level.
- **Pressure altitude.** This is the atmospheric pressure corrected to sea level according to the International Standard Atmosphere (ISA). Pressure altitude is primarily used for airplane performance calculations using 101 kPa as the standard for atmospheric pressure at sea level. See the following chart.

| Pressure Altitude (ft) | Static Pressure (kPa) | In. Hg | PSI |
|---|---|---|---|
| 0 | 101.325 | 29.92 | 14.7 |
| 1,000 | 97.715 | 28.86 | 14.2 |
| 2,500 | 92.500 | 27.32 | 13.4 |
| 5,000 | 84.306 | 24.90 | 12.2 |
| 10,000 | 69.681 | 20.58 | 10.1 |
| 20,000 | 46.563 | 13.75 | 6.8 |
| 30,000 | 30.089 | 8.89 | 4.4 |
| 36,090 | 22.631 | | |

- **Density altitude.** This altitude factor is important for engine operation. Density altitude is the number of oxygen molecules that are entering the engine. The density is affected by temperature; therefore, the use of the intake air temperature sensor data is important in determining air density.

fuel trim after the engine has been run for a while on newer vehicles.

- TP sensor. The PCM uses the position of the throttle in three places to determine basic calculations. These three positions are:
  - Idle
  - Cruise
  - Wide-open throttle (WOT)
- The TP sensor is also monitored for rate of change. If the throttle is rapidly depressed, this indicates that a large gulp of air is going to be entering the engine and additional fuel will need to be provided up to about five times (500%) more than normal. If the throttle is rapidly released, the fuel needs to be removed (fuel cut off) from the cylinders to keep the engine from stalling.

- Battery voltage correction. The PCM attempts to keep the emissions low and protect the catalytic converter and the engine from damage. If the battery voltage becomes lower than normal, the fuel injectors will be slower to open and, as a result, deliver less than the calculated amount of fuel. Therefore, the PCM uses a program called battery voltage correction that adds time to the injector pulse width if battery voltage is low. This correction will prevent a possible lean air-fuel condition, which could cause damage to the catalytic converter and/or the engine itself.

**MAF SYSTEM MODIFIERS**   Using a mass air flow (MAF) sensor provides the PCM with a direct reading of the volume of air entering the engine. As a result, a MAF-equipped engine is able to provide a more accurate air-fuel ratio under all conditions. A MAF system has the following advantages compared with a speed density system:

- The system measures the actual mass of the air entering the engine.
- Altitude and temperature correction are not needed.
- The amount of exhaust gas recirculation does not need to be calculated.

However, some calculations need to be made to the air-fuel ratios if the throttle is rapidly depressed. Many General Motors systems use both a MAP sensor and a MAF sensor. One of the purposes of the MAP sensor, besides helping to diagnose the proper operation of the EGR system, is to provide the PCM with intake manifold pressure changes that occur when the throttle is rapidly closed or opened.

Electronic throttle control (ETC) systems help the PCM maintain proper air-fuel mixtures because the computer can control the rate of change of throttle opening. Therefore, it can determine what is happening directly rather than indicating it through information provided by the MAP sensor.

## MEASURING PULSE WIDTH

The PCM determines the base injector pulse width based on the reading from the sensors and the calculations from look-up tables stored in read-only memory. This base pulse width is the best guess as to the correct amount of fuel that the engine needs. Pulse width is measured in milliseconds (ms) and represents the amount of time the fuel injectors are commanded on. A typical engine at idle speed will have a pulse width of about 2 to 5 milliseconds, depending on the size of the engine. If there is a fault in one of the sensors, the calculated base pulse width may be incorrect. Because the air-fuel ratio is very important for the proper operation of the catalytic converter, the PCM uses data from the oxygen sensor to modify,

**One Millisecond per Liter**

A rule-of-thumb that usually works to determine if the pulse width is within reason is to remember that the size of the engine does affect the amount of fuel needed. While injector flow rates are higher for larger engines, it is generally true that, at idle on a warm engine, the injector pulse width will be about 1 millisecond per liter of displacement.

2 liters = 2 milliseconds
3 liters = 3 milliseconds
4 liters = 4 milliseconds
5 liters = 5 milliseconds
6 liters = 6 milliseconds

Therefore, if the injector pulse width is far from being normal, determine if the engine has a vacuum leak (if numbers are too high) or if the purge valve is stuck open (if the numbers are too low).

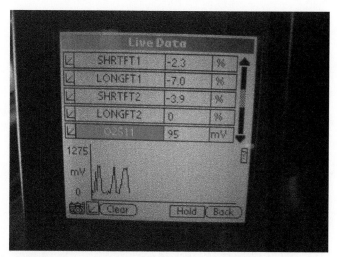

**FIGURE 17–3** Scan tool display, showing both long-term and short-term fuel trim. Both LTFT and STFT should be less than 10%.

if needed, the commanded pulse width. This correction from the base pulse width using data from the oxygen sensor is called fuel trim.

## FUEL TRIM

Based on the oxygen sensor activity, the PCM tries to keep the air-fuel mixture at 14.7:1 under most conditions.

**NOTE: If the vehicle is operating under full load, the oxygen sensor data is ignored and the PCM commands the richer-than-normal air-fuel mixture needed for maximum power based on inputs from the other sensors.**

## THE NEED FOR FUEL TRIM

The purpose of fuel trim is to provide the catalytic converter with a stoichiometric air-fuel mixture, which it needs to reduce $NO_x$ exhaust emissions and to help oxidize $HC$ and $CO$ into harmless carbon dioxide ($CO_2$) and water ($H_2O$) vapor.

If the exhaust is always rich, the catalytic converter cannot reduce CO and HC emissions. If the exhaust is always lean, the catalytic converter cannot reduce $NO_x$ emissions; therefore, the air-fuel mixture must alternate between rich and lean. The computer is therefore designed to provide as close to a 14.7:1 mixture as possible by using the oxygen sensor, as well as the short-term and long-term fuel trim program, to accomplish this feat. ● **SEE FIGURE 17–3.**

## SHORT-TERM FUEL TRIM

**Short-term fuel trim (STFT)** is a percentage measurement of the amount the computer is adding or subtracting from a calculated value. Electronic fuel-injector systems use the oxygen sensor (O2S) to determine whether the exhaust is rich or lean. Without the O2S, fuel delivery is controlled by the computer alone using the programmed pulse width commands based on other sensor inputs such as engine coolant temperature (ECT), throttle position (TP), and engine load (MAP). When the engine is operating in closed loop, the O2S signal can modify or change the preprogrammed fuel delivery. Fuel trim is expressed as a percentage (%), either positive (+) or negative (−), and represents the amount of fuel different from the anticipated amount. For example, if a small vacuum leak occurs, the O2S produces a lower voltage signal which is interpreted by the computer as meaning the air-fuel mixture is too lean. As a result, the pulse width is increased slightly to compensate for this slight vacuum leak. The amount of this additional fuel is seen on a scan tool as a positive short-term fuel trim.

**NOTE: Before 1993, General Motors referred to short-term fuel trim as the *integrator* and expressed it in binary numbers. A reading of 128 was the midpoint and a reading of + or − 10 from 128 (118–138) was usually considered to be a normal reading.**

A short-term fuel trim of +20% indicates that 20% additional fuel had to be added to achieve the proper air-fuel mixture. A −20% short-term fuel trim indicates that fuel had to be removed by shortening the injector pulse width to achieve the proper air-fuel mixture.

Short-term fuel trim represents actions by the computer over a relatively short time. The purpose of the STFT is to provide a varying air-fuel mixture so that the catalytic converter can efficiently reduce HC, CO, and $NO_x$ exhaust emissions. If, for example, a large vacuum leak were to occur, then the fuel delivery would have to be increased even more and for a longer

**The Red S-10 Pickup Truck Story**

A 4-cylinder 2.2-liter engine was replaced under the new vehicle warranty due to excessive oil consumption. The replacement engine never did run correctly, especially at idle and low speeds. The scan tool data showed a −25% long-term fuel trim, indicating that the oxygen sensor was measuring a very rich (low oxygen content) exhaust stream. Because the engine was operating so badly, the service technician believed the oxygen sensor was indicating a false rich condition. The service technician then checked the following:

- Poor $O_2$ sensor ground (this can cause a higher-than-normal $O_2$ sensor voltage)
- $O_2$ sensor wiring shorted to voltage or near a spark plug wire
- A contaminated (coated) $O_2$ sensor that will read higher than normal

None of the false rich conditions was found. Remembering that the engine ran terribly even when cold and the problem started after the engine was replaced, the technician started to look for faults that could have occurred when parts were switched from the original engine to the replacement engine. The technician found an incorrect EGR gasket. This caused exhaust gases to flow into the cylinders all the time. The exhaust gases also displaced the oxygen that normally would be in the cylinder, thereby reducing the amount of oxygen measured by the $O_2$ sensor. Replacing the EGR gasket restored proper engine operation.

time. Therefore, electronic fuel-injection system computers also incorporate a long-term fuel trim program.

## LONG-TERM FUEL TRIM

**Long-term fuel trim (LTFT)** is designed to add or subtract fuel for a longer amount of time than short-term fuel trim. For this reason, LTFT should be looked at by the service technician as a guide to whether the computer has been adding or subtracting fuel in order to achieve the proper air-fuel mixture. For example, if a vacuum hose splits open, the engine will be leaner than normal. Short-term fuel trim will attempt to add fuel right away to adjust. If the resulting air (vacuum) leak remains for longer than a few seconds to a minute, the computer will revise the long-term fuel trim to compensate for the leak over a larger period of time.

When the LTFT makes an adjustment, the STFT can still make short and quick changes in the air-fuel mixture needed to provide the catalytic converter with an alternating rich, then lean, then rich exhaust. *The purpose of long-term fuel trim is to keep short-term fuel trim as close to zero as possible.*

## USING FUEL TRIM AS A DIAGNOSTIC AID

Fuel trim values can only be observed with a scan tool. A scan tool will display both short-term and long-term fuel trim. For system diagnosis, refer to the long-term fuel trim because it represents a longer amount of time (history) and a greater amount of mixture correction.

**NOTE: The object of STFT and LTFT is to be able to make corrections to the amount of fuel delivered to the engine to achieve the proper air-fuel mixture. For example, a reading of +30% LTFT will indicate the computer must deliver 30% more than the calibrated amount of fuel to achieve the proper air-fuel mixture. This also means that the engine is now operating with the correct air-fuel mixture. The LTFT number simply tells the technician what the computer had to do to achieve the proper mixture.**

The following are three examples of readings and possible explanations:

### Example

**Vehicle 1.** STFT = +5%, LTFT = 20%
Explanation: The computer is responding to a lean condition. The LTFT indicates that the programmed amount of fuel had to be increased by 20% to achieve the proper air-fuel mixture to the level where the STFT could "toggle" the mixture rich and lean for the most catalytic converter efficiency. Look for a vacuum leak or low fuel pressure.

### Example

**Vehicle 2.** STFT = +10%, LTFT = 0%
Explanation: These readings are perfect. It is normal for the STFT to add or subtract up to 20% to achieve the proper air-fuel mixture.

### Example

**Vehicle 3.** STFT = −10%, LTFT = −30%
Explanation: The engine was rich because the LTFT had to remove 30% of the anticipated amount of fuel to achieve the proper air-fuel mixture. Look for a defective (stuck-open) injector, defective fuel pressure regulator, or a restriction in the intake air passage.

## FUEL TRIM CELLS

Both STFTs and LTFTs react to oxygen sensor voltage to modify fuel delivery. Most vehicles set aside different **fuel trim cells** for each combination of engine speed (RPM) and load. The computer can then correct for slight differences in fuel mixture separately for each cell. For example, General Motors uses 16 cells plus 2 for deceleration and 2 for idle only.

### Think of a Small Faucet and a Large Faucet

The purpose of fuel trim is to add or subtract fuel as needed to maintain the proper air-fuel mixture so the catalytic converter can operate properly. STFT is fast but can add or subtract only a small amount of fuel. This can be visualized as being similar to a small water faucet adding water to a sink. For example, if a small vacuum hose becomes disconnected, the STFT will add a little extra fuel to compensate for the added amount of air being drawn into the engine. If a large hose becomes disconnected, the STFT cannot supply the needed fuel required; therefore, the LTFT is needed to supply additional fuel to overcome the large air leak. This can be visualized as being similar to a large water faucet adding a greater amount of water to a sink. Because the LTFT indicates a larger amount of fuel being added or subtracted than STFT, many service technicians simply ignore the STFT readings and use the LTFT numbers to see if they are within 10%. If LTFT is greater than 10%, either positive (+) or negative (−), then a fault should be corrected. The maximum value for STFT and LTFT depends on the exact make, model, and year of vehicle but is usually limited to 25% to 30% for either.

| | | | |
|---|---|---|---|
| 12 | 13 | 14 | 15 |
| 8 | 9 | 10 | 11 |
| 4 | 5 | 6 | 7 |
| 0 | 1 | 2 | 3 |

Load (vertical axis)

RPM ──────────→

| Deceleration Cells | Idle Cells |
|---|---|
| Greater than 1225 RPM = 17 | A/C on = 18 |
| Less than 1225 RPM = 16 | A/C off = 19 |

## FUEL TRIM CELL DIAGNOSIS

To use fuel trim as a diagnostic aid, the data should be observed during the same condition as the problem. For example, notice that there are two cells for idle—one with the air conditioning (A/C) on and one for the A/C off. If the problem or customer's concern only occurs when the A/C is on, then observe the fuel trim numbers on the scan tool with the engine operating at idle and with the A/C on.

The same thing is true of a problem that may be occurring at 55 MPH (90 km/h). Looking at fuel trim in the service bay (stall) with the engine at idle will not help the technician at all. The vehicle must be driven under similar conditions to best duplicate

### Movie Mode Diagnosis

A scan tool will display fuel trim values but only those in the cell where the engine is operating. For example, if an engine lacks power while towing a trailer up a hill, looking at the fuel trim values at idle in the shop will show the values in the cell or cells that the engine is operating. To observe the true fuel trim values, the vehicle will have to be operated under similar conditions and the data recorded on the scan tool. Use snap-shot or movie mode during the test drive, scroll through the recorded values, and look for the fuel trim cell and the LTFT and STFT values to help determine if there is a fuel delivery or other fuel trim-related problem.

the condition when the problem occurs. Only then will the correct fuel cell be displayed. Then the long-term fuel trim information should be valid. See the following fuel trim diagnostic chart.

**Fuel Trim Diagnostic Chart**

| Fuel Trim @ Idle | Fuel Trim @ 3000 RPM | Possible Cause(s) |
|---|---|---|
| Adding fuel | No correction | Vacuum leak |
| No correction | Adding fuel | Low fuel volume, weak fuel pump, or restricted fuel filter |
| Adding fuel | Adding fuel | Dirty (clogged) fuel injectors, low fuel pump pressure |
| Subtracting fuel | No correction | Gasoline in the engine oil (drawn into the engine through the PCV valve) |
| Subtracting fuel | Subtracting fuel | High fuel pressure, defective fuel pressure regulator, leaking or stuck-open injector(s) |

## MAF SENSOR ACCURACY

In an engine equipped with a MAF sensor, the accuracy of the sensor is critical for the PCM to provide the current pulse-width command to the fuel injectors. Factors that can affect the accuracy of the MAF sensor readings include:

1. **Vacuum leaks.** A vacuum leak represents air entering the combustion chambers that was not measured by the MAF sensor, and affects the air-fuel mixture mostly at idle. Above idle, the effects of a vacuum leak are reduced.

2. **False air.** False or unmeasured air is air that is entering the intake system after the MAF sensor. This false air can have a

**FIGURE 17–4** Any fault in the air cleaner assembly can disrupt the airflow through the MAF sensor.

great effect on the air-fuel mixture at idle and, like a vacuum leak, tends to have less of an effect at higher engine speeds.

3. **PCV airflow.** The airflow through the PCV system is not measured by the MAF sensor. Therefore, all openings to the crankcase must be sealed to prevent unmeasured air from entering.

4. **Airflow disturbance (disruption).** If the incorrect air filter is installed or the air inlet system is modified, airflow through the MAF sensor may not be straight. If air turbulence passes through the MAF sensor, the accuracy of the amount of airflow will not be correct. ● **SEE FIGURE 17–4.**

# VOLUMETRIC EFFICIENCY

**DEFINITION OF VOLUMETRIC EFFICIENCY** Volumetric efficiency (VE) is the percentage of air entering the engine compared to the theoretical airflow. Typical normally aspirated engines will test having a VE of 75% to 90%. Older two-valve cylinder head engines will test lower than newer engines equipped with four valves per cylinder. Percentages above 100% are possible on supercharged or turbocharged engines. A VE calculator can be downloaded here (free):

*www.lindertech.com/guru3*

User name: GURU3

Password: LTS2004

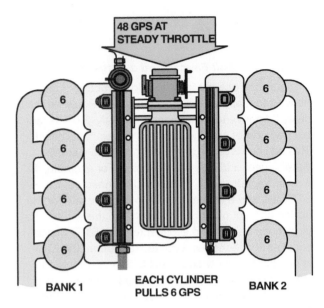

**FIGURE 17–5** This properly operating engine is drawing in 48 grams per second of air for all eight cylinders. This indicates that each cylinder will be receiving 6 grams per second (GPS).

The calculation requires data to be captured using a scan tool while the vehicle is being driven at wide-open throttle. This test should be conducted in a safe location away from traffic and does not need to be performed at high vehicle speeds. The data needed includes:

- Engine size in cubic inches
- Engine speed (RPM)
- MAF (grams per second)
- Intake air temperature (IAT)

**Example 1**

A Chevrolet Trailblazer equipped with a 4.2-liter 6-cylinder engine is tested using the following information and results:

Engine size = 256 cu. in. (4.2 liters)

Engine RPM = 6097

MAF (gm/s) = 225.4

IAT (°F) = 66

The calculated airflow through the engine is 395 cu. ft per sec. The theoretical airflow through the engine is 451 cu. ft per second. The VE is 87%.

This result indicates that the MAF sensor is accurately measuring the airflow and the engine is in good mechanical condition.

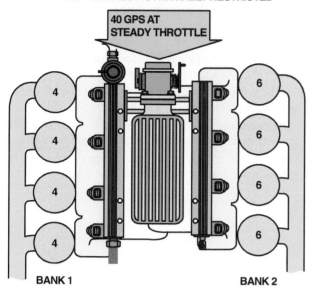

LEFT EXHAUST IS PARTIALLY RESTRICTED

40 GPS AT STEADY THROTTLE

BANK 1          BANK 2

**FIGURE 17–6** If the exhaust system on the left bank (bank #1) were to become restricted, the total airflow through the MAF sensor would also decrease. The cylinders on the right bank (bank #2) would draw the same 6 GPS as before and the cylinders on bank #1, which have a restricted exhaust, would draw just 4 GPS.

MAF SENSOR READS ONLY 40 GRAMS PER SECOND

BANK 1     EACH CYLINDER     BANK 2
            40 / 8 = 5GPS

**FIGURE 17–7** If all cylinders were equal and showed the 40 grams per second, then each cylinder will be drawing 5 grams per second (5 × 8 cylinders = 40 GPS). Bank 1 is being supplied 4/5ths of the air needed whereas bank 2 is being supplied 6/5ths of the air needed causing bank 1 to operate too rich and bank 2 to operate too lean.

### Example 2

A Cadillac Deville is equipped with a 4.6-liter V-8. The customer's concern is poor performance. Fuel trim numbers are within ± 2% from idle to cruise. A check of the VE indicates the following:

Engine size = 281 cu. in. (4.6 liters)

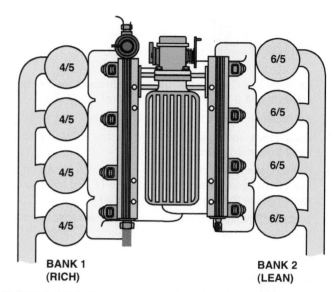

BANK 1          BANK 2
(RICH)          (LEAN)

**FIGURE 17–8** As a result of the restricted exhaust on bank #1, the restricted bank will operate too rich and bank #2 will operate too lean. The long-term fuel trim will be negative for bank #1 and positive for bank #2.

🔧 **TECH TIP**

**MAF Sensor or Airflow Problem?**

If a MAF sensor reading is lower than normal, such as at wide-open throttle, it could be an engine breathing problem or a defective/contaminated MAF sensor. To determine which is the case, check the following:

- If the fuel trim numbers follow the airflow, then there is an airflow measurement error (MAF sensor-related problem).
- If the fuel trim numbers are okay, the MAF is okay.
- If the BARO reading is lower than normal, then there is an engine breathing issue, such as a restricted intake or exhaust.

🔧 **TECH TIP**

**Possible Restricted Exhaust? Check the IAT.**

If the exhaust system is restricted, all of the exhaust will be unable to exit the engine, especially at wide-open throttle. Using a scan tool, look at the values displayed for the intake air temperature (IAT) sensor. The IAT temperature should decrease slightly at WOT normally due to the increased airflow. If the IAT temperature reading increases, this is an indication of a restricted exhaust.

Engine RPM = 3400
MAF (gm/s) = 80
IAT (°F) = 95
The calculated volumetric efficiency is 53%. A clogged catalytic converter is discovered to be the cause.

## SUMMARY

1. Lambda is a Greek letter used to represent air-fuel ratio. Lambda of 1.0 is equal to an air-fuel rate of 14.7:1.

2. Equivalence ratio is the inverse of lambda.

3. Base pulse width is determined by the PCM based on input from many sensors.

4. Speed density fuel control uses calculations based on the input from various sensors such as the TP and MAP sensor to determine the amount of fuel needed.

5. Mass air flow systems use a mass air flow sensor to measure the mass of the air entering the engine directly.

6. Fuel trim uses the oxygen sensor data to fine tune the air-fuel mixture to ensure lowest emissions.

7. Short-term fuel trim (STFT) is capable of quickly adding or subtracting fuel, but only a limited amount.

8. Long-term fuel trim (LTFT) is capable of adding or subtracting more fuel than STFT, but is slower to react.

9. Volumetric efficiency is the percentage of air entering the engine compared to the theoretical airflow.

## REVIEW QUESTIONS

1. What is the difference between lambda and equivalence ratio?

2. How is base pulse width determined?

3. Why is fuel trim needed?

4. What is the difference between short-term and long-term fuel trim?

## CHAPTER QUIZ

1. If the air-fuel ratio is 14.7:1, what is lambda?
   a. 1.0
   b. 0.9
   c. 1.1
   d. 14.7

2. If lambda is 0.98, this means the _____.
   a. Mixture is lean
   b. Air-fuel mixture is within 2% of stoichiometric
   c. Air-fuel mixture is slightly rich
   d. Both b and c

3. Base pulse width is determined by _____.
   a. Oxygen sensor data
   b. Computer calculations
   c. Input from many sensors, except the oxygen sensor
   d. Both b and c

4. The air at high altitude has _____.
   a. 21% oxygen
   b. Less than 21% oxygen
   c. A higher pressure
   d. A higher density

5. In a speed density system, what does *not* need to be corrected for?
   a. Air temperature
   b. Oxygen in the exhaust from the oxygen sensor
   c. Amount of EGR
   d. BARO sensor data

6. In a MAF system, which is correct?
   a. The system measures the actual mass of the air entering the engine.
   b. The amount of EGR flow must be subtracted from the MAF sensor reading.
   c. Altitude correction is not needed.
   d. Temperature of the air correction is not needed.

7. Injector pulse width is measured in _____.
   a. Percentage (%)      c. Duty cycle (%)
   b. Milliseconds (ms)   d. Frequency (Hz)

8. What is *not* true about short-term fuel trim?
   a. It is able to react quickly to add or subtract fuel.
   b. It can add or subtract a large amount of fuel.
   c. It uses the oxygen sensor.
   d. It is expressed in percentages.

9. A Nissan is being checked, using a scan tool, and Alpha is 107. This means _____.
   a. The PCM is adding fuel
   b. The PCM is subtracting fuel
   c. The PCM represents STFT only
   d. The PCM represents LTFT only

10. A contaminated or defective MAF sensor is indicated if _____.
    a. The fuel trim number follows the airflow
    b. The VE is bad
    c. The fuel trim numbers are within ±2%
    d. The BARO reading is lower than normal

# chapter
# 26

# IN-VEHICLE ENGINE SERVICE

OBJECTIVES: **After studying Chapter 26, the reader will be able to:** • Prepare for ASE certification test content area "A" (General Engine Diagnosis) • Diagnose and replace the thermostat. • Diagnose and replace the water pump. • Diagnose and replace an intake manifold gasket • Determine and verify correct cam timing • Replace a timing a belt • Describe how to adjust valves • Explain hybrid engine precautions

KEY TERMS: EREV 365 • Fretting 363 • HEV 365 • Idle stop 365 • Skewed 362

## THERMOSTAT REPLACEMENT

**FAILURE PATTERNS** All thermostat valves move during operation to maintain the desired coolant temperature. Thermostats can fail in the following ways:

- **Stuck Open**—If a thermostat fails open or partially open, the operating temperature of the engine will be less than normal. ● **SEE FIGURE 26–1.**

- **Stuck Closed**—If the thermostat fails closed or almost closed, the engine will likely overheat.

- **Stuck Partially Open**—This will cause the engine to warm up slowly if at all. This condition can cause the powertrain control module (PCM) to set a P0128 diagnostic trouble code (DTC) which means that the engine coolant temperature does not reach the specified temperature.

- **Skewed**—A **skewed** thermostat works, but not within the correct temperature range. Therefore, the engine could overheat or operate cooler than normal or even do both.

**REPLACEMENT PROCEDURE** Before replacing the thermostat, double-check that the cooling system problem is not due to another fault, such as being low on coolant or an inoperative cooling fan. Check service information for the specified procedure to follow to replace the thermostat. Most recommended procedures include the following steps:

**STEP 1** Allow the engine to cool for several hours so the engine and the coolant should be at room temperature.

**STEP 2** Drain the coolant into a suitable container. Most vehicle manufacturers recommend that new coolant be used and the old coolant disposed of properly or recycled.

**FIGURE 26–1** A stuck-open thermostat. This caused the vehicle to set a diagnostic trouble code P0128 (coolant temperature below thermostat regulating temperature).

**STEP 3** Remove any necessary components to get access to the thermostat.

**STEP 4** Remove the thermostat housing and thermostat.

**STEP 5** Replace the thermostat housing gasket and thermostat. Torque all fasteners to specifications.

**STEP 6** Refill the cooling system with the specified coolant and bleed any trapped air from the system.

**STEP 7** Pressurize the cooling system to verify that there are no leaks around the thermostat housing.

**STEP 8** Run the engine until it reaches normal operating temperature and check for leaks.

**STEP 9** Verify that the engine is reaching correct operating temperature.

**FIGURE 26–2** Use caution if using a steel scraper to remove a gasket from aluminum parts. It is best to use a wood or plastic scraper.

**FIGURE 26–3** An intake manifold gasket that failed and allowed coolant to be drawn into the cylinder(s).

## WATER PUMP REPLACEMENT

**NEED FOR REPLACEMENT**   A water pump will require replacement if any of the following conditions are present:

- Leaking coolant from the weep hole
- Bearing noisy or loose
- Lack of proper coolant flow caused by worn or slipping impeller blades

**REPLACEMENT GUIDELINES**   After diagnosis has been confirmed that the water pump requires replacement, check service information for the exact procedure to follow. The steps usually include the following:

**STEP 1**   Allow the engine to cool to room temperature.

**STEP 2**   Drain the coolant and dispose of properly or recycle.

**STEP 3**   Remove engine components to gain access to the water pump as specified in service information.

**STEP 4**   Remove the water pump assembly.

> **NOTE: Always compare the replacement pump with the original to be sure that they are the same.**

**STEP 5**   Clean the gasket surfaces and install the new water pump using a new gasket or seal as needed. ● **SEE FIGURE 26–2.** Torque all fasteners to factory specifications.

**STEP 6**   Install removed engine components.

**STEP 7**   Fill the cooling system with the specified coolant.

**STEP 8**   Run the engine, check for leaks, and verify proper operation.

## INTAKE MANIFOLD GASKET INSPECTION

**CAUSES OF FAILURE**   Many V-type engines leak oil, coolant, or experience an air (vacuum) leak caused by a leaking intake manifold gasket. This failure can be contributed to one or more of the following:

1. Expansion/contraction rate difference between the cast-iron head and the aluminum intake manifold can cause the intake manifold gasket to be damaged by the relative motion of the head and intake manifold. This type of failure is called **fretting.**

2. Plastic (Nylon 6.6) gasket deterioration caused by the coolant. ● **SEE FIGURE 26–3.**

### DIAGNOSIS OF LEAKING INTAKE MANIFOLD GASKET

Because intake manifold gaskets are used to seal oil, air, and coolant in most causes, determining that the intake manifold gasket is the root cause can be a challenge. To diagnose a possible leaking intake manifold gasket, perform the following tests:

**Visual inspection**—Check for evidence of oil or coolant between the intake manifold and the cylinder heads.

**Coolant level**—Check the coolant level and determine if the level has been dropping. A leaking intake manifold gasket can cause coolant to leak and then evaporate, leaving no evidence of the leak.

**Air (vacuum) leak**—If there is a stored diagnostic trouble code (DTC) for a lean exhaust (P0171, P0172, or P0174), a leaking intake manifold gasket could be the cause. Use propane to check if the engine changes when dispensed around the intake manifold gasket. If the engine changes in speed or sound, then this test verifies that an air leak is present.

FIGURE 26–4 The lower intake manifold, attaches to the cylinder heads.

FIGURE 26–5 The upper intake manifold, often called a plenum, attaches to the lower intake manifold.

## INTAKE MANIFOLD GASKET REPLACEMENT

When replacing the intake manifold gasket, always check service information for the exact procedure to follow. The steps usually include the following:

**STEP 1** Be sure the engine has been off for about an hour and then drain the coolant into a suitable container, if required.

**STEP 2** Remove covers and other specified parts needed to get access to the retaining bolts.

**STEP 3** To help ensure that the manifold does not warp when removed, loosen all fasteners in the reverse order of the tightening sequence. This means that the bolts

FIGURE 26–6 Many aftermarket replacement intake manifolds have a different appearance from the original manifold.

should be loosened starting at the ends and working toward the center.

**STEP 4** Remove the upper intake manifold, if equipped, and inspect for faults. ● **SEE FIGURES 26–4 AND 26–5.**

**STEP 5** Remove the lower intake manifold, using the same bolt removal procedure of starting at the ends and working toward the center.

**STEP 6** Thoroughly clean the area and replace the intake manifold if needed. Check that the correct replacement manifold is being used, and even the current part could look different from the original. ● **SEE FIGURE 26–6.**

**STEP 7** Install the intake manifold using new gaskets as specified. Some designs use gaskets that are reusable. Replace as needed.

**STEP 8** Torque all fasteners to factory specifications and in the proper sequences. The tightening sequences usually start at the center and work outward to the ends.

> **CAUTION: Double-check the torque specifications and be sure to use the correct values. Many intake manifolds use fasteners that are torqued to values expressed in pound-inches and not pound-feet.**

**STEP 9** Reinstall all parts needed to allow the engine to start and run, including refilling the coolant if needed.

**STEP 10** Start the engine and check for leaks and proper engine operation.

**STEP 11** Reset or relearn the idle if specified, using a scan tool.

**STEP 12** Install all of the remaining parts and perform a test drive to verify proper operation and no leaks.

**STEP 13** Check and replace the air filter if needed.

**STEP 14** Change the engine oil if the intake manifold leak could have caused coolant to leak into the engine, which would contaminate the oil.

**FIGURE 26–7** A single overhead camshaft engine with a timing belt that also rotates the water pump.

## TIMING BELT REPLACEMENT

**NEED FOR REPLACEMENT** Timing belts have a limited service and a specified replacement interval ranging from 60,000 miles (97,000 km) to about 100,000 miles (161,000 km). Timing belts are required to be replaced if any of the following conditions occur:

- Meets or exceeds the vehicle manufacturer's recommended timing belt replacement interval.
- The timing belt has been contaminated with coolant or engine oil.
- The timing belt has failed (missing belt teeth or broken).

**TIMING BELT REPLACEMENT GUIDELINES** Before replacing the timing belt, check service information for the recommended procedure to follow. Most timing belt replacement procedures include the following steps:

**STEP 1** Allow the engine to cool before starting to remove components to help eliminate the possibility of personal injury or warpage of the parts.

**STEP 2** Remove all necessary components to gain access to the timing belt and timing marks.

**STEP 3** If the timing belt is not broken, rotate the engine until the camshaft and crankshaft timing marks are

aligned according to the specified marks. ● **SEE FIGURE 26–7.**

**STEP 4** Loosen or remove the tensioner as needed to remove the timing belt.

**STEP 5** Replace the timing belt and any other recommended items. Components that some vehicle manufacturers recommend replacing in addition to the timing belt include:
- Tensioner assembly
- Water pump
- Camshaft oil seal(s)
- Front crankshaft seal

**STEP 6** Check (verify) that the camshaft timing is correct by rotating the engine several revolutions.

**STEP 7** Install enough components to allow the engine to start to verify proper operation. Check for any leaks, especially if seals have been replaced.

**STEP 8** Complete the reassembly of the engine and perform a test drive before returning the vehicle to the customer.

## HYBRID ENGINE PRECAUTIONS

**HYBRID VEHICLE ENGINE OPERATION** Gasoline engines used in **hybrid electric vehicles (HEVs)** and in **extended range electric vehicles (EREVs)** can be a hazard to be around under some conditions. These vehicles are designed to stop the gasoline engines unless needed. This feature is called **idle stop.** This means that the engine is not running, but could start at any time if the computer detects the need to charge the hybrid batteries or other issue that requires the gasoline engine to start and run.

**PRECAUTIONS** Always check service information for the exact procedures to follow when working around or under the hood of a hybrid electric vehicle. These precautions could include:

- Before working under the hood or around the engine, be sure that the ignition is off and the key is out of the ignition.
- Check that the "Ready" light is off. ● **SEE FIGURE 26–8.**
- Do not touch any circuits that have orange electrical wires or conduit. The orange color indicates dangerous high-voltage wires, which could cause serious injury or death if touched.
- Always use high-voltage linesman's gloves whenever depowering the high-voltage system.

**HYBRID ENGINE SERVICE** The gasoline engine in most hybrid electric vehicles specifies low viscosity engine oil as a

**FIGURE 26–8** A Toyota/Lexus hybrid electric vehicle has a ready light. If the ready light is on, the engine can start at anytime without warning.

**FIGURE 26–9** Always use the viscosity of oil as specified on the oil fill cap.

way to achieve maximum fuel economy. ● **SEE FIGURE 26–9.** The viscosity required is often:

- SAE 0W-20
- SAE 5W-20

Many shops do not keep this viscosity in stock so preparations need to be made to get and use the specified engine oil.

In addition to engine oil, some hybrid electric vehicles such as the Honda Insight (1999–2004) require special spark plugs. Check service information for the specified service procedures and parts needed if a hybrid electric vehicle is being serviced.

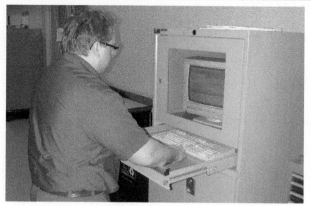

**1** Before starting the process of adjusting the valves, look up the specifications and exact procedures. The technician is checking this information from a computer CD-ROM-based information system.

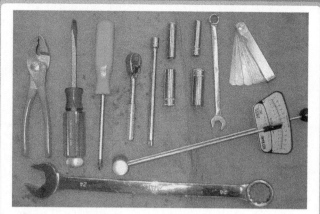

**2** The tools necessary to adjust the valves on an engine with adjustable rocker arms include basic hand tools, feeler gauge, and a torque wrench.

**3** An overall view of the four-cylinder engine that is due for a scheduled valve adjustment according to the vehicle manufacturer's recommendations.

**4** Start the valve adjustment procedure by first disconnecting and labeling, if necessary, all vacuum lines that need to be removed to gain access to the valve cover.

**5** The air intake tube is being removed from the throttle body.

**6** With all vacuum lines and the intake tube removed, the valve cover can be removed after removing all retaining bolts.

CONTINUED ▶

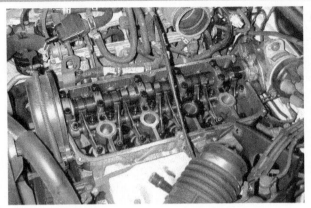

**7** Notice how clean the engine appears. This is a testament of proper maintenance and regular oil changes by the owner.

**8** To help locate how far the engine is being rotated, the technician is removing the distributor cap to be able to observe the position of the rotor.

TIMING MARK

**9** The engine is rotated until the timing marks on the front of the crankshaft line up with zero degrees—top dead center (TDC)—with both valves closed on #1 cylinder.

**10** With the rocker arms contacting the base circle of the cam, insert a feeler gauge of the specified thickness between the camshaft and the rocker arm. There should be a slight drag on the feeler gauge.

**11** If the valve clearance (lash) is not correct, loosen the retaining nut and turn the valve adjusting screw with a screwdriver to achieve the proper clearance.

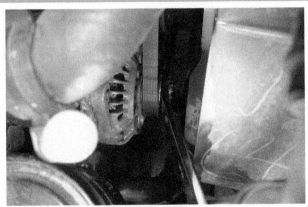

**12** After adjusting the valves that are closed, rotate the engine one full rotation until the engine timing marks again align.

TIMING MARK

**13** The engine is rotated until the timing marks again align indicating that the companion cylinder will now be in position for valve clearance measurement.

**14** On some engines, it is necessary to watch the direction the rotor is pointing to help determine how far to rotate the engine. Always follow the vehicle manufacturer's recommended procedure.

**15** The technician is using a feeler gauge that is one-thousandth of an inch thinner and another one-thousandth of an inch thicker than the specified clearance as a double-check that the clearance is correct.

**16** Adjusting a valve takes both hands—one to hold the wrench to loosen and tighten the lock nut and one to turn the adjusting screw. Always double-check the clearance after an adjustment is made.

**17** After all valves have been properly measured and adjusted as necessary, start the reassembly process by replacing all gaskets and seals as specified by the vehicle manufacturer.

**18** Reinstall the valve cover being careful to not pinch a wire or vacuum hose between the cover and the cylinder head.

CONTINUED ▶

**19** Use a torque wrench and torque the valve cover retaining bolts to factory specifications.

**20** Reinstall the distributor cap.

**21** Reinstall the spark plug wires and all brackets that were removed to gain access to the valve cover.

**22** Reconnect all vacuum and air hoses and tubes. Replace any vacuum hoses that are brittle or swollen with new ones.

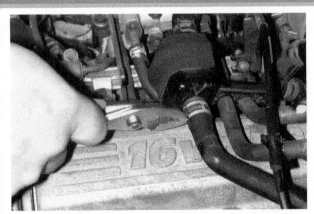

**23** Be sure that the clamps are properly installed. Start the engine and check for proper operation.

**24** Double-check for any oil or vacuum leaks after starting the engine.

## SUMMARY

1. Thermostats can fail in the following ways:
   - Stuck open
   - Stuck closed
   - Stuck partially open
   - Skewed

2. A water pump should be replaced if any of the following conditions are present:
   - Leaking from the weep hole
   - Noisy bearing
   - Loose bearing
   - Lack of normal circulation due to worn impeller blades

3. A leaking intake manifold gasket can cause coolant to get into the oil or oil into the coolant, as well as other faults, such as a poor running engine.

4. When a timing belt is replaced, most vehicle manufacturers also recommend that the following items be replaced:
   - Tensioner assembly
   - Water pump
   - Camshaft seal(s)
   - Front crankshaft seal

5. When working on a Toyota/Lexus hybrid electric vehicle (HEV), be sure that the key is off and out of the ignition and the READY light is off.

## REVIEW QUESTIONS

1. How can a thermostat fail?
2. How can a water pump fail requiring replacement?
3. What will happen to the engine if the intake manifold gasket fails?
4. Why must timing belts be replaced?
5. Why is it important that the READY light be out on the dash before working under the hood of a hybrid electric vehicle?

## CHAPTER QUIZ

1. A thermostat can fail in which way?
   a. Stuck open
   b. Stuck closed
   c. Stuck partially open
   d. Any of the above

2. A skewed thermostat means it is _____
   a. Working, but not at the correct temperature
   b. Not working
   c. Missing the thermo wax in the heat sensor
   d. Contaminated with coolant

3. Coolant drained from the cooling system when replacing a thermostat or water pump should be _____
   a. Reused
   b. Disposed of properly or recycled
   c. Filtered and reinstalled after the repair
   d. Poured down a toilet

4. A water pump can fail to provide the proper amount of flow of coolant through the cooling system if what has happened?
   a. The coolant is leaking from the weep hole
   b. The bearing is noisy
   c. The impeller blades are worn or slipping on the shaft
   d. A bearing failure has caused the shaft to become loose

5. Intake manifold gaskets on a V-type engine can fail due to what factor?
   a. Fretting
   b. Coolant damage
   c. Relative movement between the intake manifold and the cylinder head
   d. All of the above

6. A defective thermostat can cause the Powertrain Control Module to set what diagnostic trouble code (DTC)?
   a. P0171
   b. P0172
   c. P0128
   d. P0300

7. A replacement plastic intake manifold may have a different design or appearance from the original factory-installed part.
   a. True
   b. False

8. The torque specifications for many plastic intake manifolds are in what unit?
   a. Pound-inches
   b. Pound-feet
   c. Ft-lbs per minute
   d. Lb-ft per second

9. When replacing a timing belt, many experts and vehicle manufacturers recommend that what other part(s) should be replaced?
   a. Tensioner assembly
   b. Water pump
   c. Camshaft oil seal(s)
   d. All of the above

10. Hybrid electric vehicles usually require special engine oil of what viscosity?
    a. SAE 5W-30
    b. SAE 10W-30
    c. SAE 0W-20
    d. SAE 5W-40

# chapter 27

# SYMPTOM-BASED DIAGNOSIS

**OBJECTIVES:** **After studying Chapter 27, the reader will be able to:** • Prepare for ASE Engine Performance (A8) certification test content area "A" (General Engine Diagnosis) and ASE Advanced Level (L1) certification test content area "A" (General Powertrain Diagnosis). • List the possible causes of an engine performance problem based on its symptoms. • List the possible causes of a rich air-fuel mixture. • List the possible causes of a lean air-fuel mixture. • Describe what symptoms may occur if a particular sensor is defective. • List the possible causes of excessive HC, CO, and $NO_x$ exhaust emissions.

**KEY TERMS:** Backfire 378 • Detonation 375 • Dieseling 378 • Fuel economy 377 • Hesitation 372 • Lean misfire 383 • Misfire 380 • Ping 375 • Rough (unstable) idle 374 • Run-on 378 • Sag 372 • Spark knock 375 • Stall 374 • Stumble 373 • Surges 380 • Symptom 381

About 80% of problems can be solved using a systematic approach. However for the remaining 20%, it is the skill and experience of the service technician that will help narrow the problem to the root cause.

This chapter is different from the previous chapters in this textbook, as it will be devoted to providing:

- Lists for common causes of problems based on their symptoms
- Lists of symptoms that a particular component could cause if it were defective
- Typical causes of a too rich or too lean condition that are included to help find those exhaust emission testing failures

This chapter is similar to having an experienced service technician next to you while you are working on a problem that seems difficult to solve. Enjoy.

## ENGINE HESITATES, SAGS, OR STUMBLES DURING ACCELERATION

**Hesitation** means a delay in the operation of the engine when the accelerator pedal is depressed. Sometimes hesitation is described as **sag** or "lack of response" as the accelerator is pushed down.

The most common cause of hesitation is a too lean air-fuel mixture being delivered to the engine during the time the accelerator is depressed. When the accelerator pedal is depressed, additional air can quickly flow into the engine. Gasoline is

heavier than air and cannot flow as fast into the engine as the air. As a result, the engine normally would hesitate until the correct amount of gasoline flow matches the increased amount of air entering the engine. Fuel systems are designed to compensate for this lag or hesitation by providing an additional shot

**FIGURE 27–1** Valve deposits on the intake valves can cause hesitation during acceleration, especially if the engine is cold.

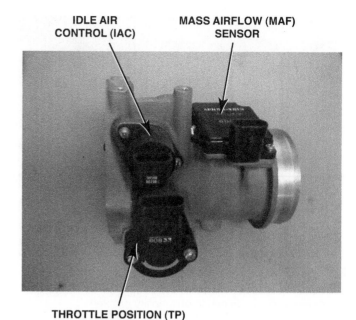

IDLE AIR CONTROL (IAC)

MASS AIRFLOW (MAF) SENSOR

THROTTLE POSITION (TP) SENSOR

**FIGURE 27–2** Typical throttle-position (TP) sensor.

or squirt of fuel into the intake manifold or cylinder just as the accelerator pedal is depressed.

- Carbon buildup on the backside of the intake valves absorbs gasoline vapors and can cause a hesitation, especially when the engine is cold. ● **SEE FIGURE 27–1.**
- A throttle-position (TP) sensor is used on electronic fuel-injection systems to signal the computer to provide an extra pulse to the fuel injector(s) just as the accelerator pedal is depressed to prevent a hesitation (● **SEE FIGURE 27–2).**

| Possible Cause | Reason |
|---|---|
| Throttle-position (TP) sensor | • The TP sensor voltage should be within the specified range at idle. If too high or too low, the computer may not provide a strong enough extra pulse to prevent a hesitation.<br>• An open or short in the TP sensor can result in hesitation because the computer would not be receiving correct information regarding the position of the throttle. |
| Throttle-plate deposit buildup (port fuel-injected engines) | • An air flow restriction at the throttle plates creates not only less air reaching the engine but also swirling air due to the deposits. This swirling or uneven air flow can cause an uneven air-fuel mixture being supplied to the engine, causing poor idle quality and a sag or hesitation during acceleration. |

| | |
|---|---|
| Manifold absolute pressure (MAP) sensor fault | • The MAP sensor detects changes in engine load and signals to the computer to increase the amount of fuel needed for proper operation. Check the vacuum hose and the sensor itself for proper operation. |
| Check the throttle linkage for binding | • A kinked throttle cable or cruise (speed) control cable can cause the accelerator pedal to bind. |
| Contaminated fuel | • Fuel contaminated with excessive amounts of alcohol or water can cause a hesitation or sag during acceleration. |

**NOTE: To easily check for the presence of alcohol in gasoline, simply get a sample of the fuel and place it in a clean container. Add some water and shake. If no alcohol is in the gasoline, the water will settle to the bottom and be clear. If there is alcohol in the gasoline, the alcohol will absorb the water. The alcohol-water combination will settle to the bottom of the container, but will be cloudy rather than clear. ● SEE FIGURE 27–3.**

| | |
|---|---|
| Clogged, shorted, or leaking fuel injectors | Any injector problem that results in less than an ideal amount of fuel being delivered to the cylinders can result in a hesitation, a sag, or **stumble** during acceleration. |
| Spark plugs or spark plug wires | Any fault in the ignition system such as a defective spark plug wire or cracked spark plug can cause hesitation, a sag, or stumble during acceleration. At higher engine speeds, a defective spark plug wire is not as noticeable as it is at lower speeds, especially in vehicles equipped with a V-8 engine. |

**FIGURE 27–3** Many areas of the country use gasoline that is blended with up to 10% ethanol (ethyl alcohol). Sometimes too much alcohol can cause driveability problems.

**FIGURE 27–4** The deposits on the back (engine) side of the throttle plate can cause rough idle or stalling due to lack of proper air flow into the engine.

| Possible Cause | Reason |
| --- | --- |
| EGR valve operation | • Hesitation, a sag, or stumble can occur if the EGR valve opens too soon or is stuck partially open. |
| False air | • A loose or cracked intake hose between the MAF sensor and the throttle plate can be the cause. |

## ROUGH IDLE OR STALLING

**Rough** (or **unstable**) **idle** is a common occurrence because many different systems have a direct effect on idle quality. If the engine **stalls** (stops running), most customers are very concerned because it can be a safety-related malfunction. For the engine to idle correctly, each cylinder has to have the same (or nearly the same) compression, air-fuel mixture, ignition timing, and quality of spark.

| Possible Cause | Reason |
| --- | --- |
| Vacuum leak | • A vacuum leak (also called an air leak) allows extra air to enter the intake manifold or an individual cylinder, thereby leaning the air-fuel mixture to one or more cylinders. Because the cylinder(s) is not receiving the *same* air-fuel mixture, the engine will not run smoothly and a rough idle can result. |
| | • In some cases, a vacuum leak can cause a higher-than-normal idle speed or even cause the engine to stall. |
| Dirty throttle plate(s) (port fuel-injected engines) | • Dirty throttle plates can restrict the amount of air entering the engine. ● **SEE FIGURE 27–4.** This is especially noticeable when the engine is idling. Often, the idle air control valve can offset the effect of the dirty throttle by increasing the amount of air that bypasses the throttle plate. Although this may restore the proper idle speed, idle quality may still be poor. |
| | • In severe cases, dirty throttle plates can cause stalling, especially when coasting to a stop. |
| Clogged, shorted, or leaking fuel injectors | • A clogged or inoperative fuel injector causes the cylinder or cylinders affected to be leaner than usual. Because all cylinders are not receiving the same amount of fuel, the engine will run roughly and may even stall. |
| | • If an injector is leaking and not shutting off when power is removed from the injector, the injector will cause excessive amounts of fuel to be drawn into the affected cylinder or cylinders. |
| | • If an injector is electrically shorted, excessive current will flow through the windings of the injector coil. Two situations can occur: (1) The shorted injector may operate, but will draw current from another injector that shares the same injector driver inside the computer. In this case, the injector that is shorted will work okay, but the "good" injector will not work. (2) The shorted injector may work depending on how badly the injector is shorted and how the injector driver circuit inside the computer controls (limits) the current flow through the injector. |

| Ignition system fault | • Defective spark plug wires can cause a rough running or idling engine, and in severe cases can cause the engine to stall. |
| | • Dirty, cracked, unevenly gapped, or excessively worn spark plugs can cause poor engine operation, a rough idle, or even stalling. |
| | • Weak ignition may result from a shorted ignition coil, defective ignition module (igniter), or defective pickup coil or crankshaft position sensor. |
| Exhaust gas recirculation (EGR) valve stuck open | • An open EGR valve allows inert exhaust gases to be mixed with the proper air-fuel mixture. The exhaust gases cannot burn and the EGR being open at idle is likely to cause a rough idle or stalling. |
| | • At higher engine speeds, exhaust gases can be introduced into the cylinder as is normally done; therefore, the engine runs okay above idle speed. |
| Positive crankcase ventilation (PCV) systems fault | • About 20% of the air going into the engine at idle comes from the PCV system. |
| | • Check that a replacement PCV valve may not be correctly calibrated for the engine (wrong PCV valve application during a previous service). |
| | • All vacuum hoses should be carefully inspected for cracks. |
| | • All vacuum passages should be carefully inspected for obstructions such as carbon buildup in manifold ports where the PCV hose attaches to the manifold. |
| Secondary air injection system malfunction | • Inspect the one-way check valves. A hole in a check valve can cause exhaust gases to flow into the air pump system and into the intake manifold, greatly affecting the air-fuel mixture. |
| Idle air control (IAC) problems | • If the IAC is stuck, the valve cannot provide the correct idle speed. Usually, this results in too high an idle speed, but it can result in a too low idle speed, causing the engine to idle roughly and, in severe cases, even stall. |
| | • Restricted IAC passages can limit the amount of air going into the engine at idle. |
| Manifold absolute pressure (MAP) or mass airflow (MAF) sensor fault | • A MAP sensor vacuum hose, either split open or collapsed, can greatly affect the operation of the MAP sensor. An incorrect MAP sensor signal to the computer can cause the computer to supply either a too rich or too lean command. |
| | • A defective MAP or MAF sensor can also cause a rough idle or stalling. |

| Malfunction or misadjusted park-neutral switch | • The computer will not command the proper air-fuel mixture if the gear selection is in drive or reverse, yet the computer "thinks" that the gear selector is still in park or neutral. |
| | • The idle speed is affected by the park-neutral switch and the engine may idle roughly or even stall. |

# SPARK KNOCK (PING OR DETONATION)

Spark knock (also called detonation or ping) is most noticeable during acceleration. Spark knock is usually due to excessively lean air-fuel mixtures or excessively hot engine operation. The noise or knock is a result of a secondary rapid burning of the last 3 to 5% of the gases inside the combustion chamber. When this secondary flame front hits the primary spark-ignited flame front, two situations occur:

1. Temperature greatly increases at the instant the two flame fronts collide.
2. Pressure greatly increases at the same time due to the temperature rise.

These two factors combine to cause the piston to "ring" like a bell, creating the characteristic sound of spark knock.

| Possible Cause | Reason |
| --- | --- |
| Vacuum leak | Causes a leaner-than-normal air-fuel mixture. |
| Defective EGR valve/system | Exhaust gas recirculation (EGR) system uses inert gases to slow the burning process. If not enough exhaust gas is recirculated spark knock can occur. |
| Low coolant level | Could cause the engine to operate too hot. |
| Contaminated $O_2$ sensor | Causes the computer to deliver a too lean air-fuel mixture. |
| Electric cooling fan inoperative | Can cause the engine to operate at too high a temperature. |
| Too low fuel pressure | Can cause the engine to operate with a too lean air-fuel mixture. |
| Too advanced ignition timing | Causes excessive pressure buildup in the combustion chamber. |
| Knock sensor or system is not operating | If the knock sensor (KS) system is not operating, the ignition timing will not be retarded when spark knock is detected. |
| Park-neutral switch | The computer is not seeing a drive gear and the EGR is not commanded on if the vehicle is not in a drive gear (drive or reverse). |

| Possible Cause | Reason |
|---|---|
| Defective valve stem seals | • Causes excessive carbon buildup inside the combustion chamber, creating higher-than-normal compression.<br>• Defective valve stem seals are sources of carbon that can glow, which could be an ignition source that ignites the air-fuel mixture before the spark plug fires, causing preignition. |
| Engine mechanical faults | Incorrect engine parts such as pistons, camshaft, or cylinder heads that can cause excessive compression. |
| PROM | An updated PROM (programmable read-only memory) may have been released that changes the ignition timing or air-fuel mixture to solve a spark knock concern. |

**FIGURE 27–5** A vacuum gauge is an excellent and low-cost tool to use to make sure that the engine is functioning normally.

## ENGINE CRANKS OKAY, BUT IS HARD TO START

In order for engines to start, the correct air fuel ratio must be delivered to the cylinders and a strong spark must be present to ignite the mixture. Worn engine parts can also cause an engine to not have enough compression or to have the valves open and close at the proper time and duration.

| Possible Cause | Reason |
|---|---|
| Weak spark to the spark plugs | A weak spark caused by faults in the ignition coil(s), secondary spark plug wires, or distributor cap or rotor (if so equipped) can prevent the air-fuel mixture from igniting when the cylinder is under compression when the engine is being cranked. |
| Low fuel pressure | Low fuel pressure due to a weak fuel pump or defective fuel-pressure regulator can cause a lack of fuel being supplied to the engine. A defective check valve in the fuel pump can also cause the fuel pressure to drop to zero and can cause a long cranking period to occur before starting. |
| Contaminated or stale gasoline | Gasoline with excessive amounts of alcohol can cause hard starting, especially in cold weather. Stale gasoline is gasoline that has been stored for a long time (several months) and the light ends have evaporated, leaving the heavier portions of the gasoline that are hard to ignite. |
| Leaking, clogged, or inoperative fuel injectors | • If a fuel injector were to stick open, an excessive amount of fuel would fill the cylinder, causing the spark plug(s) to foul and make starting difficult.<br>• If an injector were clogged or inoperative, a lack of fuel would cause the cylinder to be too lean, and hard starting (or no starting) may occur. |
| Low cranking vacuum | • Low cranking vacuum (lower than 2.5 in. Hg) can result from an idle air control (IAC) being stuck open or from an excessively worn engine.<br>• Another cause of low cranking vacuum is the installation of a high-performance camshaft with too much duration. ● **SEE FIGURE 27–5.** |
| Excessively advanced or retarded ignition timing | • Excessively advanced ignition timing causes the spark to occur too soon while the piston(s) is coming up at the end of the compression stroke. This overadvanced timing usually causes the engine to crank slowly and unevenly.<br>• Excessively retarded ignition timing causes the spark to occur near or after the piston reaches top dead center (TDC). This causes the engine to have to crank a long time before starting. |
| Excessively advanced or retarded valve timing | • Incorrect valve timing can occur due to wear (stretching) of the timing chain.<br>• Incorrect installation of a replacement timing chain or timing belt may have occurred. Look for evidence of a previous timing belt or chain repair or replacement. |

**FIGURE 27-6** This meter indicates a cranking voltage of 10.32 volts, which is within specifications (above 9.6 volts during cranking).

## ENGINE DOES NOT CRANK OR CRANKS SLOWLY

The starter motor is designed to crank the engine between 80 and 250 revolutions per minute (RPM) to permit proper intake of a combustible air-fuel mixture to start. If the engine does not crank, then the fault is in the cranking circuit, which consists of the following components:

- Battery
- Starter motor
- Starter solenoid
- Ignition switch
- Park-neutral or clutch safety switch
- Cables, wires, and connectors

A fault in any of these components can cause slow cranking or no cranking of the engine when the ignition switch is turned to the Start position.

| Possible Cause | Reason |
| --- | --- |
| Weak or discharged battery | The battery should be at least 75% charged with at least 12.4 volts for proper operation of the starter. ● SEE FIGURE 27-6. |
| Loose or dirty battery connections at the battery | Loose or corroded connections can cause an excessive voltage drop, resulting in lower voltage across the starter motor. |
| Defective or misadjusted park-neutral safety switch | The safety switch (either park-neutral with an automatic transmission or the clutch with a manual transmission) may cause an open circuit to the starter solenoid. With no voltage to the solenoid, a no-crank condition occurs. |
| Defective or misadjusted ignition switch | A defective or misadjusted ignition switch may cause an open circuit to the starter solenoid. With no voltage to the solenoid, a no-crank condition is noticed. |
| Blown fuse or fusible link | Most circuits are protected by a fuse and a fusible link. If either is blown or defective, no voltage can reach the starter solenoid; therefore, no cranking of the engine is possible. |

## POOR FUEL ECONOMY

Poor **fuel economy** means lower-than-usual miles per gallon (or liters per 100 kilometers in the metric system) as determined by an actual road test. The test procedure should include the following steps:

1. Fill the fuel tank (DO NOT overfill) and record the mileage (for example, 52,168 miles).
2. Drive the vehicle normally for 100 to 200 miles or more.
3. Fill the tank again. Record the gallons of fuel used and the ending mileage (for example, 10.6 gallons and 52,406 miles).
4. Calculate the miles per gallon:

$$52{,}406 - 52{,}168 = 238 \text{ miles}$$
$$238 \text{ miles} \div 10.6 \text{ gallons of fuel} = 22.4 \text{ MPG}$$

Fuel efficiency is determined by many factors including:

- Proper air-fuel mixture
- Proper ignition timing
- Proper gear ratio (this ensures as low a piston speed as practical while cruising in high gear)
- Mechanically sound engine including proper valve timing components
- Engine operating at its most efficient coolant temperature
- Proper operation of the exhaust emissions and fuel evaporative control systems
- Whether the vehicle has been operating with the A/C or defrost on all the time (This can reduce fuel economy.)

| Possible Cause | Reason |
| --- | --- |
| The engine is not operating at the proper coolant temperature | • A defective or stuck-open thermostat can cause the engine to operate less efficiently. Using a lower-than-specified temperature thermostat can also reduce fuel economy. The temperature of the thermostat represents the opening temperature, and the thermostat is fully open 20°F higher than the opening temperature. For example: (1) a 180°F thermostat starts to open at 180°F and is fully open at 200°F. (2) A 195°F thermostat opens at 195°F and is fully open at 215°F. ● SEE FIGURE 27-7 for an example of a stuck-open thermostat. |

**FIGURE 27-7** This stuck-open thermostat caused the engine to fail to reach normal operating temperature. As a result, the fuel economy was much lower than normal and it failed a state vehicle exhaust emission test due to excessive hydrocarbons (HC).

| Possible Cause | Reason |
| --- | --- |
| | • Inoperative torque converter clutch (lockup torque converter). When a vehicle equipped with an automatic transmission/transaxle with a lockup converter reaches cruising speed, the torque converter clutch is applied, reducing the normal slippage that occurs inside a torque converter. When the torque converter clutch applies, the engine speed drops 150 to 250 RPM and increases fuel economy. Use a scan tool or tachometer to monitor the engine speed (RPM). The engine speed should drop as soon as the computer commands the torque converter clutch to apply. |
| | • Check the evaporative emission control system for proper operation. A hole in the vacuum diaphragm can cause liquid gasoline to be drawn from the fuel tank directly into the engine, greatly reducing fuel economy. Use a hand-operated vacuum pump to check all charcoal canister vacuum diaphragms. |
| | • Check the following engine-related systems: (1) ignition timing, (2) vacuum leaks, (3) dirty (clogged) air filter or air intake, and (4) exhaust system for restrictions. |

## DIESELING OR RUN-ON

**Dieseling** or **run-on** is a term used to describe the engine continuing to run after the ignition is turned off. A diesel engine operates by ignition of the fuel by heat of compression without the need for a spark to occur. Therefore, if the engine continues to run, an ignition source and fuel must be available. The ignition source is usually hot carbon deposits inside the combustion chamber.

| Possible Cause | Reason |
| --- | --- |
| Leaking injectors | For the engine to continue to run with the key off, a source of fuel is necessary. An injector(s) that is leaking can provide the fuel, and the carbon deposit inside the combustion chamber can provide the ignition source. |
| Defective fuel-pressure regulator | A hole in the rubber diaphragm can provide a source of fuel after the ignition is turned off. |

## BACKFIRE

A **backfire** is the burning of fuel in the intake manifold or in the exhaust system. It is accompanied by a loud popping noise.

| Possible Cause | Reason |
| --- | --- |
| Vacuum leak | A vacuum leak causes a leaner-than-normal air-fuel mixture. A lean mixture burns hotter and slower than the correct mixture. This slow burning mixture can continue burning throughout the exhaust stroke and can ignite the incoming air-fuel mixture when the intake valve opens at the end of the exhaust stroke. This burning of the intake charge in the intake manifold causes a backfire. |
| Low fuel pressure | Causes a leaner-than-normal air-fuel mixture. |
| Clogged or inoperative fuel injector | Causes a leaner-than-normal air-fuel mixture. |
| • **Incorrect ignition timing** • **Crossed spark plug wire** | If the ignition timing is incorrect, either too advanced or retarded, the spark will not occur when it should. Due to the time it takes for |

- **Crossfire between two cylinders side-by-side**
- **Cracked or carbon-tracked distributor cap**
- **Defective or worn spark plugs**
- **Worn camshaft**
- **Fault in the valve train that could prevent proper valve opening and closing**

Exhaust gas recirculation (EGR) valve open all the time or defective EGR valve gasket

Air pump fault such as a defective switching valve

Hole in the exhaust

the air-fuel mixture to burn (about 3 ms), it may cause the mixture to be burning in the exhaust system or into the intake manifold when the intake valve opens at the end of the exhaust stroke.

If the valves do not open fully and close fully at the proper time, a backfire can occur. If the intake valve does not open as far as it should, a leaner-than-normal air-fuel mixture will be in the cylinder when the spark plug fires. This can cause the fuel to still be burning when the intake valve opens at the end of the exhaust stroke. A leaking valve can cause the burning air-fuel mixture to escape and can cause a backfire.

Exhaust gases are inert and do not react chemically with the air-fuel mixture. The purpose and function of the EGR system are to slow down the rate of burning of the air-fuel mixture by introducing a metered amount of exhaust gas into the cylinders. Too much EGR can drastically slow the burning of the fuel. This slowing down of the burning of the air-fuel mixture can cause the burning of the fuel to continue as the intake valve opens at the end of the exhaust stroke, which causes a backfire.

Air pump operation injects extra air into the exhaust manifold or catalytic converter, depending on engine temperature and other factors. To prevent a backfire, the air pump output should be directed to the atmosphere or air cleaner during deceleration when the intake manifold vacuum is high.

An exhaust leak can cause excessive noise, which could be interpreted by the owner as a backfire.

## LACK OF POWER

A lack of power may also be noticeable as *sluggish* or *spongy* performance. This means that the engine delivers less-than-expected power and the vehicle speed does not increase as desired when the accelerator pedal is depressed.

| Possible Cause | Reason |
| --- | --- |
| Retarded ignition timing | If the spark occurs later than normal, a decrease in power is the result. For example, the ignition timing is retarded if the spark occurs at 2 degrees before top dead center (BTDC) rather than at the specification of 10 degrees BTDC. |
| Retarded camshaft timing | A stretched timing chain or incorrect installation of a timing chain or belt can cause low power at low engine speeds. When the engine speed increases, however, the engine will perform correctly because the air-fuel mixture is better able to get into and out of the engine at a higher speed if the camshaft timing is retarded. |
| Exhaust system restriction | A restricted exhaust system can cause low power because some of the burned exhaust is still in the cylinder at the end of the exhaust stroke. This causes a less-than-ideal air-fuel mixture to be drawn into the cylinder on the next intake stroke. Check the following for possible restriction: |

- Exhaust system for collapsed or damaged sections.
- Inspect and pound on the catalytic converter(s) and muffler(s) by hand to check for possible broken internal baffles.
- Use a fitting that takes the place of the oxygen sensor and measure the amount of back pressure with the engine running using a pressure/ vacuum gauge. Most vehicle manufacturers specify a reading of less than 2.5 PSI at 2500 engine RPM.

| Possible Cause | Reason |
| --- | --- |
| Weak ignition coil or worn spark plugs | The ignition output of the coil should be capable of providing a high enough voltage to fire a spark tester that has a minimum required voltage of 25,000 volts (25 kV). A weak coil or an excessively worn spark plug can prevent the proper burning of the air-fuel mixture inside the cylinder. If the air-fuel mixture is not ignited, a lack of power results. |

| Possible Cause | Reason |
| --- | --- |
| Restricted fuel filter, low fuel pump pressure, or contaminated gasoline | A lack of clean fuel at the proper pressure can cause the engine to produce less-than-normal power. A lack of fuel causes a lean air-fuel mixture that can also cause spark knock (ping or detonation), backfire, hesitation, and related problems. |
| Excessive knock sensor activity | If an engine knock is detected, the computer retards the ignition timing to reduce or eliminate the spark knock. When the ignition timing is retarded, the engine produces less-than-normal power. Excessive spark knock activity can result from one or more of the following: <br><br>• Too low octane-rated gasoline <br><br>• Too lean air-fuel mixture <br><br>• Excessive carbon buildup inside the combustion chamber <br><br>• Engine mechanical or accessory drive belt faults causing a vibration or noise that is being sensed by the knock sensor as being caused by spark knock. |
| Engine mechanical faults | If the engine has a worn camshaft or low compression, it cannot produce normal power. |
| Accelerator pedal not opening the throttle all the way | If the mechanical linkage is out of adjustment or the interior carpet or mat prevents the throttle from opening all the way, a loss of power will be noticed. Have an assistant check that the throttle opens all the way when the accelerator pedal is depressed from inside the vehicle. |

## SURGES

A **surge** is a change in engine power under steady throttle conditions. A driver may feel a surge as if the vehicle was speeding up and slowing down with no change in the accelerator pedal. A lean air-fuel mixture is the most common cause of this condition.

| Possible Cause | Reason |
| --- | --- |
| Lean air-fuel mixture | • A false rich condition caused by a contaminated oxygen sensor could cause the computer to reduce the amount of fuel delivered to the cylinders. <br><br>• A restricted fuel line or fuel filter can cause a lean condition. |

| Possible Cause | Reason |
| --- | --- |
| Excessive exhaust gas recirculation | A defective EGR valve or solenoid can cause an excessive amount of exhaust gas to enter the combustion chamber, resulting in a less-than-efficient mixture. |
| Weak spark | A weak ignition coil, worn spark plugs, or defective spark plug wires can cause an ignition misfire, resulting in a lack of power that could be intermittent and cause a surge. |
| A clogged or defective fuel injector | Proper engine operation depends on each cylinder receiving the same amount of clean fuel at the proper pressure. |

## CUTS OUT OR MISFIRES

When an engine **misfires,** it jerks or pulsates and is usually more noticeable when the engine is accelerated. Because the engine is not running smoothly, the cause of the misfire is usually due to faults in one or more cylinders, either with a lack of spark, fuel, or compression.

| Possible Cause | Reason |
| --- | --- |
| Spark plugs and/or spark plug wires | Any fault in the secondary ignition system results in uneven firing of the cylinders, causing the engine to miss or cut out. |
| Engine mechanical faults such as: <br><br>• **Worn camshaft** <br><br>• **Bent pushrod** <br><br>• **Broken valve spring** <br><br>• **Lack of compression** | Any malfunction in the valve train would cause an uneven firing of the cylinders. |

## RICH EXHAUST

A rich exhaust can be determined by a variety of methods, including:

- High CO exhaust readings (over 0.5%)
- Exhaust smell
- Poor fuel economy
- High O2S readings (consistently over 700 mV)
- More than −20% long term fuel trim (LTFT).
- Black exhaust smoke

Although the oxygen sensor should provide a rich signal (O2S high) to the computer and the computer should restore proper operation, many faults in the engine management system can cause the engine to operate too rich, including:

1. Oxygen sensor skewed low or defective
2. False lean signals to the oxygen sensor caused by:
   - Ignition misfire (defective spark plug wires or fouled plugs)
   - Exhaust leak upstream of O2S such as a cracked exhaust manifold or leaking crossover pipe connections
3. Defective fuel-pressure regulator—a hole in the diaphragm can allow gasoline to flow from the fuel line directly into the intake manifold

## LEAN EXHAUST

A lean exhaust can be determined by a variety of methods including:

- High $O_2$ exhaust readings (over 2%).
- Engine hesitates, bucks, jerks, or backfires through the air inlet.
- Low O2S reading (consistently less than 200 mV).
- High block lean numbers (more than 150 or more than a +20% long-term fuel-trim correction factor).

Although the oxygen sensor should provide a lean signal (O2S low) to the computer and the computer should restore proper operation, many faults in the engine management system can cause the engine to operate too lean, including:

1. Oxygen sensor skewed high or defective
2. False rich signal from O2S caused by silicon-contaminated or coated oxygen sensor
3. Large intake manifold or vacuum hose leak
4. Broken intake valve spring causing large internal vacuum (air) leak
5. Low fuel-pump pressure
6. Low voltage to the injectors
7. Poor computer ground causing improper opening of the injectors

 **TECH TIP**

**The Lighter Fluid Trick**

A vacuum (air) leak is often difficult to find. A common technique is to use lighter fluid and carefully squirt along the intake manifold gasket and other possible sources of a leak. The small nozzle of the lighter fluid container makes it easy to find even a small leak. For hard-to-reach areas, attach a straw to the nozzle of the container to direct the lighter fluid. Propane also can be used effectively to locate vacuum leaks.

## SYMPTOMS OF A DEFECTIVE COMPONENT

It is a good idea to know what **symptoms** a particular part or component will cause if defective. In this section, a component part or sensor is listed with typical symptoms the part or sensor could cause if defective.

**NOTE: Many symptoms are similar for more than one component part or sensor. This section should *not* be used for diagnosis of an engine performance problem.**

| Engine Part or Sensor | Problem if Defective |
| --- | --- |
| Ignition coil | • No start or hard to start<br>• Misfire under load<br>• Intermittent missing/stalling<br>• Cuts out at high engine speeds |
| Manifold absolute pressure (MAP) sensor | • A MAP sensor is used to measure atmospheric pressure (altitude) when the ignition key is first turned on and to signal engine vacuum, which is a measure of engine load, to the computer.<br>• Light load—less fuel, more ignition timing is possible.<br>• Heavy load—more fuel, less ignition timing is possible.<br>• Therefore, a fault in the MAP sensor can have a major effect on the air-fuel mixture supplied to the engine.<br>• Some characteristic symptoms include: Rough idle and stalling<br>Poor fuel economy<br>Hesitates on acceleration<br>Failed exhaust emissions tests for excessive HC and CO |
| Oxygen sensor | • Poor fuel economy, rough running, stalling, and excessive exhaust emissions (high HC and CO likely) can occur. |

**NOTE: The engine will usually operate correctly at or near wide-open throttle (WOT) because the computer ignores the oxygen sensor during these conditions and simply supplies the engine with a rich mixture needed for maximum acceleration.**

| | |
| --- | --- |
| | • Oxygen sensors usually fail low, meaning that the computer gases appear leaner than they actually are and, therefore, the computer will command a richer-than-needed amount of fuel. This is another reason why a defective oxygen sensor is not noticed during rapid acceleration. |
| Spark plug wires | • Engine misfire (especially in wet weather)<br>• Loss of power |

| Engine Part or Sensor | Problem if Defective |
|---|---|

Caution: If a spark plug wire is defective, high voltage can cause a carbon track in the distributor cap or rotor (if equipped) or cause the ignition coil to become tracked (ruining the coil and requiring replacement).

| | |
|---|---|
| Throttle-position (TP) sensor | • The TP sensor signals the computer regarding not only the position of the throttle, but also the rate of change (speed) at which the throttle is being depressed or released. The TP sensor is an important input device for the torque converter clutch (TCC). The TP voltage has to be greater than a certain percentage (usually about 10%) and less than a certain percentage (usually about 80%). |

CORRODED TERMINAL

**FIGURE 27–8** This corroded coil terminal on a waste spark-type ignition system caused a random misfire DTC to set (P0300) and it affected both cylinders and not just the one than had the corroded terminal.

# EXCESSIVE CO EXHAUST EMISSIONS

The chemical abbreviation CO stands for carbon monoxide, which is formed during the combustion process inside the engine by combining the carbon (C) from the gasoline (HC) and the oxygen (O) from the air. An efficient engine should produce very little CO if there is enough oxygen in the cylinder to create $CO_2$. However, if the air-fuel mixture is too rich, an excessive amount of CO emissions will be created. Therefore, CO is called the *rich indicator* exhaust gas.

| Possible Cause | Reason |
|---|---|
| Clogged or restricted positive crankcase ventilation (PCV) system including the valve itself, the rubber hose, or the manifold vacuum port | Because about 20% of the air needed comes from the PCV system, a restriction in the system reduces the amount of air and increases the amount of CO produced by the engine. |
| Defective fuel-pressure regulator | A fuel-pressure regulator uses a spring-loaded rubber diaphragm to control fuel pressure. The strength of the spring determines the fuel pressure. On most port fuel-injected engines, a vacuum hose from the intake manifold attaches above the rubber diaphragm which changes the fuel pressure in relation to manifold vacuum. A hole in the rubber diaphragm can draw fuel from the fuel rail directly into the intake manifold. This extra fuel can cause the engine to run too rich and produce excessive CO exhaust emissions. |
| Too high fuel pressure | A restricted fuel return line or defective regulator can cause excessive fuel pressure. This excessive fuel pressure often results in excessively rich air-fuel mixture and excessive CO emissions. |
| Degraded catalytic converter | A degraded catalytic converter can cause the vehicle to fail an emission test for excessive CO emissions. |

# EXCESSIVE HC EXHAUST EMISSIONS

The chemical abbreviation for hydrocarbons (gasoline) is HC. Excessive HC exhaust emissions mean that the gasoline is not being properly burned inside the engine. Because the ignition system is used to ignite the air-fuel mixture, any malfunction in this system can result in higher-than-normal HC exhaust emissions.

| Possible Cause | Reason |
|---|---|
| Ignition system faults | Allows unburned fuel to exit the engine. The entire ignition system should be inspected and tested, including:<br>• Spark plugs.<br>• Spark plug wires.<br>• Distributor cap and rotor (if so equipped). ● SEE FIGURE 27–8.<br>• Ignition timing. |

| Excessively lean air-fuel mixture | A very lean air-fuel mixture is often too lean to ignite. As a result, this unburned fuel is pushed out of the engine during the exhaust stroke. This is called a **lean misfire**. |
| --- | --- |
| Thermostat inoperative (stuck open) or opening temperature too low | An engine operating colder than normal causes a greater-than-normal amount of fuel to condense on the cylinder walls. Because liquid fuel cannot burn without oxygen, this layer of unburned fuel (HC) is pushed out the exhaust system by the piston on the exhaust stroke. Using the specified-temperature thermostat reduces the amount of this quenched fuel, reduces HC emissions, and improves fuel economy. |
| Degraded catalytic converter | A degraded catalytic converter can cause a vehicle to fail an emission test for excessive HC emissions. |

**FIGURE 27–9** This badly eroded water (coolant) pump caused the engine to overheat.

# EXCESSIVE NO$_x$ EXHAUST EMISSIONS

The chemical abbreviation for oxides of nitrogen is NO$_x$. Both nitrogen (N) and oxygen (O$_2$) are normally part of our atmosphere. It requires heat and/or pressure to combine them to form oxides of nitrogen. Excessive NO$_x$ emissions, therefore, mean that the engine combustion chamber temperatures are too high or the chamber has excessive compression.

| Possible Cause | Reason |
| --- | --- |
| Inoperative or restricted flow EGR valve | The purpose and function of the exhaust gas recirculation system are to introduce inert burned exhaust gases into the combustion chamber to reduce the peak temperatures to reduce NO$_x$ emissions. |
| Cooling system fault such as low coolant level, clogged radiator, restricted air flow through the radiator | Any fault in the cooling system can cause an increase in engine operating temperatures, and therefore cause the engine to create excessive NO$_x$ emissions. ● **SEE FIGURE 27–9.** |
| Too far advanced ignition timing | Advanced ignition timing causes the spark to occur too soon while the piston is coming up on the compression stroke. As a result, the temperature and pressures inside the combustion chamber are increased, which increases the formation of NO$_x$. |
| Too low octane-rated fuel | Using a gasoline with an octane rating lower than specified by the vehicle manufacturer can cause the engine to spark knock (ping). Spark knock or ping is caused by a secondary explosion inside the combustion chamber, which causes a rapid pressure and temperature rise to occur. Therefore, if an engine is spark knocking (pinging), it is also emitting an excessive amount of NO$_x$. |
| Degraded catalytic converter | A degraded catalytic converter can cause a vehicle to fail an emission test for excessive NO$_x$ emissions. |

# SUMMARY

1. A lean air-fuel mixture is the usual cause of hesitation or stumble during acceleration.

2. A vacuum leak and lean air-fuel mixture can cause a rough idle or stalling.

3. Spark knock (ping or detonation) is often caused by a too lean air-fuel mixture, or if the engine operating temperature is too high.

4. A hard-start problem is often due to a lack of fuel.

5. A slowly cranking engine is usually due to low battery voltage. A no-crank condition is usually due to an open circuit in the cranking circuit.

6. Poor fuel economy is usually due to an excessively rich air-fuel mixture.

7. A lean air-fuel mixture is usually due to a vacuum leak.

8. A rich air-fuel mixture can be caused by a defective oxygen sensor or the engine getting fuel from another source not controlled by the computer or fuel system.

## REVIEW QUESTIONS

1. List five engine performance faults that can occur if a vacuum (air) leak occurs.

2. What symptom(s) may occur if the EGR valve is inoperative (never opens)?

3. List four items that can cause excessive CO exhaust emissions.

4. List four items that can cause excessive HC exhaust emissions.

5. List four items that can cause excessive $NO_x$ exhaust emissions.

## CHAPTER QUIZ

1. Technician A says that a partially stuck-open EGR valve can cause ping (spark knock) during wide-open throttle engine operation. Technician B says that the partially stuck-open EGR valve could cause the engine to stall while operating at idle speed. Which technician is correct?
   a. Technician A only
   b. Technician B only
   c. Both Technicians A and B
   d. Neither Technician A nor B

2. Technician A says that a too rich air-fuel mixture can be caused by a defective fuel-pressure regulator. Technician B says that a defective pressure regulator can cause a too lean air-fuel mixture. Which technician is correct?
   a. Technician A only
   b. Technician B only
   c. Both Technicians A and B
   d. Neither Technician A nor B

3. Technician A says that excessive $NO_x$ exhaust emissions can be due to a defective PCV valve. Technician B says that a too lean air-fuel mixture can cause excessive $NO_x$ exhaust emissions. Which technician is correct?
   a. Technician A only
   b. Technician B only
   c. Both Technicians A and B
   d. Neither Technician A nor B

4. Technician A says a defective TP sensor can cause the engine to hesitate during acceleration. Technician B says that dirty throttle plate(s) on a port-injected engine could cause a hesitation during acceleration. Which technician is correct?
   a. Technician A only
   b. Technician B only
   c. Both Technicians A and B
   d. Neither Technician A nor B

5. Technician A says that defective spark plug wires can cause the engine to misfire. Technician B says a fouled spark plug can cause the engine to misfire. Which technician is correct?
   a. Technician A only
   b. Technician B only
   c. Both Technicians A and B
   d. Neither Technician A nor B

6. Technician A says a rough idle on a fuel-injected engine can be caused by dirty throttle plates. Technician B says the wrong PCV valve could cause the engine to idle roughly. Which technician is correct?
   a. Technician A only
   b. Technician B only
   c. Both Technicians A and B
   d. Neither Technician A nor B

7. Technician A says that spark knock (ping or detonation) can be caused by a lean air-fuel mixture. Technician B says an inoperative cooling fan could cause the engine to spark knock. Which technician is correct?
   a. Technician A only
   b. Technician B only
   c. Both Technicians A and B
   d. Neither Technician A nor B

8. Technician A says that a stretched (worn) timing chain can cause the engine to lack power at slow speeds. Technician B says a clogged exhaust system can cause the engine to lack power at high speeds. Which technician is correct?
   a. Technician A only
   b. Technician B only
   c. Both Technicians A and B
   d. Neither Technician A nor B

9. Technician A says that poor fuel economy can be caused by a defective thermostat. Technician B says a defective evaporative charcoal canister can cause poor or reduced fuel economy. Which technician is correct?
   a. Technician A only
   b. Technician B only
   c. Both Technicians A and B
   d. Neither Technician A nor B

10. Technician A says a rich exhaust could be caused by a hole in the rubber diaphragm of the fuel-pressure regulator on a port-injected engine. Technician B says that a defective spark plug wire can cause the engine computer to supply a too rich air-fuel mixture. Which technician is correct?
    a. Technician A only
    b. Technician B only
    c. Both Technicians A and B
    d. Neither Technician A nor B